GREAT ADVENTURES IN MEDICINE

SECOND, REVISED EDITION

EDITED BY
SAMUEL RAPPORT
HELEN WRIGHT

WITH AN INTRODUCTION BY
DETLEV W. BRONK,
President of the Rockefeller Institute
and
President of the National Academy of Sciences

D1209097

THE DIAL PRESS · 1961 · NEW YORK

DESIGNED BY WILLIAM R. MEINHARDT

MANUFACTURED IN THE UNITED STATES OF AMERICA BY

THE HADDON CRAFTSMEN, SCRANTON, PENNA.

ACKNOWLEDGMENTS:

Adams, Samuel Hopkins: "Peruna and the Bracers" from *The Great American Fraud;* copyright 1905 by the American Medical Association, Chicago, Illinois. By permission of *The Journal of the American Medical Association,* Chicago.

Agramonte, Aristides: *The Inside Story of a Great Medical Discovery,* copyright 1915 by The Science Press, Lancaster, Pennsylvania. Reprinted from the December 1915 issue of *Scientific Monthly. By permission of the American Association for the* Advancement of Science, Washington, D. C.

Alvarez, Walter C.: *The Emergence of Modern Medicine from Ancient Folkways.* Reprinted from September 1936 issue of Sigma Xi Quarterly. By permission of *American Scientist.*

Aubrey, John: "The Only Contemporary Character Sketch of William Harvey" (17th Century). Reprinted from *The Story of Medicine* by Victor Robinson. Copyright 1943 by Froben Press, New York.

Bernard, Claude: "The Truth Seekers" from *The Life of Pasteur* by René Vallery-Radot; published 1910 by Doubleday, Page and Company.

Billings, John Shaw: "The Johns Hopkins Hospital." From Billings' report on Johns Hopkins, July 15, 1876. Reprinted from *John Shaw Billings—A Memoir,* by Fielding H. Garrison; published 1915 by G. P. Putnam's Sons, New York.

Boccaccio, Giovanni: "The Plague." From *The Decameron of Boccaccio.* Translated 1353.

Brill, A. A.: "The Psychology of Sigmund Freud" from *The Basic Writings of Sigmund Freud,* copyright by Dr. A. A. Brill. Reprinted from Modern Library edition (1938). By permission of Mrs. Rose Owen Brill.

Buley, R. Carlyle and Pickard, Madge E.: "On Dr. Richard Carter," from *The Midwest Pioneer, His Ills, Cures and Doctors,* by Madge Evelyn Pickard and R. Carlyle Buley, published 1945 by R. E. Banta, Crawfordsville, Indiana. By permission of Dr. Buley.

Burnett, F. M.: "Influenza." From *Viruses and Man* by F. M. Burnett. Reprinted by permission of Penguin Books Ltd.

Cannon, Walter Bradford: "The Career of the Investigator." Reprinted from July

21, 1911 issue of *Science*. By permission of American Association for the Advancement of Science, Washington, D. C.

Cannon, Walter Bradford: "On Becoming a Doctor." Reprinted from *The Way of an Investigator*, by Walter Bradford Cannon. Copyright, 1945, by W. W. Norton & Company, Inc.

Cannon, Walter Bradford: "Gains from Serendipity." Reprinted from *The Way of an Investigator* by Walter Bradford Cannon, M.D. By permission of W. W. Norton & Company, Inc. Copyright 1945 by W. W. Norton & Company, Inc.

Clendening, Logan: "Science and Surgery—John Hunter" and "The Medicine Man." Reprinted from *Behind the Doctor*, by Logan Clendening, by permission of Alfred A. Knopf, Inc. Copyright 1933 by Alfred A. Knopf, Inc.

Cushing, Harvey: "The Art of Medicine," from *The Medical Career*, published 1940 by Little, Brown & Company, Boston, Mass. By permission of Dr. John F. Fulton, literary executor of Estate of Dr. Harvey Cushing.

de Ropp, Robert S.: "Sick Minds, New Medicines." From *Drugs and the Mind* by Robert S. Ropp. Reprinted by permission of St. Martin's Press Incorporated.

Dickens, Charles: "Sairey Gamp," from *Martin Chuzzlewit* (1843).

Doyle, A. Conan: "His First Operation," from *Round the Red Lamp*. Published 1894 by D. Appleton & Co.

Ellis, Havelock: "On Becoming a Doctor." Reprinted from *My Life, Autobiography of Havelock Ellis*. Published 1939 by Houghton Mifflin Company, Boston, Mass.

Finney, John Miller Turpin: "My Professional Colleagues." From *A Surgeon's Life* by J. M. T. Finney. Copyright, 1940, by John Miller Turpin Finney. Courtesy of G. P. Putnam's Sons.

Fleming, Alexander: "Chemotherapy." From *Chemotherapy: Yesterday, Today, Tomorrow*. Published 1946, by Cambridge University Press, London.

Fletcher, Thomas F., Jr. and Procopio, Frank: "Organized Medicine and Polio Control with Sabin Vaccine." Prepared as a scientific exhibit by the American Medical Association for its Annual Meeting, 1961 and used with permission.

Flexner, James Thomas: "The Death of Pain" and "A Backwoods Galahad: Ephraim McDowell" from *Doctors on Horseback* by James Thomas Flexner. Copyright 1937 by James Thomas Flexner. Reprinted by permission of The Viking Press, Inc., New York.

Foster, Sir. Michael: "Vesalius and Harvey: The Founding of Modern Anatomy and Physiology." From *Lectures On the History of Physiology During the Sixteenth, Seventeenth and Eighteenth Centuries*. Published 1901, reprinted 1924, by Cambridge University Press, London.

Fracastoro, Girolamo: "The Sinister Shepherd." Metrical English translation copyright 1934, by William Van Wyck. By permssion of Dr. William Van Wyck.

Franklin, Benjamin: "Observations." From *Experiments and Observations on Electricity Made at Philadelphia in America*. Published 1774, London.

Freud, Sigmund: "On Becoming a Doctor." From *Sigmund Freud: Autobiography*, translated by James Strachey. Published 1935, by W. W. Norton and Company, New York.

Galen, Clarissimus: "On Various Medical Subjects." Translated by Arthur J. Brock in *Greek Medicine In Rome*, published 1929 by E. P. Dutton & Co., Inc., New York.

Grenfell, Wilfred Thomas: "On Becoming a Doctor." From *A Labrador Doctor, the Autobiography of Wilfred Thomas Grenfell*. Published 1919 by Houghton Mifflin Company, Boston, Mass.

Guttmacher, Alan F.: "Bootlegging Bodies." From *Bulletin of the Society of Medical History* of Chicago, January 1935, Vol. IV no. 4. By permission of Dr. George H. Coleman, editor of the *Bulletin* and of Dr. Alan F. Guttmacher.

Guttmacher, Alan F.: "Ambroise Paré Does a Delivery" from *Into This Universe*, by

Alan Frank Guttmacher. Copyright 1937 by Alan Frank Guttmacher. Reprinted by permission of The Viking Press, Inc., New York.

Haggard, Howard W.: "Treatment of King Charles." From *Devils, Drugs and Doctors,* by Howard W. Haggard, Copyright 1920, by Harper & Brothers.

Harrison, George Russell: "The Doctor and the Physicist." From *Atoms in Action,* by George Russell Harrison, Copyright 1941 by William Morrow & Company, Inc., Publishers, and used with their permission.

Heiser, Victor: "Leprosy in the Philippines." Reprinted from *An American Doctor's Odyssey,* by Victor Heiser, M.D. By permission of W. W. Norton & Company, Inc. Copyright 1936 by Dr. Victor Heiser.

Hertzler, Arthur E.: "The Horse and Buggy Doctor." From *The Horse and Buggy Doctor* by Arthur E. Hertzler, Copyright, 1938, by Paul B. Hoeber, Inc.

Holmes, Oliver Wendell: "On Becoming a Doctor." From *Yankee From Olympus—Justice Holmes and His Family,* by Catherine Drinker Bowen. Copyright 1945. By permission of Little, Brown & Company, Boston, Mass., and The Atlantic Monthly Press, Boston, Mass.

Holmes, Oliver Wendell: "Bishop Berkeley and Tar Water" and "The Young Practitioner." From *Medical Essays,* Edition of 1891. Published by Houghton Mifflin Company.

Hunter, John: "Experiments Made to Ascertain the Progress and Effects of the Venereal Poison." From *A Treatise on the Venereal Diseases,* 1786.

Huxley, Thomas Henry: "Medical Education." From *American Addresses,* published by D. Appleton & Co., 1877.

Keen, William W.: "The Surgical Operations on President Cleveland in 1893." Published by George W. Jacobs & Company, Philadelphia, 1917. Reprinted from *The Saturday Evening Post,* issue of September 22, 1917.

Koch, Robert: "The Etiology of Tuberculosis" (1882). Translated from the German, 1932, by Dr. Max Pinner and Berna Pinner. Reprinted with permission from *The American Review of Tuberculosis* of March 1932. Copyright 1932 by National Tuberculosis Association, New York, N. Y.

Kuhn, Robert A.: "Hope for Victims of Stroke." From *New Hope for Stroke Victims* by Robert Kuhn. © 1960 by Robert Kuhn. Reprinted by permission of the author, the *Ladies Home Journal* and the publisher, Appleton-Century-Crofts, Inc.

Laënnec, René Théophile Hyacinthe: "The Invention of the Stethescope." From *On Mediate Ausculation*—1819, translated by John Forbes, London, 1834.

Le Sage, Alain René: "Doctor Sangrado." From *The Adventures of Gil Blas of Santillane,* Book II, Chapter II.

Lister, Joseph: "On the Antiseptic Principle of the Practice of Surgery." From the *British Medical Journal,* September 21, 1867. Reprinted from C.N.B. Camac, *Epoch Making Contributions to Medicine, Surgery and Allied Sciences,* published 1909 by W. B. Saunders Company.

Lot, Fernand: "The Therapeutical Use of Radioactive Isotopes." From *Radioisotopes in the Service of Man* by Fernand Lot. © 1958 by Unesco, and used by permission.

Merrill, John P.: "The Transplantation of the Kidney." Reprinted with permission of *Scientific American* and the author. Copyright © 1959 by Scientific American, Inc. All rights reserved.

Minot, George Richards: "Anemia." From *The Scientists Speak,* edited by W. Warren Weaver. Copyright 1947 by Boni and Gaer. Used by permission of United States Rubber Company.

Montagu, Lady Mary Wortley: "Inoculation Against Smallpox." From *Letters From the East,* published 1716-1718.

Ordronaux, John: "The Medical School of Salernum." From *Code of Health of the School of Salernum*, translated into English by John Ordronaux. Published 1869, by J. B. Lippincott & Company, Philadelphia.

Paracelsus: "On Authority and Experiment." Quoted in Paracelsus in the *Light of Four Hundred Years*, by Henry E. Sigerist, M. D., in New York Academy of Medicine: *The March of Medicine*, 1941. Copyright 1941, by Columbia University Press. By permission of Columbia University Press.

Paré, Ambroise: "A Fresh-Water Soldier." From *Journeys in Divers Places*, by Ambroise Paré (16th Century). Translated in *Life and Times of Ambroise Paré*, by Francis R. Packard, published 1921, by Paul B. Hoeber, Inc., New York.

Parsons, Robert P.: "Joseph Goldberger and Pellagra." From *Trail to Light*, by Robert Parsons, copyright 1943, used by special permission of the publishers, The Bobbs-Merrill Company, Inc.

Pasteur, Louis: "On Experimental Science" and "On Claude Bernard and His Work" from *The Life of Pasteur* by René Vallery-Radot. Published 1910 by Doubleday, Page and Company.

Radford, E. and M. A.: "Two Cures for the Ague and Remedies in 18th Century England and Ireland." Reprinted from *Encyclopedia of Superstitions*, by E. and M. A. Radford, published 1949 by Philosophical Library. By permission of Philosophical Library.

Robinson, Victor: *The Place of Paracelsus in Medicine*. From *The Story of Medicine*. Copyright by Froben Press, New York, 1943. By permission of Ellen H. Ringer for Victor Robinson Estate.

Roentgen, Wilhelm Conrad: "On a New Kind of Rays." Translated (1933) in *Wilhelm Conrad Roentgen and the Early History of the Roentgen Rays*, by Dr. Otto Glasser. Published and Copyright 1934, by Charles C. Thomas, Springfield, Illinois. By permission of Dr. Otto Glasser and the publishers.

Ross, Sir Ronald: "Malaria." From *Memoirs*, published 1923 by John Murray, Publishers, Ltd., London and used with their permission.

Roueché, Berton: "A Pig From Jersey." The article, "A Pig From Jersey," reprinted by permission; copyright 1950 *The New Yorker Magazine, Inc.*

Sarton, George: "The History of Medicine." From *The History of Medicine Versus the History of Art*, by Professor George Sarton. Fielding H. Garrison Lecture, read at the Seventeenth Annual Meeting of the American Association of the History of Medicine, May 1941. By permission of Professor Sarton.

Schweitzer, Albert: "On the Edge of the Primeval Forest." Reprinted from *On the Edge of the Primeval Forest*, Copyright 1931 by the Macmillan Company and used with their permission and that of A. & C. Black, Ltd., London.

Shakespeare, William: "An Apothecary's Shop." From *Romeo and Juliet*.

Sims, J. Marion: "On Becoming a Doctor." From *The Story of My Life*, by J. Marion Sims. Published 1888, by D. Appleton & Company.

Slosson, Edwin E.: "Chemistry in the Service of Medicine." Reprinted from pamphlet with Introduction by E. E. Slosson, Forum Director of *Science Service* at time of issuance of pamphlet (1920's) at Cambridge, Mass., by the Committee to Extend the National Service of Harvard University. By permission of Preston Slosson, for Estate of Edwin E. Slosson.

Snow, John: "On the Mode of Communication of Cholera." From *The Autobiography of Science*, edited by Forest Ray Moulton and Justis J. Schifferes, published 1945 by Doubleday and Company.

Spencer, Steven M.: "The New Weapons Against Cancer." From the *Saturday Evening Post*, July 12, 1958. Copyright © 1958 The Curtis Publishing Company. Reprinted by permission of the Curtis Publishing Company and the author.

Stanley, Wendell M.: "On the Nature of Viruses, Cancer, Genes and Life—A Declaration of Independence." From the *Proceedings of the American Philosophical*

Society, Vol. 101, No. 4, August 1957. Reprinted by permission of the American Philosophical Society and the author.

Stevenson, Robert Louis: "The Doctor." Quoted from "Medicine at the Crossroads," By Harvey Cushing in his *The Medical Career,* published 1940, by Little, Brown & Company, Boston.

Sydenham, Thomas: "Descriptions of Disease. On the Measles and On St. Vitus Dance" taken from *Processus Integri,* published 1691. Translation from the Latin by R. G. Latham published by Sydenham Society, 1848. "On Scarlet Fever" taken from *Observationes Medicas Circa Morborum Acutorum Historiam et Curationem,* 1676.

Thompson, Morton: "The Cry and the Covenant." From *The Cry and the Covenant,* by Morton Thompson. Copyright 1949 by Morton Thompson. Reprinted by permission of Doubleday and Company, Inc.

Thwaites, John G.: "Surgery." From *Modern Medical Discoveries* by John G. Thwaites. © 1958 by John Thwaites. Reprinted by permission of E. P. Dutton & Co. and Routledge & Kegan Paul Ltd.

Timme, Walter: "The Story of the Glands of Internal Secretion." From *Milestones In Medicine.* Copyright, 1938, D. Appleton-Century Co., Inc. Reprinted by permission of Appleton-Century-Crofts, Inc.

Vallery-Radot, René: "Louis Pasteur and the Conquest of Rabies." From *The Life of Pasteur,* by René Vallery-Radot, published 1910 by Doubleday, Page & Company.

Van Leeuwenhoek, Anton: "Very Small Living Creatures." Reprinted from *The Autobiography of Science,* edited by Forest Ray Moulton and Justis J. Schifferes, published 1945 by Doubleday and Company.

Vogel, Karl: "Medicine at Sea in the Days of Sail." From *Milestones In Medicine.* Copyright, 1938, by D. Appleton-Century Co., Inc. Reprinted by permission of Appleton-Century-Crofts, Inc.

Warren, Mrs. Lena: "Experiences With Yellow Fever." From *Walter Reed and Yellow Fever,* by Howard A. Kelly. Copyright 1906 by Howard A. Kelly. Published by Medical Standard Book Company, Baltimore, Maryland.

Weaver, Warren: "Radiations and the Genetic Threat." Reprinted by permission of the author.

Woodham-Smith, Cecil: "Florence Nightingale." From *Florence Nightingale,* published by the McGraw-Hill Book Co., Inc., and used with their permission and that of Constable & Company Limited, London. Copyright, 1951, by Cecil Woodham-Smith.

Zinsser, Hans: "Laboratories and Medical Practice." From *As I Remember Him,* by Hans Zinsser, by permission of Little, Brown & Company and the Atlantic Monthly Press. Copyright 1939, 1940 by Hans Zinsser.

Zinsser, Hans: "Epidemics and the Fall of Rome." From *Rats, Lice and History,* by Hans Zinsser, by permission of Little, Brown & Company and the Atlantic Monthly Press. Copyright 1934, 1935 by Hans Zinsser.

Also:

"Ancient Remedies: Egyptian: The Ebers Papyrus." H. Joachim *Papyros Ebers, Das älteste Buch über Heilkunde,* (page 41), Berlin, 1890. Quoted in Mettler & Mettler, *History of Medicine,* (page 321) Blakiston Company, Philadelphia, 1947.

Babylonian: "For Gastric Complaint." From M. Jastrow, Jr.: *The Medicine of the Babylonians and Assyrians,* Lancet, 2:1137, 1913.

Byzantine: Paul of Aegina (625-690)—"On the Curative Powers of the Blood of Animals." See F. Adams, *The Seven Books of Paulus Aegineta,* London 1844-1847, 3 volumes; quotation on Blood from vol. 3, page 25.

"Code of Health of the School of Salernum" (*Regimen Sanitatis Salernitanum*). Translation into English by John Ordronaux, published by J. B. Lippincott & Company, Philadelphia, 1869

ACKNOWLEDGMENTS

ix

"Dietary and Sanitary Laws; Diagnosis and Treatment of Leprosy." From the *Book of Leviticus*, King James Version of the Bible, published in 1611.

From the Writings of William Osler: "Personal Ideals and The Master Word in Medicine." From "Farewell Address," May 2, 1905, quoted in *The Great Physician*, by Edith Gittings Reid (page 176), Oxford Unversity Press. Bed-Side Library for Medical Students from *Aequanimitas*, edition of 1932.

"Hippocratic Oath, The:" estimated between 5th and 6th Centuries B. C. From *A Source Book of Medical History*, compiled by Logan Clendening. Copyright ·1942 by Paul B. Hoeber, Inc.

Medieval Remedies:

From the *Leech Book of Bald in the 10th Century:* "Dysentery:" quoted from Charles H. LaWall, *The Curious Lore of Drugs and Medicine* (originally entitled *Four Thousand Years of Pharmacy*), Copyright 1927, by J. B. Lippincott Company.

"Medieval Celtic Remedy for Baldness and Formula for an Electuary of Precious Stones," by Bulleyn, Pharmacist and Physician in the reign of Henry VIII, from Charles H. LaWall (same as above). By permission of Joseph W. E. Harrisson, Sc.D., of LaWall and Harrisson, Philadelphia, Penna.

New World Remedies:

"Remedies of Dr. Richard Carter of Kentucky"—1825. From *A Short Sketch of the Author's Life, and Adventures from His Youth until 1818*, in the First Part. In Part II: "A Valuable, Vegetable, Medical Prescription, with table of Detergent and Corroborant Medicines to Suit the Treatment of the Different Certificates." Published at Versailles, Indiana, 1825.

"Oath and Prayer of Maimonides" (12th Century A.D.) quoted from Charles H. LaWall, *The Curious Lore of Drugs and Medicine* (originally entitled *Four Thousand Years of Pharmacy*), Copyright 1927 by J. B. Lippincott Company. By permission of Joseph W. E. Harrisson, Sc.D., of LaWall and Harrisson, Philadelphia, Penna.

"Wisdom of Hippocrates, The:" from *The Works of Hippocrates*. Translated from the Greek by Francis Adams. Sydenham Society, London, 1849.

Contents

Part 4: Into Modern Times

A. THE OLD WORLD . . .

B. . . . AND THE NEW

Part 5: The Turn of the Century—and Beyond

Part 6: Contemporary Medicine

Preface

SEVERAL years ago, the famous explorer Stefansson edited a collection of "Great Adventures and Explorations." The book contained accounts of stormy sea voyages, journeys to the poles and travels overland to countries never before penetrated by civilized men. There is vast appeal to our love of adventure in these trips to unknown lands. Yet the voyages man has made into the frontiers of the mind are fully as dramatic, and to many individuals enormously more exciting.

The present book concerns itself with some of these other adventures. The territory explored is that which lies beneath the skin of the animal man. Snow, ice and other hazards are replaced by the "very small living creatures," the microbes of van Leeuwenhoek. The early blundering attempts to find a passage to the Indies find their counterpart in the first fantastic, often horrifying, remedies for disease. The death of Scott in the Antarctic is no more heroic than that of Lazear, martyr to yellow fever. The discoveries of Vesalius and Harvey opened new vistas as surely as did those of Columbus.

As originally conceived, the volume was intended to collect for the layman some of the most significant and dramatic writings from the entire field of medicine. A period of over five years of reading and research, carried on from one coast to the other, began. The most ancient documents in translation, as well as the most up-to-date periodicals, were examined. Innumerable books and articles were discarded as being too technical or too specialized, or simply because something better was available.

There remained a manuscript roughly three times the length of the present book. From this, the works which best fitted into the overall plan were finally selected.

The arrangement, after the Introductory section, is roughly chronological. In order to fit the articles into a comprehensible pattern, we have divided the book into five divisions, representing five great eras of medicine's growth. However, the chronological method has not been slavishly followed—for example, Dr. Benjamin Rush on the ravages of yellow fever in 1793 appears next to Dr. Agramonte's story of the first great conquest of the disease in 1900. When read consecutively, from cover to cover, in conjunction with the Synopses which appear at the beginning of each section, the volume gives an idea of the historical growth, the slow accretion of knowledge, which has resulted in the massive structure of modern medicine. Or the reader may choose an article at random, jumping from viruses to medicine men, from x-rays to medieval remedies. In either case, it is hoped that he will gain an appreciation of how the doctor has come to learn what he knows, of the problems which still remain, and of the overpowering human interest of every facet of the search.

The book should have reference value, for here are some of the papers that have made medical history, written by the masters themselves—Paré on the treatment of gunshot wounds, Jenner on vaccination, Lister on antisepsis, Koch on tuberculosis. Sometimes, it has seemed advisable to use the words of those who have been best able to evaluate discoveries in the perspective of history. Thus a noted modern physiologist, Sir Michael Foster, looks back on the early days of his science to write on Vesalius and Harvey. Thus A. A. Brill, one of the first to introduce psychoanalysis into the United States, describes the contributions of Freud. Nor do we limit ourselves to scientific discovery. Dorothea Lynde Dix's impassioned Memorial to the Legislature of Massachusetts in 1843 grew out of no medical training but only out of her sickness of heart when she saw the awful condition of the insane in her day. Unlike most documents of the first importance, the paper is written with consummate journalistic skill. From it grew a whole new conception of the handling of the mentally ill in America.

However, mere lists of discoveries and achievements "are to the history of medicine hardly more than a skeleton is to a living body," to quote Professor George Sarton of Harvard, one of the greatest modern historians of science. "Discoveries may be im-

portant,· but personalities are infinitely more so," he says in a
selection which is included in the Introductory section because it
helps explain the aim and purpose of the book. For this reason
we include the heart-moving story of Pasteur's battle against
rabies, taken from the biography by his son-in-law. Here too is the
incredible and horrifying account of how Semmelweiss struggled
to end the murder of mothers and infants at childbirth, his words
unheard and he himself dying a martyr. John Hunter, famed 18th
century surgeon, tells how he inoculated himself with a venereal
infection in order to study its progress. Cecil Woodham-Smith
describes Florence Nightingale's conquest of the filth and suffering of the Crimean War. James Thomas Flexner shows how the
discovery of one of mankind's greatest blessings, anesthesia, resulted in misery for the discoverers.

The story of medicine has other aspects. It has been said that
there is nothing man will not do and has not done to rid himself
of disease. In the pages that follow are dozens of examples of his
utterly unavailing self-torture. Here also are the great doctors—
Osler, Halsted, Welch and Kelly, the "big four" of Johns
Hopkins; Hertzler, the famous "horse and buggy doctor";
Schweitzer, the musical and philosophical genius who became a
medical missionary. Great modern experimenters—Cannon,
Fleming, Stanley—tell something about their problems. Medical
students appear through the eyes of Oliver Wendell Holmes and
A. Conan Doyle.

By its very nature, "Great Adventures in Medicine" does not
attempt to present a detailed and connected history of the subject.
Nor, as has been made obvious, can any volume of this size even
approximate encyclopedic treatment. Space limitations have made
it necessary to omit great names, distinguished writers, important
subjects. However, the writings here included may well inspire
readers to go further afield. It is hoped that these readers will
number doctors themselves, who sometimes know too little about
the literature of medicine which is not immediately applicable to
their daily practice; medical students; young men and women
who look forward to medicine and nursing as careers—as well as
intelligent laymen to whom the book is primarily directed.

Preface to the Second Edition

IN THE period of nearly a decade since *Great Adventures in Medicine* was first published, medicine has marched with ever-lengthening strides. Polio in large measure has been conquered. Surgery has dared to perform operations unheard of even during World War II. Chemistry begins to control mental illness. Yet much remains to be done. Cancer is an ever-present curse. The fear of radiation hangs over us—although that is not so much a problem of medicine as of mankind itself. Above all, the great mysteries of life and growth await their Newton and their Einstein. In this new edition, it has been the intention of the editors to describe some of the most important recent advances in medicine, and in so doing to illuminate once more the constant growth and the organic structure of the great edifice whose beginnings are hidden in the mists of prehistory.

Introduction

THIS book is appropriately entitled GREAT ADVENTURES
IN MEDICINE for scientific research is a great intellectual adventure. It is well to emphasize this quality of science at a time
when science is valued most by many people for the material benefits it provides. The material benefits are obvious. The intellectual
or spiritual values are subtle, but they have a profound influence
on our thoughts and on the conduct of our lives. The discoveries
of science have given us knowledge and understanding which
have dissolved old prejudices and superstitions which were rooted
in ignorance of nature. The endless frontiers of knowledge have
stimulated man's curiosity and have kept alive his will to know.
This curiosity is the primary motive of the scientist. It is a human
characteristic which invigorates our culture and gives zest to life.
The great discoveries described in this volume are recounted by
adventurers who pioneered in the timeless quest for greater understanding. Those who read of their adventures will gain greater
hope for a better future for these are accounts of great undertakings of the human mind.

The publication of this book follows closely an announcement
of great historic significance: the death rate in this country has
declined forty-five percent in fifty years. This achievement has
been made possible by the scientists who here tell of their adventures. It is a spectacular achievement, but it is only the first fruit
of their investigation. The knowledge which they have provided
is also the foundation for new discoveries in the future; it is

scientific capital which will be utilized in still unknown ways for the further prolongation of life, for the prevention of disease and for the better relief of suffering. Accordingly, the reader has before him a book which records achievements of the past and forecasts the future. It is of timeless significance and interest.

As is characteristic of all intellectual adventures, science is not static. Each new discovery suggests new questions concerning the nature of man and the world in which he lives. New knowledge provides new means for answering those questions. A civilization based on science is not static. The applications of science reshape the relations of man to man and of man to his environment. By the use of science, men recreate their environment and modify the structure of the society in which they live. These changes, born of science and technology, pose new problems for solution by scientists primarily concerned with the furtherance of human welfare. If our civilization is to provide lives that are more satisfying as well as longer, machines must be better adapted to their users, new sources of energy must be utilized in accordance with biological needs and limitations, social relations must be shaped with regard for the characteristics and requirements of individuals. There is a growing realization of the need for greater recognition of these biological requirements and human values in the planned evolution of our civilization. The knowledge of man revealed by the writers of this book will be the foundation for such a wholesome social evolution.

The rapid increase of scientific knowledge has fostered scientific specialization. Few scientists are now able to comprehend more than a small body of scientific knowledge; progress is made by solving limited problems. But the advance of any field of science is furthered by new developments in other areas of science. The significance of new discoveries is enhanced when they are related to other fields of knowledge. Accordingly, GREAT ADVENTURES IN MEDICINE has a special value in these days of specialization for it was written by scientists who had a broad grasp of science; few of them were narrow specialists or technicians. Readers will better comprehend the unity of all science.

I believe the greatest value of this book is its emphasis on the humanitarian values of science. This is especially significant at a time when the leaders of totalitarian nations seek to use science for the suppression of human freedoms. Science depends upon those freedoms. Science, in turn, furthers those freedoms if science is used for the benefit of man as did those who engaged in these great adventures in medicine.

DETLEV W. BRONK

Part 1

Introductory

Introductory

SYNOPSIS

ANY *collection of the most significant writings in the field of medicine should rightfully begin with "The Hippocratic Oath." Even today, more than twenty centuries after it was composed, it is subscribed to by physicians all over the world. Some of its original provisions no longer apply. Its greatest significance lies in the ethical standard, the moral code which it established, and which no reputable physician will transgress. It has inspired physicians in a way which is itself inspiring. Surely no other art or business or profession can boast such a record of devotion to human welfare. There are men like the Chamberlins who invented the obstetrical forceps and kept the secret for generations while women died in childbirth; but for each of these there are thousands of general practitioners who die of overwork, or medical scientists who infect themselves with loathsome or fatal diseases to observe the symptoms and test possible cures.*

The Code survived even the intellectual sleep of the Middle Ages, when charlatanism was at its peak. Amidst the ignorance and quackery of the time, Maimonides, a Jewish physician, composed his moving "Oath and Prayer," which compared to "The Hippocratic Oath" is comparatively unknown, but which ranks with the great personal credos of all time.

We have already commented in the Preface on "The History of Medicine" by Professor Sarton, the distinguished Harvard historian. As has been stated, this short selection owes its place

3

here to the light it throws on the aims of the editors in preparing this book. One additional point should be made. Professor Sarton says, "A deeper study of almost any discovery reveals that what we call the discovery is only the final clinching of an argument developed by many men throughout a long period of time." That point should be borne in mind time and again, as we consider Harvey's discovery of the circulation of the blood, made after many men had stopped just short of the final idea, or Pasteur's annihilation of the theory of spontaneous generation, which had been argued for generations.

The final article in the section is the fascinating "From Folk-ways to Modern Medicine" by the noted physician Walter C. Alvarez. In it he considers the miraculous changes which have taken place since the days of the cave man. It is his thesis, as it is that of other students, that medicine as we know it began when mankind ceased to believe in disease as the work of malevolent gods and so began to search for earthly causes. He shows further, with a wealth of illustration, how the old-time witch doctor has existed side by side with the scientific man of medicine from the earliest times to the present. The Century Dictionary, under "medicine," gives two distinct definitions:

> *1. The art of preventing, curing or alleviating disease . . .*
> *2. Something which is supposed to possess curative, supernatural or mysterious power; any object used or any ceremony performed as a charm . . .*

As Alvarez shows so clearly, the second is always ready to take over when the first fails, ready to promise anything from a cure for cancer to eternal youth. The evidence appears time after time in the contents of this book. The magical remedy is accepted by gullible millions. Even so great a philosopher as Bishop Berkeley swallows his tar water with relish (see page 149). Newsweek for Jan. 22, 1951 reports on a Better Business Bureau publication entitled "Facts You Should Know About Health Cures." In that year of grace, the booklet feels called on to state that magic horse collars are worthless for the treatment of any condition . . . honey is not a cure for whooping cough . . . grape juice will not reduce weight . . . blueberry juice is not a cure for diabetes . . . olive oil will not prevent appendicitis.

This is a situation which faces us constantly, which is overcome only to rise again. Each time it must be eliminated before scientific medicine can take over. Alvarez not only exposes the condition, he points the way to the cure.

The Hippocratic Oath

I SWEAR by Apollo Physician, by Asclepius, by Health, by Panacea and by all the gods and goddesses, making them my witnesses, that I will carry out, according to my ability and judgment, this oath and this indenture. To hold my teacher in this art equal to my own parents; to make him partner in my livelihood; when he is in need of money to share mine with him; to consider his family as my own brothers, and to teach them this art, if they want to learn it, without fee or indenture; to impart precept, oral instruction, and all other instruction to my own sons, the sons of my teacher, and to indentured pupils who have taken the physician's oath, but to nobody else. I will use treatment to help the sick according to my ability and judgment, but never with a view to injury and wrong-doing. Neither will I administer a poison to anybody when asked to do so, nor will I suggest such a course. Similarly I will not give a woman a pessary to cause abortion. But I will keep pure and holy both my life and my art. I will not use the knife, not even, verily, on sufferers from stone, but I will give place to such as are craftsmen therein. Into whatsoever houses I enter, I will enter to help the sick, and I will abstain from all intentional wrong-doing and harm, especially from abusing the bodies of man or woman, bond or free. And whatsover I shall see or hear in the course of my profession, as well as outside my profession in my intercourse with men, if it be what should not be published abroad, I will never divulge, holding such things to be holy secrets. Now if I carry out this oath, and break it not, may I gain for ever reputation among all men for my life and for my art; but if I transgress it and forswear myself, may the opposite befall me.

460-377 B.C.

The Oath and Prayer
of Maimonides

THE Eternal Providence has appointed me to watch over the life and health of Thy creatures. May the love for my art actuate me at all times; may neither avarice, nor miserliness, nor the thirst for glory, nor for a great reputation engage my mind; for the enemies of Truth and Philanthropy could easily deceive me and make me forgetful of my lofty aim of doing good to Thy children.

May I never see in the patient anything but a fellow creature in pain.

Grant me strength, time and opportunity always to correct what I have acquired, always to extend its domain; for knowledge is immense and the spirit of man can extend infinitely to enrich itself daily with new requirements. Today he can discover his errors of yesterday and tomorrow he may obtain a new light on what he thinks himself sure of today.

O God, Thou hast appointed me to watch over the life and death of Thy creatures; here I am ready for my vocation.

And now I turn unto my calling:

O stand by me, my God, in this truly important task;
Grant me success! For—
Without Thy loving counsel and support,
Man can avail but naught.
Inspire me with true love for this my art
And for thy creatures,
O grant—
That neither greed for gain, nor thirst for fame, nor vain ambition,
May interfere with my activity.
For these I know are enemies of Truth and Love of men,
And might beguile one in profession
From furthering the welfare of Thy creatures.
O strengthen me.

Grant energy unto both body and the soul
That I might e'er unhindered ready be
To mitigate the woes,
Sustain and help
The rich and poor, the good and bad, enemy and friend.
O let me e'er behold in the afflicted and suffering,
Only the human being.

Twelfth Century A.D.

The History of Medicine

GEORGE SARTON

I AM afraid that many physicians think of it too much in terms of a list of discoveries and achievements. In fact, such lists have been compiled in such a dry and impersonal manner that the names of physicians associated with each "item" might almost be replaced by an x, y, or z. Such lists are useful, but they are to the history of medicine hardly more than a skeleton is to a living body. The skeleton is indispensable to be sure, but insufficient.

A mere list of discoveries is a falsification of the history of medicine, even from the purely scientific point of view, for such a list exaggerates the discontinuities in medical progress. A deeper study of almost any discovery reveals that what we call the discovery is only the final clinching of an argument developed by many men throughout a long period of time. However, such a list is a far greater falsification from the broad human point of view.

The history of science, and in particular the history of medicine (we can not repeat it too often) is not simply an account of discoveries. Its purpose is to explain the development of the scientific spirit, the history of man's reactions to the truth, the history of the gradual revelation of truth, the history of the gradual liberation of our minds from darkness and prejudice. Discoveries are evanescent, for they are soon replaced by better ones. The historian must try not only to describe these evanescent discoveries but to find in science that which is timeless. When he does that he comes very close to the historian of art. To put it in other words, a man's name may be immortalized by his discoveries. Perhaps there was nothing else in him deserving of remembrance? He may have been a poor sort of man, a man whose mind was as sharp and narrow as a knife-edge? Or else the historian betrayed him? In so far as a scientist is also an artist, his personality can survive, otherwise not. It is the historian's main duty to revive the personalities, rather than to enumerate their scientific excrescences. Discoveries may be important, but personalities are infinitely more so.

1941

The Emergence of Modern Medicine from Ancient Folkways

WALTER C. ALVAREZ

In all matters relating to disease, credulity remains a permanent fact, uninfluenced by civilization or education.

Sir Wm. Osler.

Some time ago when I began to arrange the notes for this lecture on the emergence of modern scientific medicine from the folkways of the past, the realization gradually came to me that it hasn't yet quite emerged, and that this fact would have to be taken into account in any discussion of the subject. What I came to see as I looked about me more thoughtfully was that although in its achievements and in its promise for the future, scientific medicine has immeasurably outdistanced the folk medicine, faith healing, cult medicine, and out-and-out quackery which has always competed with it, these competitors, which one would think might now be abandoned as superfluous, still flourish in the land, and still maintain their original hold on the affections of mankind.

As I shall emphasize later on in this lecture, a savage community usually has two types of medical practitioner: One, the witch doctor who cures by incantation and ceremonial and jugglery, and the other, the herb doctor and bone setter, who, according to his lights, practices much as does a scientific physician. Among the savages the witch doctor is usually held in higher esteem than is the herb doctor, and so also in the supposedly civilized parts of the world the quack often pulls in the crowds and waxes rich while the less spectacular but well-trained physician plods on without much acclaim.

For instance, a few years ago in the environs of Paris, crowds flocked to the booth of a man who was selling herbs to the accompaniment of an attractive and plausible line of patter. When the police arrested him for practicing medicine without a license, they discovered to their surprise that he was not a quack but really a licensed physician, and they were still more surprised when he begged them not to reveal this fact. As he said, if his customers were ever to hear that he was an educated physician they would all leave him, and he would have to go back to poverty.

MANY PERSONS VOTE FOR QUACKERY

In States which use the initiative and the referendum, the people commonly vote down laws designed to debar ignoramuses from the practice of medicine, and sometimes they will go even further. Thus, in a certain city of this land, when a wealthy man presented the citizens with a much-needed hospital, they accepted the gift with the donor's proviso that the place be maintained always as a class A institution, that is, one in which only reputable and licensed physicians are allowed to see patients. But soon the few back-manipulators in town were protesting volubly that as taxpayers they had a right to practice in the city hospital, and so the people went to the polls again and voted to break their covenant with the donor and to turn the building over to the back-rubbers. Hence, when last I had news of the situation, the regular physicians were out, and the town was back where it was before, without a satisfactory hospital.

Actually, the presence of this large group of people in some communities, unappreciative of, or militantly hostile to, scientific medicine makes it impossible for health officers to stamp out diseases such as smallpox and diphtheria, against which, for years, science has offered adequate means of protection.

MANY GO TO IRREGULAR PRACTITIONERS BECAUSE REGULAR MEDICINE FAILED TO HELP

Now I know that there are several reasons for the great faith many people have in irregular practice by poorly trained and inexperienced men. . . . Perhaps the main reason why quackery thrives today is that there are still so many diseases which the scientific physician cannot cure. I feel confident that eventually many of these will be conquered, but I doubt if my profession will ever be able to make over those millions of poor, broken-down men and women who either inherited bodies and nerves too frail to stand up to the strain of life or else had burdens laid on them heavier than they could bear. These people throng our offices every day begging for help, but in so many cases "the contractor put in poor materials," and the only way in which one could hope to work a cure would be to begin with a different set of grandparents.

Nor can the physician yet replace defective or worn-out parts, or parts already destroyed by disease, when the patient comes for help. When a fire in a big conduit burns out some wires, and part of a town is left in darkness, down the manholes go the linemen and soon new wires are strung. But when the poison of infantile paralysis has eaten a hole through the cable of nerves supplying the leg muscles of a little boy or girl, there is no way in which the neurologist can get in and repair the damage, and no one who knows what has happened would think of promising the poor, worried parents a complete cure. Much that is helpful can be done by an expert orthopedist, but he cannot put back the injured nerve cells.

Similarly, the physician cannot take out grandmother's creaky knees and say, like an automobile repair man might do: "See, there, the rubber cushions and the oiling system are practically gone and the surface of the bone is burred over from much pounding, just as in the case of an old chisel. You'd better let us get you a new pair of joints from the factory!". . . .

The huge army of the weak, the unfit, the psychopathic, the crippled, and the ailing will ever be on the lookout for a worker of miracles. And one cannot blame them: They are desperate and ready to try anything once. They and their loved ones will always be scanning the horizon for hope, and they will always be ready to spend the last penny of their savings on a journey to the home of some new wonderworker.

WHY QUACKS OFTEN APPEAR TO WORK MIRACLES

But some of you will remind me that sometimes the quack does cure after able physicians have failed. And you are right; I have seen this myself, but no one who knows anything of quackery, or human suggestibility, or hysteria, or the tendency of most diseases to let up without any treatment at all, is ever going to conclude that simply because a man is curing some people and is gathering crowds on his doorstep he is a good physician, and his system of practice is worth investigating or imitating. This statement will doubtless seem so paradoxical to some of you that probably I should digress for a moment and explain. . . .

STRIKING PERSONALITIES THAT HEAL

Often the cure, when it does come from an irregular practitioner, is worked not so much by the massage or the manipulation as by the influence of an unusual and commanding personality. A few months ago while lunching at a club I couldn't take my eyes off a big, tall, striking-looking man, with piercing black eyes, long black hair shot with gray, and a strangely moving, deep and musical voice. I said to the friends with me, "What a wonderful quack he would make," and then they told me that actually he was a sort of faith healer. He was a preacher who, having discovered one day that he had the gift of healing by the laying on of hands, had gone over into the practice of medicine.

Actually, all great physicians seem to possess some of this ability to inspire sick persons with confidence and hope, and to lift them up out of a bog of worry and fatiguing thoughts and onto the road to health.

CURES DO NOT JUSTIFY A QUACK

As I have already said, the fact that a healer is besieged by hordes of patients, many of whom depart singing his praises, does not indicate for a moment that his methods are rational or worth using by other men. In the hands of the next man they may fail utterly, and for that matter, they usually fail after a time even in the hands of the original user. For this reason nearly all forms of quackery have their day, and then they lose ground and disappear.

Perkins' tractors.—Thus, toward the close of the eighteenth century, Elisha Perkins, an American physician, was curing disease right and left with two little, supposedly magnetic, pieces of metal called tractors. He did so well that even George Washington got a pair. After Elisha died, his son took the tractors to England, where he made a great stir and enlisted the support of the nobility. Unfortunately for him, the famous Dr. Haygarth was skeptical. First he held clinics at which he demonstrated how patients lost their pains when the affected parts were stroked with the tractors. Then, when everyone was much impressed, he took out his penknife and cut the supposed magnets in two; they were imitations made of wood. In the reaction that followed, educated England laughed, and Perkins left for home.

Asuero.—In Madrid, a few years ago, an unimportant physician named Asuero announced that all diseases were due to trouble in a little nerve in the nose, and easily curable by local treatments. The idea caught on, and soon there was a line of people on the sidewalk each morning waiting to get into his office. As commonly happens with quacks, the wealthy and the aristocratic made much of him, and in two or three years he accumulated a large fortune.

Then, apparently, he ran out of suckers, and with nothing to do, he left for Italy to see if he could start there all over again. But the Italians did not take to the idea, and when last I heard of the man he had failed to get going even with the help of his old prestige, his wealth, and the support of some dukes and duchesses. His imitators also failed. Some of you may ask: But didn't the method have some value? Yes; it was nothing new. Nose specialists have used it for years, and with it have helped occasional patients with hay fever and headache.

Albert Abrams.—Another typical story is that of Albert Abrams, a licensed physician of no great reputation in California. For years he promoted a scheme for curing disease by pounding the spine with a little rubber hammer. But the idea never took hold, and until he was about sixty, Abrams had only a mediocre practice. Then one day as he sat looking at one of the first little radio sets, he got an idea that was soon to bring him in a million dollars. He took a couple of cheap resistance boxes and an old Ford spark coil, hooked them together in the silliest way, and announced to the world that with this magic detector he could tune in on the electronic vibrations coming from a drop of blood and could tell exactly what disease the patient was suffering with. For good measure he would tell if the sample of blood came from a Chinese or a Jew, or from a Presbyterian or a Catholic! Just as easily he could connect the patient to another silly box of wires and tune the disease right out of him.

To people who were just beginning to realize what marvels the radio tube could perform, this all sounded so reasonable and so up to date that thousands flocked to him and paid $100 or more to sit for a while holding onto the end of a wire out of which was flowing—absolutely nothing. Many felt that they were cured, and writers like Upton Sinclair, who swallowed hook, line and sinker, wrote articles accusing the leaders of the medical profession of narrowness, backwardness, and jealousy, and an inability to recognize genius when they saw it. The fact that Professor Millikan, on the witness stand in a malpractice suit, swore that he had examined the instruments and that they couldn't possibly do what they were supposed to do, did not seem to discourage anyone.

And then Abrams died, and without his frequent startling pronouncements, which had served to keep his name in the newspapers, his disciples found themselves with but few patients, and most of them were compelled to shift over into some other better advertised and more popular form of quackery.

SELF-LIMITED DISEASES

But some of you may still be saying that you know of a man who was lying at death's door and, after treatment by some irregular practitioner, got well. Yes, this happens all the time and yet it usually proves nothing. Many is the time that I have received great credit for cures which I know good old Mother Nature had more to do with than I. I can remember one of the lucky breaks that came to me when I was a young man starting out in the practice of medicine. A man lay ill with penumonia and, as usually happens in this disease, each morning of the first week found him worse. Not knowing enough about the disease to expect this, the wife became convinced that the nice old doctor in attendance did not know his business and dismissed him. I was then called and I barely had time to change the medicines before the crisis came—and my reputation was made! I tried to explain to the people that they must not blame the old doctor because in this case the pneumonia had run a very typical course to recovery, but they thought I was just trying to be modest; and so finally I gave in, and said no more, salving my conscience with the conviction that sooner or later I would get my share of disgrace perhaps as undeserved as was my present credit. And so it happened; my next patient with pneumonia did so badly that I was dismissed; the old doctor was called in shortly before the crisis came, and thus he got even with me. . . .

Curing a disease that wasn't there.—Or here is the fairly common story of another type of case in which the irregular practitioner triumphs because either he or some good physician diagnosed wrongly. The case is that of a very wealthy woman who was operated on years ago for a tumor of the large bowel. It looked so much like an inoperable cancer that the famous surgeon in attendance did not attempt to remove it, but simply made a bypass around it. Later, as more experience came to him, he realized that what he had seen was not a cancer at all but only an inflammatory mass that would probably disappear after the type of operation that he had performed. But in the meantime, the patient had gone to a faith healer; and when years passed and she remained well, she built for this healer and her faith a beautiful church. Always, then, when one hears that some healer has cured a cancer, it is well to remember the possibility that the diagnosis was wrong.

Cures that won't work twice.—And here is yet another type of case. Recently I saw a woman with severe arthritis. She told me that five years before, when the disease first flared up and put her in a wheel chair, she went to a quack who cured her with the help of an herb tea. Naturally, I asked her why she wasn't back taking the same treatment again, and her answer was that she had gone but that this time the tea wouldn't work. The chances are, then, that the first spectacular cure was not a cure at all but only one of those spontaneous remissions which are so common in the course of a lifelong disease. . . .

BELIEF IN THE MIRACULOUS INCULCATED IN EARLY LIFE

But there are yet other reasons, and very strong ones too, why all of us look for miracles when it comes to the treatment of disease. We may have spent four years at college learning that the universe is run according to immutable laws, but throughout our youth, and almost from the moment that we could understand speech, we were taught to believe stories of miraculous suspensions of these laws, and we were urged to ask daily that such miracles of protection be performed for us and for our loved ones.

Furthermore, in our daily contacts with the people about us and with the world of books, we absorb, willy nilly and unconsciously, much medical folklore which inevitably has an influence on our thinking and our behavior. And if it influences the behavior of an educated man, how much more must it dominate the thought and the behavior of the ignorant and the naturally credulous? None of us can escape it. You sneeze, and some old person near you says, "God bless you." Why did she do that? She probably does not know, but her ancestors in Europe could have told us that you sneezed because a little devil was just then entering your body with evil intent, and when your friend called upon the name of God, that devil had to get out in a hurry. Unconsciously, you subscribe to the same idea when you say, "I wonder what possessed me to do that?" or "I wonder what can have gotten into that child."

Or let us suppose that, without thinking in time to stop myself, I remark to my wife that it is almost a year since I had a cold. I immediately rap wood, but why? Actually, on looking this up in my library on folklore, I found that I do not do it right. I really should be pounding so hard on a log and making so much noise while I am bragging that the devil will not be able to hear me and to say, "Watch me and see how I take that cocky fellow down a peg." Now isn't that silly, and yet I keep on rapping wood on every appropriate occasion, just because it makes me feel safer.

But you can't laugh at me because you have your own pet superstitions. Perhaps you have a horseshoe over the barn door to keep out the elves that would ride the horses all night and sicken the cows and poison the churn. Or let us suppose that you start to pick a sliver out of your finger with a pin and your grandmother catches you at it. You know that she will insist that you use a needle. But why? For 20 years I have been asking grandmothers that question. They all agree that one must use iron and not brass, but the two lame explanations which they give can easily be shown to be inadequate. I searched for years through the literature on folklore for information on this point until at last I became convinced that the original reason was that if iron is used it will keep the wicked elves away from the wound just as iron over the door will keep them out of the house. When you use a brass pin you have no protection, and the wound may fester.

But some of you may ask: Why should the iron protect? Briefly, it is because the elves and the old gods and demons were very conservative; so much so that for thousands of years they clung to the use of the old chipped flint axes and knives of our cave-dwelling ancestors. Eventually they got so that they could tolerate bronze, but even yet they cannot abide nor even go near the newfangled iron which came into use about 1000 B.C.

Or, let us suppose that today, as a young mother sits trimming for the first time her baby's nails, the grandmother comes in. Why will she be so upset and why will she perhaps get down on the rug and pick up all the little parings so as to destroy them in the fire? Why will she say that for the first year of the baby's life the nails must be bitten off? Ask her and she will probably say that if this is not done the baby will grow up to be a thief or it will sicken and die. But let us ask the official nail-paring swallower of a Madagascar chief (I have read in scientific treatises that there is such a man) or let us ask any savage anywhere on the face of the earth, and he will tell us that when the nails are bitten off the pieces must be swallowed. If they were to be left around, and a bad witch were to get hold of a piece, she could easily say some spells over it, and disaster would soon come to the baby.

I never cease marveling at the antiquity and the wide dissemination of scores of these beliefs. For instance, there are many poor homes in England today in which, if a child is seriously ill, the grandmother will want to administer a skinned mouse as a medicine. But why a mouse? To find out we have to go to Egypt where each year as the Nile subsides and the peasants go back to their fields, they find in the cracks in the mud an abundance of mice. They think that these mice sprang from the mud, and therefore must represent an essence of the life-giving virtues of the river. What is more appropriate, then, than to save a dying child with a medicine which represents life abundant? And now comes what, to my mind, is the most interesting part of the story, and this is that when Elliott Smith was studying the mummies of some little children who lived in Egypt over 6,000 years ago, long before the pyramids were built, he found in each stomach— a mouse!

ANCIENT THEORIES OF THE CAUSATION OF DISEASE

Now it will be noticed in the examples which I have given of present-day medical superstition that disease is usually supposed to be due to the malevolence of the devil or of witches or wicked elves, or of men who know enough of the magic arts to summon help from the powers of darkness. What is more natural, then, than to assume that health is to be maintained by warding off evil in some magic or symbolic way.

But where did we get these ideas? I feel sure that we got them from our remote beetling-browed ancestors who hunted the reindeer and the woolly mammoth in the days when the great ice sheets were retreating northward toward the pole. But someone says: How can anyone know what those ancient savages thought? Well, we cannot know for certain, but here and there in the few remaining wildernesses, explorers come upon men who live in a stone age very similar to that of our ancient ancestors, and always these men are found to have about the same ideas in regard to disease. Never having heard of germs or high blood-pressure or hardening of the arteries, it never occurs to them that a man might die of natural causes. If he wasn't injured in an accident or mauled by an enemy or a wild beast, then he must have been harmed by witchcraft or he must have offended some deity or broken some tabu.

One of these ideas has come down to us embalmed in a word. Thus, when an old man drops to the floor unable to speak or to use his right arm or leg, we physicians say that a blood-vessel in the brain has either ruptured or been plugged in some way. But the layman says that it is a stroke, which implies that God was angry and reached out and struck the man down. I never realized how fully a college graduate could believe this until one day when, as I sat by the minister's wife, encouraging her to learn to talk again after a bad cerebral thrombosis, I found that the endlessly recurring question in her mind was: "Wherein have I sinned so terribly that God has struck me down in this cruel way; why has He done this to me who have served Him lovingly all my days?"

But to get back to the savages and their ideas of medicine: Seeing that to them disease is due purely to the malevolence of gods and witches, it is easy to understand why their most prized physicians are not expected to have any knowledge of the body or of surgery or of healing herbs; all they are asked to do is to find out which god is angry and why, or which witch is at work and who is employing him. After that they must know how to appease the god, or to nullify the evil charms of the witch with yet stronger charms and spells.

THE TWO TYPES OF HEALER·AND THEIR DESCENDANTS

And so it is that wherever on this earth one encounters primitive people one is likely to find that the most respected and most feared man in the tribe is the witch doctor. Often he is a sort of Pooh Bah who exercises the functions of physician, seer, prophet, priest, sorcerer, master of ceremonies, and perhaps even king. Some times he represents the finest flower of the development of his people, and then again he may be little more than a juggler and an assassin who will kill for a price.

But what happens when a savage falls out of a tree and breaks his legs, or comes back from a raid with part of his scalp hanging over his ear, or what is done to help the man who gets constipated or has a boil that needs lancing? Will the witch doctor bother with such small practice? No, that is usually beneath his notice, and hence in every tribe there is another kind of healer, a man or woman who can clean wounds and bring the edges together, who can splint a broken leg or pull a dislocated bone back into place, who can incise an abscess or knock out an aching tooth, who can massage stiff muscles or give a sweat bath, and who knows the lore of medicinal plants.

And here I get to the central theme of my discourse, and this is that from the time when man first stepped down out of the trees and made himself a stone ax down to the present moment, there have always been, in every community, two types of medical practitioner: One a believer in some supernatural or similarly unprovable and ready-made explanation of disease as a whole; the other, a student of the many diseases as he finds them; the one disdainful of the study of the structures and workings of the human body; the other a deep student of these sciences; the one treating by means of charms and spells, ceremony, hocus-pocus, exorcism, and sacrifice; the other treating with physical and chemical measures; one whose forte is the cure of nervous troubles, hysteria, and self-limited diseases; the other whose greatest success is found in the healing of those lesions such as deep wounds or bad fractures in which Mother Nature, unaided, either fails to cure or else ends up with a bad result.

THE CONSERVATISM OF THE WITCH DOCTORS

As one would expect, the descendants of the witch doctor have not changed their technique very much through the ages, and if tomorrow they were to be called upon to cope with some terrible epidemic their methods would be practically the same as those of their savage ancestors. They would doubtless begin as they did in Biblical times, in the Middle Ages, and in the terrible winter of 1918, by fixing the blame on some group of persons who had offended the deity. Then there would be sacrifice and ceremony, solemn processions and pilgrimages and the making of vows, all undertaken with the hope of expiating sin and propitiating an angry God.

The average individual would keep his windows tightly closed at night to keep out the flying demons of disease, and he would certainly wear a protective amulet. If during the epidemic, a savage were to come to our shores with some explorer, he would see nothing new in all this, and could only approve heartily of every detail.

HOW PROGRESS IS MADE BY THE DESCENDANTS OF THE HERB DOCTORS

But now let us see what the descendants of the herb doctor did when, some 30 years ago, they were asked to send men to India to try to stop the bubonic plague which was raging there as it has done so many times in the past.

Did the physicians on that commission go into the temples and offer sacrifices to the hideous goddess of epidemic disease? No, they went to work with microscopes and guinea pigs. First, reckless of their lives, they opened the bodies of people dying with the plague, and studied the characteristic changes in the several organs. Then they put under the microscope a little juice from the enlarged glands in the groin, and always they found millions of tiny germs such as are never found in the tissues of normal persons. Then these germs were cultivated in glass tubes, and a drop of the culture was injected into a guinea pig, and when the animal sickened and died, the autopsy always showed lesions like those of the patients. And so, gradually, it became clear that the cause of the scourge was a living thing, a tiny germ which went into a man and kept multiplying until it killed him.

The next question was: How did this germ get into the people? Did they drink it or eat it or did it travel through the air? At this point the physicians were helped by a bit of knowledge that had been available for centuries, namely, that always, preceding an epidemic of plague, rats crawl out of their holes and die. Accordingly, hundreds of rats from the affected regions were caught and dissected, and in the sickly ones again there appeared the same lesions and the same little germs that had been found in the guinea pigs and in the patients. But how were the germs getting from the rats into the people? Soon the rats' fleas came under suspicion, and when some were removed from a rat dying of the plague and dissected, there again were the germs.

Then the scientists collected fleas from sick rats and put them on guinea pigs, and the pigs sickened and died of plague. They always got the disease also when they were left in cages on the floors of the huts where men were dying of plague and their fleas were hopping about looking for a new host. But when the cages were made of wire gauze too fine for the passage of fleas, or when ordinary cages were suspended some distance off the floor, too high for a flea to jump in, none of the guinea pigs succumbed.

At last, then, the essential facts about the disease were available, and bubonic plague could no longer range as a terrible scourge up and down the earth. Now, whenever a few cases appear in a city, health officers rush in and destroy rats and fleas, and the epidemic is stopped before it can get well started. . . .

EVERY WORTH-WHILE DISCOVERY
OF THE PAST IS USED TODAY

I must hurry on to point out a fact which to me is a source of pride, and this is that every worth-while discovery ever made and remembered, and every accurate bit of information ever obtained and passed onward by the ancient herb doctors and by all true students of disease throughout the ages is used in scientific medicine today. I feel that every well-educated regular physician today is the lineal descendant and heir of the old herb doctor and primitive surgeon, just as every faith healer and every irregular practitioner who treats all cases alike, and every ignorant quack who treats by hocus-pocus of one kind or another is a lineal descendant of the witch doctor.

In my library I have translations of the two oldest medical papyri in the world. So far as scholars can tell, these two books date back to between two and three thousand years before Christ. The Smith papyrus was written by a remarkably modern surgeon who described the several types of fracture of the skull and the symptoms that go with each so clearly that we can follow him today. He sutured wounds and brought their edges together with adhesive tape; he knew that an injury to one side of the brain caused paralysis of the other side of the body, and he was often able to pick the patient who would die and the others who would probably get well. If he could only wake up today, to crawl out of his sarcophagus, I believe that a modern brain surgeon would find in him a helpful associate, and would defer to his judgment in the handling of many a wound.

The other ancient book, the Ebers papyrus, is not so satisfying today, because the witch doctor had too much to do with writing it. It is largely a collection of prescriptions in which drugs are mixed with unpleasant things such as the dried excrement of men and animals. Why did they use such things? In order to make the indwelling demon of disease so disgusted that he would get out and not come back. Actually some of the prescriptions were labeled "for the expelling or *terrifying* of the disease."

The Chinese have the same idea today, and in the Flowery Kingdom, when a man lies desperately ill his relatives will sometimes hire orchestras to keep up such an infernal din all day and all night that the devil causing the disease will get worn out from lack of rest and sleep and will depart for a quieter place!

MIXTURES OF THE MAGICAL
AND THE PRACTICAL

But to get back to the Ebers papyrus: As I have already pointed out, one finds there many instances of a very common medical practice, and this is the mixture of the magical and the practical. As one would expect, all through the ages the two systems have been combined more or less unconsciously by practitioners of the two types. Sometimes the witch doctor or the mental healer has used manipulations and even drugs, and the old herb doctor has taken care to gather his plants with a certain ritual or while mumbling spells, and only during certain phases of the moon. Furthermore, the herb doctor has often fallen from grace, scientifically speaking, and has prescribed a drug not because experience showed him that it was useful but perhaps because the astrologers believed that it and the disease to be treated were both under the protection of the same sign of the zodiac. Or perhaps because a walnut looks like a brain with all its convolutions, the old doctor gave powdered walnuts for insanity; or he gave red medicines for anemia and yellow ones for jaundice. Or he shaved elder bark downward to get a cure for vomiting and upward to get a cure for diarrhea!

Archeologists who, years ago, unearthed the archives of an ancient king of Nineveh found two letters of great interest to the medical historian. One was from a magician telling his master, the king, of his illness and begging that a physician be sent to him, the other was from a prominent physician who had prescribed for the king. Unfortunately, the treatment did not help, and later when the physician wrote, admitting that he did not know what the trouble was, he went on to suggest that while the local physicians continued to administer the medicines he had prescribed they had better also call in a magician.

And so it goes today; the faith healer calls in an obstetrician to help with a difficult case of labor, the spinopath prescribes diet and insulin for a diabetic, and the regular physician cures many a hysterical patient with a combination of pills, impressive apparatus, suggestion, and personal magnetism. . . .

THE TRUE PHYSICIAN USES
EVERYTHING EVER FOUND USEFUL

And this leads me to emphasize again the fact that a scientific physician today uses gladly any drug and any method of healing that he can hear of that was ever found really useful by anyone anywhere. Just let us go into a drug store and glance over the shelves. There we will find the castor oil, senna, ox gall, aloes, and opium which were used in ancient Egypt; another purgative, magnesia, came originally from an ancient city of that name in Greece; jalap comes from Mexico, and cascara from California; the aspirin which is so popular today is first cousin to the smelly oil of wintergreen which our grandmothers used to put on flannel and tie around aching joints, and quinine and cocain and ipecac come from South America. Digitalis, our most valuable heart medicine, came to us from an old English herb woman. When, 100 years ago, Dr. Withering found that this woman was curing some patients whom he had failed to help, he went to her and paid a good price for her secret. Then, like the true physician that he was, he picked out of her messy concoction the one essential drug and gave it freely to the world.

Lest this story about Withering serve to strengthen the belief that many persons have that it pays sometimes to go to a Chinese herb doctor or to an American Indian or to a Hindu or some other foreign healer because he must know many things that the American physician does not know, especially about medicines of vegetable origin, I will say that there may have been something in this idea long ago but there is not much in it now after all the years that pharmacologists have spent in studying drugs from all over the world. . . .

HIPPOCRATES, THE FATHER OF MEDICINE

But to get back to the beginnings of medical writing; let me tell you a little about the greatest of all the ancient books. Really it is a series of books written in large part by Hippocrates, he whom we now call the father of medicine. He lived and worked in Greece some 400 years before Christ. He was a modern type of scientific physician in that he observed closely with a surprisingly open mind; he described what he saw, he recorded his failures as well as his successes, and he used everything of curative value that he could find. As one would expect from this, much of what he wrote so long ago is still of interest and value today. The few chapters that are of little value are the ones, probably written by disciples, in which the facts of observation were warped to fit one of those unprovable theories of disease which are still so popular with irregular practitioners today.

As many of you know, the Greeks looked upon the world as made up of four elements: Fire, air, earth, and water, and the body of four humors: Blood, phlegm, yellow bile, and black bile. These humors were affected by the four qualities of matter: Heat, cold, dryness, and moisture, and disease resulted when a humor became too hot or too cold, or too dry or too moist.

You who know something of modern chemistry and physics will say: "How silly," and yet these humoral ideas dominated and restricted and largely sterilized medical thought for 2,000 years. Even today, they affect our speech, and we say that a man is of a sanguine, a phlegmatic, a choleric, a bilious, or a melancholy nature, that he is good or bad humored, or that he has a warm or a cold temperament.

We physicians revere Hippocrates because he was the first man to teach, first, that many diseases clear up best if the physician does not meddle too much, and, second, that medicine can advance only when it breaks away from magic. Gradually, through the two milleniums before the birth of Christ, physicians had been coming to see that some diseases are due to injury and contagion and the wearing out of parts, but so far as we have a record, Hippocrates was the first to go the whole way and state that no disease is purely miraculous in origin. He would not exclude even epilepsy, which then was called the sacred disease, because of those terrifying fits which seem so obviously to be due to possession by a god or a devil.

And if through the ages, religiously minded people had only listened to Hippocrates and had given his successors the freedom to dissect, to perform autopsies, to experiment on animals, and to report honestly and fearlessly what they found, how almost certain it is that today medical knowledge would be hundreds of years ahead of where it is, with tuberculosis and cancer and arthritis perhaps only memories of the past.

THE EVER-PRESENT OPPOSITION
TO MEDICAL ADVANCEMENT

But all through the ages a large section of the people in every country have kept saying, "No, you mustn't do this and you mustn't do that," thus making it hard or impossible for physicians to carry on their studies and their beneficent work for the relief of human suffering.

Really, aren't we human beings curious in our mental processes? In the middle ages they loved to hitch a dray horse to each of a man's hands and feet and drive these horses off in four different directions; they loved to strip off a man's skin while he was still alive, or to break his bones on the wheel, or to roast him over a slow fire; but just let the crowd which had looked on with approval and pleasure discover next day that an eminent teacher of medicine, trying to learn how better to help suffering humanity, had dissected what was left of the poor prisoner after the hangman was done, and they would turn in wrath to rend the impious wretch who had dared to so desecrate a human body!

But we must not smile at this in a superior way because even today, it is not always easy to get human bodies for dissection, and so bitter is the opposition of some animal lovers to the progress of scientific medicine, that in many cities the pound man does not dare to sell even a dead dog for study in the local medical school.

Just think of Aristotle, the greatest naturalist, and one of the greatest physicians of all time, having to admit that even with the backing of his pupil and patient, Alexander, the most powerful ruler of the then known world, he had been unable to dissect even one human body, and he had never seen a man's kidney or a woman's uterus!

It was not until the sixteenth century that the opposition to dissection of the human body died down sufficiently in a few Italian cities so that the great Vesalius was able to learn how a man is made inside, and to publish (in 1543) the first accurate book on anatomy. Obviously, until such knowledge was secured, the practice of surgery was impossible.

The next big step in the progress of medical science came in 1628 with Harvey's great discovery of the circulation of the blood. With this work was begun an era in which the functions of the many organs of the body were studied. In 1683, Leeuwenhoek discovered bacteria, and in 1719, Morgagni founded the science of pathology, which deals with the changes that are to be found in the bodies of persons dead of disease.

Later there came much progress in the differentiation of diseases by careful study of the symptoms and the physical findings, until physicians were able to distinguish malaria from typhoid fever, measles from German measles, diphtheria from croup, and appendicitis from ordinary stomach ache. Around 1877 Pasteur discovered the role that germs play in the causation of disease; protective vaccines and sera began to be made, and Lister showed how to banish suppuration from surgical wounds. In 1846, Morton and others discovered anesthesia, and surgery came into its own. Finally, with the development of bacteriology, there came wonderful triumphs in the prevention and cure of many of the infectious diseases that have plagued mankind.

THE LATEST PHASE OF MEDICAL PROGRESS

Today we are entering on a marvelous phase of medical development, and many seeming miracles are already being performed. The physiological chemist is having his inning, and every few months, someone discovers a new substance which has uncanny powers in the way of controlling growth and development. One of these substances makes giants, another makes midgets, another produces goiter, another makes the breasts of a virgin animal fill with milk, and other substances produce cancer at the will of the investigator. I feel sure that we are but on the threshold from which we shall soon glimpse great wonders.

As yet we do not know how to use curatively all these gifts of the chemist, and many are not yet even on the market, but with time and experience, there must surely come from some of them great benefits to the human race.

THE NEED FOR PROTECTING RESEARCH WORKERS FROM MISGUIDED PEOPLE

All of these great gifts of science are for you and your children. No one knows on what day some disease, as yet incurable, is going to strike down someone dear to you; and when that day comes the only hope your physician may be able to give you will be that in several laboratories in this country, or abroad, devoted men and women are working late into the night, hot on the trail of a cure for this very disease which now interests you so much. Under those circumstances the one thing left for you to do will be to pray that the discovery will not come too late.

Surely when such days of sorrow and anxiety come you do not want to have the door of hope slammed shut in your face with the announcement that certain people who care for animals more than they care for men and women and little children have succeeded in stopping work in those very laboratories in which this most promising research was going on. I am sure that most of you would never consent to such a thing if only you understood the problem, and if only you believed university authorities when they assure you that today laboratory animals are well taken care of, and, when operated on, are always kept under surgical anesthesia.

The story goes that once upon a time a man of God was treed by an angry bear which started to climb up after him. At first the minister said: "O Lord, help me," but as the bear kept climbing higher, he finally prayed: "O Lord, if you won't help me, at least don't help the bear." And so I close with this plea: That while teachers of medicine and investigators struggle to advance medical science and to supply you and your children with ever better and abler and finer physicians and with ever more efficient treatments for disease, will you please refrain from helping those many persons who are always trying to lower standards of medical education and licensure, and are always trying to stop the work being carried on in the research laboratories. As Dr. John Abel, that grand old man of American medicine, once said, "Greater even than the greatest discovery is to keep open the way to future discoveries."

1936

Part 2

67786

Ancient and Medieval Times

Ancient and Medieval Times

SYNOPSIS

OUT *of primeval darkness comes primitive man into a world of fear, peopled by ghosts and demons, ruled by angry gods, dominated by mystery and magic. To protect himself from supernatural powers, he wears amulets. To ward off disease he carries fetishes. To allow the devil to escape, he cuts a hole in his head.*

In "The Medicine Man" Logan Clendening paints a fanciful picture of one of the first operations. He tells what it was expected to accomplish and how disease must have appeared to our early forbears. We are still deep in the age of magic. Yet something, aside from exorcism, has been done to drive out the devil of disease; and indeed the operation—cutting a hole in the head, or trephining, is still used in surgery. Unwittingly a step has been taken in the direction of scientific cure.

T. H. Huxley, the great nineteenth century scientist and lecturer, said, "I suppose that medicine and surgery first began by some savage more intelligent than the rest, discovering that a certain herb was good for a certain pain, and that a certain pull, somehow or other, set a dislocated joint right. I suppose all things had their humble beginnings, and medicine and surgery were in the same condition."[1] One of the earliest attempts to write down such methods of cure is the Ebers Papryus, described by Alvarez in the preceding section. The prescriptions given follow an incantation to be recited at the beginning. In the Egyptian mind magic and science are still blended, as in the Babylonian and

[1] From "On Medical Education" in "Science and Education," Appleton, 1894.

Byzantine prescriptions which follow. These illustrate the conception of disease as good or evil, the efficacy of the amulet, the mystic power of blood and of stones. The gods and superstition were still the ruling forces in medicine. The human body was sacred; no study of anatomy, no real analysis of disease could be made.

The best known of all these ancient formulations, which still influence the daily actions of millions, are the "Dietary and Sanitary Laws" of the Book of Leviticus. If they seem strange to sophisticated ears, they do at least attempt to codify rules of public health. The account of leprosy reflects Egyptian tabus, but shows an effort to observe the progress of disease.

Some four hundred years later, in 460 B.C. according to tradition, a child named Hippocrates was born on the island of Cos near the Asclepion, where his father was a priest. He was destined to become the greatest doctor of ancient Greece and to earn the title "The Father of Medicine." "To know is one thing," he said; "merely to believe one knows is another; to know is science, but merely to believe one knows is ignorance."

From his earliest years, Hippocrates set out to know—to observe for himself, to learn from actual observation instead of from magical belief. He brought medicine down to earth, into the hands of man and out of the hands of gods. He no longer feared their anger, no longer confused devils and diseases. To many this was heresy, but he gathered a school of disciples around him and his influence was profound.

Disease, said Hippocrates, was a part of the order of nature. Its progress could be watched; it could be cured by natural means. Therefore he observed the patient closely, noted the changing symptoms day by day, recorded case histories and prescribed accordingly. In the passages quoted in "The Wisdom of Hippocrates," we can watch him at work, this man who was the first great bedside physician, whose method of observation marked the true beginning of modern medicine.

"It appears to me," said Hippocrates of the "sacred disease," epilepsy, "to be nowise more divine nor more sacred than other diseases, but has a natural cause from which it originates like other affections." If the theory and the method implicit in this sentence had prevailed during succeeding centuries, the Dark Ages might never have engulfed Europe. But after his death, while lip service was paid to his name, the method which underlay his teachings

was ignored. His skepticism, his questioning spirit were buried under an immovable weight of dogma, dogma often justified on the grounds that it stemmed from Hippocrates himself.

Five hundred years later, another child, destined to have even greater influence, was born in Pergamun, Asia Minor. This child, named Galen, grew up to become a conceited and boastful man who claimed, "Whoever seeks fame need only become familiar with all that I have achieved." For twelve hundred years, Galen held sway over the Medieval world. His doctrines were strengthened rather than weakened with the years. For Galen took the observations of Hippocrates, combined them with other beliefs, made his own assumptions, drew his own conclusions, and worked out a dogmatic system of medicine that, like Aristotle's, appeared so perfect that it was never questioned.

Like Hippocrates, Galen made observations some of which you will read in "On Various Medical Subjects." He dissected a pig and the Barbary Ape to find out how they were formed. He examined the skeleton of a robber, and named the various parts of the body and the muscles—names still retained today. Unfortunately, he assumed that the anatomies of apes and men had much more similarity than is the case, and it remained for Vesalius, over a thousand years later, to point out Galen's numerous errors. He also made suggestions about the movement of the blood through the body, by veins and arteries. He believed that this movement was a kind of ebb and flow, and this error was not completely overthrown until Harvey's monumental publication in 1628. His greatest fault was that he fettered medicine with hypotheses. To quote Professor Victor Robinson in "The Story of Medicine," "Galen admired Euclid's method of proving things, and he tried to make medicine as exact a science as geometry ... In his system, everything was explained; everything was catalogued and tabulated. He answered all questions, he solved all problems. There seemed nothing left for others to do except to say, Amen. And so it was. Galen was the last of the Greeks and when he spoke no more, the voice of the ancient world was hushed. Galen was the final star that shone in the twilight of antiquity, and when his effulgence was extinguished, there settled over Europe a darkness that was not lifted for many centuries."

Out of that darkness, the historians bring us a story of quackery, of complete submission to authority, of brutal remedies and of plagues that sometimes wiped out whole populations. Hans

Zinsser, the famous epidemiologist, shows the disastrous effects of plague on history in "Epidemics and the Fall of Rome," taken from his best-selling book "Rats, Lice and History." What happened in a city stricken by plague is described with graphic detail in Boccaccio's classic "The Plague," taken from the "Decameron" and considered one of his finest pieces of writing.

Galen died about 200 A.D. His influence, with that of all Greek civilization, spread not only over Europe, but also into Syria and Arabia, with stagnating effect. Finally, in the Ninth Century, in Arabia, a doctor named Rhazes began again to question and observe. He was the first to give authentic descriptions of smallpox and measles. With his successor Avicenna, born in the following century, he helped relight the flame of learning. Unfortunately this inquiring spirit continued to be tempered too strongly by the dogmas of Galen. Therefore, when Avicenna, physician-in-chief to the hospital of Bagdad, decided to draw up a new classification of medicine and wrote it down in his great Canon of Medicine, his influence was more detrimental than helpful to future progress. "Avicenna," says Sir William Osler, "is the author of the most famous medical textbook ever written. It is safe to say that the 'Canon' was a medical bible for a longer period than any other work."[2] This book, which was indeed a monument of learning and of philosophical thought was read, not only in Arabia but soon, with the spread of Arabic influence after the Crusades, was translated into Latin and read throughout Europe. Its influence was even profounder than that of Galen.

It was a mixture of Hippocratic, Galenic and Arabian medicine which was taught at the medical schools that began to have importance in the Middle Ages. Yet in the best of these schools, an enlightened attitude appeared. John Ordronaux's comment on "The Medical School of Salernum" reveals a point of view which is in some respects strikingly modern. His translation of the "Code of Health of the School of Salernum," shows a common sense which makes its enormous popularity completely understandable. (According to Ordronaux, the Code was translated into eight languages from the original Latin, and appeared in a grand total of 163 editions, extending over several centuries.)

Yet it must be remembered that even in the best of the schools, dominated by church authority and by the infallibility of Galen and Avicenna, the training of the student was largely theoretical.

[2] In "The Evolution of Modern Medicine," Yale, 1921.

He never entered a laboratory, never dissected a corpse. Once a year, it is true, a pig was publicly dissected at Salerno, but it was considered sacrilegious to touch the human body. The first medical school to break away from this stifling rule was that of Bologna where, as early as 1200, it is said, a human dissection was made. But the practice was not carried farther for many years.

Meanwhile Fracastoro, writing on "The Sinister Shepherd" in 1530, could attribute syphilis, which was spreading in a terrifying way, to the dire influence of the sun and planets, particularly Venus. This poem, which named the venereal disease, is one of the most famous in medical history. Meanwhile, also, "Medieval Remedies," of which we give a short sampling, continued to be compounded of spider webs and mice and precious stones, to say nothing of ingredients far more horrible. As a result, people continued to die swiftly and surely. There was dire need for a Reawakening in the Medieval world ruled by the gods, the church and the alchemists.

The Medicine Man

LOGAN CLENDENING

In the dawn of time on a river-bank in the green land! Caves, piles of rudely fashioned stones, skins hung to dry—the litter of humans.

Htebh stood at the cave mouth, sadly gazing at his son. The youth was in the throes of his terrible malady again.

He had felt it coming on. That was the strange thing about this demon that possessed him. It gave warnings. The boy had known the fit was coming and had staggered up to the plot of grass under the great tree. He had learned from experience that it was safer for him to be on the grass away from stones or logs.

There he lay panting now, for the fit had passed. First he had emitted a great shout—a tortured cry of agony as his head was thrown back, his arms and legs were drawn into convulsion after convulsion which racked him, his eyes turned up and the froth formed in his mouth.

The women came crowding to the mouth of the cave. Most of them gave one glance and went back to their work, for the wretched boy's attacks were a familiar sight by this time. Only his mother sat down and, covering her face with her hands, rocked herself to and fro, moaning.

One of the boy's brothers, coming up the steep slope from the river below, glanced at the quivering figure under the tree and laughed derisively. But Htebh rebuked him.

"Fool! And of a fool's litter!" he cried. "Do you wish to court devils? The fiend that inhabits thy brother may spawn and send some of his brood into thy head."

36

The awesome warning served to quiet the scoffer.

The grandmother came out of the cave and waddled over to the prostrate figure. Taking out of her bag a sharpened fish-bone, she grasped the lad's arm and thrust the point of the bone into one of the veins that could be plainly seen beneath the skin. The blood flowed freely.

Htebh made no sign at this, nor any attempt to stop her. But they had tried that before. The devils which caused this malady did not flow out of the body with the blood.

"Go fetch the medicine man, Astur," he commanded the youth who had laughed.

By the time the priest and medicine man with his train of assistants could be seen coming up the river path, the sick boy was to all outward appearances perfectly well. His mother sat over him crooning and rubbing his forehead.

"The demon still tortures my son," Htebh announced to Astur.

The medicine man frowned portentously at this, as if to rebuke boy and demon both.

"I have tried everything," Htebh continued. "The demon resists all my magic. Do not forget that I have tried the incantation of the seven fishes, and still the demon returns. His blood has flown over and over again, and still the demon does not leave him."

"Ay," said the medicine man, solemnly, "these devils which cause convulsions inhabit the head." Here the priest tapped his forehead. "We must give them a way to get out. We must make an opening there."

Htebh nodded in agreement and acquiescence.

"Send for Achot, the trephiner," commanded the priest.

"I know these demons," explained the medicine man while they awaited the arrival of the trephiner. "When I was young, my father pointed out to me one of our tribesmen who had been in the great battle with the warriors of the Folk Beyond the East. In the battle he had been struck on the right side of the head by a spear. The spear was flung with great force and broke the bone. But on the point of that spear the medicine worker of the Folk Beyond the East had witched a demon, and it entered the head of our tribesman and he suffered as does your boy. Hy!" Here the medicine man's voice sunk to a whisper. "Do you know something else that was strange about that demon? My father pointed it out to me and I have seen it since with my own eyes. Though the hole was in the right side of the head, it was the left arm and leg that was convulsed. These are subtle demons. They roam through all parts."

The trephiner was a man of venerable appearance. He had been brought up to do this work. His father and his father's father had been trephiners before him.

With him had come also the high priest and the headman of the tribe.

The patient was laid out on the ground. His hands and feet were bound with thongs. His head was laid on a stone.

The priest stood at his head. A circle of priests and tribesmen sat around the prostrate form. The medicine man walked round and round inside this circle chanting a religious hymn. The circle of helpers rocked back and forth emitting long-drawn wails for help.

The trephiner laid out several sharp-edged flints on a flat rock. He put some soft dried moss beside him, and, speaking gently and encouragingly to the boy, he made a swift cut through the skin of the scalp. He mopped the blood up with his dry moss and put his hand out for a glowing brand of wood which his assistant handed him from the fire. He seared the edges of the scalp wound, and the victim for the first time let out a long wail of pain. The incantations rose in volume.

Exposing the smooth plate of bone, the trephiner now took one of his sharp-edged flints and began to scrape the bone. The victim writhed a little from time to time, but did not complain much. It probably hurt him less than the dentist of our own day hurts one of his patients with his drill.

A priest came forward and put a cup of mistletoe wine to the boy's lips. He drank several cups during the operation, so that by the time the opening was completed, he was snoring happily.

The surgeon packed wet moss over the wound and left him sleeping in the cave. For several days he tossed with fever. Matter came running from the wound. The priest said it was the sign the devil inside was dying. Wine was poured on the wound. The old grandmother brought herbs from the woods to quiet him.

Finally he was able to be up and about. And, sure enough, the demons did not trouble him for all of that summer and the winter following and the next winter.

But then the demon returned. He had another convulsion, and the trephiner, with the help of the priest, made a hole on the opposite side of his head. For a while again there was no falling sickness, and then the boy disappeared. Search of the country-side failed to find him. Weeks later his body was found at the foot of a cliff. Probably, they said, the demon returned and attacked him as he was standing on the edge, and in his convulsion he threw himself over and was killed. . . .

This story of mine, while it is entirely fanciful, has firm basis in reality.

Skulls with round trephine openings in them have been found in prehistoric human excavations all over the world. These holes were not made in the skull after death, because many of them show, around the edges of the opening, evidence that the bone has grown in an attempt at healing. From the same signs we decide that the trephining did not kill the patient. Some skulls show several trephine openings of different dates—some more healed than others.

Further conviction is added by the knowledge that certain primitives still perform trephining. "Lucas Championnière saw a Kabyle thonbit who told him it was quite common among his tribe; he was the son of a family of trephiners, and had undergone the operation four times; his father, twelve times; he had three brothers, also experts; he did not consider it a dangerous operation. He did it most frequently for pain in the head, and occasionally for a fracture." (Osler: "Evolution of Modern Medicine.")

Trephining, of course, is performed as one of the standard operations of modern surgery. It consists in taking a plate out of the bony dome of the skull. It is performed for various purposes. Remember that the skull is an unyielding casket for the brain—very useful because it protects perfectly this most vital of all structures. But the arrangement has its disadvantages. When disease occurs inside the skull—when, for instance, a tumour begins to grow—the vital brain substance is compressed and destroyed. The surgeon renders help in these circumstances by making an opening in the skull—trephining. This opening allows the contents to bulge and reduces the headache and other sufferings, preserves the intellect, and prolongs life. Sometimes through such openings it is possible to remove the tumour or loosen adhesions which are causing trouble.

This primitive operation of trephining represents one of the first upward steps we can discern in the development of scientific medicine.

Before that, all explanation of disease was magic. Devils had entered the sick man's body.

The cure for this was exorcism—driving the devils out by incantation. Ceremonies of exorcism—sometimes a ritual dance, sometimes a personal service of prayer, fast, and confession—were performed by the medicine man.

The most primitive human community may be compared to a unicellular animal. There was no specialization, no division of work. Just as the primitive animal, a single cell, takes on all the functions of the body—it digests, moves, reacts, excretes, etc.—so the primitive family did all the work of a complex society—growing edible plants, fishing, hunting, making clothes and pots, house-building, herding, defending, etc. When specialization began, it was by the formation of a caste—the priestly caste, which at first included the functions of king, judge, and medicine man, as well as priest.

The reason for the formation of just this caste, which seems to us the least important branch of practical business, is to be found in the leaning of the primitive mind towards a mystical explanation for the universe. The priest, the medicine man, could influence unseen powers which brought rain for the crops, could prevent cataclysms of nature, such as floods, earthquakes, and volcanoes, and could also bring and take away disease.

To perform this work the medicine man was especially selected. Usually he was marked out from birth. In Liberia twins are regarded as particularly gifted. Seventh sons, as is well known, are attuned to the whisperings of the infinite. And, of course, the seventh son of a seventh son is doubly dyed. One such, a fiery old fellow, in the Highlands of Scotland, who was a militant atheist, was nevertheless up to a few years ago constantly besieged by his neighbours and even awakened in the dead of night to touch sick people brought to his door.

Babies who come into the world feet first are adept at setting fractures and curing lumbago. Those who have fits, trances, convulsions, dreams, or nightmares are obviously the tabernacles of divine visitation. . . .

Another branch of magic, which may be called witchcraft, supposes that it is possible for one person to "send" disease upon another.

A simple form of witchcraft lies in the theory of the effigy. If a savage makes an effigy of a man, he somehow controls that man's mana. All primitive people object violently to being photographed or painted. Magical law says that their images are themselves. An Ojibway medicine man will construct a wooden doll—an image of his petitioner's enemy—and run a needle into the eye or heart: then the enemy will go blind or die of heart pangs.

Any part of the body must be kept out of the hands of an enemy: hair, nail parings, fæcal matter, even clothes or soil in which are bare footprints. For the enemy will use these in lieu of the body itself and work destruction. The Victorian Blacks burn an enemy's cast-off hair and cause fever. In Scotland up to thirty years ago to burn fæces caused dysentery.

Even the enemy's name is an effigy. The curse which you just breathed against the county assessor is a witness of your belief in the power of "sending" disease.

Human beings may possess the power to confer disease and misfortune, as witness the evil eye.

Just as the treatment for demoniacal possession was exorcism, so the prevention of witchcraft was a charm.

To ward off the evil eye, raise the hand with the middle fingers closed.

Amulets, talismans, cryptic writings! There is the story of a youth at Oxford who went out into the fields and sat beneath a tree to study. Idly he traced some Greek letters upon a sheet of paper—one lovely phrase that caught his fancy. Idly he fell asleep, and when he woke, the twilight was grey about him. A young girl—a country lass—had been watching him and shyly asked for the paper on which the Greek words were written. He gave it to her and, gathering up his books, strolled back to his study. And time went on and he left Oxford. He succeeded in his work and was made a judge. One day he was presiding at Oxford and they brought before him a miserable old woman, accused of being a witch. The country-folk said she charmed the cattle with a paper on which was cabbalistic writing. The judge asked to see it, and they passed it up to him. Dimly the old man seemed to remember something familiar. Then suddenly it came to him: the so potent charm was that chorus ending from Euripides which he had scribbled and left beneath the grey towers of Oxford long ago when all the world was young.

Of other charms and healing ways:
Iron is widely regarded as having specially valuable properties:

"Let the superstitious wife
Near the child's head lay a knife,
Point be up and haft be downe
While she gossips in the towne
This 'mong other mystic charms
Keep the sleeping child from harms."

Stones.—Mad stones are still used for the bite of a mad dog. The milpreve is a blue stone supposed to be concentrated crystallized snake-venom. In the west of England they are hung around the necks of cattle to prevent the bites of adders. If one gets a stone from the stomach or gall-bladder of an animal (a bezoar stone), it is naturally more powerful than any ordinary stone.

Rings, bands, belts, and necklaces.—Constriction cures are everywhere practised. Rheumatism rings are an example. In Derbyshire a red thread is tied around the neck to prevent goitre. In Los Angeles an "electric" belt worn about the waist produces sexual virility.

Healing wells and waters.—Though largely used for skin troubles and eye diseases, the use of running water or spring water is not confined to those maladies exclusively.

"Now, there is at Jerusalem by the sheep market a pool, which is called in the Hebrew tongue Bethesda, having five porches. In these lay a great multitude of impotent folk, of blind, halt, withered, waiting for the moving of the water. For an angel went down at a certain season into the pool and troubled the water; whosoever then first after the troubling of the water stepped in was made whole of whatsoever disease he had." (John v. 2-4.)

Spittle.—"Everybody has heard of cures by saliva. . . . Warts, contracted sinews, wounds, sores, and skin-rashes in general, are to this day treated by the application of saliva, that secreted in the morning before breakfast being considered the most efficacious. . . .

"When a Dyak of Borneo is seized with vomiting and sweating he thinks that an unfriendly ancestral spirit has chased out his soul and has taken its place. So he sends for a wise woman . . . and after she has identified the intruding spirit . . . an effigy is moulded from the ashes of the hearth, and . . . the wise woman moves it seven times up and down before the patient. Then the patient spits upon the image, and the disease is thereby transferred to the spirit via his effigy." (Dan McKenzie: *The Infancy of Medicine*.)

"In Ireland, fasting spittle is considered of great efficacy by the peasants for sore eyes, especially if mixed with clay taken from a holy well. This is made into a paste and applied to the eyes." (Lady Wilde: *Ancient Cures of Ireland*. London, 1890.)

Transference of disease to animals.—"Frog in the throat" is a disease of Cheshire which is treated by holding the head of a frog in the child's mouth for a few moments; the disease passes into the animal.

The orthodox method of curing abdominal cramps is to hold a live animal on the belly. For gripes, according to Marcellus (A.D. 300), a live duck was applied to the abdomen, and the pains passed into the duck, "to whom they prove fatal."

Goitre can be transferred to a corpse, by having the hand of the corpse (especially of a young child or a suicide) touch the enlarged thyroid nine times. A young woman was led on the scaffold of Old Bailey in order to get rid of a wen by having it touched by the hand of the man just executed. In Northampton patients used to congregate around the gallows in order to receive the "dead stroke." The fee went to the hangman.

To be cured of a particularly obstinate venereal disease the patient must have intercourse with a *virgo intacta*, the disease being entirely transferred to the second person.

Scourging and whipping.—"In case a man be lunatic, take skin of a mere swine, work it into an whip and swinge the man therewith: soon he will be well." (Saxon Leechdoms.)

The Quixos Indians treat illness by whipping the patient with nettles.

Compared with such things, trephining was a sheer intellectual leap.

The devil was still the cause of the disease. But they had located the devil. The symptoms of epilepsy or headache or insanity were those belonging to the head. The devil who caused this sort of mischief was in the skull. Therefore, make a hole there to drive him out.

It was the beginning of reason.

1933

Ancient Remedies

EGYPTIAN

The Ebers Papyrus

If thou examinest a person with a misery in the epigastrium, he has pain in the arm, the breasts, and the belly and he is told that it is the uat disease (the green-sickness) sayest thou, accordingly, "It is caused by death which has entered the mouth and taken up its abode there." Make him a medicine of the following plants: tehua berries, poppies, peppermint, annek, the red seeds of sechet, cook it in oil and let the patient drink thereof.

Lay thy hand upon him, his arm is easily extended and free of pain. Say, "This disease has passed through its proper intestinal route to the anus, I shall not repeat the medicine."

Circa 850 B.C.

BABYLONIAN

For Gastric Complaint: If a man has stomach pain, let that man kneel on his feet and have burning juice of cassia poured over him, and he will recover. If *ditto* let him kneel on his feet and let cold water flow over him. If *ditto*, place his head downwards and his feet up, strike his cheek forcibly, rub him violently, say to his stomach, "Be Good."

BYZANTINE

Alexander of Tralles (525-605)

For Colic: Remove the nipple-like projection from the caecum of a young pig, mix myrrh with it, wrap it in the skin of a wolf or dog, and instruct the patient to wear it as an amulet during the waning of the moon. Striking effects may be looked for from this remedy.

Paul of Aegina (625-690)

On the Curative Powers of the Blood of Animals: Sanguis, Blood; no kind of it is of a cold nature, but that of swine is liquid and less hot, being very like the human in temperament. That of common pigeons, the wood pigeons, and the turtle, being of a moderate temperament, if injected hot, removes extravasated blood about the eye from a blow; and when poured upon the durameter, in cases of trephining, it is anti-inflammatory. That of the owl, when drunk with wine or water, relieves dyspnoea. The blood of bats, it is said, is a preservative to the breasts of virgins, and, if rubbed in, it keeps the hair from growing; and in like manner also that of frogs and the blood of the chameleon and the dog-tick. But Galen, having made trial of all these remedies, says that they disappointed him. But that of goats, owing to its dryness, if drunk with milk, is beneficial in cases of dropsy, and breaks down stones in the kidneys. That of domestic fowls stops hemorrhages of the membranes of the brain, and that of lambs cures epilepsies. The recently coagulated blood of kids, if drunk with an equal quantity of vinegar, to the amount of half a hemina, cures vomiting of blood from the chest. The blood of bears, of wild goats, of buck goats, and of bulls, is said to ripen apostemes. That of the land crocodile produces acuteness of vision. The blood of stallions is mixed with septic medicines. The antidote from bloods is given for deadly poisons, and contains the blood of the duck, of the stag, and of the goose.

On stones used in the treatment of disease.

Bloodstone—for hemorrhages, fungous ulcers, hemoptysis, and trachoma.

Jasper—as an amulet—for treatment of gastric complaints.

Judaic-stone—used as a restorative from hysterical fits.

Sapphirus (usually lapis-lazuli)—for ophthalmic diseases and internal ulcerations.

Dietary and Sanitary Laws; Diagnosis of Leprosy

From *THE BOOK OF LEVITICUS*
DISTINCTION OF MEATS, CLEAN AND UNCLEAN

AND the LORD spake unto Moses and to Aaron, saying unto them,

Speak unto the children of Israel, saying, These *are* the beasts which ye shall eat among all the beasts that *are* on the earth.

Whatsoever parteth the hoof, and is clovenfooted, *and* cheweth the cud, among the beasts, that shall ye eat.

Nevertheless these shall ye not eat of them that chew the cud, or of them that divide the hoof: *as* the camel, because he cheweth the cud, but divideth not the hoof; he *is* unclean unto you.

And the coney, because he cheweth the cud, but divideth not the hoof; he *is* unclean unto you.

And the hare, because he cheweth the cud, but divideth not the hoof; he *is* unclean unto you.

And the swine, though he divide the hoof, and be cloven-footed, yet he cheweth not the cud; he *is* unclean to you.

Of their flesh shall ye not eat, and their carcass shall ye not touch; they *are* unclean to you.

These shall ye eat of all that *are* in the waters: whatsoever hath fins and scales in the waters, in the seas, and in the rivers, them shall ye eat.

And all that have not fins and scales in the seas, and in the rivers, of all that move in the waters, and of any living thing which *is* in the waters, they *shall be* an abomination unto you:

They shall be even an abomination unto you; ye shall not eat of their flesh, but ye shall have their carcasses in abomination.

Whatsoever hath no fins nor scales in the waters, that *shall be* an abomination unto you.

And these *are they which* ye shall have in abomination among the fowls; they shall not be eaten, they *are* an abomination: the eagle, and the ossifrage, and the ospray,

And the vulture, and the kite after his kind;

Every raven after his kind;

And the owl, and the night hawk, and the cuckow, and the hawk after his kind,

And the little owl, and the cormorant, and the great owl,

And the swan, and the pelican, and the gier eagle,

And the stork, the heron after her kind, and the lapwing, and the bat.

All fowls that creep, going upon *all* four, *shall be* an abomination unto you.

THE PURIFICATION OF A WOMAN

And the Lord spake unto Moses, saying,

Speak unto the children of Israel, saying, If a woman have conceived seed, and born a man child: then she shall be unclean seven days; according to the days of the separation for her infirmity shall she be unclean.

And in the eighth day the flesh of his foreskin shall be circumcised.

And she shall then continue in the blood of her purifying three and thirty days; she shall touch no hallowed thing, nor come into the sanctuary, until the days of her purifying be fulfilled.

But if she bear a maid child, then she shall be unclean two weeks, as in her separation: and she shall continue in the blood of her purifying threescore and six days. . . .

DIAGNOSIS OF LEPROSY

And the LORD spake unto Moses and Aaron, saying,

When a man shall have in the skin of his flesh a rising, a scab, or bright spot, and it be in the skin of his flesh *like* the plague of leprosy; then he shall be brought unto Aaron the priest, or unto one of his sons the priests:

And the priest shall look on the plague in the skin of the flesh: and *when* the hair in the plague is turned white, and the plague in sight *be* deeper than the skin of his flesh, it *is* a plague of leprosy: and the priest shall look on him, and pronounce him unclean.

If the bright spot *be* white in the skin of his flesh, and in sight *be* not deeper than the skin, and the hair thereof be not turned white; then the priest shall shut up *him that hath* the plague seven days:

And the priest shall look on him the seventh day: and, behold, *if* the plague in his sight be at a stay, *and* the plague spread not in the skin; then the priest shall shut him up seven days more:

And the priest shall look on him again the seventh day: and, behold, *if* the plague *be* somewhat dark, *and* the plague spread not in the skin, the priest shall pronounce him clean: it *is but* a scab: and he shall wash his clothes, and be clean.

But if the scab spread much abroad in the skin, after that he hath been seen of the priest for his cleansing, he shall be seen of the priest again:

And *if* the priest see that, behold, the scab spreadeth in the skin, then the priest shall pronounce him unclean: it *is* a leprosy.

When the plague of leprosy is in a man, then he shall be brought unto the priest;

And the priest shall see *him:* and, behold, *if* the rising *be* white in the skin, and it have turned the hair white, and *there be* quick raw flesh in the rising;

It *is* an old leprosy in the skin of his flesh, and the priest shall pronounce him unclean, and shall not shut him up: for he *is* unclean.

And if a leprosy break out abroad in the skin, and the leprosy cover all the skin of *him that hath* the plague from his head even to his foot, wheresoever the priest looketh;

Then the priest shall consider: and, behold, *if* the leprosy have covered all his flesh, he shall pronounce *him* clean *that hath* the plague: it is all turned white: he *is* clean.

But when raw flesh appeareth in him, he shall be unclean.

And the priest shall see the raw flesh, and pronounce him to be unclean: *for* the raw flesh *is* unclean: it *is* a leprosy.

Or if the raw flesh turn again, and be changed unto white, he shall come unto the priest;

And the priest shall see him: and, behold, *if* the plague be turned into white; then the priest shall pronounce *him* clean *that hath* the plague: he *is* clean. . . .

And the leper in whom the plague *is*, his clothes shall be rent, and his head bare, and he shall put a covering upon his upper lip, and shall cry, Unclean, unclean.

All the days wherein the plague *shall be* in him he shall be defiled; he *is unclean*: he shall dwell alone; without the camp *shall* his habitation be. . . .

From the King James version of the Bible.
Circa 850 B.C.

The Wisdom of Hippocrates

APHORISMS

LIFE is short, and the Art long; the occasion fleeting; experience fallacious, and judgment difficult. The physician must not only be prepared to do what is right himself, but also to make the patient, the attendants and externals co-operate.

A slender and restricted diet is always dangerous in chronic diseases, and also in acute diseases, where it is not requisite. And again, a diet brought to the extreme point of attenuation is dangerous; and repletion, when in the extreme, is also dangerous.

Old persons endure fasting most easily; next, adults; young persons not nearly so well; and most especially infants, and of them such as are of a particularly lively spirit.

In whatever disease sleep is laborious, it is a deadly symptom; but if sleep does good, it is not deadly.

When sleep puts an end to delirium, it is a good symptom.

Both sleep and insomnolency, when immoderate, are bad.

It is better that a fever succeed to a convulsion, than a convulsion to a fever.

Persons who are naturally very fat are apt to die earlier than those who are slender.

In every movement of the body, whenever one begins to endure pain, it will be relieved by rest.

Phthisis most commonly occurs between the ages of eighteen and thirty-five years.

In persons who cough up frothy blood, the discharge of it comes from the lungs.

Sneezing coming on, in the case of a person afflicted with hiccup, removes the hiccup.

Eunuchs do not take the gout, or become bald.

A woman does not take the gout, unless her menses be stopped.

A young man does not take the gout until he indulges in coition.

In acute diseases, coldness of the extremities is bad.

A chill supervening on a sweat is not good.

If a dropsical patient be seized with hiccup the case is hopeless.

METHOD OF PROGNOSIS

I

It appears to me a most excellent thing for the physician to cultivate prognosis; for by foreseeing and foretelling, in the presence of the sick, the present, the past, and the future, and explaining the omissions which patients have been guilty of, he will be the more readily believed to be acquainted with the circumstances of the sick; so that men will have confidence to intrust themselves to such a physician. And he will manage the cure best who has foreseen what is to happen from the present state of matters. For it is impossible to make all the sick well; this, indeed, would have been better than to be able to foretell what is going to happen; but since men die, some even before calling the physi-

cian, from the violence of the disease, and some die immediately
after calling him, having lived, perhaps, only one day or a little
longer, and before the physician could bring his art to counteract
the disease, it therefore becomes necessary to know the nature
of such affections, how far they are above the powers of the
constitution; and, moreover, if there be anything divine in the
diseases, and to learn a foreknowledge of this also. Thus a man
will be the more esteemed to be a good physician, for he will be
the better able to treat those aright who can be saved, from having long anticipated everything; and by seeing and announcing
beforehand those who will live and those who will die, he will
thus escape censure.

II

He should observe thus in acute diseases; first, the countenance
of the patient, if it be like itself, for this is the best of all; whereas
the most opposite to it is the worst, such as the following: a sharp
nose, hollow eyes, collapsed temples; the ears cold, contracted,
and their lobes turned out; the skin about the forehead being
rough, distended, and parched; the color of the whole face being
green, black, livid, or lead-colored.[1] If the countenance be such
at the commencement of the disease and if this cannot be accounted for from the other symptoms, inquiry must be made
whether the patient has long wanted sleep; whether his bowels
have been very loose; and whether he has suffered from want of
food; and if any of these causes be confessed to, the danger is to
be reckoned so far less; and it becomes obvious, in the course of a
day and a night, whether or not the appearance of the countenance proceed from these causes. But if none of these be said to
exist, and if the symptoms do not subside in the aforesaid time,
it is to be known for certain that death is at hand. And, also, if
the disease be in a more advanced stage either on the third or
fourth day, and the countenance be such, the same inquiries as
formerly directed are to be made, and the other symptoms are to
be noted, those in the whole countenance, those on the body, and
those in the eyes; for if they shun the light, or weep involuntarily,
or squint, or if the one be less than the other, or if the white of
them be red, livid, or has black veins in it; if there be a gum upon
the eyes, if they are restless, protruding, or are become very
hollow; and if the countenance be squalid and dark, or the color

[1] The Hippocratic facies.

of the whole face be changed—all these are to be reckoned bad and fatal symptoms. The physician should also observe the appearance of the eyes from below the eyelids in sleep; for when a portion of the white appears owing to the eyelids not being closed together, and when this is connected with diarrhea or purgation from medicine, or when the patient does not sleep thus from habit, it is to be reckoned an unfavorable and very deadly symptom; but if the eyelid be contracted, livid, or pale, or also the lip, or nose, along with some of the other symptoms, one may know for certain that death is close at hand. It is a mortal symptom also, when the lips are relaxed, pendent, cold, and blanched.

CHILDBIRTH FEVER

The wife of Epicrates, who was lodged at the house of Archigetes, being near the term of delivery, was seized with a violent rigor, and, as was said, she did not become heated; next day the same. On the third, she was delivered of a daughter, and everything went on properly. On the day following her delivery she was seized with acute fever, pain in the cardiac region of the stomach, and in the genital parts. Having had a suppository, was in so far relieved; pain in the head, neck, loins; no sleep; alvine discharges scanty, bilious, thin, and unmixed; urine thin and blackish. Toward the night of the sixth day from the time she was seized with the fever, became delirious. On the seventh, all the symptoms exacerbated; insomnolency, delirium, thirst; stools bilious and high-colored. On the eighth, had a rigor; slept more. On the ninth, the same. On the tenth, her limbs painfully affected; pain again of the cardiac region of the stomach; heaviness of the head; no delirium; slept more; bowels constipated. On the eleventh, passed urine of a better color and, having an abundant sediment, felt lighter. On the fourteenth, had a rigor; acute fever. On the fifteenth, had a copious vomiting of bilious and yellow matters; sweated; fever gone; at night acute fever; urine thick, sediment white. On the seventeenth, an exacerbation; night uncomfortable; no sleep; delirium. On the eighteenth, thirsty; tongue parched; no sleep; much delirium; legs painfully affected. About the twentieth, in the morning, had a slight rigor; was comatose; slept tranquilly; had slight vomiting of bilious and black matters; towards night deafness. About the twenty-first, weight generally in the left side, with pain; slight cough; urine thick, muddy, and reddish; when allowed to stand, had no sediment; in other respects

felt lighter; fever not gone; fauces painful from the commencement, and red; uvula retracted; defluxion remained acrid, pungent,
and saltish throughout. About the twenty-seventh, free of fever;
sediment in the urine; pain in the side. About the thirty-first was
attacked with fever, bilious diarrhea; slight bilious vomiting on
the fortieth. Had a complete crisis, and was freed from the fever
on the eightieth day.

Blood Poisoning

Criton, in Thasus, while still on foot, and going about, was
seized with a violent pain in the great toe; he took to bed the same
day, had rigors and nausea, recovered his heat slightly, at night
was delirious. On the second, swelling of the whole foot, and
about the ankle erythema, with distension, and small bullae
(phlyctaenae); acute fever; he became furiously deranged; alvine
discharges bilious, unmixed and rather frequent. He died on the
second day from the commencement.

On the Sacred Disease

It appears to me to be nowise more divine nor more sacred
than other diseases, but has a natural cause from which it originates
like other affections. Men regard its nature and cause as divine
from disease and wonder, because it is not at all like to other
diseases. And this notion of its divinity is kept up by their inability to comprehend it, and the simplicity of the mode by which
it is cured, for men are freed from it by purifications and
incantations. But if it is reckoned divine because it is wonderful,
instead of one there are many diseases which would be sacred; for,
as I will show, there are others no less wonderful and prodigious,
which nobody imagines to be sacred. The quotidian, tertian, and
quartan fevers, seem to me no less sacred and divine in their origin
than this disease, although they are not reckoned so wonderful.
And I see men become mad and demented from no manifest
cause, and at the same time doing many things out of place; and
I have known many persons in sleep groaning and crying out,
some in a state of suffocation, some jumping up and fleeing out of
doors, and deprived of their reason until they awaken, and afterwards becoming well and rational as before, although they be
pale and weak; and this will happen not once but frequently. And
there are many and various things of the like kind, which it would
be tedious to state particularly. And they who first referred this

disease to the gods, appear to me to have been just such persons as the conjurors, purificators, mountebanks, and charlatans now are, who give themselves out for being excessively religious, and as knowing more than other people. Such persons, then, using the divinity as a pretext and screen of their own inability to afford any assistance, having given out that the disease is sacred, adding suitable reasons for this opinion, they have instituted a mode of treatment which is safe for themselves, namely, by applying purifications and incantations, and enforcing abstinence from baths and many articles of food which are unwholesome to men in diseases.

460-377 B.C.

On Various Medical Subjects

CLARISSIMUS GALEN

GALEN'S CONCEIT OF HIMSELF

I HAVE done as much to medicine as Trajan did to the Roman Empire, in making bridges and roads throughout Italy. It is I alone that have pointed out the true method of treating diseases: it must be confessed that Hippocrates had already chalked out the same road, but as the first discoverer, he has not gone so far as we could wish; his writings are defective in order, in the necessary distinctions; his knowledge in some subjects is not sufficiently extensive; he is often obscure after the manner of the ancients, in order to be concise; he opened the road, but I have rendered it passable.

BONES OF APES AND MEN

First of all, then, I would ask you to make yourself well acquainted with the human bones, and not to look on this as a matter of secondary importance. Nor must you merely read the subject up in one of these books which are called by some "Osteology," by others "The Skeleton," and by others simply "On Bones," as is my own book; which, by the way, I am certain is better than any previously written, both as regards the exactitude of its matter and the brevity and clearness of its explanations. Make it your earnest business, then, not only to learn exactly from the book the appearance of each of the bones, but to become yourself by the use of your own eyes an eager firsthand observer of human osteology.

At Alexandria this is very easy, since the physicians in that country accompany the instruction they give to their students with opportunities for personal inspection. Hence you must try to get to Alexandria for this reason alone, if for no other. But if you cannot manage this, still it is not impossible to obtain a view of human bones. Personally I have very often had a chance to do this where tombs or monuments have become broken up. On one occasion a river, having risen to the level of a grave which had been carelessly constructed a few months previously, easily disintegrated this; then by the force of its current it swept right over the dead man's body, of which the flesh had already putrefied, while the bones were still closely attached to one another. This it carried away downstream for the distance of a league, till, coming to a lakelike stretch with sloping banks, it here deposited the corpse. And here the latter lay ready for inspection, just as though prepared by a doctor for his pupil's lesson.

Once also I examined the skeleton of a robber, lying on a mountainside a short distance from the road. This man had been killed by some traveler whom he had attacked, but who had been too quick for him. None of the inhabitants of the district would bury him; but in their detestation of him they were delighted when his body was eaten by birds of prey; the latter, in fact, devoured the flesh in two days and left the skeleton ready, as it were, for anyone who cared to enjoy an anatomical demonstration.

As regards yourself, then, even if you do not have the luck to see anything like this, still you can dissect an ape, and learn each of the bones from it, by carefully removing the flesh. For this purpose you must choose the apes which most resemble man. . . .

Thus if you should also later meet with a human skeleton, you would easily recognize and remember everything. . . .

A PSYCHIATRIC DIAGNOSIS

I was called in to see a woman who was stated to be sleepless at night and to lie tossing about from one position into another. Finding she had no fever, I made a detailed inquiry into everything that had happened to her, especially considering such factors as we know to cause insomnia. But she either answered little or nothing at all, as if to show that it was useless to question her. Finally she turned away, hiding herself completely by throwing the bedclothes over her whole body, and laying her head on another small pillow, as if desiring sleep.

After leaving I came to the conclusion that she was suffering from one of two things: either from a melancholy dependent on black bile, or else trouble about something she was unwilling to confess. I therefore deferred till the next day a closer investigation of this. Further, on first arriving I was told by her attendant maid that she could not at present be seen; and on returning a second time, I was told the same again. So I went yet a third time, but the attendant asked me to go away, as she did not want her mistress disturbed. Having learned, however, that when I left she had washed and taken food in her customary manner, I came back the next day, and in a private conversation with the maid on one subject and another I found out exactly what was worrying the patient. And this I discovered by chance.

After I had diagnosed that there was no bodily trouble, and that the woman was suffering from some mental uneasiness, it happened that, at the very time I was examining her, this was confirmed. Somebody came from the theater and said he had seen Pylades dancing. Then both her expression and the color of her face changed. Seeing this, I applied my hand to her wrist and noticed that her pulse had suddenly become extremely irregular (*anomalous*). This kind of pulse indicates that the mind is disturbed; thus it occurs also in people who are disputing over any subject. So on the next day I said to one of my followers that, when I paid my visit to the woman, he was to come a little later and announce to me, "Morphus is dancing today." When he said this, I found that the pulse was unaffected. Similarly also on the next day, when I had an announcement made about the third member of the troupe, the pulse remained unchanged as before. On the fourth evening I kept very careful watch when it was announced that Pylades was dancing, and I noticed that the pulse was very much disturbed. Thus I found out that the woman was in love with Pylades, and by careful watch on the succeeding days my discovery was confirmed.

Similarly, too, I diagnosed the case of a slave who administered the household of another wealthy man, and who sickened in the same way. He was concerned about having to give an account of his expenses, in which he knew that there was a considerable sum wanting; the thought of this kept him awake, and he grew thin with anxiety. I first told his master that there was nothing physically wrong with the old man, and advised an investigation to be made as to whether he feared his master was about to ask an account of the sums he had entrusted to him, and for this reason was worried, knowing that a considerable amount would be found wanting. The master told me I had made a good suggestion, so in order to make the diagnosis certain, I advised him to do as follows: he was to tell the slave to give him back all the money he had in hand, lest, in the event of his sudden death, it should be lost, owing to the administration passing into the hands of some other servant whom he did not know, for there would be no use asking for an account from such an one. And when the master said this to him, he felt sure he would not be questioned. So he ceased to worry, and by the third day had regained his natural physical condition.

Now what was it that escaped the notice of previous physicians when examining the aforesaid woman and the aforesaid slave? For such discoveries are made by common inductions (*epilogisms*) if one has even the smallest acquaintance with medical science. I suppose it is because they have no clear conception (*diagnosis*) of how the body tends to be affected by mental conditions. Possibly also they do not know that the pulse is altered by quarrels and alarms which suddenly disturb the mind.

THE EMPEROR'S CASE HISTORY

What happened in the case of the Emperor [Marcus Aurelius] himself was really wonderful. His own opinion and that of the physicians of his entourage who had gone abroad with him was that some febrile paroxysm had begun. But they all proved wrong both on the second and third day, in the morning and at the third hour. He had on the preceding day taken a draught of bitter aloes at the first hour, and then some theriac, as was his daily custom. Next he took some food about the sixth hour, washed at sunset, and had a small meal. During the whole night there ensued colicky pains with intestinal evacuations. This made him feverish, and when his attendant physicians observed this, they gave orders that he should be kept quiet; then they prescribed slop diet at the ninth hour. After this I was myself also summoned to come and sleep in the palace. Then, when the lamps were newly lit, a messenger came to call me at the Emperor's bidding. Three doctors had been observing him since about daybreak, and two of them feeling his pulse, and they all considered this the beginning of a febrile attack. I stood by, however, without saying anything; so the Emperor, looking at me first, asked why, when the others felt his pulse, I alone did not do so. I said to him, "Two of these gentlemen have already done this, and probably when they were abroad with you they already learned by experience the characteristics of your pulse; hence I expect they will be better able to judge its present condition [diathesis]." On my saying this he bade me also feel his pulse. It seemed to me that, taking his age and constitution into account, the pulse was far from indicating the beginning of a febrile attack. I declared that this was no onset of fever, but that his stomach was overloaded by the food he had taken, which had turned to phlegm prior to ejection.

My diagnosis seemed praiseworthy to the Emperor, and he repeated three times in succession: "That's it. It is just what you say. I feel I have taken too much cold food." And he asked what was to be done. I answered what I knew, and said to him: "If it were anyone else who was in this state, I should follow my custom and give him wine sprinkled with pepper. But in the case of kings like yourself, physicians are in the habit of giving safer remedies; hence it will be enough to apply over your stomach some wool impregnated with warm spikenard ointment." The Emperor said that in any case when his stomach was out of order he was in the habit of applying warm spikenard ointment enveloped in purple wool. So he gave orders to Pitholaus to do this, and to let me go. When this application had been made, and his feet thoroughly heated by rubbing with the warm hand, he asked for some Sabine wine, sprinkled pepper in it, and drank. He then declared to Pitholaus that he had "one physician, and he was a perfect gentleman." Further, as you know, he keeps constantly saying about me that I am "first among the physicians and alone among the philosophers." For he had already had experience of many who were not only mercenary, but also quarrelsome, conceited, selfish, and malicious. . . .

Second Century.
Translated in 1929

Epidemics and the Fall of Rome

HANS ZINSSER

THE effects of a succession of epidemics upon a state are not measurable in mortalities alone. Whenever pestilences have attained particularly terrifying proportions, their secondary consequences have been much more far-reaching and disorganizing than anything that could have resulted from the mere numerical reduction of the population. In modern times, these secondary effects have been—to some extent—mitigated by knowledge which has removed much of the terror that always accompanies the feeling of complete helplessness in the face of mysterious perils.

In this respect, modern bacteriology has brought about a state of affairs which may exert profound influence upon the future economic and political history of the world. Some epidemic diseases it has converted from uncontrolled savagery into states of relatively mild domestication. Others it can confine to limited territories or reservations. Others again, though still at large, can be prevented from developing a velocity which—once in full swing—is irresistible. But even in cases where no effective means of defense have as yet been discovered—as, for instance, in influenza, infantile paralysis, and encephalitis—the enemy can be faced in an orderly manner, with determination and with some knowledge of his probable tactics; still, no doubt, with terror, but at least without the panic and disorganization which have been as destructive to ancient and medieval society as the actual mortalities sustained.

In earlier ages, pestilences were mysterious visitations, expressions of the wrath of higher powers which came out of a dark nowhere, pitiless, dreadful, and inescapable. In their terror and ignorance, men did the very things which increased death rates and aggravated calamity. They fled from towns and villages, but death mysteriously traveled along with them. Panic bred social and moral disorganization; farms were abandoned, and there was shortage of food; famine led to displacement of populations, to revolution, to civil war, and, in some instances, to fanatical religious movements which contributed to profound spiritual and political transformations.

The disintegration of the Roman power was a gradual process brought about by complex causes . . . The problem has been dealt with from every conceivable angle, for there is no greater historic puzzle than that of the disappearance of the ancient civilization— a disappearance so complete that not a spark from its embers shone through the barbaric darkness of several hundred years . . . We are far from wishing to make the error against which Pareto warns, *"d'envisager comme simples des faits extrêmement compliqués"*; and we do not mean to add to other one-sided views an epidemic theory of the Roman decline. But we believe that a simple survey of the frequency, extent, and violence of the pestilences to which Roman Europe and Asia were subjected, from the year one to the final barbarian triumph, will convince the unprejudiced that these calamities must be interpolated in any appraisal of the causes that wore down the power of the greatest state the world has known. Indeed, we are inclined to believe, from a consideration of the circumstances prevailing at that time, that it would be impossible to maintain permanently a political and social organization of the type and magnitude of Rome in the face of complete lack of modern sanitary knowledge. A concentration of large populations in cities, free communication with all other parts of the world,—especially Africa and the East,—constant and extensive military activity involving the mobilization of armies in camps, and the movement of large forces back and forth from all corners of the world—these alone are conditions which inevitably determine the outbreak of epidemic disease.[1] And against such outbreaks there was absolutely no defense available at the

---

[1] This is still entirely applicable to modern times. Experience in the cantonments of 1917 and in the sanitation of active troops convincingly showed that war is to-day [this refers to World War I], as much as ever, 75 per cent an engineering and sanitary problem and a little less than 25 per cent a military one. Other things being approximately equal, that army will win which has the best engineering and sanitary services. The wise general will do what the engineers and the sanitary officers let him. The only reason why this is not entirely apparent in wars is because the military minds on both sides are too superb to notice that both armies are simultaneously immobilized by the same diseases.

Incidentally, medicine has another indirect influence on war which is not negligible. There seems little doubt that some of the reckless courage of the American troops in the late war was stimulated by the knowledge that in front of them were only the Germans, but behind them there were the assembled surgeons of America, with sleeves rolled up.

time. Pestilences encountered no obstacles. They were free to sweep across the entire world, like flames through dry grass, finding fuel wherever men lived, following trade routes on land, and carried over the sea in ships. They slowed down only when they had burned themselves out—and even then, when they had traveled as slowly as did the plagues of Cyprian and Justinian, they often doubled on their own paths, finding, in a new generation or in a community with fading immunity, materials on which they could flame up again for another period of terror. As soon as a state ceases to be mainly agricultural, sanitary knowledge becomes indispensable for its maintenance.

Justinian died in 565. Charlemagne was crowned in 800. Between 600 and 800, Italy was the battleground of barbarian immigrants who were fighting for the spoils. Rome, in the ancient sense, had ceased to exist. The final collapse of its defensive energy corresponds, in time, with the calamity of the great pestilence which bears Justinian's name. And while it would not be sensible to hold this plague alone responsible, it can hardly be questioned that it was one of the factors—perhaps the most potent single influence—which gave the *coup de grâce* to the ancient empire.

Moreover, the history of the preceding six hundred years furnishes any number of examples to show that, again and again, the forward march of Roman power and world organization was interrupted by the only force against which political genius and military valor were utterly helpless—epidemic disease. There is no parallel in recent history by which the conditions then prevailing can be judged, unless it is the state of Russia between 1917 and 1923. There, too, the unfettered violence of typhus, cholera, dysentery, tuberculosis, malaria, and their brothers exerted a profound influence upon political events . . . It was only the highly developed system of sanitary defense on the Polish and the southern fronts that prevented, during those years, an invasion—first of disease, misery, and famine; then of political disruption—from spreading across Europe. This statement may, perhaps, be debatable. But it is, at least, a reasonable probability.

At any rate, during the first centuries after Christ, disease was unopposed by any barriers. And when it came, as though carried on storm clouds, all other things gave way, and men crouched in terror, abandoning all their quarrels, undertakings, and ambitions, until the tempest had blown over. . . .

II

There is relatively little information in the literature of the first century A.D. in regard to epidemics. In the reign of Nero (after 54 B.C.), a plague occurred which is described by Tacitus as "extraordinarily destructive"—though his text gives no clues from which a diagnosis can be made. In the cities of Italy, there raged a disease which was so severe that corpses were in all the houses, and the streets were filled with funeral processions, "Slaves as well as citizens died" (we quote from Schnurrer), "and many who had mourned a beloved victim died themselves with such rapidity that they were carried to the same pyre as those they had mourned." Whether this particular malady was confined to Italy or not, we have no means of telling. But during the same period there were a number of other epidemic diseases in the provinces, one of which is described as "anthrax," and was probably similar or identical with the infection known by this name to-day, since it attacked cattle and horses as well as men. According to some writers, it was this disease which, occurring among the Huns about 80 A.D., started 30,000 of them, with 40,000 horses and 100,000 cattle, on their westward wanderings (Johannes von Müller).

Throughout the first century, there were earthquakes, famines, volcanic eruptions, and vaguely reported epidemics. However, the first pestilence of which we have reliable accounts is that which is spoken of as the "Plague of Antoninus" (or of Galen). This disease started in the army of Verus, which was campaigning in the East in 165 A.D. According to Ammianus Marcellinus, the original infection came from a chest in a temple which the soldiers had looted. As the army returned homeward, it scattered the disease far and wide, and finally brought it to Rome. By this time, the infection had radiated into all corners of the world, and before long had extended "from Persia to the shores of the Rhine," even spreading through the Gallic and Germanic tribes. The mortality in many of the cities was such that, as Marcus Aurelius says, "corpses were carried in carts and wagons." Orosius states that so many people died that cities and villages in Italy and in the provinces were abandoned and fell into ruin. Distress and disorganization were so severe that a campaign against the Marcomanni was postponed. When, in 169, the war was finally resumed, Haeser records that many of the Germanic warriors—men and women—were found dead on the field without wounds, having died from the epidemic. Marcus Aurelius contracted the disease and, recognizing the contagiousness of his affliction, refused to see his son. He died on the seventh day, his illness aggravated by his refusal to take nourishment. Since this was in 180 A.D., at which time Galen's description, *Methodus Medendi*, was written, it is plain that the pestilence in Europe lasted at least fourteen years. There is no definite information of the approximate number of deaths, but there is no doubt about the fact that the mortality was so great that it completely demoralized social, political, and military life and created such terror that there were none who dared nurse the sick. Our authority for this is Ammianus Marcellinus. The temporary arrest of the epidemic in 180 lasted only nine years. Dio Cassius tells us that it broke out again under Commodus in 189. "There arose the greatest plague of any I know of. Often there were 2000 deaths a day at Rome." It appears that the later phases were even more deadly than the earlier ones.

The nature of this disease is uncertain. It is, as usual, more than likely that no single infection was responsible, but that a number of different ones were raging at the same time. The most fatal of these, the one which gave the epidemic its chief characteristics, was a condition which, if not smallpox, was closely related to it. Indeed, the epidemic of Antoninus seems to have closely resembled the plague of Athens. Galen tells us that a majority of the cases began with inflammations of the pharynx, fever, and diarrhea. On the ninth day, there was—in most cases— an eruption which was sometimes pustular and sometimes dry. We are again faced with the difficulty of accurately interpreting the words referring to the nature of the exanthemata, but there is less uncertainty in connection with this disease than there was in descriptions of the plague of Athens, in regard to the raised, often vesicular and pustular nature of the eruption. Haeser, whose opinion in this matter we share, after reading the evidence, inclines to the belief that the epidemic was one of smallpox, or of a disease closely related to the modern form of the disease. This fact is rendered particularly likely by the speed and extensiveness with which the malady spread across the entire known world.

There can be little room for doubt that a calamity of this kind, lasting for over a decade, during a political period rendered critical by internal strife and constant war against encircling hostile barbarians, must have had a profound effect upon the maintenance of the Roman power. Military campaigns were stopped, cities depopulated, agriculture all but destroyed, and commerce paralyzed.

Apart from the military and camp disease which at brief intervals afflicted the frontier armies, the Roman world remained relatively free of great pestilences from the time of Commodus until the year 250, a period when the empire was entering into its turbulent, ever-increasing struggle against the barbarian inroads. The threat became especially serious after the victory of the Goths over Decimus at Forum Trebronii. There started at this time a pandemic which is described, among others, by Saint Cyprian—and is therefore often spoken of as the epidemic of Cyprian. This disease, like the Athenian plague, was said to have originated in Ethiopia, reaching Europe after passing across Egypt. It lasted no less than fifteen or sixteen years, during which it spread over the entire known world "from Egypt to Scotland." It swept over the same regions repeatedly, after intervals of several years. Its contagiousness was extreme and, according to Cedrenus, it was transmitted not only by direct contact, but indirectly—through clothing. Gregory of Nyssa[1] and Eusebius have left records of the suddenness of its appearance, and of its terrifying violence. In a city of Pontus, in 256, it appeared after the gathering of a great crowd in a theatre, as a punishment for the temerity of the spectators in challenging Jupiter, in whose honor the performance was given. In Alexandria, the mortality was enormous. The speed of extension was favored by the active warfare going on in many of the provinces. The Germanic tribes were invading Gaul and the Near East. The Far Eastern provinces were being attacked by the Goths, and the Parthians were conquering Mesopotamia. Terror was extreme, and phantoms were seen to hover over the houses of those who were about to fall sick. Saint Cyprian made many conversions to Christianity by exorcising these evil spirits. Throughout the early Christian

---

[1] In Gregory of Nyssa, the same plague is referred to as occurring during the life of Gregorius Thaumaturgus. There is also a description in *Patrologia Græca, Gregorius III*, in which the symptoms are given as follows: "When once the disease attacked a man, it spread rapidly over all his frame. A burning fever and thirst drove men to the springs and wells; but water was of no avail when once the disease had attacked a person. The disease was very fatal. More died than survived, and not sufficient people were left to bury the dead."

period, every great calamity—famine, earthquake, and plague—
led to mass conversions, another indirect influence by which
epidemic diseases contributed to the destruction of classical
civilization. Christianity owes a formidable debt to bubonic plague
and to smallpox, no less than to earthquake and volcanic eruptions.

The nature of the plague of Cyprian is even more difficult to
determine than is that of the Athenian pestilence. Haeser believes
that bubonic plague played a dominant rôle, and bases this chiefly
upon the seasonal factor—that is, upon the reports that in Egypt
successive outbreaks began in the autumn and lasted until the very
hot weather in July. In the absence of any definite information of
glandular swellings or buboes, however, this view is pure surmise.
Cyprian describes the disease as beginning with redness of the
eyes, inflammation of the pharynx and throat, violent diarrhea
and vomiting.[1] He mentions gangrene of the feet, paralysis of the
lower extremities, deafness, and blindness. No skin eruption is
described. One must assume again a synchronous prevalence
of many diseases, among which forms of meningitis and probably
acute bacillary dysenteries were frequent, but no specific diagnosis is possible from the symptoms observed by writers of the
period.

Whatever the conditions may have been, their violence was so
extreme that one cannot doubt their serious effects upon political
and social development. A conception of the extreme distress
may be obtained from the following, which we quote literally
from Haeser: "Men crowded into the larger cities; only the
nearest fields were cultivated; the more distant ones became overgrown, and were used as hunting preserves; farm land had no
value, because the population had so diminished that enough
grain to feed them could be grown on the limited cultivated
areas." Even in the centre of Italy, large territories became
vacant; swamps developed, and rendered unhealthy the formerly
wholesome coast lands of Etruria and Latium. Hieronymus writes
that the human race had been "all but destroyed," and that the
earth was returning to a state of desert and forests.

During the plague of Cyprian, according to Baronius, the

[1] Cyprian's description in *De Mortalitate* is as follows: "The bowels,
relaxed into a constant flux, use up the strength of the body. A fire, conceived in the marrow, ferments into wounds in the jaw [*fauces*]. The
intestines are shaken with continual vomiting. The eyes burn with blood.
Sometimes the feet or other parts of the limbs are cut off because of the
infection of disease, [*causing*] putrefaction [*morbida putredo*]."

Christian custom of wearing black as a color of mourning originated. It had been used before by Hadrian, who, says Schnurrer,
wore black for nine days after the death of Plotina.

Between the pestilence of Cyprian and the next great pandemic,
spoken of as the plague of Justinian, there occurred a succession
of calamities—earthquakes, famines, and the severe, but relatively
localized, epidemic diseases such as one would expect in an empire
in which there was a constant movement of large armed forces
and uninterrupted communication with the East and with the
north coast of Africa. At the same time, the migration of agricultural populations to the cities had already produced a great
crowding of people into small areas, without any of the indispensable safeguards of modern medicine.

In the reign of Diocletian and Maximian, a plague is described,
without any specific symptomatology, by Cedrenus. Eusebius
places this outbreak a little later, and also speaks of a new disease
—possibly anthrax—which affected thousands of people, appeared in the form of acute ulcerations and swellings of different
parts of the body, and blinded many in whom it occurred. Numbers of domestic animals died at the same time. Disease and famine
continued into the year 313.

There follows a period about which we have relatively little
record, though it probably had its usual measure of disease. It is
the period during which *Völkerwanderung* was in one of its
most active stages. This phenomenon was like the impact of
human waves from east to west. The movement may have been
started when the Huns, or Hiong-nus, were pushed out of China,
and wandered to the Caspian Sea. Impelled to move, possibly by
disease, they began to migrate westward. Their first collision was
with the Alani, whom they scattered or carried along with them
in a thrust against the Goths. The latter had wandered from the
north along the river beds toward the Black Sea. Crowded out
by Huns and Alani, the Goths fled into Roman territory, where
they temporarily settled along the Danube.

By 406, a general movement of barbarian tribes—Suebi, Alani,
Burgundi, and Vandals—was taking place into Italy, Gaul, and
across the Pyrenees to Spain. According to Idatius, it was a
period of war, famine, and pestilence. In 444, there was a terrible
epidemic in Britain, which seems to have been in part responsible
for the historically momentous conquest of Britain by the Saxons.
Baeda, in his *Historia Ecclesiastica Gentis Anglorum*, states that

Voltiger, hard pressed and in distress, called upon the Saxon chieftains, Hengist and Horsa, for assistance: "A terrible plague fell upon them, which destroyed so many that the living could barely suffice to bury the dead. They consulted what was to be done, and where to seek aid against the frequent incursions of the northern races [apparently their fighting forces were greatly depleted by the plague], and agreed to call in the Saxon nation from across the Sea. The Saxons arrived in 449, and acted as mercenary guards for the Britons." It requires little exercise of the imagination, therefore, to conclude that the history of the British Isles in all its subsequent developments of race, customs, architecture, and soforth, was in large part determined by an epidemic disease.

Eusebius tells of an epidemic which occurred throughout the Roman provinces and near Vienna (then known as Orae Favianae) in 455 and 456. It began with inflamed eyes, swelling and redness of the skin over the entire body, and it ended—sometimes fatally —on the third or fourth day, with severe pulmonary symptoms. It is impossible to say what this disease might have been—possibly general streptococcus infection, or a form of scarlet fever, with secondary streptococcic pneumonia.

In 467, Rome itself suffered from a disease about which we know, from Baronius, only that it killed a great many people. In the immediately succeeding years, much scattered—but localized —epidemic disease occurred in the Gallic provinces; and in 477, when the Saxon King, Odoacer, reached Anjou on his way to Italy, a severe plague broke out among citizens and invaders alike. Shortly after this, a famine and plague in North Africa decimated the Vandals, thus preparing them for defeat by the Mohammedans.

Of great diseases there is no record during the ensuing fifty years, but in 526 occurred the great earthquake of Antioch, which was responsible for the death of several hundred thousand people.

This brings us to the greatest of all the pandemics that helped to undermine the ancient civilization—namely, that of Justinian, details of which we know very largely from the writings of Procopius.

The sixth century was a period of calamity rarely equaled in history. Seibel in his *Die Grosse Pest zur Zeit Justinians*, has thoroughly compiled the available information, and is the authority from which most subsequent writers quote. According to him, a succession of earthquakes, volcanic eruptions,—Vesuvius in 513 was one,—and famines preceded and accompanied the series of pestilences which wrought terror and destruction throughout all of Europe, the Near East, and Asia for over sixty years. Of the natural convulsions, the most destructive was an earthquake, followed by conflagration, which destroyed Antioch in 526, killed between 200,000 and 300,000 inhabitants, and frightened away most of the remainder. There also were earthquakes in Constantinople and in other cities of the East, as well as in many places in Europe proper. Among others, there was a severe one in Clermont, then called Civitas Averna. A succession of floods and famines added to the general misery. The impoverishment, the displacement of populations, the agricultural disorganization and famine which attended these calamities must have contributed materially to the origin and spread of the pestilence. Modern experience has demonstrated this a number of times, when tidal waves, earthquakes, and floods have wrought similar havoc.

The great plague of Justinian began in Egypt, near Pelusium. The suggested Ethiopian origin is vague; there was a sort of ancient and traditional suspicion that disease usually came out of Ethiopia. Procopius writes of this:—

> At this time [540], there started a plague. It appeared not in one part of the world only, not in one race of men only, and not in any particular season; but it spread over the entire earth, and afflicted all without mercy of both sexes and of every age. It began in Egypt, at Pelusium; thence it spread to Alexandria and to the rest of Egypt; then went to Palestine, and from there over the whole world; in such a manner that, in each place, it had seasonal occurrence. And it spared no habitations of men, however remote they may have been. And if, at times, it seemed as though it had spared any region for a time, it would surely appear there later, not then attacking those who had been afflicted at an earlier time; and it lasted always until it had claimed its usual number of victims. It seemed always to be spread inland from the coastal regions, thence penetrating deeply into the interior.
>
> In the second year, in the spring, it reached Byzantium and began in the following manner: To many there appeared phantoms in human form. Those who were so encountered, were struck by a blow from the phantom, and so contracted the sickness. Others locked themselves into their houses. But then the phantoms appeared to them in dreams, or they heard voices that told them that they had been selected for death.

Since Procopius himself believed these things, his account reflects the terrified helplessness and panic which spread with this pestilence.

Four months the plague remained in Byzantium. At first, few died—then there were 5000, later 10,000 deaths a day. "Finally, when there was a scarcity of gravediggers, the roofs were taken off the towers of the forts, the interiors filled with the corpses, and the roofs replaced." Corpses were placed on ships, and these abandoned to the sea. "And after the plague had ceased, there was so much depravity and general licentiousness, that it seemed as though the disease had left only the most wicked."

Procopius devotes a number of paragraphs to a description which is our only clue to diagnosis:—

"They were taken with a sudden fever: some suddenly wakened from sleep; others while they were occupied with various matters during the daytime. The fever, from morning to night, was so slight that neither the patients nor the physician feared danger, and no one believed that he would die. But in many even on the first day, in others on the day following, in others again not until later, a bubo appeared both in the inguinal regions and under the armpits; in some behind the ears, and in any part of the body whatsoever.

To this point, the disease was the same in everyone, but in the later stages there were individual differences. Some went into a deep coma; others into violent delirium. If they neither fell asleep nor became delirious, the swelling gangrened and these died from excess of pain. It was not contagious to touch, since no doctor or private individual fell ill from the sick or dead; for many who nursed or buried, remained alive in their service, contrary to all expectations. Some of the physicians unacquainted with this disease and in the belief that the buboes were the chief site of the sickness, examined the bodies of the dead, opened the buboes and found a great many pustular places.

Some died at once; others after many days; and the bodies of some broke out with black blisters the size of a lentil. These did not live after one day, but died at once; and many were quickly killed by a vomiting of blood which attacked them. Physicians could not tell which cases were light and which were severe, and no remedies availed."

Agathius, speaking of the year 558, describes the same disease at Byzantium and again mentions buboes and sudden death which usually occurred on the fifth day. It attacked all ages, but killed more men than women.

It is interesting to note that this epidemic displayed one of the characteristics so often referred to in modern epidemiology —namely, when the outbreaks began, the number of sick and the mortality were relatively slight, but both rose with appalling violence as the epidemic gathered velocity.

There can be little doubt that the pestilence of Justinian was mainly one of bubonic plague, but the references to the general eruption of black blisters in many cases indicate that smallpox of a very severe type participated. Whatever it was, its extent and severity were such that commentators like Haeser believe it to have exerted an influence upon the decline of the Eastern empire which historians have too often overlooked. In the course of sixty to seventy years, a considerable part of the known world was devastated by the disease. Cities and villages were abandoned, agriculture stopped, and famine, panic, and the flight of large populations away from the infected places threw the entire Roman world into confusion.

Gibbon, speaking of this plague, says: "No facts have been preserved to sustain an account or even a conjecture of the numbers that perished in this extraordinary mortality. I only find that, during three months, five and at length ten thousand persons died each day at Constantinople; and many cities of the East were left vacant, and that in several districts of Italy the harvest and the vintage withered on the ground. The triple scourges of war, pestilence and famine afflicted the subjects of Justinian; and his reign is disgraced by a visible decrease of the human species which has never been regained in some of the fairest countries of the globe."

Procopius was an eyewitness of most of the events which he describes. He was associated closely with Belisarius in his campaigns, and occupied a position of sufficient importance to have the "inside" of what was going on in Constantinople at the court. One may, therefore, assume that his accounts of the turbulence of the period—wars, political corruption, and pestilence—are not unduly exaggerated. And since we have recently had a greater, more widespread, and more destructive war than most others of history, and since political corruption to-day is probably quite as

well developed and general as at any time, it is a reasonable conjecture that it may have been only our relative ability to control
pestilence which has preserved the modern world, for a time,
from breaking up as did the empire of Justinian.

In studying, through the eyes of Procopius, the reign of Justinian, one obtains an extraordinarily vivid picture of the manner
in which the three major agencies cooperated in bringing the
empire to its knees. Justinian was making a final effort to restore
the imperial world power. Wars with Persia, wars against the
Vandals in Africa and against the Goths in Italy, armies to maintain on all fronts, in widely separated parts of the world, strained
the resources of the government to their utmost. Everywhere
the ring of defense was being pushed back by ever-increasing
hordes of barbarians, who had by this time learned much of the
art of war and of organization from their former overlords.
Internal insurrections, as at Byzantium in 532, threatened the rear.
Treachery and graft weakened the administrative power at court.
And superimposed upon these almost, perhaps entirely insuperable difficulties was the pestilence,—sweeping from east to west,
north to south, again and again, for almost sixty years,—killing,
terrifying, and disorganizing.

The plague lasted until 590, or a little later. Between 568 and
570, most of Italy was conquered by the Lombards, who, as
Cunimund, another barbarian, said, "resemble in figure and in
smell the mares of the Sarmatian plains." The power and the
grace and the administrative logic that once were Rome had died.

1934

The Plague

GIOVANNI BOCCACCIO

In the year of our Lord 1348, there happened at Florence, the
finest city in all Italy, a most terrible plague; which whether
owing to the influence of the planets, or that it was sent from God
as a just punishment for our sins, had broken out some years
before in the Levant; and after passing from place to place, and
making incredible havoc all the way, had now reached the West;
where, spite of all the means that art and human foresight could

suggest, as keeping the city clear from filth, and excluding all suspected persons; notwithstanding frequent consultations what else was to be done; nor omitting prayers to God in frequent processions: in the spring of the foregoing year, it began to show itself in a sad and wonderful manner; and, different from what it had been in the East, where bleeding from the nose is the fatal prognostic, here, there appeared certain tumours in the groins, or under the arm-pits, some as big as a small apple, others as an egg; and afterwards purple spots in most parts of the body: in some cases large and but few in number, in others less and more numerous, both sorts the usual messengers of death. To the cure of this malady, neither medical knowledge, nor the power of drugs was of any effect; whether because the disease was in its own nature mortal, or that the physicians (the number of whom, taking quacks and women pretenders into the account was grown very great) could form no just idea of the cause, nor consequently ground a true method of cure; which ever was the reason, few or none escaped; but they generally died the third day from the first appearance of the symptoms, without a fever or other bad circumstance attending. And the disease by being communicated from the sick to the well, seemed daily to get ahead, and to rage the more as fire will do, by laying on fresh combustibles. Nor was it given by conversing with only, or coming near the sick, but even by touching their clothes, or anything that they had before touched. It is wonderful, what I am going to mention; which had I not seen it with my own eyes, and were there not many witnesses to attest it besides myself, I should never venture to relate, however credibly I might have been informed about it; such I say, was the quality of the pestilential matter, as to pass not only from man to man, but, what is more strange, and has been often known, that anything belonging to the infected, if touched by any other creature, would certainly infect, and even kill that creature in a short space of time; and one instance of this kind I took particular notice of; namely, that the rags of a poor man just dead, being thrown into the street, and two hogs coming by at the same time, and rooting amongst them, and shaking them about in their mouths, in less than an hour turned round, and died on the spot. These accidents, and others of the like sort, occasioned various fears and devices amongst those people that survived, all tending to the same uncharitable, and cruel end; which was, to avoid the sick, and everything that had been near them;

expecting by that means to save themselves. And some holding it best to live temperately, and to avoid excesses of all kinds, made parties, and shut themselves up from the rest of the world; eating and drinking moderately of the best, and diverting themselves with music, and such other entertainments as they might have within doors; never listening to anything from without, to make them uneasy. Others maintained free living to be a better preservative, and would baulk no passion or appetite they wished to gratify, drinking and revelling incessantly from tavern to tavern, or in private houses, which were frequently found deserted by the owners, and therefore common to every one; yet avoiding, with all this irregularity, to come near the infected. And such, at that time was the public distress, that the laws, human or divine, were not regarded; for the officers, to put them in force, being either dead, sick, or in want of persons to assist them; every one did just as he pleased. A third sort of people chose a method between these two; not confining themselves to rules of diet like the former, and yet avoiding the intemperance of the latter; but eating and drinking what their appetites required, they walked everywhere with odours and nosegays to smell to; as holding it best to corroborate the brain: for they supposed the whole atmosphere to be tainted with the stink of dead bodies, arising partly from the distemper itself, and partly from the fermenting of the medicines within them. Others of a more cruel disposition, as perhaps the more safe to themselves, declared, that the only remedy was to avoid it: persuaded, therefore of this, and taking care for themselves only, men and women in great numbers left the city, their houses, relations, and effects, and fled into the country: as if the wrath of God had been restrained to visit those only within the walls of the city; or else concluding, that none ought to stay in a place thus doomed to destruction. Divided as they were, neither did all die nor all escape; but falling sick indifferently, as well those of one as of another opinion; they who first set the example by forsaking others, now languished themselves, without mercy. I pass over the little regard that citizens and relations showed to each other; for their terror was such, that a brother even fled from his brother, a wife from her husband, and what is more uncommon, a parent from its own child. On which account numbers that fell sick could have no help but what the charity of friends, who were very few, or the avarice of servants supplied; and even these were scarce, and at extravagant wages, and so little used to the business, that they were only fit to reach what was called for, and observe when they died; and this desire of getting money often cost them their lives.

From this desertion of friends, and scarcity of servants, an unheard of custom prevailed; no lady, however young or handsome, would disdain being attended by a man-servant, whether young or old it mattered not; and to expose herself naked to him, the necessity of the distemper requiring it, as though it was to a woman; which might make those who recovered, less modest for the time to come. And many lost their lives, who might have escaped, had they been looked after at all. So that, between the scarcity of servants, and violence of the distemper, such numbers were continually dying, as made it terrible to hear as well as to behold. Whence, from mere necessity, many customs were introduced, different from what had been before known in the city. It had been usual, as it now is for the women who were friends and neighbours to the deceased, to meet together at his house, and to lament with his relations; at the same time the men would get together at the door, with a number of clergy, according to the person's circumstances; and the corpse was carried by people of his own rank, with the solemnity of tapers and singing, to that church where the person had desired to be buried; which custom was now laid aside, and, so far from having a crowd of women to lament over them, that great numbers passed out of the world without a single person: and few had the tears of their friends at their departure; but those friends would laugh, and make themselves merry; for even the women had learned to postpone every other concern to that of their own lives. Nor was a corpse attended by more than ten, or a dozen, nor those citizens of credit, but fellows hired for the purpose; who would put themselves under the bier, and carry it with all possible haste to the nearest church; and the corpse was interred, without any great ceremony, where they could find room.

With regard to the lower sort, and many of a middling rank, the scene was still more affecting; for they, staying at home either through poverty, or hopes of succour in distress, fell sick daily by thousands, and, having nobody to attend them, generally died: some breathed their last in the streets, and others shut up in their own houses, when the stench that came from them, made the first discovery of their deaths to the neighbourhood. And, indeed, every place was filled with the dead. A method now was taken, as well out of regard to the living, as pity for the dead, for the neighbours, assisted by what porters they could meet with, to clear all the houses, and lay the bodies at the doors; and every morning great numbers might be seen brought out in this manner; from whence they were carried away on biers, or tables, two or three at a time; and some times it has happened, that a wife and her husband, two or three brothers, and a father and son, have been laid on together: it has been observed also, whilst two or three priests have walked before a corpse with their crucifix, that two or three sets of porters have fallen in with them; and where they knew but of one, they have buried six, eight, or more: nor was there any to follow, and shed a few tears over them; for things were come to that pass, that men's lives were no more regarded than the lives of so many beasts. Hence it plainly appeared, that what the wisest in the ordinary course of things, and by a common train of calamities, could never be taught, namely, to bear them patiently; this, by the excess of those calamities, was now grown a familiar lesson to the most simple and unthinking. The consecrated ground no longer containing the numbers which were continually brought thither, especially as they were desirous of laying every one in the parts allotted to their families; they were forced to dig trenches, and to put them in by hundreds, piling them up in rows, as goods are stowed in a ship, and throwing in little earth till they were filled to the top. Not to rake any farther into the particulars of our misery, I shall observe, that it fared no better with the adjacent country; for to omit the different castles about us, which presented the same view in miniature with the city, you might see the poor distressed labourers, with their families, without either the plague or physicians, or help of servants, languishing on the highways, in the fields, and in their own houses, and dying rather like cattle than human creatures; and growing dissolute in their manners like the citizens, and careless of everything, as supposing every day to be their last, their thoughts were not so much employed how to improve, as to make use of their substance for their present support: whence it happened that the flocks, herds, etc., and the dogs themselves, ever faithful to their masters, being driven from their own homes, would wander, no regard being had to them, among the forsaken harvest; and many times, after they had filled themselves in the day, would return of their own accord like rational creatures at night. What can I say more, if I return to the city? unless that

such was the cruelty of Heaven, and perhaps of men, that between March and July following, it is supposed, and made pretty
certain, that upwards of a hundred thousand souls perished in the
city only; whereas, before that calamity, it was not supposed to
have contained so many inhabitants. What magnificent dwellings,
what noble palaces were then depopulated to the last person!
what families extinct! what riches and vast possessions left, and no
known heir to inherit! what numbers of both sexes in the prime
and vigour of youth, whom in the morning neither Galen, Hippocrates, nor Asclepius himself, but would have declared in perfect health; after dining heartily with their friends here, have
supped with their departed friends in the other world!

1358

The Medical School of Salernum

JOHN ORDRONAUX

THE Medical School of Salernum dates back to the ninth century,
although writers disagree so extensively upon the question of its
origin, whether ecclesiastical or lay, that it is hardly worth our
while to open any discussion upon it. That a school existed
there, flourished, and was the acknowledged head of all European
medical academies during the Middle Ages, is an established fact
no longer to be gainsaid. . . .

   The Statutes of the college of Salernum are remarkable for the
jealous guardianship which they exercise over the purity and
proficiency of candidates for medical degrees. The school had
selected for its patron St. Matthew, and for the motto on its seal
the words "*Civitas Hippocratica.*" Its Faculty consisted of ten
professors or *Magistri*, who succeeded each other according to
seniority. The examination of candidates was conducted with
great strictness, and consisted in expositions either of Galen's
Therapeutics, or the first book of Avicenna; also in the Apho-
risms of Hippocrates and the Analytics of Aristotle. If successful,
the candidate received the title of M.A. and Physician.

   Candidates were required to be twenty-one years of age, and
to produce proofs of having studied Medicine for seven years. As
yet the degree thus obtained did not authorize one to practice

indiscriminately in every department; for, if the candidate desired to be admitted to practice Surgery, it was required in addition that he should study Anatomy for one whole year. But
every one, to whatever degree admitted, must first swear to be
true and obedient to the Society of Physicians—to refuse all fees
from the poor, *and to have no share of gains with apothecaries.*
A book was then put into his hands—a ring upon his finger—his
head was crowned with laurel, and he was dismissed with a kiss.

These statutes were modified from time to time, although the
spirit of rigid honor and medical orthodoxy in which they were
cast was never abated to the last. Again, another law required
that the candidate should have accomplished three years of study
in logic, and five years in both medicine and surgery, before he
could be admitted to an examination. He must also swear to conform to established rules, and among other things *servare formam
curiae hactenus observatum*, and inform the authorities whenever
an apothecary falsified drugs.

On the other hand, apothecaries were obliged to compound
medicines as the physician directed and to sell them at an established price. . . .

A still later law required, after five years' study, another year
of practice with an old physician. But during these five years the
candidate might still teach in public. Another rule, which was
evidently considered of more than ethical obligation, forbade
every physician to share in the profits of apothecaries or to keep
a drug store himself.

The instruction imparted in the school was restricted to such
principles alone as were found in the authenticated texts of Hippocrates and Galen.

The *fees* of practitioners were duly regulated according to
time and *distance.* Thus, for office-calls and those within the city
limits during the day, physicians received half a *tarenus*;[1] for calls
outside the city three tareni if entertained at the patient's house,
otherwise four; and the patient might call in the physician twice

[1] The *tarenus* was a gold coin equal in value to two Neapolitan *carlini*,
or about eight cents of our money, gold standard. At this rate, our illustrious
Masters of Salernum received *four* cents for office-calls and such as were
made in the city; and *twenty-four* cents for those made out of town.

> Content with little, like Hippocrates,
> They practiced more for honor, than for fees.
> But when the fee was earned, the visit made,
> Without delay, they asked to be repaid.

during the day and once during the night. The poor always to be attended gratuitously.

Druggists (*stationarii*) and apothecaries (*confectionarii*) were placed under the supervision of physicians, who were forbidden to merchandise with them as to prices, or to own any share in their profits. And both those who sold and those who manufactured drugs were first sworn to a strict adherence to the Codex; their number was limited, and the cities or towns in which they could follow their avocations carefully designated. The prices allowed to be charged by them were based chiefly upon the perishable nature of the articles. Two Imperial inspectors were charged, in connection with the Medical Faculty, with the duty of superintending the preparation of all electuaries and syrups. In matters appertaining to medical police, such as contagious diseases, sales of poison or love-philters and other charms, the laws at Salernum were in advance of the age, and hardly surpassed even in our own day. Those, in particular, relating to apothecaries are worthy of imitation and adoption in every civilized country.

Frederick II . . . dealt a fatal blow to the school at Salernum when he erected a rival academy at Naples. By whatsoever motive induced, his knowledge of, and respect for the sacred traditions clustering around this old Hippocratic shrine, should have made him hesitate and refrain from dealing it a wound destined to sap its existence. But so it was; and from that moment the active life of the institution began to diminish. Bologna and Paris, both jealous rivals of Salernum, and who had essayed by imitation of her teachings to eclipse her didactically, soon took advantage of their opportunity. The infusion of Saracenic Medicine into the Hippocratic doctrines at Salernum became more and more apparent, and only in the department of surgery do the Greek traditions still appear to hold their original sway during the period of her decline. And yet, such is the ingrained respect of the human mind for whatever has survived the erosions of time, that we instinctively retrace our steps in periods of doubt to consult ancient authorities, if even but traditional; such, in fact, is the historical momentum of a great name, which, once crowned in the temple of Fame, can never be dethroned or stripped of its sovereignty, that, as late as the middle of the last century Salernum was still considered the *mater et caput* of medical authority in ethical matters, for in 1748 disputes as to precedence in rank between physicians and surgeons having occasioned painful dif-

ferences among French practitioners, the Medical Faculty of
Paris addressed an official letter to the Faculty of Salernum, requesting their counsel and assistance in the formation of a judgment upon the issues then raised before them. This is the last
historical appearance of the famous School of Salernum, for a
sweeping royal decree of 1811, centralizing instruction in a few
designated centres, virtually completed her downfall, by assigning
to her a place among gymnasia or preparatory institutes only.

Thus died the venerable and venerated mother of all Christian
medical schools amid the splendors of a meridional civilization,
of which, in her own department, she had been the day-star and
morning-glory. The first to rise from the darkness of the Middle
Ages, and to aid in the revival of medical letters, she continued
faithful to her trust and her tenets for more than *nine centuries.*
What school ever did as much for medical learning? Or where
did rational Medicine ever find so firm and enduring a shrine?
It is sad to think that not a stone of the old University is now
standing—that not a fragment of the valuable collection of MSS.
contained in her once opulent library still remains in Salernum;
but scattered here and there on dusty shelves and in unfrequented
corners, they have been left to the chance discovery of some
mousing antiquary. . . .

THE SCHOLA SALERNITANA

Not to have been familiar with it from beginning to end, not
to have been able to quote it orally as the occasion might require,
would, during the Middle Ages, have cast serious suspicion upon
the professional culture of any physician. Indeed, it was a general
favorite among the educated of every class, and looked upon, like
Solomon's Proverbs, as a People's Book, useful to all who could
appreciate its wide yet broad and common-sense suggestions as
to the conduct of our physical life. So universally were its merits
recognized and endorsed that an edition of it was printed as early
as 1480. Since that time, according to Mr. Baudry de Balzac, *two
hundred and forty* editions of this famous Poem have been published, and in almost all the languages of modern Europe. . . .

The first edition, with the commentary of Arnaldus de Villa
Nova, appears to have been printed at Montpelier, A.D. 1480, in
quarto; and there have been subsequently issued in the *original*
Latin no less than one hundred and seven editions. . . .

It is the condensation of truth in compact, suggestive sentences, adorned by the elegance of rhyme, and thus invoking the harmony of numbers to the aid of memory, which has given to this Poem an undying charm. Written in plain, untechnical language, saturated with the broad common sense of daily experience, and prescribing for all the necessities and all the dangers of practical life, it at once comes home, as Bacon said of his Essays, to "Men's Businesse and Bosomes"; and the innumerable imitations of it which sprang up in medieval Europe, wherever a rival medical school existed, attest in the most forcible manner possible the high and fixed reverence it commanded in public estimation.

1869

Code of Health of the
School of Salernum

OF MENTAL CONDITIONS, AND OF CERTAIN REMEDIES

Salerno's School, in conclave high, unites
To counsel ENGLAND's KING, and thus indites:

If thou to health and vigor wouldst attain,
Shun weighty cares—all anger deem profane,
From heavy suppers and much wine abstain.
Nor trivial count it, after pompous fare,
To rise from table and to take the air.
Shun idle, noonday slumber, nor delay
The urgent calls of Nature to obey.
These rules if thou wilt follow to the end,
Thy life to greater length thou mayst extend.

(*Addition* A. v.[1])

Shouldst Doctors need? be these in Doctors' stead—
Rest, cheerfulness, and table thinly-spread.

[1] These letters, wherever they occur, refer to ARNOLD OF VILLA NOVA's Commentary, whose text we have followed.

REFRESHMENT FOR THE BRAIN

At early dawn, when first from bed you rise,
Wash, in cold water, both your hands and eyes.
With comb and brush then cleanse your teeth and hair,
And thus refreshed, your limbs outstretch with care.
Such things restore the weary, o'ertasked brain;
And to all parts ensure a wholesome gain.
Fresh from the bath get warm. Rest after food,
Or walk, as seems most suited to your mood.
But in whate'er engaged, or sport, or feat,
Cool not too soon the body when in heat.

(*Addition* A. V.)

Recreation for the Sight.

Groves, Brooks and Verdure, weary eyes relieve,
At dawn, seek Mountains, Streams at dusky eve.

(*Addition* from Paris Ed., 1861.)

At eve the shore, at morn the groves, frequent,
Whose varied hues, to cheer the sight, present
Blue tints and green, with dusky-yellow blent.

OF NOONTIDE SLEEP

Let noontide sleep be brief, or none at all;
Else stupor, headache, fever, rheums will fall
On him who yields to noontide's drowsy call.

(*Addition* from Paris Ed. of 1861.)

Perchance, should some one crave a midday nap
From habit—then, t'will cause him less mishap.
But let none sleep soon after having fed,
Nor long, and always with uplifted head.
To point these rules, 'tis fitting to rehearse,
To him who sleeps, this rude, untutored verse:
Post-prandial sleep, ye mortals, put afar,
In any month whose name includes an R.
Post-prandial sleep's alone salubrious,
In months, whose names their ending have in US.

OF ENCARCERATED FLATUS

Four ills from long-imprisoned flatus flow,
Convulsions, colics, dropsies, vertigo;
The truth of this the thing itself doth show.

OF SUPPER

Great suppers will the stomach's peace impair.
Wouldst lightly rest? curtail thine evening fare.

THE RULE FOR APPORTIONING MEALS

Eat not again till thou dost certain feel
Thy stomach freed of all its previous meal.
This mayst thou know from hunger's teasing call,
Or mouth that waters—surest sign of all!

(*Addition* from Paris Ed., 1861.)

An empty stomach, calling loud for food,
To hear long tales is in no willing mood.

FOOD TO BE AVOIDED

The luscious peach, the apple and the pear,
Cheese, ven'son, salted meats and e'en the hare,
With flesh of goats, dyspeptic throes provoke,
And crush the weak 'neath melancholy's yoke.

(*Addition* from Paris Ed., 1861.)

Salt is the flesh of ruffled ducks and geese;
Fried meats do harm; while boiled give peptic peace;
And fragrant roasts, digestive powers increase.
Bitters will purge—crude things in all cause wind,
And salted meats the body dry and bind,
While crusts give rise to bile of darkest kind.
Salt things consume virility and sight,
And psoric torments breed of direst might.

FOOD THAT BOTH NOURISHES AND FATTENS

Eggs newly laid and broths of richest juice,
With ruby wine, increase of strength produce,
Wheat and milk make flesh, brains and tender cheese,
Marrow and pork, as taste they chance to please.
Or eggs, with art prepared, or honeyed wine;
Ripe figs and grapes, fresh gathered from the vine.

OF THE QUALITIES OF GOOD WINE

The taste of wines, their clearness, odor, shade,
Are living proofs of their specific grade;
You'll find all those that are of highest source,
Fragrant, frigid, fair, fuming high with force.

OF SWEET WHITE WINE

Rich, heavy wines that are both sweet and white,
The body's size increase, and e'en its might.

OF MILK FOR CONSUMPTIVES

Goats' milk and camels', as by all is known,
Relieve poor mortals in consumption thrown;
While asses' milk is deemed far more nutritious,
And, e'en beyond all cows' or sheeps', officious.
But should a fever in the system riot,
Or headache, let the patient shun this diet.

(*Addition* from Paris Ed., 1861.)

The stomach's gently soothed, and moistened too,
The liver nourished with fresh heat anew;
The loins more active are, the fat's dispelled,
The bowels freed, and every taint expelled.
Cows' milk gives wonted heat to every part,

And quickly dissipates the acrid smart
Of tainted humors, with a soothing art;
Increases flesh, to pangs of womb gives ease,
Can moist the body, and its heat appease;
And whatsoever things remain still crude
Within, converts to salutary food.

OF BUTTER AND WHEY

Butter soothes, moistens—all this without fever;
Whey proves a cleanser and a full reliever.

OF FIGS

Fig-poultice will our bodies rid of tumors,
Scrofula, boils and even peccant humors;
'Twill surely draw—add poppy-heads alone—
The splintered fragments from a broken bone.

(*Addition* A. V.)

Breed lice and lust in all who use the fruit,
And yet Love's call, in turn, chill at its root.

(*Addition* from Paris Ed., 1861.)

Figs soothe the chest, and figs the bowels scour,
When raw or cooked with corresponding power
Both feed and fatten and relieve us too,
From every kind of swelling, old or new.

OF PEPPER

All peppers black make food digest with haste,
Cure phlegm, and help us to repair our waste.
White pepper is the stomach's dearest friend,
And coughs and pains brings to an early end.
'Twill interrupt the chill of any fever,
Or prove, if raging high, supreme reliever.

OF DULLNESS OF HEARING

To sleep soon after having taken food,
And exercise when frequently renewed,
With drunkenness—all these in turn appear
To dull, betimes, the sharpness of the ear.

OF RINGING IN THE EARS

Emetics, blows, all accidents and fear,
Dangers, long fasts and drunkards' wild career,
Will cause continued ringing of the ear.

OF SOME EFFECTS OF BLOOD-LETTING

Bleeding soothes rage, brings joy unto the sad,
And saves all lovesick swains from going mad.

OF THE SIZE OF THE WOUND IN BLOOD-LETTING

A medium-sized incision always make,
Whate'er amount of blood you wish to take;
The copious vapor rising sudden, flees,
And thus the blood escapes with greater ease.

THINGS TO BE CONSIDERED IN BLOOD-LETTING

When one is bled he should for full six hours
Most vigilant maintain his mental powers,
Lest fumes of artful slumber too profound
Should all his mortal nature sadly wound.
For fear that thou some slender nerve shouldst mar,
Conduct not the incision deep nor far;
And being purged through blood, and thus renewed,
Haste not at once to sate thyself with food.

THINGS TO BE AVOIDED AFTER BLEEDING

All things from milk as are in gen'ral made,
And draughts of wine, of whatsoever grade,
Should every one dismissed, avoided be
By recent subjects of phlebotomy.
Cold things are also hurtful to the weak,
Nor let them, dauntless, brave damp skies or bleak;
For vigor only comes once more to these
From sunshine mingled with the passing breeze.
To all rest proves an everlasting gain,
While exercise occasions certain pain.

IN WHAT DISEASES, AGES AND QUANTITIES BLOOD-LETTING SHOULD OCCUR

Acute disease, or only so in part,
Demands blood-letting freely from the start.
In middle age, bleed largely without fear,
But treat old age like tender childhood here.
In spring you may bleed doubly at your pleasure—
At other times alone in single measure.

WHAT PARTS ARE TO BE DEPLETED AND AT WHAT SEASONS

In spring, and likewise in the summer tide,
Blood should be drawn alone from the right side.

The text followed in making this translation by John Ordronaux is that of 1480, with commentary by Arnaldus de Villa Nova, a distinguished physician of the 13th century, in the edition of Zaccharius Sylvius, published in Rotterdam, 1657. The translation includes Villa Nova's commentary, and further ones derived from the Paris edition of 1861.

Translation published 1869

The Sinister Shepherd

GIROLAMO FRACASTORO

WITHIN the purple womb of night, a slave,
The strangest plague returned to sear the world.
Infecting Europe's breast, the scourge was hurled
From Libyan cities to the Black Sea's wave.
When warring France would march on Italy,
It took her name. I consecrate my rhymes
To this unbidden guest of twenty climes,
Although unwelcomed, and eternally.

O Muse, reveal to me what seed has grown
This evil that for long remained unknown!
Till Spanish sailors made the west their goal,
And plowed the seas to find another pole,
Adding to this world a new universe.
Did these men bring to us this latent curse?
In every place beneath a clamorous sky
There bursts spontaneously this frightful pest.
Few people has it failed to scarify,
Since commerce introduced it from the West.
Hiding its origin, this evil thing
Sprawls over Europe. . . .

This pestilence's savage voice I hear,
And wandering to our houses, will it sow
In tender virgin breasts a wicked seed,
Hatched from a poison that no vice has wrought.
And from its evil clutches none is freed.
It is at home in hovel and the court,
Its symptoms never twice the same, indeed. . . .

Within the body, long its ferment rests,
To nourish at some hidden source of breasts.
Then suddenly, beneath a languor's weight,
The victim creeps about in fearful state,

The heart defective and the slightest strain
Tiring the limbs, while energies remain
All sapped. A gloomy eye and saddened face
Of sickly pallor bend to this disgrace,
And soon a vicious ulcer eats its way
Into the privates. And a vengeful sway
Takes cancerous possession to remain.
Extended to the groin is its fell bane. . . .

Soon is the body ulcerous and vile.
The face becomes within a little while
A mask of running pustules small and great.
A horny shell will glands well imitate.
Breaking and emptying an acrid humor,
From pus-corroded skin, pours every tumor.
And bloody ulcers deeply dig away,
Gnawing the tissues that they make their prey.
Then is man stripped until his piteous moans
Come from a skeleton of putrid bones.
The lips are torn to shreds for this vile ill,
And, ere the voice dies, it is harsh and shrill. . . .

Gone is the brilliance of his youth and spring.
Dying by inches, as his soul sinks, he
Finds on his limbs a hideous leprosy.
Upon his very bones would caries fling
Its banners, till they open to the eyes.
His lovely eyes that were so long alight—
Ulcers devour these—a hideous sight.
Purulent poison too his nose corrodes,
Until for viscous humors, it explodes. . . .

Seek out the strongest remedies, nor fear
Fatigue, though it belabors somewhat drear.
And if you haste, success will crown your pains.
Then is the plague less harsh within your veins. . . .

Exile your mistress that a lonely bed
Shuns Venus and her altars and embraces.
And shun your love for all her tender graces,
Or for your lack of faith will she be dead. . . .

Touch not the truffle or the artichoke
Leeks and cucumbers leave to other folk.
And vinegar and milk you must let be
For this will you be better off, and see
That your cup contains no ichor
Of a full bodied wine or foaming liquor. . . .

Soon is repaired the ruin of the flesh,
If lard be well applied that's good and fresh . . .
Oxide of lead, mercury, frankincense,
Antimony and storax will provoke
If spread upon the flesh their caustic smoke,
Released to stop the progress of this ill,
And that they may attack with mighty will.
But there may be a source of wild regret,
If unsuccessful. Deeper driven yet
May be the ulcer on its biting path.

All men concede that mercury's the best
Of agents that will cure a tainted breast . . .
Each acrid molecule will in its turn
Seize upon every humor that will burn
The scourge away . . .
Of this distemper. Let me give its history.

"An ancient king had we, Alcithous,
Who had a shepherd lad called Syphilus.
On our prolific meads, a thousand sheep,
A thousand kine this shepherd had to keep.
One day, old Sirius with his mighty flame,
During the summer solstice to us came,
Taking away the shade from all our trees,
The freshness from the meadow, coolth from breeze.
His beasts expiring then did Syphilus
Turn to this horror of a brazen heaven,
Braving the sun's so torrid terror even,
Gazing upon its face and speaking thus:
'O Sun, how we endure, a slave to you!
You are a tyrant to us in this hour.
What matters it that bulls be killed, no few?
No father are you, nor supreme of power,

If fields be burned and sheep and kine and I.
Though jealous gods may never wish to see
Cattle submitted to my might, ah me,
My flocks are helpless for your brazen sky.
If the old tales be true, which is absurd,
You have one goat, one bull, and just one ram.
As guardian of this foolish little herd,
You have a mangy cur. The thing's a sham.
Why honor you? Alcithous is worth
Worship divine. He rules the sea and earth.
Stronger than gods and stronger than the sun,
He'll bring back verdant pastures, every one.
Life will he give to an expiring breeze,
He will revive the cattle and the trees.'

"Thus spake he. Braving gods, upon a hill
He reared an altar with a mighty will
To Prince Alcithous. The herdsmen bold
And all the ploughmen did as they were told,
Denying gods, deserting temples fair.
And to their king alone they worshipped there,
Reserving sacred bulls and frankincense
For him, and honoring him with joy immense.

"Upon his throne sat King Alcithous,
Whom a mad joy, alas, had blinded thus!
The outlawed gods no longer would he believe,
And he commanded that each state receive
Him as a god. Unto the thunder he sent
The gods, their cult—their domain his intent.

"But one who gazes, and with open eyes,
Embracing all the universe indeed,
Perceived the crime. Our island paradise
Received the evil of a subtle seed.
And foetid fogs and humid air became
The fardels of our impious, wicked shame.

"The sun went pallid for his righteous wrath
And germinated poisons on our path.
And he who wrought this outrage was the first

To feel his body ache, when sore accursed.
And for his ulcers and their torturing,
No longer would a tossing, hard couch bring
Him sleep. With joints apart and flesh erased,
Thus was the shepherd flailed and thus debased.
And after him this malady we call
SYPHILIS,[1] tearing at our city's wall
To bring with it such ruin and such a wrack,
That e'en the king escaped not its attack.

"The folk in fear, within the wood, Carthesis
Ran to consult the dryad, Ameresis.
Behind a clump of trees was her retreat.
Infallible, interpretive and sweet
Was she. They asked why gods condemned them and
Whom should they seek to cure them. She replied:
'All of the gods are wrathful. Understand,
Perverted race, you perish for your pride.
You braved the sun. The sun has punished you.
Incense is not for man. Immortals too
Find this a horror. You were prideful, mad.
Erect once more your altars and be glad
That sacrificial flesh shall smoke again.
Immortal justice is not stayed by men.
Your punishment must be eternal bane.
Apollo swears this by the sacred Styx.
He'll ease this ravage if you lunatics
Will worship gods again. To banish pain,
The sky reserves a mighty remedy
For you born of these shores. A black cow's blood
To Tellus[2] must be poured upon the grass.
And a white heifer might change Juno's mood,
Ere aught be granted that this ill may pass.
Some fecund seeds in Tellus's vast breast
Can grow a wide and leafy tree to scorn
This poison's energy. Peace! Be at rest!
Tellus will see that this tree shall be born.'

[1] The word may be derived from the Greek: sus-philos which means hog-love.
[2] *Tellus mater* is the ancient Latin deity of earth. She was the Goddess of marriage and of fertility and she was invoked in solemn oaths as the grave of all things. Several festivals were celebrated in her honor.

"Silent grew Ameresis and the sun
Sought the soft couch of west. The trees, the caves
Trembled at her soft voice when day was done.
The people reared their altars by the waves.
Juno and Tellus were given sacrifices.
O miracle! Anon, a great tree rises,
And, by the gods, it was not seen before,
By any people living on this shore.
The fertile land was shaded by this tree,
Covering our fields and hillsides, every lea.
And temples were reopened to the sun.
For expiation, all the gods chose one
Poor victim for a folk so impious;
Their common choice, the shepherd, Syphilus.
He bent his head beneath a sacred band,
Resigned and calm. And then, at a command,
The steel is raised to make his blood to flow.
But Juno turns the sword aside and so
The execution's stayed and by her grace.
Apollo's bull shall take the shepherd's place.

"Our fathers founded this so solemn rite,
Hoping to expiate a crime thereby.
And good are all the gods who dwell on high,
And every year they gather for this sight,
And every year a shepherd symbolizes
The victim; ancient are these sacrifices.
Each generation celebrates this feast.
It never ceases and our punishment
Continues 'til some clemency is sent
To us by all the gods. This crowd and priest
Assemble that the people purify
Them by infusions of this sacred tree,
In hopes to quench the fires for which they die,
When blazes in them this fierce malady."

1530
Translated in 1934

Medieval Remedies

FROM *THE* LEECH BOOK OF BALD *IN THE TENTH CENTURY*

DYSENTERY

Against dysentery, a bramble of which both ends are in the earth, take the nether root, delve it up, cut nine chips with the left hand and sing three times the Miserere Mei Deus and nine times the Pater Noster; then take mugwort and everlasting, boil these worts and the chips in milk until they get red, then let the man sip at night fasting a pound dish full, let him rest himself soft and wrap himself warm; if more need be let him do so again; if thou still need do it a third time thou wilt not need oftener.

MEDIEVAL CELTIC REMEDY FOR BALDNESS:

Let calcine a raven, his ashes boil in sheep's suet, and rub to the head, it cures.

With mice fill an earthen pipkin, stop the mouth with a lump of clay, and bury it beside a fire, but so as the fire's too great heat reach it not. So let it be then for a year, and at the year's end take out whatever may be found therein. But it is urgent that he who shall lift it have a glove on his hand, lest at his finger's end the hair come sprouting forth.

PLAGUE—DURING THE THIRTEENTH AND FOURTEENTH CENTURIES

Treatment of the Plague according to John of Burgundy, also known as the traveler, Sir John Mandeville:

Plague is held to be the effect of miasms or corrupt vapors upon the humoral complexion of the patient, the pestilence entering as an evil emanation through the pores of the skin and traveling thence to the heart, the liver, and the brain. To combat this, bathing was interdicted, lest the pores of the skin be opened, light diet, acid fruits and drinks, and especially liberal potations of vinegar were recommended. The air of rooms was purified by burning juniper branches or throwing powders on live coals for the patients' inhalation. Aromatic drugs were exhibited internally and carried in the hand mixed with resin or amber, and if the disease was acquired, bloodletting was immediately resorted to. Vinegar acquired a prominent status as a preventive.

FORMULA FOR AN ELECTUARY OF PRECIOUS STONES OF BULLEYN, PHARMACIST AND PHYSICIAN IN THE REIGN OF HENRY VIII

Take two drachms of white perles; two little peeces of saphyre; jacinthe, corneline, emerauldes, granettes of each an ounce; setwal, the sweat root doronike, the rind of pomecitron, mace, basel seede, of each two drachms; roots of both white and red behen, ginger, long pepper, spicknard, folium indicum, saffron, cardamon, of each one drachm; troches of diarodon, lignum aloes, of each a small handful; cinnamon, galinga, zurubeth, which is a kind of setwal, of each one and one-half drachms; thin peeces of gold and sylver, of each half of scruple; musk, half a drachm.

To be made with: honey emblici, which is the fourth kind of mirobalans, with roses, strained, in equal parts as much as will suffice.

Result: Kings and noblemen have used this for their comfort. It causeth them to be bold-spirited, the body to smell well, and ingendereth to the face a good color.

FOR PAIN IN THE EYE (SIXTEENTH CENTURY)

Take the right eye of a Frogg, lap it in a piece of Russet cloth and hang it about the neck; it cureth the right eye if it be enflamed or bleared. And if the left eye be greved, do the like by the left eye of the said Frogg.

Part 3

The Rebirth of Medicine

The Rebirth of Medicine

SYNOPSIS

IN ANATOMY, *in chemistry, in physics and astronomy, the situation at the beginning of the Revival of Learning was similar. In each science, it was necessary to overthrow blind belief in the written words of men centuries dead, and substitute methods of experiment and observation. A small group of geniuses accomplished the task—in physics, Galileo; in astronomy, Copernicus, Galileo and Newton; in medicine Vesalius and Harvey.*

It was the unique contribution of Paracelsus that he was the first great rebel whose attack on the medical gods had some effect on his·contemporaries. It is this fact, not his clinical skill nor his use of minerals in medicine, which assures his place in history. "On Authority and Experiment," from his own writings and "The Place of Paracelsus in Medicine," by Professor Robinson show the irascible, egotistical, bombastic quality of the man.

To destroy error was only part of the battle; truth had to be substituted. The basic principles controlling the body mechanism must be firmly established. A number of experimenters worked on the problem. Notable among these was Leonardo da Vinci. Somewhat earlier than Paracelsus, he dissected human bodies and made magnificent drawings of the human skeleton. He made physiological experiments on the heart and blood vessels; he seemed to understand the action of the valves of the great arteries. But he did not publish his anatomical drawings and he was too bound by tradition to discover the circulation of the blood._ His influence on the main stream of medical history was small.

Leonardo, it should be repeated, was only one of those who stood on the edge of great discovery—the spirit of creation was abroad. But it remained for two men, Vesalius and Harvey, to establish the sciences of human anatomy and physiology, to place them on the foundation of established fact which holds up the entire edifice of medicine. Sir Michael Foster, one of the most famous British physiologists, who is also a skilful and charming writer, tells the story in "Vesalius and Harvey."

As we have stated, Galen himself had some notion of the ebb and flow of the blood, during which, he thought, it was infused by the liver with "natural spirits." Galen further believed that blood passed from the right to the left side of the heart through invisible pores in the septum, the partition dividing the two sides of the heart. While Vesalius disbelieved this idea, he was content to teach it. Michael Servetus, who died at the stake for his religious beliefs in 1553, rejected it. Further, Servetus understood at least one aspect of the movement of the blood, the pulmonary circulation. Others too solved various aspects of the difficult problem. It was Harvey's special contribution that he was able to build on all the facts that had been discovered before him and explain, with exact proof, just how the blood does move: the minor, or pulmonary circulation, from the right side of the heart, through the lungs and back to the left side of the heart; and the major, or systemic circulation, from the left side of the heart to the rest of the body through the arteries, and its return through the veins to the right side of the heart again, constantly moving "as it were, in a circle." How the blood was collected from the lungs and how it passed from the arteries to the veins remained a mystery to Harvey. The microscope, which he lacked, was necessary to discover the capillaries (first observed by Malpighi) and thus close the circle.

Another important innovator, Ambroise Paré, ranks close to these two for his contributions to clinical medicine and surgery. Paré recognized the importance of the structure beneath the skin in the practice of surgery, lifting the despised art, practiced only by barbers, to a respected place in medicine. We quote here from his "Journeys in Divers Places" a famous passage in which he describes how he abolished the terrible ordeal of pouring boiling oil on gunshot wounds. Paré was also among the first to practice the method of turning the child in the mother's womb known as podalic version, a fact which serves as the basis for the fanciful

*and moving "Ambroise Paré Does a Delivery," by Professor Alan
Frank Guttmacher of Johns Hopkins. A measure of Paré's modesty is the remark which he made famous, "I dressed him and
God healed him." A measure of his humanity is the fact that after
curing his soldier patients, he devised artificial limbs for them.*

*Yet contemporaneous with these prodigious feats of discovery,
there remained the doctors who bled their patients to death,
typified by "Doctor Sangredo," taken from Alain-René Le Sage's
famous novel "Gil Blas;" the starveling apothecaries who dealt
in charms and poisons, immortalized in Shakespeare's "Romeo
and Juliet;" the physicians who prescribed remedies such as those
in "Seventeenth and Eighteenth Century Remedies," curing toothache by carrying the tooth of a dead man, curing "the passion of
the heart" with a mixture containing, among other things, damask
roses and the powders of precious stones. As shown in this selection, even so distinguished a natural philosopher as Robert Boyle
dealt in such nostrums. The great Bishop Berkeley swallowed
them with relish. Charles II was probably killed by them a bit
sooner than he would have died naturally.*

*Unfortunately, the discoveries of Vesalius and Harvey did not,
in themselves, help the suffering and bedridden patient, no matter
how enlightened his physician might be. The study of what
disease really was, how it was caused and how it might be cured
was still in its infancy. A group of great clinicians now arose who
met the need, slowly advancing the arts of differentiation of
disease and treatment. The efficacy of Cinchona bark in treating
malaria was recognized about the middle of the Seventeenth
Century. Among others, the Italian Morgagni, the Englishman
Sydenham, and the Dutchman Boerhave contributed to the abolition of the "schools," "systems" and metaphysical explanations
which sought to channel all medical information into rigid patterns. Beside the nonsensical remedies of Berkeley and the
king's physicians, we have the rational observation of Sydenham,
"The English Hippocrates." Sydenham set himself the task of
describing the course of actual cases as they occurred in his own
practice. In so doing he differentiated among the various diseases,
since each affected the body differently. He gave clear, accurate
descriptions of smallpox, malaria, scarlet fever, gout and others
(see "Descriptions of Disease" which follows). Moreover, he
had a truly modern conception of the role of the physician as a
passive aid to nature in helping the patient recover.*

It was Sydenham's weakness that he sneered at the medical writings of his predecessors and contemporaries and was thus unaware of anatomical and physiological progress. Nor did he make use of the powerful tool of the post-mortem—the study of the morbid changes which result in the death of the patient. How John Hunter, born nearly forty years after Sydenham died, made full use of the post-mortem, is the subject of Clendening's "Science and Surgery—John Hunter." Yet this was only one of his claims to importance. He was the greatest surgeon of his day, initiating several new techniques. He was the founder of the first natural history museum, the forerunner of similar museums throughout the world. He had the extraordinary courage and curiosity to inoculate himself with venereal disease, a story he himself tells in "Experiments Made to Ascertain the Progress and Effects of the Venereal Poison." It is a tragic and ironic fact that this heroic experiment served only to confuse and mislead the medical profession for decades. For the inoculation, Hunter used gonorrheal pus. Unknown to him, however the patient from whom he obtained this pus was also syphilitic. (The syphilitic chancre which resulted and which Hunter described is still known as the Hunterian chancre.) As a result, Hunter became convinced that syphilis and gonorrhea were the same, and his prestige was so great that other physicians accepted his opinion. Moreover, the treatment which he believed to be successful was in reality a failure. Hunter was thirty-eight when he contracted the disease. He continued his heroic labors for decades thereafter, but his health was poor until his death.

Not the least of Hunter's accomplishments was the fact that he was the teacher of Edward Jenner, who made one of the great medical discoveries of all time, which has all but wiped out smallpox in every civilized country on earth. A method of inoculation had been known in Oriental countries since ancient times. The method, which resulted in a mild case only, was introduced into England by Lady Mary Wortley Montagu, wife of the British Ambassador to Turkey, in 1718, and is described in her "Inoculation Against Smallpox" which follows. There were disadvantages to the process—the problem of getting infected matter and the fact that those infected were capable of passing on a virulent case to those with whom they came in contact. Nevertheless, it was workable and no doubt would have spread, had Jenner's method of vaccination with cowpox not intervened.

It is hard to overestimate the importance of the discovery described so dramatically in Jenner's "An Inquiry Into the Causes and Effects of the Variolae Vaccinae, Known by the Name of the Kine Pox." It has been instrumental in saving the lives of hundreds of millions of people from that day to this. For smallpox travelled everywhere, to the igloos of the Eskimos and the wigwams of the Indians. It decimated China and Mexico. No corner of the earth was free from the scarred and pitted faces which today are a rarity. The news spread rapidly. Benjamin Waterhouse performed the first vaccination in America in 1800, as described in his "The History of the Kine Pox." Everywhere the gratitude of the people was overwhelming. As Howard W. Haggard remarks in "The Doctor in History," "The American Indians sent a delegation to thank him personally and to bring him gifts. The Dowager Empress of Russia sent him a ring and gave the name Vaccinoff to the first child vaccinated in Russia."

One other enormously valuable aid to the diagnostician and clinician appeared toward the end of this period with the discovery of the stethoscope by René Laënnec. The work describing it was published in 1819 and a section of it is here reprinted under the title "The Invention of the Stethoscope." Laënnec was a French physician who himself was a victim of tuberculosis. His device has proved to be one of the most important tools in the recognition of a variety of diseases. Its discovery, incidentally, is usually coupled with that of percussion by Leopold Auenbrugger of Austria in 1761. Anyone who has visited a doctor becomes immediately aware of these two indispensable methods of diagnosis.

Our final selection in the present section is "Bootlegging Bodies," by Professor Guttmacher who wrote "Ambroise Paré Does a Delivery." Here he tells about one of the most gruesome episodes in the history of medicine. The horrors of the trade, brought on by the need for bodies for dissection, resulted in reforms which drove the body snatchers out of business, but not before every form of crime, including wholesale murder, had been committed. It is an exciting and authentic selection.

On Authority and Experiment

AUREOLUS THEOPHRASTUS BOMBASTUS VON HOHENHEIM
Known as PARACELSUS

But we shall free the art of medicine from its worst errors. Not by following that which those of old taught, but by our own observation of nature, confirmed by extensive practice and long experience. Who does not know that most doctors today make terrible mistakes, greatly to the harm of their patients? Who does not know that this is because they cling too anxiously to the teachings of Hippocrates, Galen, Avicenna, and others? . . .

Day after day I publicly elucidate for two hours, with great industry and to the great advantage of my hearers, books on practical and theoretical medicine, internal medicine, and surgery, books written by myself. I did not, like other medical writers, compile these books out of extracts from Hippocrates or Galen, but in ceaseless toil I created them anew, upon the foundation of experience, the supreme teacher of all things. If I want to prove anything, I shall not try to do it by quoting authorities, but by experiment and by reasoning thereon. If therefore, my dear readers, one of you should feel the impulse to penetrate these divine mysteries, if within a brief space of time he should want to fathom the depths of medicine, let him come to me at Basle, and he will find much more than I can utter in a few words. To express myself more plainly, let me say, by way of example, that I do not believe in the ancient doctrine of the complexions and the humors, which have been falsely supposed to account for all diseases. It is because these doctrines prevail that so few physicians have a precise knowledge of illnesses, their causes, and their critical days. I forbid you, therefore, to pass a facile judgment upon Theophrastus until you have heard him for yourselves. Farewell, and come with a good will to study our attempt to reform medicine. *Basle, June 5, 1527.*

The Place of Paracelsus
in Medicine

VICTOR ROBINSON

AMONG the surgical thinkers of the Renaissance, first place belongs to the abused and abusive Paracelsus, who refused to recognize the cleft between medicine and surgery. Erratic and unbalanced, and often lost in incomprehensible mysticism, he nevertheless enunciated principles—in most vehement vernacular—which furnished an impetus to all the rebellious spirits of the time, and have since been incorporated into modern surgery.

Paracelsus tells us why he became a reformer: "Since I saw that the doctrine accomplished nothing but the making of corpses, deaths, murder, deformity, cripples, and decay, and had no foundation, I was compelled to pursue the truth in another way, to seek another basis, which I have attained after hard labor." He had a noble conception of the duty of a physician, and was so anxious to cure that he exclaimed, "If God will not help me, so help me the Devil!" In the presence of the sick, Paracelsus was a changed man: his arrogance and bombast turned to humanity and charity. The maimed, the diseased, the suffering, came to him:

A man named Bartholomew who had for two years a pain in his side, a woman who had a great swelling on her thigh, a soldier who was shot in the breast with a forked arrow, a young man who had a crusty ulcer on his chin, one whose stomach was swollen and standing out, a lad whose finger was eaten to the bone with disease, a goldsmith whose skull had been injured, one Jonas who fell in love with one Sabina and then fell beside himself, the daughter of one Oliver who was pale and ate small

stones and chalk, a boy of eighteen who had a black bladder
appear where a tooth was drawn, a young gentlewoman named
Ascania who had pain all over her body, one who had a flux of
blood from a severed artery, a knight who suffered a stroke of
apoplexy, a man of the country who was stung by an adder, one
who was wounded in the tunicle of the heart, a young man who
was vexed with a continual and violent cough, a certain woman
who was troubled with a disease in her secret parts, one named
Vermundus who was so weak in his head that he staggered as if
drunk, a fair young man who was infected with the pox through
the act of the Sodomites, one named Gallenus who had lost his
speech, one who was troubled with a great burning of the urine,
one who had a cataract of the eyes, a woman whose courses were
so long that she was ready to give up the ghost, a sucking child
whose palate was full of pustules, one Gotius who had a bone
out of joint for several days, a lawyer who was long sick of the
colic, a man of threescore years who was full of melancholy
humors, a woman who three months after conception feared
abortion, a certain man who had carnal company with his wife
but could void no sperm, a certain Queen who through the retention of her menses had her tongue inflamed, a German prince
who was sick with the frenzy, a gentlewoman of name who was
troubled with a suffocation of the matrix, a certain baron who
was sorely afflicted with syphilis.

Because of his famous cures, Paracelsus was made professor
at Basel. In this pretty town, near a chestnut-covered terrace
that overlooks the hills of the Black Forest, still stands the house
where lived two illustrious friends and patients who sought health
at the hands of Paracelsus—Frobenius the printer and Erasmus
the philosopher. "I cannot," wrote Erasmus, "offer thee a reward
equal to thy art and knowledge, but I surely offer thee a grateful
soul. Thou hast called from the shades Frobenius who is my other
half: if thou restorest me also thou restorest each through the
other. May fortune favor that thou remain in Basel."

So Paracelsus came to the University, looking as natural as
the portrait of himself, wrongly ascribed to the great Tintoretto.
He regarded the students with those strange eyes which have
been described as "wild, intense, hungry, homeless, defiant and
yet complaining eyes; the eyes of a man who struggles to tell a
great secret, and cannot find words for it, and yet wonders why
men cannot understand, and will not believe what seems to him

as clear as day." The new professor did many astonishing things that day. Instead of using monkish Latin, he lectured in native German, which then seemed "even to the German emperor, suitable only to address horses." Paracelsus had with him a pile of books—the works of Galen, Avicenna, Averroes and other medical masters. It was surprising to see the iconoclast in company with the authorities. But Paracelsus did not quote from them. He placed some sulphur in a brazier, set fire to it, cast in the sacred volumes, and burnt up the idols:

"Follow me," he cried, "not I you, follow me Avicenna, Galen, Rhazes, Montagnana, Mesuë, and ye others! Follow me, not I you! ye of Paris, Montpellier, ye of Suabia, ye of Meissen, ye of Cologne, ye of Vienna and the banks of the Danube and the Rhine, ye islands of the sea, Italy, Dalmatia, Sarmatia, Athens, ye Greeks, ye Arabs, ye Israelites, not one of you shall remain in the remotest corner upon whom the dogs shall not void their urine! How does this please you, Cacophrastus? This dung must ye eat! And ye Calefactores, ye shall become chimney-sweeps! What will you think when I triumph? I am to be the monarch, and the monarchy will belong to me. For I tell you boldly that the hair from the back of my head knows more than all your writers put together; my shoe-buckles have more wisdom in them than either Galen or Avicenna; and my beard more experience than your whole Academy."

The academic career of Paracelsus was brief and stormy; his life was a constant battle, and he would have aroused even greater turmoil if he had published his theological writings, since they contained these sentiments: "Those who stand with the Pope consider him a living saint, those who stand with the Arian also hold him a righteous man, those who hold with Zwingli likewise consider him a righteous man, those who stand with Luther hold him a true prophet. Thus are the people deceived. Every fool praises his own motley. He who depends on the Pope rests on the sand, he who depends on Zwingli depends on hollow ground, he who depends upon Luther depends on a reed. They all deem themselves each above the other, and denounce one another as Antichrists, heathens and heretics, and are but four pairs of breeches from one cloth. It is with them as with a tree that has been twice grafted and bears white and yellow pears. Whoever opposes them and speaks the truth, he must die. How many thousands have they strangled and caused to be strangled

in recent years." Had Frobenius put this manuscript into print
for its author, the fate of Paracelsus would have been that of
Charles Estienne—classicist and scientist, first to demonstrate
the spinal canal, whose reward was to perish in the dungeons of
religious intolerance. The only man of that age who remained
immune while he thrust his pen at fanaticism was Erasmus—the
unique monk who scorned a cardinal's hat in his lifetime, and
refused a priest's attendance at his death-bed; the unapproachable Erasmus whose wit mocked the wickedness of kings and
the corruption of prelates.

The·complacent cocksureness of Paracelsus was enough to
stir the ire of a turtledove. "Tell me, Galenic doctor," he jauntily
asks, "on what foundation you stand? Have you ever cured
podagra, have you ever dared to attack leprosy, or healed
dropsy? Truly I think you will be silent and allow that I am
your master. If you really wish to learn, listen to what I say,
attend to what I write." Such vanity overtops the loftiest peaks
of his native Alps, but much can be forgiven the man who in the
age of polypharmacy was able to say: "Bah! this miserable compounding business! Yet the woman requires only one man to
father her child; many seeds only corrupt it. Mix many kinds
of seeds and bray them like an apothecary and bury them in the
earth; no fruit will come from them . . . My accusers complain that I have not entered the temple of knowledge through
the legitimate door. But which one is the truly legitimate door?
Galenus and Avicenna or Nature? I have entered through the
door of Nature: her light, and not the lamp of an apothecary's
shop has illuminated my way."

He advanced our understanding of syphilis, was the first to
point out the connection between goiter of the parent and
cretinism of the offspring, wrote an admirable description of
hospital gangrene, and truly roared against what he termed "the
damnable precept which teaches that it is necessary to make
wounds suppurate." His insistence on the cleanliness of wounds
is found in various declarations which at that time were revolutionary: "In wounds nature is the real physician. All that is
necessary is to prevent infection in wound diseases. The humors
and complexions, diet and weather, and the stars have no influence. Only the proper treatment, that which lets nature act in
peace, determines the result."

When Paracelsus is in a strange mood, and begins with his

aniadum, aquastor, evestrum, erodinium, his hidden iliasters, ultimate essences, astral corpses, haunted houses and poisoned moons, we feel all the superstitions of the age creeping over us. Not only did he accept the occultism of the sixteenth century, with its witchcraft and magic, but he was the father of the *homunculus*—a motherless miniature man produced in a glass bottle by mixing horse-dung with human semen and adding the appropriate chemicals. In spite of his adherence to mysticism, Paracelsus had the luminous intelligence to inform his time: "In Nature's battle against disease the physician is but the helper, who furnishes Nature with weapons, the apothecary is but the smith who forges them. The business of the physician is there-fore to give to Nature what she needs for her battle. Nature is the physician . . . Ere the world perishes, many arts now ascribed to the work of the devil will become public, and we shall then see that the most of these effects depend upon natural forces."

1931

Vesalius and Harvey: The Founding of Modern Anatomy and Physiology

MICHAEL FOSTER

THE WHOLE story of the rise and growth of the art of healing is too vast to be gathered into one set of lectures, too varied to be treated of by one man alone . . . I will ask you to let me start with the middle of the sixteenth century, and indeed with the particular year 1543. . . .

In this year 1543 the printing-press of J. Oporinus (or Herbst) in Basel gave to the world in a folio volume the *Fabrica Humani Corporis*, the Structure of the Human Body, by Andreas Vesa-lius. This marked an epoch in the history of Anatomy, and so of Physiology and of Medicine. Who was Andreas Vesalius, and why did his book mark an epoch?

Let me briefly answer the latter question first. In the times of the Greeks mankind had made a fair start in the quest of natural knowledge, both of things not alive and of things living; the search had been carried on into the second century of the Christian Era when Galen expounded the structure and the use of the parts of the body of man. As Galen passed away inquiry, that is to say inquiry into natural knowledge, stood still. For a thousand years or more the great Christian Church was fulfilling its high mission by the aid of authority; but authority, as with the growth of the Church it became more and more potent as an instrument of good, became at the same time more and more potent as a steriliser of original research in natural knowledge.

As spiritual truths were learned by the study of the revealed word, so anatomical and medical truths were to be sought for, not by looking directly into the body of man, not by observing and thinking over the phenomena of disease, but by studying what had been revealed in the writings of Hippocrates and Galen. As the Holy Scriptures were the Bible for all men, so the works of the Greek and Latin writers became the bible for the anatomist and the doctor. Truth and science came to mean simply that which was written, and inquiry became mere interpretation.

The "new birth" of the fifteenth and sixteenth centuries was in essence a revolt against authority as the guide in knowledge; and the work of Andreas Vesalius of which I am speaking marks an epoch, since by it the idol of authority in anatomical science was shattered to pieces never to be put together again. Vesalius described the structure of the human body such as he found it to be by actual examination, by appealing to dissection, by looking at things as they are. He dared not only to show how often Galen was wrong, but to insist that when Galen was right he was to be followed, not because he had said it, but because what he said was in accordance with what anyone who took the pains to inquire could assure himself to be the real state of things. . . .

Who then was this Andreas Vesalius?

He was born at Brussels at midnight as the last day of 1514 was passing into the first of 1515. His family, which had dwelt for several generations at Nymwegen and which originally bore the name of Witing, had produced many doctors and learned men, and his father was apothecary to Charles V. His mother, to judge by her maiden name, Isabella Crabbe, was probably of English extraction.

The young Vesalius (or Wesalius, for so it was sometimes spelt) was sent to school at Louvain and afterwards entered the University there, which then as later was of great renown. Though he diligently pursued the ordinary classical and rhetorical studies of the place, the bent of his mind early showed itself; while yet a boy he began to dissect such animals as he could lay his hands on. Such a boy could not do otherwise than study medicine, and in 1533, a lad of seventeen or eighteen, he went to Paris to sit at the feet of Sylvius, then rising into fame.

The ardent young Belgian was however no docile hearer, receiving open-mouthed whatever fell from the master. Sylvius' teaching was in the main the reading in public of Galen. From time to time however the body of a dog or at rarer intervals the corpse of some patient was brought into the lecture room, and barber servants dissected in a rough, clumsy way and exposed to the view of the student the structures which the learned doctor, who himself disdained such menial, loathsome work, bid them show. This did not satisfy Vesalius. At the third dissection at which he was present he, already well versed in the anatomy of the dog, irritated beyond control at the rude handling of the ignorant barbers, pushing them on one side, completed the dissection in the way he knew it ought to be done.

"My study of anatomy," says he, "would never have succeeded had I when working at medicine at Paris been willing that the viscera should be merely shewn to me and to my fellow-students at one or another public dissection by wholly unskilled barbers, and that in the most superficial way. I had to put my own hand to the business."

Besides listening to Sylvius, he was a pupil of Johannes Guinterius (Günther), a Swiss from Andernach, who also was teaching anatomy and surgery at Paris at the time, and with whom his relations seem to have been closer than with Sylvius.

Neither Sylvius, however, nor Guinterius, nor any one at the time was able to supply Vesalius with that for which he was obviously longing, the opportunity of dissecting thoroughly the human body. Complete dissection was then well-nigh impossible, the most that could be gained was the hurried examination of some parts of the body of a patient who had succumbed to disease. One part of the human body, the foundation of all other parts, the skeleton, could however be freely used for study. In those rude times burial was rough and incomplete, and in the cemeteries bones lay scattered about uncovered. In the burial-

ground attached to the church of the Innocents at Paris Vesalius
spent many hours, studying the bones; and he also tells us how in
another burial-ground, on what is now "Les Buttes Chaumont,"
he and a fellow-student nearly left their own bones, being on one
occasion attacked and in great risk of being devoured by savage,
hungry dogs who too had come there in search of bones. By
such a rough, perilous study Vesalius laid the foundation of his
great work, a full and exact knowledge of the human skeleton.
He tells us how he and a fellow-student were wont to try their
knowledge by a test which has been often used since, the recognition of the individual bones by touch alone, with the eyes shut.

After three years the wars drove him back from Paris to
Louvain, where he continued to pursue his anatomical studies
with unflagging zeal. Here as at Paris he was driven to use
strange means to gain the material for his studies. Walking one
day with a friend in the outskirts of the city and coming to the
public gibbet, where "to the great convenience of the studious,
the bodies of those condemned to death were exposed to public
view," they came upon a corpse "which had proved such a sweet
morsel to the birds that they had most thoroughly cleaned it,
leaving only the bones and ligaments." With his friend's help
he climbed up the gallows and attempted to carry off the skeleton,
but in the hurry of such a theft in open daylight he only succeeded in getting part of it; accordingly that evening he got
himself shut out of the city gates, secured in the quiet of night
the rest of the skeleton, and returning home by a roundabout way
and re-entering the city by a different gate, safely carried it in.

In 1537, after a year's stay at Louvain where, in the February
of that year, he put forth his first juvenile effort, a translation of
the ninth book of Rhazes, he migrated to Venice, the enlightened
if despotic government of which was in all possible ways foster-
ing the arts and sciences, and striving to develop in the dependent
city of Padua a University which should worthily push on the
new learning. It may be worth while to note, as an instance of
how in the web of man's history threads of unlike kind are made
to cross, that among the monks who had charge of the Hospital
at Venice, at which Vesalius pursued his medical studies, was
one who bore the name of Ignatius Loyola. . . .

The brilliant talents of the young Belgian at once attracted
the notice of the far-sighted rulers of Venice. He was in December of that same year, 1537, made Doctor of Medicine in their

University of Padua, was immediately entrusted with the duty
of conducting public dissections, and either then or very shortly
afterwards, though he was but a lad of some one or two and
twenty summers, was placed in a Chair of Surgery with care
of Anatomy.

He at once began to teach anatomy in his own new way. Not
to unskilled ignorant barbers would he entrust the task of laying
bare before the students the secrets of the human frame; his own
hand, and his own hand alone, was cunning enough to track out
the pattern of structures which day by day were becoming more
and more clear to him. Following venerated customs he began his
academic labours by "reading" Galen, as others had done before
him, using his dissections to illustrate what Galen had said. But
time after time the body on the table said plainly something different from that which Galen had written.

He tried to do what others had done before him, he tried to
believe Galen rather than his own eyes, but his eyes were too
strong for him; and in the end he cast Galen and his writings to
the winds and taught only what he himself had seen and what he
could make his students see too.

Thus he brought into anatomy the new spirit of the time, and
the men of the time, the young men of the time answered to the
new voice. Students flocked to his lectures, his hearers amounted
it is said to some five hundred, and an enlightened Senate recognized his worth by repeatedly raising his emoluments.

Such a mode of teaching laid a strain on the getting of the
material for teaching. Vesalius was unwearied in his search for
subjects to dissect. He begged all the doctors to allow him to
examine the bodies of their fatal cases. He ingratiated himself
with the judges, so that when a criminal was condemned to death
they gave directions that the sentence should be carried out at
such a time, and the execution should be conducted now in this
manner, now in that as might best meet the needs of Vesalius'
public dissections. Nor did he shrink apparently from robbing
the grave, for he relates how, learning of the death and hurried
burial of the concubine of a monk, he got possession of the body,
and proceeded at once to remove the whole of the skin in order
that the peccant holy man, who had got wind of the matter,
might be unable to recognize his lost love. And he made dissections in Bologna as well as Padua. . . .

Five years he thus spent in untiring labours at Padua. Five years he wrought, not weaving a web of fancied thought, but patiently disentangling the pattern of the texture of the human body, trusting to the words of no master, admitting nothing but that which he himself had seen; and at the end of the five years, in 1542, while he was as yet not 28 years of age, he was able to write the dedication to Charles V of a folio work, entitled the "Structure of the Human Body," adorned with many plates and woodcuts, which appeared at Basel in the following year, 1543. He had in 1538 published, under the sanction of the Senate of Venice, "Anatomical Tables," and in the same or succeeding year had brought forth an edition of Guinterius, a treatise on blood-letting, and an edition of Galen. There is a legend that the pictures in the great work were by the hand of Titian, but there seems no doubt that they, like the Tables, were done by one John Stephen Calcar, a countryman of Vesalius.

This book is the beginning not only of modern anatomy but of modern physiology.

We cannot it is true point to any great physiological discovery as Vesalius' own special handiwork, but in a sense he was the author of discoveries which were made after him. He set before himself a great task, that of placing the study of human anatomy on a sound basis, on the basis of direct, patient, exact observation. And he accomplished it. Galen had attempted the same thing before him; but the times were not then ripe for such a step. Authority laid its heavy hand on inquiry, and Galen's teaching instead of being an example and an encouragement for further research, was, as we have said, made into a bible, and interpretation was substituted for investigation. Vesalius, inspired by the spirit of the new learning, did his work in such a way as to impress upon his age the value not only of the results at which he arrived, but also and even more so, of the method by which he had gained them. He taught in such a way that his disciples, even when they thought him greater than Galen, never made a second Galen of him; they recognized that they were most truly following his teaching as a whole when they appealed to observation to show that in this or that particular point his teaching was wrong. After him backsliding became impossible; from the date of the issue of his work onward, anatomy pursued an unbroken, straightforward course, being made successively fuller and truer by the labours of those who came after.

Vesalius' great work is a work of anatomy, not of physiology.

Though to almost every description of structure there are added observations on the use and functions of the structures described, and though at the end of the work there is a short special chapter on what we now call experimental physiology, the book is in the main a book of anatomy, the physiology is incidental, occasional, and indeed halting. Nor is the reason far to seek. Vesalius had a great and difficult task before him. He had to convince the world that the only true way to study the phenomena of the living body was, not to ask what Galen had said, but to see for oneself with one's own eyes how things really were. And not only was a sound and accurate knowledge of the facts of structure a necessary prelude to any sound conclusions concerning function, but also the former was the only safe vantage ground from which to fight against error. When he asserted that such a structure was not as Galen had described it but different, he could appeal to the direct visible proof laid bare by the scalpel. Even then he found it difficult to convince his hearers, so ready were men still to trust Galen rather than their own eyes. Much harder was the task when, in dealing with function, he had to leave the solid ground of visible fact, and to have recourse to arguments and reasoning. . . .

Obviously his vigorous and active young mind was starting many inquiries of a purely physiological kind, and he was aware that much of the physiology which he had put into his book would not stand the test of future research. He knew more particularly that the chapter in that book in which he treated of the use of the heart and its parts was as he says "full of paradoxes." But he was no less aware that his bold attempt to expound the plain visible facts of anatomy such as they appeared to one who had torn from his eyes the bandages of authority, was of itself enough to raise a storm of opposition; he feared to jeopardize his success in that great effort by taking upon himself further burdens.

Experience showed that in this he was right. Even while he was writing his book, timorous friends urged him not to publish it; its appearance they said would destroy his prospects in life. And in one sense it did. Towards the end of 1542 after the completion of his great task, although in August of that year he had been reappointed to the Chair of Surgery and Anatomy for three years, he, with the sanction of the Senate, left Padua for a while, his pupil Realdus Columbus being appointed his deputy. He made a short stay at Venice; he visited Basel either once or twice, chiefly it would seem to confer with his printers; but while in that city he prepared with his own hands from the body of an executed criminal a complete skeleton which is still religiously preserved there. He also probably made a hurried journey to the Netherlands. During his absence from Padua, after the appearance of his book the storm broke out. The great Sylvius and others thundered against him, reviling him in a free flow of adjectives. Coming back to Padua, after about a year's absence, he found opposition to his new views strong even there . . . The spirit shewn entered like iron into his soul. If the work on which he had labored so long and which he felt to be so full of promise met with such a reception, why should he continue to labour? Why should he go on casting his pearls before swine? He had by him manuscripts of various kinds, the embodiment of observations and thoughts not included in the *Fabrica*. What they were we can only guess; what the world lost in their loss we shall never know. In a fit of passion he burnt them all, and the Emperor Charles V, offering him the post of Court Physician, he shook from his feet in 1544 the dust of the city in whose University he had done so much, and still a youth who had not yet attained the thirties, ended a career of science so gloriously begun.

Ended a career; for though in the years which followed he from time to time produced something, and in 1555 brought out a new edition of his *Fabrica*, differing chiefly from the first one, so far as the circulation of the blood is concerned, in its bolder enunciation of his doubts about the Galenic doctrines touching the heart, he made no further solid addition to the advancement of knowledge. Henceforward his life was that of a Court Physician much sought after and much esteemed, a life lucrative and honourable and in many ways useful, but not a life conducive to original inquiry and thought. The change was a great and a strange one. At Padua he had lived amid dissections; not content with the public dissections in the theatre, he took parts at least of corpses to his own lodgings and continued his labours there. No wonder that he makes in his *Fabrica* some biting remarks to the effect that he who espouses science must not marry a wife, he cannot be true to both. A year after his arrival at the Court he sealed his divorce from science by marrying a wife; no more dissections at home, no more dissections indeed at all, at most some few post-mortem examinations of patients whose lives his skill had failed to save. . . .

When in 1556 Charles withdrew from the world and took

refuge in the Cloister, Vesalius transferred to the son Philip II the services which he had paid to the father, and in 1559 returned with him to Spain.

Spain, as it then was, could be no home for a man of science. The hand of the Church was heavy on the land; the dagger of the Inquisition was stabbing at all mental life, and its torch was a sterilizing flame sweeping over all intellectual activity. . . .

We cannot wonder that amid such surroundings the feelings that the past years had been years of a wasted life grew strong upon him, and that wistful memories of the earlier happy times gathered head. He was still in the prime of life, a man of some forty-five summers; many years of intellectual vigour were perhaps still before him. Was he to spend all these in marking time to the music of an Imperial Court?

Just at this time, in 1561, there came into his hands the anatomical observations of Falloppius (Gabrielo Falloppio), a man of whom I shall presently have to speak, who in 1551 had after a brief interval succeeded Vesalius in the Chair of Padua. This book came to the wearied and despondent Vesalius, banished to the intellectual desert of Madrid, as a living voice from a bright world outside. Putting everything else on one side, he gave himself, as he says, "wholly up to the instant greedy reading of the pages" which brought vividly back to him the delights of his youth. Calling back from the past the memory of things observed long ago, for new observations, as we have seen, were out of his power, he put together bit by bit some notes criticizing Falloppius' work, put them together hurriedly and rapidly, in order that Tiepolo, the Venetian ambassador, then at Madrid but about to return to Venice, might carry the manuscript with him. In that "Examen," as he calls it, Vesalius says how the reading of Falloppius' notes had raised in him "a glad and joyful memory of that most delightful life which, teaching anatomy, I passed in Italy, the true nurse of intellects." He looks forward, he says, "to see the ornaments of our science continue to bud forth in the school from which I was while yet a youngster dragged away to the dull routine of medical practice and to the worries of continual journeys. I look forward to the accomplishment of that great work for which, to the best of my powers so far as my youth and my then judgment allowed, I laid foundations, such that I need not be ashamed of them."

And even more, he was nursing the idea that his present barren life might be exchanged for a more fruitful one. "I still," says he, "live in hope that at some time or other, by some good fortune I may once more be able to study that true bible, as we count it, of the human body and of the nature of man. . . ."

But it was not to be. In 1563 he suddenly determined to make a pilgrimage to Jerusalem. There are various legends as to the reasons which led him to this step. It is said that in making what was supposed to be a post-mortem examination on a noble man, or according to others a woman suffering from some obscure disease, it turned out that the body was still living, and that the Church insisted upon the pilgrimage as an expiation for an act deemed to be a sacrilege. The truer account is probably that told by the botanist Clusius, that Vesalius, ill in body, and we may add even more sick at heart, wearied of the Court, and harassed by the Church, seized an opportunity, and made the proposed pilgrimage an excuse for bringing to an end his then mode of life.

On his way to Jerusalem he stopped at Venice and renewed his intercourse with scientific friends. He there learnt that the manuscript on Falloppius had never reached that anatomist, who had somewhat suddenly died in 1562, but was still in Tiepolo's hands. His friends at once obtained it from Tiepolo, and it saw the light in the following May.

The Senate at Venice were just then at a loss for a fit successor to Falloppius, and it is possible that Vesalius during his stay in the city made known his willingness to desert the Court and to return to academic life; for it is said, though documentary evidence is lacking, that during his eastern journey he received an invitation to occupy his old Chair. Alas, on his way back in 1564 he was taken ill, or possibly a latent malady openly developed itself, he was put ashore on the island of Zante, and there he passed away.

The influence of Vesalius on the history of science may be regarded on the one hand in its general, on the other in its more special aspect.

Taking the general aspect first we may say that he founded modern anatomy. He insisted upon, and through his early unwearied labours by his conspicuous example he ensured the success of the new method of inquiry, the method of observation as against interpretation; he overthrew authority and raised up experience, he put the book of nature, the true book, in place of the book of Galen, and thus made free and open the paths of inquiry. Others before him, as we have said, Mundinus to wit and Carpi, had made like efforts, but theirs were partial and unsuccessful; Vesalius' efforts were great, complete, and successful. Upon the publication of the *Fabrica*, the pall of "authority" was once and for ever removed. Vesalius' results were impugned, and indeed were corrected by his compeers and his followers; but they were impugned and corrected by the method which he had introduced. Inquirers asserted that in this or that point Galen was right and Vesalius was wrong, but they no longer appealed to the authority of Galen as deciding the question, they appealed now to the actual things as the judge between the two, as the judge of Galen as of others. And even those who were Vesalius' most devoted disciples never made of him a second Galen; they never appealed to him as an authority, they were content to show on the actual body that what he had said was right.

Under a more special aspect he may be regarded as the founder of physiology as well as of anatomy in as much as he was the distinct forerunner of Harvey. For Harvey's great exposition of the circulation of the blood did, as we shall see, for physiology what Vesalius' *Fabrica* did for anatomy; it first rendered true progress possible. And Harvey's great work was the direct outcome of Vesalius' teaching. . . .

When in 1542 after the completion of his great work Vesalius had leave to absent himself from Padua a young man, Matheus Realdus Columbus, a native of Cremona, was appointed as his deputy, and when in 1544 Vesalius finally left Padua, the Senate of Venice entrusted for two years the duty of reading the lectures on Surgery and Anatomy to the same Columbus. But Columbus did not remain Vesalius' successor even for the two years; in the next year, 1545, Cosimo de Medici appointed him as the first Professor of Anatomy in the newly renovated University of Pisa; and Vesalius' Chair was not adequately filled until 1551, when Gabrielus Falloppius was placed in it.

Falloppius, born in Modena in 1523, a favourite and a devoted pupil of Vesalius, an accomplished and travelled scholar, a careful and exact observer and describer, a faithful, modest, quiet man, has left his name in anatomy in the terms Falloppian canal and Falloppian tubes. We owe to him many valuable observations on the skeleton, especially on the skull, on the tympanum, on the muscles, and on the generative organs. But he made no large con-

tribution to knowledge such as distinctly influenced the progress
of physiology; and he left no mark on the doctrines of the circulation. I have already spoken of his Anatomical Observations as
stirring up Vesalius in his later years to revived anatomical long-
ings; in these Falloppius says that if he had been able to advance
any new truth, that was largely due to Vesalius "who so showed
me the true path of inquiry that I was able to walk along it still
farther than had been done before."

Born, in 1537, of humble parents, in the little Tuscan town or
rather village bearing that name, Hieronymus Fabricius[1] studied
under Falloppius at Padua, and, on the death of his master, in
1565, succeeded him in the Chair of Anatomy, holding it for 40
years, until 1619, when he died at the ripe old age of 82.

A distinguished surgeon and a learned anatomist, well acquainted with the anatomy not only of man but of other verte-
brates, he was the author of many treatises, most of which had
distinct physiological bearings and which contained many contributions to the advancement of knowledge. He was the first
after Aristotle to describe the formation of the chick in the egg;
he wrote well on locomotion, on the eye, on the ear, on the skin,
on the larynx and on speech; but the one work which concerns
the subject which we have in hand is that on the valves of the
veins, the book *De venarum ostiolis*, "the little doors of the veins,"
which saw the light in 1574.

Johannus Baptista Cannanus, Professor at Ferrara, is said to have
observed the valves long before, namely in 1547, and indeed to
have told Vesalius of his observation; and even before that, these
structures it is said were noticed by Sylvius. But they were not
really laid hold of until Fabricius published his book. In that work
he most carefully and accurately described their structure, position 'and distribution, illustrating his observations by fairly good
figures. He moreover clearly recognized that the valves offered
opposition to the flow of blood from the heart towards the pe-
riphery, and even gives the now well-known demonstration of
their action on the living arm.

He says, *De venarum ostiolis*:

"Little doors of the veins is the name I give to certain very thin
little membranes occurring on the inside of the veins, and distributed at intervals over the limbs, placed sometimes one by itself,

---

[1] Often spoken of, from the place of his birth, as ab Aquapendente.

and sometimes two together. They have their mouths directed towards the root of the veins (*i.e.* the heart), and in the other direction are closed. Viewed from the outside they present an appearance not unlike the swellings which are seen in the branches and stem of a plant. In my opinion they are formed by nature in order that they may to a certain extent delay the blood and so prevent the whole of it flowing at once like a flood either to the feet, or to the hands and fingers, and becoming collected there. For this would give rise to two evils; on the one hand the upper parts of the limbs would suffer from want of nourishment, and on the other the hands and feet would be troubled with a continual swelling. In order therefore that the blood should be everywhere distributed in a certain just measure and admirable proportion for maintaining the nourishment of the several parts, these valves of the veins were formed. . . ."

But he wholly failed to recognize their true function. Still labouring under the influence of the old doctrines and believing that the use of the veins was that of carrying crude blood, blood not vivified by the vital spirits, from the heart to the tissues, he thought that he had fully explained the value of the veins, by pointing out that they opposed the flow from the heart to the tissues, not of all blood but only of an excess of blood; their purpose was to prevent the blood as it flowed along the veins from the heart being heaped up too much in one place. But he also thought that they were the means of furnishing temporary local reservoirs of blood; and he likens them to the devices by which in mills and elsewhere water is dammed up. He left for another, for a pupil of his, the opportunity of putting to its right use the discovery which he had made. . . .

I need not take up time by entering largely into the details of the oft-told story of William Harvey's life.

Born at Folkestone, on the south coast of England, in April 1578, just four years after Fabricius had published his treatise on the valves of the veins, admitted to Gonville and Caius College, Cambridge, in 1593, taking his degree in Arts in 1597, he left England the following year to study medicine under the great master at Padua. There he spent the greater part of four years, years very nearly overlapping the period between the writing and the publication of Fabricius's treatise on Respiration, of which I have just spoken as being, in great measure, an exposition of the Galenic doctrine of the circulation. At the end of the period, in 1602, he received at Padua the degree of Doctor of Medicine, and on his return to England in the same year was incorporated into the Doctorate at Cambridge.

Setting up his abode in London, joining the Royal College of Physicians in 1604, and becoming Physician to St Bartholomew's Hospital in 1609, he ventured in 1615 to develop, in his Lectures on Anatomy at the College of Physicians, the view which he was forming concerning the movements of the heart and of the blood. But his book, his *Exercitatio*, on that subject did not see the light until 1628.

"The little choleric man," as Aubrey calls him, attained fame among his fellows, and favour at Court. As Physician to King Charles I he accompanied that monarch on his unhappy wanderings, and every one knows the tale or legend of how at the battle of Edgehill, taking care of the Princes he sat, on the outskirts of the fight under a hedge, reading a book. In 1646, after the events at Oxford, he retired into private life, publishing in 1651 his treatise, *De generatione animalium*, in which he followed up some of the researches of his Paduan master, and on June 3, 1667, he ended a life remarkable for its effects rather than for its events.

It is a fashion to speak of Harvey as "the immortal Discoverer of the Circulation"; but the real character of his work is put in a truer light when we say that he was the first to demonstrate the circulation of the blood. His wonderful book, or rather tract, for it is little more, is one sustained and condensed argument, but an argument founded not on general principles and analogies but on the results of repeated "frequent appeals to vivisection" and ocular inspection. He makes good one position, and having done that advances on to another, and so marches victoriously from position to position until the whole truth is put clearly before the reader, and all that remains is to drive the truth home by further striking illustrations.

His first position is the true nature and purpose of the movements of the heart itself, that is, of the ventricles. When, in the beginning of the inquiry, he "first gave his mind to vivisections" he found the task of understanding the "motions and uses of the heart so truly arduous, so full of difficulties" that he began to think with Fracastorius (a Veronese doctor of the middle of the sixteenth century (1530) and more a poet than a man of science), "that the motion of the heart was only to be comprehended by

God." But the patient and prolonged study of many hearts of many animals shewed him that "the motion of the heart consists in a certain universal tension, both of contraction in the line of its fibres, and constriction in every sense, that when the heart contracts it is emptied, that the motion which is in general regarded as the diastole of the heart is in truth its systole," that the active phase of the heart is not that which sucks blood in, but that which drives blood out. Caesalpinus alone of all Harvey's forerunners had in some way or other dimly seen this truth. Harvey saw it clearly and saw it in all its consequences. It is, he says, the pressure of the constriction, of the systole, which squeezes the blood into and along the arteries, it is this transmitted pressure which causes the pulses; the artery swells at this point or that along its course, not in order that it may suck blood into it, but because blood is driven into it, and that by the pressure of the constricting systole of the heart.

With this new light shining in upon him, he was led to a clear conception of the work of the auricles and the ventricles, with their respective valves. He saw how the vena cava, on the one side, and the vein-like artery, the pulmonary veins, on the other side, empty themselves into and fill the ventricles during the diastole, and how the ventricles in turn empty themselves during the systole into the artery-like vein, the pulmonary artery on the one side and the great artery or aorta on the other. And this at once led him to a truer conception of the pulmonary circulation than was ever grasped by Servetus or Columbus. On the old view, only *some* of the blood of the right ventricle passed through the septum into the left ventricle; the rest went back again to the tissues; and it was this "some" only which Servetus and Columbus believed to pass through not the septum but the lungs. Harvey saw that all the reasons for thinking that any of the contents of the ventricle so passed were equally valid for thinking that all passed, and that the latter view alone was consonant with the facts.[1]

This new view, new in reality, though having so much resemblance to old ones that Harvey speaks of it as one "to which some, moved either by the authority of Galen or Columbus or the reasonings of others, will give their adhesion," led him at once

[1] Readers who have forgotten their elementary physiology and find themselves somewhat confused by Sir Michael's discussion are referred to page 98 for a simple description of the movement of the blood. Eds.

to another conception which however "was so new, was of so novel and unheard of a character that in putting it forward he not only feared injury to himself from the envy of a few, but trembled lest he might have mankind at large for his enemies." This new view consisted simply in applying to the greater circulation the same conclusions as those at which he had arrived in regard to the lesser circulation.

It is important to note that to this new view he was guided by distinctly quantitative considerations. He argued in this way. At each beat of the heart a quantity of blood is transferred from the vena cava to the aorta. Even if we take a low estimate (he had made observations with a view to determining the exact amount but he leaves this aside for the present as unessential), say half an ounce, or three drachms, or only one drachm, and multiply this by the number of beats, say in half-an-hour, we shall find that the heart sends through the arteries to the tissues during that period as much blood as is contained in the whole body. It is obvious, therefore, that the blood which the heart sends along the arteries to the tissues cannot be supplied merely by that blood which exists in the veins as the result of the ingesta of food and drink; only a small part can be so accounted for; the greater part of that blood must be blood which has returned from the tissues to the veins; the blood in the tissues passes from the arteries to the veins, in some such way as in the lungs it passes from the veins (through the heart) to the arteries; the blood moves in a circle from the left side of the heart, through the arteries, the tissues and the veins to the right side of the heart, and from thence through the lungs to the left side of the heart.

This is what he says:

"I frequently and seriously bethought me, and long revolved in my mind, what might be the quantity of blood which was transmitted, in how short a time its passage might be effected, and the like; and not finding it possible that this could be supplied by the juices of the ingested aliment without the veins on the one hand becoming drained, and the arteries on the other hand becoming ruptured through the excessive charge of blood, unless the blood should somehow find its way from the arteries into the veins, and so return to the right side of the heart; I began to think whether there might not be *a motion, as it were, in a circle.* Now this I afterwards found to be true; and I finally saw that the blood, forced by the action of the left ventricle into the arteries, was distributed to the body at large, and its several parts, in the same manner as it is sent through the lungs, impelled by the right ventricle into the pulmonary artery, and that it then passed through the veins and along the vena cava, and so round to the left ventricle in the manner already indicated, which motion we may be allowed to call circular."

As the sun of this truly new idea rose in Harvey's mind, this new idea that the blood is thus for ever moving in a circle, the mists and clouds of many of the conceptions of old faded away and the features of the physiological landscape hitherto hidden came into view sharp and clear. This idea once grasped, fact after fact came forward to support and enforce it. It was now clear why the heart was emptied when the vena cava was tied, why it was filled to distension when the aorta was tied. It was now clear why a middling ligature which pressed only or chiefly on the veins made a limb swell turgid with blood, whereas a tight ligature which blocked the arteries made it bloodless and pale. It was now clear why the whole or nearly the whole of the blood of the body could be drained away by an opening made in a single vein. And now for the first time was clear the purpose of those valves in the veins, whose structure and position had been demonstrated doubtless to Harvey, by the very hands of their discoverer, his old master Fabricius, but "who did not rightly understand their use, and concerning which succeeding anatomists have not added anything to our knowledge."

Fabricius, as we have seen, had used the now well-worn experiment of pressing on the cutaneous veins of the bared arm to demonstrate the existence of the valves; but he had used it to demonstrate their existence only. Blinded by the conceptions of his time he could not see that the same experiment gave the lie to his explanation of the purpose of the valves, and demonstrated not only their existence, but also their real use. Harvey, with the light of his new idea, at once grasped the true meaning of the knotty bulgings.

These however were not the only phenomena which now for the first time received a reasonable explanation. Harvey was able to point to many other things, to various details of the structure and working of the heart, to various phenomena of the body at large both in health and in disease as intelligible on his new view, but incomprehensible on any other.

If we trust, as indeed we must do, Harvey's own account of

the growth of this new idea in his own mind, we find that he was not led to it in a straight and direct way by Fabricius' discovery of the valves. It was not that the true action of these led to the true view of the motion of the blood, but that the true view of the motion of the blood led to the true understanding of their use. To that true view of the motion of blood he was led by a series of steps, each in turn based on observations made on the heart as seen in the living animal, or as he himself says "repeated vivisections," the great step of all being that one by which he satisfied himself that the quantity of blood driven out from the heart could not be supplied in any other way than by a return of the blood from the arterial endings in the body through the veins. As he himself says: "Since all things, both argument and ocular demonstration, show that the blood passes through the lungs and heart by the action of the ventricles, and is sent for distribution to all parts of the body, where it makes its way into the veins and pores of the flesh, and flows by the veins from the circumference on every side to the centre, from the lesser to the greater veins, and is by them finally discharged into the vena cava and right auricle of the heart, and this in such a quantity or in such a flux and reflux thither by the arteries, hither by the veins, as cannot possibly be supplied by the ingesta, and is much greater than can be required for mere purposes of nutrition; it is absolutely necessary to conclude that the blood in the animal's body is impelled in a circle, and is in a state of ceaseless motion; that this is the act or function which the heart performs by means of its pulse; and that it is the sole and only end of the motion and contraction of the heart. . . ."

The new theory of the circulation made for the first time possible true conceptions of the nutrition of the body, it cleared the way for the chemical appreciation of the uses of blood, it afforded a basis which had not existed before for an understanding of how the life of any part, its continued existence and its power to do what it has to do in the body, is carried on by the help of the blood. And in this perhaps, more than its being a true explanation of the special problem of the heart and the blood vessels, lies its vast importance.

1901

The Only Contemporary
Character Sketch of
William Harvey

JOHN AUBREY

HE WAS wont to say that man was but a great mischievous baboon.

He would say, that we Europaeans knew not how to order or governe our woemen, and that the Turkes were the only people used them wisely.

He was far from bigotry.

He had been physitian to the Lord Chancellor Bacon, whom he esteemed much for his witt and style, but would not allow him to be a great philosopher. "He writes philosophy like a Lord Chancelor," said he to me, speaking in derision; "I have cured him."

About 1649 he travelled again into Italy, Dr. George (now Sir George) Ent, then accompanying him.

At Oxford, he grew acquainted with Dr. Charles Scarborough, then a young physitian (since by King Charles II knighted), in whose conversation he much delighted; and whereas before, he marched up and downe with the army, he tooke him to him and made him ly in his chamber, and said to him, "Prithee leave off thy gunning, and stay here; I will bring thee into practice."

For 20 years before he dyed he tooke no manner of care about his worldly concernes, but his brother Eliab, who was a very wise and prudent menager, ordered all not only faithfully, but better then he could have donne himselfe.

He was, as all the rest of the brothers, very cholerique; and in his young days wore a dagger (as the fashion then was, nay I remember my old schoolemaster, old Mr. Latimer, at 70, wore a dudgeon, with a knife, and bodkin, as also my old grandfather Lyte, and alderman Whitson of Bristowe, which I suppose was the common fashion in their young days), but this Dr. would be to apt to drawout his dagger upon every slight occasion.

He was not tall; but of the lowest stature, round faced, olivaster complexion; little eie, round, very black, full of spirit; his haire was black as a raven, but quite white 20 yeares before he dyed.

I have heard him say, that after his booke of the Circulation of the Blood came-out, that he fell mightily in his practize, and that 'twas beleeved by the vulgar that he was crack-brained; and all the physitians were against his opinion, and envyed him; many wrote against him, as Dr. Primige, Paracisanus, etc. (vide Sir George Ent's booke). With much adoe at last, in about 20 or 30 yeares time, it was received in all the Universities in the world; and, as Mr. Hobbes sayes in his book "De Corpore," he is the only man, perhaps, that ever lived to see his owne doctrine established in his life time.

Seventeenth Century

A Fresh-Water Soldier

AMBROISE PARÉ

MOREOVER, I will here show to my readers the towns and places where I have been enabled to learn the art of surgery, always the better to instruct the young surgeon.

And first in the year 1536 the great King François sent a great army to Turin to recover the cities and castles which had been taken by the Marquis de Guast, lieutenant general of the Emperor.

There Monsieur the Constable, then grand master, was lieutenant general of the army, and Monsieur de Montejan was colonel general of the infantry, to whom I was then surgeon. A great part of the army having arrived at the Pass of Suze, we found the enemy holding the passage and having made certain forts and trenches insomuch that to make them dislodge and quit the place, it was necessary to fight, where there were many killed and wounded, as many on one side as the other, but the enemy were constrained to retire and gain the castle, which was taken in part by Captain Le Rat, who climbed with many soldiers from his company on a little hill, from whence they fired directly on the enemy. He received a shot from an arquebus in the ankle of his right foot, wherewith he suddenly fell to the ground and then said, "Now the Rat is taken." I dressed him, and God healed him.

We thronged into the city and passed over the dead bodies and some that were not yet dead, hearing them cry under the feet of our horses, which made a great pity in my heart, and truly I repented that I had gone forth from Paris to see so pitiful a spectacle. Being in the city, I entered a stable thinking to lodge my horse and that of my man, where I found four dead soldiers and three who were propped against the wall, their faces wholly disfigured, and they neither saw, nor heard, nor spake, and their clothes yet flaming from the gunpowder which had burnt them. Beholding them with pity there came an old soldier who asked me if there was any means of curing them. I told him no. At once he approached them and cut their throats gently and without anger. Seeing this great cruelty, I said to him that he was a bad man. He answered me that he prayed God that when he should be in such a case, he might find someone who would do the same for him, to the end that he might not languish miserably.

And to return to our discourse, the enemy was summoned to surrender, which they did, and went forth, their lives only saved, and a white staff in their hands, but the greater part went to gain the Château de Villaine, where there were about two hundred Spaniards. Monsieur the Constable would not leave them in his rear in order to render the road free. The château is seated upon a little mountain, which gave great assurance to those within that we could not place the artillery so as to bear upon them. . . .

Now all the said soldiers at the château, seeing our men coming with a great fury, did all they could to defend themselves, and killed and wounded a great number of our soldiers with pikes, arquebuses, and stones, where the surgeons had much work cut out for them. Now I was at that time a fresh-water soldier, I had not yet seen wounds made by gunshot at the first dressing. It is true that I had read in Jean de Vigo, first book, "Of Wounds in General," Chapter Eight, that wounds made by firearms participate of venenosity, because of the powder, and for their cure he commands to cauterize them with oil of elder, scalding hot, in which should be mixed a little theriac and in order not to err before using the said oil, knowing that such a thing would bring great pain to the patient, I wished to know first, how the other surgeons did for the first dressing which was to apply the said oil as hot as possible, into the wound with tents and setons, of whom I took courage to do as they did. At last my oil lacked and I was constrained to apply in its place a digestive made of the yolks of eggs, oil of roses and turpentine. That night I could not sleep at my ease, fearing by lack of cauterization that I should find the wounded on whom I had failed to put the said oil dead or empoisoned, which made me rise very early to visit them, where beyond my hope, I found those upon whom I had put the digestive medicament feeling little pain, and their wounds without inflammation or swelling having rested fairly well throughout the night; the others to whom I had applied the said boiling oil, I found feverish, with great pain and swelling about their wounds. Then I resolved with myself never more to burn thus cruelly poor men wounded with gunshot.

Being at Turin, I found a surgeon who was famous above all for good treatment of gunshot wounds, into whose grace I found means to insinuate myself, to have the recipe which he called his balm, with which he treated gunshot wounds, and he made me court him for years before I could draw his recipe from him. At last by gifts and presents he gave it to me, which was to boil in oil of lilies, little puppies just born, with earthworms prepared with Venetian turpentine. Then I was joyful and my heart made glad, to have understood his remedy, which was like to that which I had obtained by chance.

See how I learned to treat wounds made by gunshot, not from books.

Sixteenth Century
Translated in 1921

Ambroise Paré Does a Delivery

ALAN FRANK GUTTMACHER

MARGUERITE DE PUIS moved fitfully in the huge bed, careful lest she disturb François, her husband. Eleven months before, in April 1548, she had come to it a bride—a slip of a girl, whom François had first seen and admired on the tennis court. She had a pretty skill at the game, and some thought her backhand the best of that of all the women of Paris. As she lay restless in her bed, she mused on the changes the months had wrought.

She wondered why her time had not come, for the moon had changed the night before and the child within her moved vigorously. Was it beginning to force its way out? A wise-woman had told her that when her time was up the baby would knock on the portals of the womb, then the portals would open wide and the child would struggle forth. Was this the knocking she felt? She dreaded her approaching accouchement and yet hoped to lie in soon; soon, before François would have to join the army before Calais. The night seemed endless. She had heard the bells of Notre Dame as they struck two and three, and now it was four and the night watch called again on their rounds:

> *Réveillez-vous, gens qui dormez*
> *Priez Dieu pour les trépassés.*

Tears of self-pity wet her soft cheeks. The past few months had proved so irksome. Her grievances paraded before her mind's eye like the reflected beam of a carriage lamp which slowly traces its way across the darkness of the ceiling. There had been the sacrifice of her beautifying alum baths, soft, luxurious rainwater, sweetened with leaves of rosemary and flowers of myrtle. Doctors forbade pregnant women to bathe lest the child become too hot within the womb and, craving the more temperate air without, come forth before its time. Then, too, she missed dancing; she hadn't danced the *gaillarde* for months, and at seventeen death alone seemed more tragic. She hadn't even been allowed to lift her arms above her head. It was said that this loosed the ligaments which held the womb in place. The coach with its blooded, prancing, gaily caparisoned stallions was denied her, and she had to go about the streets of Paris in a stuffy, curtained litter, borne by her menservants; so all Paris had known for months that she was *enceinte*. Then, too, all the other young people of her set had journeyed out beyond the wall to see the wondrous Biddenden Maids who were tented there, a marvel of nature—two complete wenches joined at the waist. Marguerite wasn't allowed to see them, for if she did, she might give birth to such a monster. In fact no one was allowed to make mention of it in her presence; just by chance she had overheard the coachman telling the scullery maid. She had to be wary lest a black cat zigzag across her path and make her baby squint-eyed. No longer could she lie curled up in bed, for that would render it crook-backed. There were a thousand wearisome "Don'ts."

But on second thought these things were trivial when she remembered her lovely trousseau so carefully selected, so soon discarded—especially the beautiful purple court dress trimmed in gold filigree, with its saffron petticoat and headdress to match, bordered with pearls.' She had to leave off her bodice stiffened with whalebone, and discontinue the tight lacing which made her waist so appealingly slim. The nursekeeper said that by enclosing the belly in so straight a mould she might hinder the infant from taking its free growth, and moreover might make it come forth horribly misshapen. And so perforce the purple dress had to be laid away in a great cedar chest with the prayerful hope of future use.

The defeat of her vanity was complete when, in order to prevent her stomach from becoming marred by knotted and broken veins or from being left wrinkled and furrowed, she had agreed to support her belly with a broad linen swath on top of a dogskin. The dogskin had to be prepared according to an exact ritual. Everyone said the belly of her Cousin Anne was so unsightly after the birth of Henri because her nursekeeper had forgetfully omitted the goosegrease. Marguerite had memorized the formula and for the hundredth time went over it, half chanting to herself: "A pregnant bitch is fresh killed and the skin dressed and washed in rose-water. After it is well dried, immerse it in the following: of the suet of a kid and the fat of a sow, take three ounces each; of a capon's fat and goose's grease each an ounce and a half, cut them small and melt them in an earthen pot, adding thereto as much water as necessary. Strain them through a cloth and wash them in water till they wax very white and lose their savour; then melt them again in a double vessel adding thereto an ounce of the marrow of a hart or a stag. Once more wash it with rose-water or other sweet-smelling water, mingling therewithal two or three grains of musk or civet. Immerse the skin in the same for three full nights and four full days. Then remove it, dry, and cut to the form and bigness of the belly." She was thankful they had let her wear a new skin every fortnight. At first the skin of a foxhound was large enough, but now they had to cut it from a mastiff.

Marguerite de Puis finally wept herself to sleep. She slept soundly and was awakened by some knave who had disobeyed

the city laws in not properly greasing the axle of his dung-cart.
A tester of thick velvet which surrounded the bed made it difficult to separate night from day; yet it must be day, for she was
alone. It was warm, she threw back her heavy covers of bearskin
sewn between two layers of silk. The linen sheet felt soft against
her naked body. Hearing her stir, the nursekeeper came with a
bowl of pleasantly scented water in which a hot iron had been
dipped. After washing her, the nurse rubbed her abdomen with a
pomade made of the marrow of sheep's feet well brushed and
broken in pieces to the number of thirty or forty, duck's grease,
spermaceti, and white wax which had been agreeably perfumed
with the oil of water lilies.

Marguerite arose and sat before the fire. With a soft hand she
anointed her privities with an hysterical[1] balsam as she had done
each morning and evening for months. Then a warm decoction of
periwinkle, sage, ground-ivy, and hemlock boiled in wine and
water was brought. With a sponge dipped therein she bathed her
breasts for a quarter-hour, wiping and drying them afterwards
with a reasonably warm cloth. After girding up her belly with
the dogskin and linen swath, she put on the loose garments which
her vanity so despised. While the maid combed and oiled her
hair, the nurse brought breakfast: figs, new-laid eggs, and white
bread toasts spread with sweet fresh butter. The bread was bought
specially at Gonesse's on the Rue Saint-Jacques, for ordinary,
coarse household bread swells the stomach.

Having dressed and finished her breakfast, she called for her
litter and ordered the bearers to repair to Notre Dame. They carried her out through the courtyard of her home into the Rue des
Augustins, a narrow crowded street. The overhanging timbered
houses darkened her passage. Street venders hawked their wares,
and Monsignor's pigs rooted enthusiastically among the refuse
cast down from the windows above. The litter jolted violently as
the bearers avoided deep ruts, and Marguerite was seized with a
sharp, sudden pain. It lasted a short time, and minutes later, just as
she reached the cathedral, the pain returned; certainly it marked
the onset of her travail. She offered a silent prayer to the Madonna
at the entrance of Her church—an imploring supplication. She
was frightened by the experience that awaited her, an experience

[1] From the Greek word *hystéra*, meaning uterus or womb. In its modern
sense "hysterical" has the same derivation; the Greeks thought the condition
was due to a disease of the uterus.

which she could in no way avoid. Inevitable pain was bad enough, but more terrifying the realization that death chooses many from among those who bring life. She found solace in the remembrance of her prayers and penances of the past months and felt that Our Gracious Lady would intervene with the Lord Jesus to spare her life. In His great compassion He might grant her a living son and perhaps even a speedy delivery. She ordered the litter to return to the Rue des Augustins, and on the way back she sobbed.

When Marguerite returned, the whole household seethed with excitement. Couriers were dispatched hither and thither. One went to the Hôtel de Ville to notify François, who had gone to a meeting of the town council, another ran for Louise Grisson, wife of the butcher Grisson, famous throughout Paris for her great knowledge in the midwife's art and in the delivery of women; and another sought the three lesser women who were to assist. The priest too had to be informed.

Madame Grisson had been selected with great care. She was not a young midwife who had but read a little in a midwife's book and not by skill, but by nature's force, had laid a woman or two in an easy and natural birth. For who would hazard his safety with a pilot that had never gone to sea, but by reading books or crossing the Seine had made himself a pilot? Madame Grisson, a skilled pilot, a seasoned seafarer, had brought many a frail ship to safe port in the perilous, uncharted sea of childbirth.

When the *sage-femme* arrived, she led Marguerite into the room where she was to lie in. The room was bare except for a low pallet bed and several wooden stools. A small fire made it neither too warm nor too cool. The window curtains were drawn, and the only light came from flickering logs and a single candle. The midwife unclasped an amulet which Marguerite wore on a gold chain about her neck. It was an eagle's stone and would keep back the child if worn above the waist; tied about her thigh it would attract the child and shorten labour.

Marguerite was urged to walk about and with each throe to hold her breath and bear down. Her aged Aunt Thérèse, the vitriolic head of her mother's family, brought some specially potent sneezewort. She commanded her niece to smell of it at frequent intervals. This Marguerite did, and each time it induced a virtual bombardment of sneezes, which reminded her of the siege of Calais and the fact that her beloved François would soon be going off to the wars. As Marguerite paced back and forth monotonously, the midwife and her helpers sat on their gossip stools, outdoing each other with the most lurid tales of tragic obstetrical happenings. Poor Marguerite began to marvel that there were five women in Paris who had survived their accouchements. When she grew very weary, she was allowed to sit on the bed for a few moments while the women rubbed her legs with oils derived from egg and nuts.

The respite was short, and once more Marguerite was made to pace the floor. As the hours passed, the pain and fatigue unnerved her. Through the closed windows the noises from the street continually filtered in till she felt that she could join the shrill-voiced hawkers as they called their wares, especially the rat-poisoner with his cry:

> Death to mice, and death to rats,
> It is a new invention.
> Housewives, save your food supplies
> By using my prevention.

She found herself making a parody:

> Death to dithering midwives,
> They are the devil's invention——

If only there were a new invention to free her from these four gibbering old fools who poked her with their fingers and terrified her with their ghastly gossip.

The throes did not come often enough to satisfy the midwives, and following a consultation, Madame Grisson determined to examine the patient. After paring her nails closely and anointing her hand with butter, she inserted her fingers into the birth-passage while Marguerite stood leaning on the shoulders of one of the helpers. The examination was thorough, long, and painful. A second consultation followed, the midwives huddling together like four goblins while Marguerite continued to parade back and forth. She heard herself discussed as though she were a common milch cow. The consensus seemed to be that something should be done to stimulate the pains of labour, and each of the four women had her favoured method; eventually all four were tried. A strong clyster[1] was followed by a large dose of midwives' powder. Next they anointed well the birthplace, the ossa pubis and coccygis, with an hysterical balsam. Finally they poured the white of an egg

[1] Enema.

into the birth-canal to render it more slippery. Though Marguerite protested, the will of the midwives was the inescapable law of the lying-in chamber.

Marguerite was so fatigued by the many unremitting hours of labour, the incessant pacing, and the strenuous medication, that she pleaded to be allowed to lie down. The midwives permitted it, and during the rest period brought her a light meal—a cup of jellied broth, a bowl of caudles,[1] and a few spoonfuls of burnt wine. Soon they made her walk again, but now a woman on each side supported her under the arms.

Another hawker was passing in the street below, the water-vender, and close on him the dispenser of sauces. Their hoarse voices unintelligibly announced their wares, but Marguerite, accustomed to them from childhood, understood the verses.

> Water, water,
> One of the four elements I cry.
> Water, water,
> Come, all good folk, come and buy,
> Water, water.

Pierre was calling; he used to give her forbidden tastes when she was small. She loved his call best:

> Here is a tart-green sauce for you,
> To eat with carp and spot,
> Come buy, all who have need of it,
> While still some's in my pot.

Night came and still there was no respite. The pains had become very bad; so bad that she was forced to cry out, imploring the aid of the Mother. At about midnight the head midwife re-examined Marguerite and pronounced her ready to lie in. She was laid upon the bed, and a long, broad, multi-layered swath was placed under her back and hinder parts. Two women, one on either side, held its ends and at each pain pulled it gently toward them, raising her off the bed in order to ease the pain in her back. As labour became more furious, two more assisting women were needed, and from the assortment of kinsfolk who waited without, Madame Grisson chose Marguerite's cousins, Anne and Renée, since they had been successfully delivered of sons within the year and so might extend good fortune to their travailing cousin. Furthermore, they were highly pleasing to her, a thing of great importance, for if there is

[1] Thin gruel mixed with wine or ale to which spices are added.

anyone in the chamber for whom the patient has any mislike or loathing, labour ceases until such a one withdraws. Madame Grisson cautioned the cousins not to cross their fingers nor to shut one within the other while in the labour-room, since that hinders birth and makes it the more difficult. The new helpers were stationed on either side of the bed and during the course of each throe clenched Marguerite's hands in one of theirs, placing the free hand on top of her shoulder to prevent her from lifting herself up. Marguerite braced her feet against a board placed across the foot of the bed, and with each pain pushed and bore down with such force that her face became suffused with scarlet and the veins of her neck protruded like small throbbing ropes. The sweat stood forth like dew on her upper lip. With each throe Madame Grisson pressed the upper part of the belly with the palm of her hand, stroking the child downward little by little.

Still the infant was not born. François and the others became alarmed, and at each cry they pushed the door ajar and demanded a fresh bulletin. Madame Grisson continually encouraged the patient, saying that after the very next throe a handsome boy would be born. The constant repetition of this unfulfilled promise made it worthless, and poor Marguerite, exhausted, sobbed with pain and terror.

At the first break of dawn François insisted that the famous master barber-surgeon, Ambroise Paré, be sent for. This was no ordinary birth, he contended, which women could handle unassisted, and they had need for a man-midwife. Madame Grisson was completely contemptuous of the idea, and her stand was strengthened by Aunt Thérèse, who was horrified that any man should be invited to look upon her niece in so delicate a situation. François hesitated until once more Marguerite's agonized screams pierced the apprehensive stillness. Then he sent his most trusted servant post-haste to fetch the great man.

Paré lived within a stone's throw, on the Place du Pont Saint-Michel, and it did not take him long to appear. Those in the company who had never seen him were much impressed by his youthful appearance and his assured but humble manner. He was large-featured, of middle height, strong and hard from military campaigns. He greeted the company, and knelt before the door of the sickroom, closing his eyes in a fervent prayer: "Jesus Christ Our Lord, the only Preserver and Saviour in danger! Since there appeareth difficulty in bringing forth this child, we implore Thee that Thou allowest me, Thy humble servant, to assist Thee in happily delivering this wretched woman. We ask it for Thy name's sake." The whole assemblage responded: "Amen." Paré arose and declared that with God's guidance he was confident he could bring the baby.

In the lying-in chamber he at once became master of the situation, assuring Marguerite that her pain would soon be over. He placed her athwart the bed, raising her buttocks on a hard stuffed pillow and propped her back with a bolster so that she was half lying, half sitting. He instructed her to bend her knees and to draw her heels close to her body. She was bound in this position with a broad linen bandage, the bandage was hung about her neck and crossed over her chest and made to encompass her feet, legs, and thighs. Maître Paré applied it so tightly that she was unable to move. To reinforce this vise in which she was held, the bystanders firmly grasped her legs and shoulders. Her privy parts and thighs were covered with a warm double cloth, that neither air nor wind might enter into the womb, and that the operation might be done with more decency. Paré noted the mask of terror which disfigured Marguerite's face and once more assured her that all would end well. They then laid her head upon a bolster and put a cloth over her eyes.

He took off his two finger rings, the one the famous thirty-écu diamond given him by Monsieur d'Estampes, and the other the seal of Monsieur de Rohan, under whose banner he had campaigned in lower Brittany. He crossed himself and without further preliminaries rolled up the sleeves of his doublet and anointed well his bare arms and hands with oil. Further, he lifted the modesty cloth and poured much oil into the birth-passage to make it slippery. He inserted his hand to determine the form and situation of the child. Immediately he encountered the intact bag of waters which he broke between two fingernails, kept especially long and sharpened for this purpose. A dark, turbid fluid gushed forth, and all who watched knew by that sign that the babe would be lost unless delivery could be speedily effected.

He pushed up the head which presented and dexterously turned the child in the womb so that it came feet foremost. Despite the imprisoning bandages Marguerite struggled and writhed in agony. She was bathed in a cold sweat. He brought forth one foot and a little above the heel tied a silk band indifferently tight. He then returned this foot into the womb, leaving the loose end of the band protruding, and manœuvred to bring down the second foot.

When he had accomplished this, he pulled on the band attached to the first foot and it too came forth. He grasped both feet close together and, pulling on them, delivered the buttocks and genitals of a male child. A murmur of excitement ran through the room, and Renée went out to tell the men that for some woman as yet unconceived a lover was being born. By this time all the women kin had crowded into the small room to be present at this miraculous and brand-new operation, for just within the month Paré, with his friend Héry, had published their *Briefve collection de l'administration anatomique*, which contained a chapter on the method of extracting an infant from the belly of the mother when nature was not able to bring it forth. The midwives were amazed, the relatives astonished—all seemed to enjoy the spectacle though poor Marguerite still screamed. Paré made further traction on the feet, and soon the belly and then the chest appeared. He then slipped a hand into the uterus past the baby, and placed one of its arms above its head and the other down alongside of its body, because only when the arms were so could the child pass out of the womb. He directed the midwives to help by pressing the patient's belly downward with their hands, and at this juncture exhorted Marguerite to close her mouth and nose and to drive her breath downward with great violence, but she was too exhausted to be of much assistance. By the combination of pulling and pushing the boy was born.

His part completed, Paré withdrew to the hall, where the women crowded about him with congratulations. He was further complimented by François and the other men. With becoming humility he said that praise and thanks were due God alone, for if He had not inclined His ear unto his petition, delivery could never have been effected. François opened his purse and counted out ten silver écus. Affected by the uncommon generosity of his host, the master barber-surgeon determined to remain in the house in case he could be of further service.

The child neither cried nor seemed to breathe, but he could be given no succour until the womb was freed of its afterburden; and all efforts were centred upon this. Forthwith, Marguerite was made to swallow a four-scruple dose of Gesner's remedy, dried and powdered stones[1] of a horse. She was also given two small bags of warm salt to clench in either hand and directed to blow into them. Meanwhile, Madame Grisson took hold of the navel

[1] Testicles.

string, wagging, shaking, and gently dragging it, while another
woman pressed the top of the belly, and stroked it lightly downward. But nothing availed until a few grains of a powder made
from old shoes, burnt feathers, castoreum,[1] pepper, and asafœtida
were put into each nostril. The acrid, stinking mixture made Marguerite sneeze and vomit—this, combined with the stroking of
the belly and the pulling on the navel cord, fairly catapulted the
afterbirth from the birth-passage.

Madame Grisson gathered in a warm blanket both the child
and the afterbirth to which it was still attached by the navel
string. She sat herself before the fire, placed the warm, blood-
dripping secundines[2] on the child's belly, and took a mouth full of
warm red wine which she spurted into his mouth, ears, and nose.
The babe was as blue as the velvet of her robe, and from the difficult labour its head was curiously moulded into a peak. It lay
limp, neither moving nor breathing. The priest hastily sprinkled
the infant with holy water, pronouncing in a rich, mellow voice:
"I baptize thee, in the name of the Father, the Son, and the Holy
Ghost." All present said "Amen." In the meantime Renée removed the afterbirth from the child's belly and tossed it into the
fire, milking the vessels of the navel string toward the babe to
communicate the strength and warmth of the blaze. Master de
Puis now began to take a few feeble breaths. At first they came
very seldom, merely an occasional sucking in of the belly. Soon
they became more frequent, the chest too taking part. Madame
Grisson applied linen dipped in warm wine to the child's breast
and belly. His face was uncovered and his mouth held open a
little, that he might draw his breath more easily. She cleansed his
nostrils with small tents[3] dipped in white wine, and chafed every
part of his body with warm cloths to awaken his spirit. Little by
little he gained strength, stirring one limb after another; he cried,
weakly at first, then with a vigour that was pleasant to hear. Led
by the priest, the whole assemblage, within the room and without,
sank on their knees in a silent prayer of thanksgiving.

Madame Grisson went back to Marguerite while Angéline, one
of the midwife's assistants, tended the child. She called Anne and
Renée to witness the navel string before she cut it, for from it
they could learn whether Marguerite would have any more chil-

---

[1] Unctuous substance having a strong smell, obtained from the inguinal
glands of beavers.
[2] Placenta or afterbirth.
[3] Pledgets of cotton.

dren. Fortunately there was no knottiness or curliness where the cord joined the infant, for that would portend future barrenness; instead there were eleven knots higher up on the cord indicating that she would be the mother of twelve. The knots were very close together, foretelling that the births would be separated by only the necessary months. Furthermore, the first knot was red and not white, which showed that the next child would also be a boy.

Angéline then proceeded to perform the most ancient operation in the realm of surgery: omphalotomy, or the cutting of the navel string; even Adam and Eve practised it on their first-born.

As she was about to begin, someone called: "Make him good measure," at which all the others laughed merrily. Everyone knew that in the case of a boy the cord must be left longer, because this extra length makes both his tongue and privy member the longer, whereby he might speak the plainer, and be more serviceable to the ladies. Moreover, tying it short in a female and close to her belly makes her tongue less free and her natural part more straight and agreeable.

Angéline dug deep into her reticule and drew forth a stout brown string which had been doubled several times and knotted on the ends. She tied a double knot about the navel string and cut it above the knot with a sharp scissors. The cut end was wrapped in a small rag dipped in oil of roses, and the whole firmly compressed by a linen swath four fingers broad. The son of Marguerite and François was then wrapped in a blanket and taken to another room, where he was to receive a warm bath in red wine and water, in which the petals of red roses and the leaves of myrtle had been boiled. This would not only wash away the filth, but also resolve and digest the hard and contused places caused on the infant's tender body by reason of the hard travail. And after the bath he would receive his first swaddling. As the child was carried through the hall, François tried to lift the blanket that covered its face, but desisted when roundly abused by the midwife for daring to expose a baby's delicate eyes so soon to the light.

Marguerite appeared strong and alert immediately after the birth, due perhaps to the vast relief she felt. When unleashed from the bonds which imprisoned her, she folded her hands in prayer. A little later her face, and her hands and feet, became cold and clammy, her speech almost inaudible, her strength dangerously enfeebled, and her pulse critically weak. Madame Grisson

wrapped Marguerite's hands and feet in warm woollens and covered her with blankets. She cupped her hand over the ill woman's
lips so that she could rebreathe her own vital spirits and her
breath, reverberating, would also warm her face. Hot cloths were
put to her forehead, and the warm face of another woman was
applied to her cold cheeks. Several stone bottles filled with hot
water and wrapped around with napkins were placed in the bed
with her. These things renewed the heat in her, and forthwith she
revived.

Marguerite's large bed in her own room was prepared with hot
bricks, and several strong bodies carried her to it, for it was preferable that she should not walk. The curtains, windows, and doors
were sealed shut and the tester about the bed drawn closed, since
it was very prejudicial for a newly lain-in woman to be exposed
in any way to cold air. Despite the exclusion of new air, it was still
possible to hear noises from without, and suddenly the quiet of
the early dawn was rent with the shrill bleats and cries of a black
sheep which the butcher was flaying alive in the court below. The
hot, dripping skin was immediately brought upstairs and applied
over her belly and loins, these parts being the most disjointed
during childbirth. The skin was to remain in place for five or six
hours, that is, until its natural heat was dissipated. A small plaster
containing a little sweet-smelling civet was put to her navel. This
is serviceable in keeping the womb in its place, for the womb
being delighted with the smell draws away from the spine and
moves forward toward the belly wall. A poultice on several thick-
nesses of linen was applied to her privy parts to prevent inflammation; it was fresh made with the oil of sweet almonds and new-laid
eggs.

Marguerite was cautioned to lie flat on her back, and to turn
neither to one side nor to the other, and she was encouraged to
cross one leg over its fellow, the better to exclude the cold air. She
was told to talk as little as possible and then only in a subdued
voice. All persons but François and Aunt Thérèse and the midwives and nurses were excluded from her chamber. A cradle containing her properly swaddled son was brought in and placed next
to her bed. Marguerite had not seen him, and since she was not
allowed to turn, she could only steal a sidelong glance. She saw by
the dim candlelight that the top of the cradle was completely covered and that every now and then the cover jumped, as though a
kitten were under it. She was weary and yearned to sleep, but
Madame Grisson would not allow her; she said that it was harmful

for a mother to go to sleep until her child was at least four hours old. The midwife babbled all sorts of dreary nonsense just to keep her awake, and Marguerite had grave doubts that a baby was worth all the torture.

At long last she was permitted to sleep, and just as she was dozing off, she heard the street-crier shout:

"Good tidings. Be it known that this very morning a man child was born to François de Puis, our Town Councillor, and his spouse Marguerite. Praise ye the Lord." The cry was repeated before each house. It became soft and distant and much confused with her dreams of a midwife with the face of a gargoyle, who was devouring her very, very slowly.

1937

Doctor Sangrado

ALAIN-RENÉ LE SAGE

I STAYED three months with the Licentiate Sédillo, without complaining of bad nights. At the end of that time he fell sick. The distemper was a fever; and it inflamed the gout. For the first time in his life, which had been long, he called in a physician. Doctor Sangrado was sent for; the Hippocrates of Valladolid. Dame Jacintha was for sending for the lawyer first, and touched that string; but the patient thought it was time enough, and had a little will of his own upon some points. Away I went therefore for Doctor Sangrado; and brought him with me. A tall, withered, wan executioner of the sisters three, who had done all their justice for at least these forty years! This learned forerunner of the undertaker had an aspect suited to his office: his words were weighed to a scruple; and his jargon sounded grand in the ears of the uninitiated. His arguments were mathematical demonstrations: and his opinions had the merit of originality.

After studying my master's symptoms, he began with medical solemnity: The question here is, to remedy an obstructed perspiration. Ordinary practitioners, in this case, would follow the old routine of salines, diuretics, volatile salts, sulphur and mercury; but purges and sudorifics are a deadly practice! Chemical preparations are edged tools in the hands of the ignorant. My methods are more simple, and more efficacious. What is your usual diet? I live pretty much upon soups, replied the canon, and eat my meat with a good deal of gravy. Soups and gravy! exclaimed the petrified doctor. Upon my word, it is no wonder you are ill. High living is a poisoned bait; a trap set by sensuality, to cut short the days of wretched man. We must have done with pampering our appetites: the more insipid, the more wholesome. The human blood is not a gravy! Why then you must give it such a nourishment as will assimilate with the particles of which it is composed. You drink wine, I warrant you? Yes, said the licentiate, but diluted. Oh! finely diluted, I dare say, rejoined the physician. This is licentiousness with a vengeance! A frightful course of feeding! Why, you ought to have died years ago. How old are you? I am in my sixty-ninth year, replied the canon. So I thought, quoth the practitioner, a premature old age is always the consequence of intemperance. If you had only drank clear water all your life, and had been contented with plain food, boiled apples, for instance, you would not have been a martyr to the gout, and your limbs would have performed their functions with lubricity. But I do not despair of setting you on your legs again, provided you give yourself up to my management. The licentiate promised to be upon his good behavior.

Sangrado then sent me for a surgeon of his own choosing, and took from him six good porringers of blood, by way of a beginning, to remedy this obstinate obstruction. He then said to the surgeon: Master Martin Onez, you will take as much more three hours hence, and to-morrow you will repeat the operation. It is a mere vulgar error, that the blood is of any use in the system; the faster you draw it off the better. A patient has nothing to do but keep himself quiet, with him, to live is merely not to die; he has no more occasion for blood than a man in a trance; in both cases, life consists exclusively in pulsation and respiration.

When the doctor had ordered these frequent and copious bleedings, he added a drench of warm water at very short intervals, maintaining that water in sufficient quantities was the grand secret in the materia medica. He then took his leave, telling Dame Jacintha and me, with an air of confidence, that he would answer for the patient's life, if his system was fairly pursued. The housekeeper, though protesting secretly against this new practice, bowed to his superior authority. In fact, we set on the kettles in a hurry; and, as the physician had desired us above all things to give him enough, we began with pouring down two or three pints at as many gulps. An hour after we beset him again; then, returning to the attack time after time, we fairly poured a deluge into his poor stomach. The surgeon, on the other hand, taking out the blood as we put in the water, we reduced the old canon to death's door in less than two days.

This venerable ecclesiastic, able to hold it out no longer, as I pledged him in a large glass of his new cordial, said to me in a faint voice—Hold, Gil Blas, do not give me any more, my friend. It is plain death will come when he will come, in spite of water; and, though I have hardly a drop of blood in my veins, I am no better for getting rid of the enemy. The ablest physician in the world can do nothing for us, when our time is expired. Fetch a notary; I will make my will. At these last words, pleasing enough to my fancy, I affected to appear unhappy; and concealing my impatience to be gone: Sir, said I, you are not reduced so low, thank God, but you may yet recover. No, no, interrupted he, my good fellow, it is all over, I feel the gout shifting, and the hand of death is upon me. Make haste, and go where I told you. I saw, sure enough, that he changed every moment: and the case was so urgent, that I ran as fast as I could, leaving him in Dame Jacintha's care who was more afraid than myself of his dying without a will. I laid hold of the first notary I could find; Sir, said I, the Licentiate Sedillo, my master, is drawing near his end; he wants to settle his affairs; there is not a moment to be lost. The notary was a dapper little fellow, who loved his joke; and enquired who was our physician. At the name of Doctor Sangrado, hurrying on his cloak and hat: For mercy's sake! cried he, let us set off with all possible speed; for this doctor dispatches business so fast, that our fraternity cannot keep pace with him. That fellow spoils half my jobs.

With this sarcasm, he set forward in good earnest, and as we pushed on, to get the start of the grim tyrant, I said to him: Sir, you are aware that a dying testator's memory is sometimes a little short; should my master chance to forget me, be so good as to put in a word in my favour. That I will, my lad, replied the little proctor; you may rely on it. I will urge something handsome, if I have an opportunity. The licentiate, on our arrival, had still all his faculties about him. Dame Jacintha was by his bedside, laying in her tears by wholesale. She had played her game, and bespoken a handsome remembrance. We left the notary alone with my master, and went together into the ante-chamber, where we met the surgeon, sent by the physician for another and last experiment. We laid hold of him. Stop, Master Martin, said the housekeeper, you cannot go into Signor Sedillo's room just now. He is giving his last orders; but you may bleed away when the will is made.

We were terribly afraid, this pious gentlewoman and I, lest the licentiate should go off with his will half finished; but by good luck, the important deed was executed. We saw the proctor come out, who, finding me on the watch, slapped me on the shoulder, and said with a simper; Gil Blas is not forgotten. At these words, I felt the most lively joy; and was so well pleased with my master for his kind notice that I promised myself the pleasure of praying for his soul after death, which event happened anon; for the surgeon having bled him once more, the poor old man, quite exhausted, gave up the ghost under the lancet. Just as he was breathing his last, the physician made his appearance, and looked a little foolish, notwithstanding the universality of his death-bed experience. Yet far from imputing the accident to the new practice, he walked off, affirming with intrepidity, that it was owing to their having been too lenient with the lancet, and too chary of their warm water. The medical executioner, I mean the surgeon, seeing that his functions also were at an end, followed Doctor Sangrado.

1715-1735

An Apothecary's Shop

WILLIAM SHAKESPEARE

ROMEO: I do remember an apothecary
    And hereabouts he dwells—whom late I noted
    In tatter'd weeds, with overwhelming brows,
    Culling of simples; meager were his looks,
    Sharp misery had worn him to the bones;
    And in his needy shop a tortoise hung,
    An alligator stuff'd and other skins,
    Of ill-shap'd fishes; and about his shelves
    A beggarly account of empty boxes,
    Green earthen pots, bladders, and musty seeds,
    Remnants of packthread, and old cakes of roses,

Were thinly scattered to make up a show.
Noting this penury, to myself I said—
An if a man did need a poison now,
Whose sale is present death in Mantua,
Here lives a caitiff wretch would sell it him.
O, this same thought did but fore-run my need;
And this same needy man must sell it me.
As I remember this should be the house;
Being holiday, the beggar's shop is shut—
What ho! Apothecary!

APOTHECARY: Who calls so loud?

ROMEO: Come hither, man. I see that thou art poor;
Hold, there is forty ducats; let me have
A dram of poison; such soon speeding gear
As will disperse itself through all the veins,
That the life-weary taker may fall dead;
And that the trunk may be discharg'd of breath
As violently as hasty powder fired
Doth hurry from the fatal cannon's womb.

APOTHECARY: Such mortal drugs I have; but Mantua's law
Is death to any he that utters them.

ROMEO: Art thou so bare, and full of wretchedness,
And fear'st to die? famine is in thy cheeks.
Need and oppression starveth in thy eyes,
Contempt and beggary hangs upon thy back,
The world is not thy friend, nor the world's law;
The world affords no law to make thee rich;
Then be not poor, but break it, and take this.

APOTHECARY: My poverty but not my will consents.

ROMEO: I pray thy poverty and not thy will.

APOTHECARY: Put this in any liquid thing you will
And drink it off; and if you had the strength
Of twenty men, it would despatch you straight.

ROMEO: There is thy gold, worse poison to men's souls
Doing more murders in this loathsome world
Than these poor compounds that thou may'st not sell.
I sell thee poison, thou hast sold me none.
Farewell; buy food, and get thyself in flesh.
Come cordial, and not poison; go with me
To Juliet's grave, for there I must use thee.

1609

Seventeenth and Eighteenth Century Remedies

MEDICINAL EXPERIMENTS
Robert Boyle (1627-1691)

No. 1—A powerful remedy for Apoplectic Fits.

Take the herb Mastick and distil by an alembick with a copper body an essential oyl, of which with such a pipe or quill, that one end may be opened or stopped at pleasure (the other still remaining open) blow up some drops, first into one of the patients nostrils, and after a while into the other.

No. 147—A Choice Remedy for the Pain of the Hemmorrhoids.

Take Album Graecum reduced to an impalpable powder, mixing it up with a sufficient quantity of goose grease, and by grinding it up well in a Leaden mortar, reduce it to a black Oyntment. to be applied moderately warm to the part affected.

No. 268

Against Epilepsies of the Falling Sickness. Take of the powder of the true mistletoe of the oak, as much as will lie upon a sixpence, early in the morning, in black cherry water, for some days near the full moon.

THE QUEEN'S CLOSET OPENED, OR THE PEARL OF PRACTICE

Teeth

If you will keep your teeth from rot, plug or aking, wash the mouth continually with Juyce of Lemons, and afterwards rub your teeth with a Sage Leaf and Wash your teeth after meat with faire water.

To cure Tooth Ach

1. Take Mastick and chew it in your mouth till it is as soft as Wax, then stop your teeth with it, if hollow, there remaining till it's consumed, and it will certainly cure you.

2. The tooth of a dead man carried about a man presently suppresses the pains of the Teeth.

To Cure Insomnia

Bruise a handful of Annis-seeds, and steep them in Red Rose Water, and make it up in little bags, and binde one of them to each Nostrill, and it will cause sleep.

To Ease the Passion of the Heart

Take Damask Roses half-blown, cut off their whites, and stamp them very fine, and straine out the juyce very strong; moisten it in the stamping with a little Damask Rose water; then put thereto fine powder Sugar, and boyl it gently to a fine Syrup; then take the Powders of Amber, Pearl and Rubies, of each half a dram, Ambergresse one scruple, and mingle them with the said syrup till it be somewhat thick, and take a little thereof on a knife's point morning and evening.

1656

TWO CURES FOR THE AGUE

Make a posset with white wine and take away the curd. Take horse-dung from a stone horse as hotte as you can get it from the horse and strain it with the posset drink, and put a little methridate and cardus benedictus and unicorne's horne—and if you have no unicorne's horne then put ivorie or seahorse tooth and give it to the sick to drink fasting in the morning. Use this two or three mornings.

Quoted in "A Closet for Ladies and Gentlewomen," 1611

If you would be rid of the ague, go by night alone to a cross-roads, and just as the clock is striking midnight turn round three times and drive a large nail into the ground up to the head. Walk backwards from the nail before the clock has finished the twelfth stroke. The ague will leave you, but will go to the person next to step over the nail.

—Soffolk superstition of the 1600's quoted in E. and M. A. Radford, "Encyclopedia of Superstitions"

OTHER REMEDIES—EIGHTEENTH CENTURY
ENGLAND AND IRELAND

Baldness

Anoint the bald patches on your head with goose dung, and the hair will grow again.

Cold (in Head)

Pare very thinly the rind of an orange. Roll it up inside out and thrust a roll into each nostril. The cold will disappear.

Drunkenness

To cure a husband of drinking to excess put a live eel in his drink.

Dyspepsia

Fix a small candle on a penny-piece, place the penny on the region of the stomach where is the suffering. Light the candle, and over all place a well-dried tumbler, when the skin will be drawn up as in "cupping." This is "lifting the evil" from the body, and will rid you of the dyspepsia.

Fits

To cure fits secure a small portion of a human skull, grate it similar to ginger, mix it with food, and give to the patient to eat.

Gall Stones

Sheep's dung boiled with new milk until dissolved, and then taken internally, is a sure cure for the removal of gall stones.

Headache

Moss growing upon a human skull, if dried and powdered and taken as snuff, will cure the headache.

Jaundice

To cure the jaundice, eat nine lice on a piece of bread and butter.

—Dorset remedy

Scarlet Fever

Cut off some of the hair of a person ill with scarlet fever, and put it down the throat of the ass.

—Irish remedy

Smallpox

To cure the smallpox, take a bun from the shop of a person who, when she was married, did not change her name. It must not be paid for, nor must the person be thanked for it. Give it to the patient to eat, and the smallpox will be cured.

—Cheshire remedy

Wen

To cure a wen, you should go to an execution, and after the criminal is dead, but still hanging, one of his hands must be rubbed twice over the wen.

Quoted in E. and M.A. Radford,
"Encyclopedia of Superstition"

BISHOP BERKELEY AND TAR WATER
Oliver Wendell Holmes

Berkeley afforded a remarkable illustration of a truth which has long been known to the members of one of the learned professions, namely, that no amount of talent, or of acquirements in other departments, can rescue from lamentable folly those who, without something of the requisite preparation, undertake to experiment with nostrums upon themselves and their neighbors. The exalted character of Berkeley is thus drawn by Sir James Mackintosh: "Ancient learning, exact science, polished society, modern literature, and the fine arts, contributed to adorn and enrich the mind of this accomplished man. All his contemporaries agreed with the satirist in ascribing

" 'To Berkeley every virtue under heaven.'

"Even the discerning, fastidious, and turbulent Atterbury said, after an interview with him, 'So much understanding, so much knowledge, so much innocence, and such humility, I did not think had been the portion of any but angels, till I saw this gentleman.' "

But among the writings of this great and good man is an Essay of the most curious character, illustrating his weakness upon the point in question, and entitled, "Siris, a Chain of Philosophical Reflections and Inquiries concerning the Virtues of TAR WATER, and divers other Subjects,"—an essay which begins with a recipe for his favorite fluid, and slides by gentle gradations into an examination of the sublimest doctrines of Plato. To show how far a man of honesty and benevolence, and with a mind of singular acuteness and depth, may be run away with by a favorite notion on a subject which his habits and education do not fit him to investigate, I shall give a short account of this Essay, merely stating that as all the supposed virtues of Tar Water, made public in successive editions of his treatise by so illustrious an author, have not saved it from neglect and disgrace, it may be fairly assumed that they were mainly imaginary.

The bishop, as is usual in such cases, speaks of himself as indispensably obliged, by the duty he owes to mankind, to make his experience public. Now this was by no means evident, nor does it follow in general, that because a man has formed a favorable opinion of a person or a thing he has not the proper means of thoroughly understanding, he shall be bound to print it, and thus give currency to his impressions, which may be erroneous, and therefore injurious. He would have done much better to have laid his impressions before some experienced physicians and surgeons, such as Dr. Mead and Mr. Cheselden, to have asked them to try his experiment over again, and have been guided by their answers. But the good bishop got excited; he pleased himself with the thought that he had discovered a great panacea; and having once tasted the bewitching cup of self-quackery, like many before and since his time, he was so infatuated with the draught that he would insist on pouring it down the throats of his neighbors and all mankind.

The precious fluid was made by stirring a gallon of water with a quart of tar, leaving it forty-eight hours, and pouring off the clear water. Such was the specific which the great metaphysician recommended for averting and curing all manner of diseases. It was, if he might be believed, a preventive of the small-pox, and of great use in the course of the disease. It was a cure for impurities of the blood, coughs, pleurisy, peripneumony, erysipelas, asthma, indigestion, cachexia, hysterics, dropsy, mortification, scurvy, and hypochondria. It was of great use in gout and fevers, and was an excellent preservative of the teeth and gums; answered all the purpose of Elixir Proprietatis, Stoughton's drops, diet drinks, and mineral waters; was particularly to be recommended to sea-faring persons, ladies, and men of studious and sedentary lives; could never be taken too long, but, on the contrary, produced advantages which sometimes did not begin to show themselves for two or three months.

"From my representing Tar Water as good for so many things," says Berkeley, "some perhaps may conclude it is good for nothing. But charity obligeth me to say what I know, and what I think, however it may be taken. Men may censure and object as they please, but I appeal to time and experiment. Effects misimputed, cases wrong told, circumstances overlooked, perhaps, too, prejudices and partialities against truth, may for a time prevail and keep her at the bottom of her well, from whence nevertheless she emergeth sooner or later, and strikes the eyes of all who do not keep them shut." I cannot resist the temptation of illustrating the bishop's belief in the wonderful powers of his remedy, by a few sentences from different parts of his essay. "The hardness of stubbed vulgar constitutions renders them insensible of a thousand things that fret and gall those delicate people, who, as if their skin was peeled off, feel to the quick everything that touches them. The tender nerves and low spirits of such poor creatures would be much relieved by the use of Tar Water, which might prolong and cheer their lives." "It [the Tar Water] may be made stronger for brute beasts, as horses, in whose disorders I have found it very useful." "This same water will also give charitable relief to the ladies, who often want it more than the parish poor; being many of them never able to make a good meal, and sitting pale, puny, and forbidden, like ghosts, at their own table, victims of vapors and indigestion." It does not appear among the virtues of Tar Water that "children cried for it," as for some of our modern remedies, but the bishop says, "I have known children take it for above six months together with great benefit, and without any inconvenience; and after long and repeated experience I do esteem it a most excellent diet drink, fitted to all seasons and ages." After mentioning its usefulness in febrile complaints, he says: "I have had all this confirmed by my own experience in the late sickly season of the year one thousand seven hundred and forty-one, having had twenty-five fevers in my own family cured by this medicinal water, drunk copiously."

And to finish these extracts with a most important suggestion for the improvement of the British nation: "It is much to be lamented that our Insulars, who act and think so much for themselves, should yet, from grossness of air and diet, grow stupid or doat sooner than other people, who, by virtue of elastic air, water-drinking, and light food, preserve their faculties to extreme old age; an advantage which may perhaps be approached, if not equaled, even in these regions, by Tar Water, temperance, and early hours."

Berkeley died at the age of about seventy; he might have lived longer, but his fatal illness was so sudden that there was not time enough to stir up a quart of the panacea. He was an illustrious man, but he held two very odd opinions; that tar water was everything, and that the whole material universe was nothing.

1842

TREATMENT OF KING CHARLES
By Howard W. Haggard

Some idea of the nature and number of the drug substances used in the medicine of the past may be obtained from the records of the treatment given King Charles II at the time of his death. These records are extant in the writings of a Dr. Scarburgh, one of the twelve or fourteen physicians called in to treat the king. At eight o'clock on Monday morning of February 2, 1685, King Charles was being shaved in his bedroom. With a sudden cry he fell backward and had a violent convulsion. He became unconscious, rallied once or twice, and after a few days died. Seventeenth-century autopsy records are far from complete, but one could hazard a guess that the king suffered with an embolism—that is, a floating blood clot which had plugged up an artery and deprived some portion of his brain of blood—or else his kidneys were diseased. As the first step in treatment the king was bled to the extent of a pint from a vein in his right arm. Next his shoulder was cut into and the incised area "cupped" to suck out an additional eight ounces of blood. After this homicidal onslaught the drugging began. An emetic and purgative were administered, and soon after a second purgative. This was followed by an enema containing antimony, sacred bitters, rock salt, mallow leaves, violets, beet root, camomile flowers, fennel seed, linseed, cinnamon, cardamom seed, saphron, cochineal, and aloes. The enema was repeated in two hours and a purgative given. The king's head was shaved and a blister raised on his scalp. A sneezing powder of hellebore root was administered, and also a powder of cowslip flowers "to strengthen his brain." The cathartics were repeated at frequent intervals and interspersed with a soothing drink composed of barley water, licorice and sweet almond. Likewise white wine, absinthe and anise were given, as also were extracts of thistle leaves, mint, rue, and angelica. For external treatment a plaster of Burgundy pitch and pigeon dung was applied to the king's feet. The bleeding and purging continued, and to the medicaments were added melon seeds, manna, slippery elm, black cherry water, an extract of flowers of lime, lily-of-the-valley, peony, lavender, and dissolved pearls. Later came gentian root, nutmeg, quinine, and cloves. The king's condition did not improve, indeed it grew worse, and in the emergency forty drops of extract of human skull were administered to allay convulsions. A rallying dose of Raleigh's antidote was forced down the king's throat; this antidote contained an enormous number of herbs and animal extracts. Finally bezoar stone was given. Then says Scarburgh: "Alas! after an ill-fated night his serene majesty's strength seemed exhausted to such a degree that the whole assembly of physicians lost all hope and became despondent: still so as not to appear to fail in doing their duty in any detail, they brought into play the most active cordial." As a sort of grand summary to this pharmaceutical debauch a mixture of Raleigh's antidote, pearl julep, and ammonia was forced down the throat of the dying king.

1929

Descriptions of Disease

THOMAS SYDENHAM

ON THE MEASLES

THE measles generally attack children. On the first day they have chills and shivers, and are hot and cold in turns. On the second they have the fever in full—disquietude, thirst, want of appetite, a white (but not a dry) tongue, a slight cough, heaviness of the head and eyes, and somnolence. The nose and eyes run continually; and this is the surest sign of measles. To this may be added sneezing, a swelling of the eyelids a little before the eruption, vomiting and diarrhoea with green stools. These appear more especially during teething time. The symptoms increase till the fourth day. Then—or sometimes on the fifth—there appear on the face and forehead small red spots, very like the bites of fleas. These increase in number, and cluster together, so as to mark the face with large red blotches. They are formed by small papulae, so slightly elevated above the skin, that their prominence can hardly be detected by the eye, but can just be felt by passing the fingers lightly along the skin.

The spots take hold of the face first; from which they spread to the chest and belly, and afterwards to the legs and ankles. On these parts may be seen broad, red maculae, on, but above, the level of the skin. In measles the eruption does not so thoroughly allay the other symptoms as in small-pox. There is, however, no vomiting after its appearance; nevertheless there is slight cough instead, which, with the fever and the difficulty of breathing, increases. There is also a running from the eyes, somnolence, and want of appetite. On the sixth day, or thereabouts, the forehead and face begin to grow rough, as the pustules die off, and as the skin breaks. Over the rest of the body the blotches are both very broad and very red. About the eighth day they disappear from the face, and scarcely show on the rest of the body. On the ninth, there are none anywhere. On the face, however, and on the extremities—sometimes over the trunk—they peel off in thin, mealy squamulae; at which time the fever, the difficulty of breathing, and the cough are aggravated. In adults and patients who have been under a hot regimen, they grow livid, and afterwards black.

1692
Translated in 1848

ON ST. VITUS DANCE

This is a kind of convulsion, which attacks boys and girls from the tenth year to the time of puberty. It first shows itself by limping or unsteadiness in one of the legs, which the patient drags. The hand cannot be steady for a moment. It passes from one position to another by a convulsive movement, however much the patient may strive to the contrary. Before he can raise a cup to his lips, he makes as many gesticulations as a mountebank; since he does not move it in a straight line, but has his hand drawn aside by spasms, until by some good fortune he brings it at last to his mouth. He then gulps it off at once, so suddenly and so greedily as to look as if he were trying to amuse the lookers-on.

1692
Translated in 1848

ON SCARLET FEVER

Scarlet Fever (Scarlatina) may appear at any season. Nevertheless, it oftenest breaks out towards the end of summer, when it attacks whole families at once, and more especially the infant part of them. The patients feel rigors and shiverings, just as they do in other fevers. The symptoms, however, are moderate. Afterwards, however, the whole skin becomes covered with small red maculae, thicker than those of measles, as well as broader, redder, and less uniform. These last for two or three days, and then disappear. The cuticle peels off; and branny scales, remain, lying upon the surface like meal. They appear and disappear two or three times.

As the disease is, in my mind, neither more nor less than a moderate effervescence of the blood, arising from the heat of the preceding summer, or from some other exciting cause, I leave the blood as much as possible to its own despumation, and to the elimination of the peccant materials through the pores of the skin. With this view, I am chary both of bloodletting and of clysters. By such remedies, I hold that a revulsion is created, that the particles inimical to the blood become more intimately mixed therewith, and, finally, that the proper movement of Nature is checked. On the other hand, I am cautious in the use of cordials. By them, the blood may be over-agitated, and so unfitted for the regular and equable separation in which it is engrossed. Besides which, they may act as fuel to fever.

I hold it, then, sufficient for the patient to abstain wholly from animal food and from fermented liquors; to keep always indoors, and not to keep always in his bed. When the desquamation is complete, and when the symptoms are departing, I consider it proper to purge the patient with some mild laxative, accommodated to his age and strength. By treatment thus simple and natural, this ailment—we can hardly call it more—is dispelled without either trouble or danger: whereas, if, on the other hand, we overtreat the patient by confining him to his bed, or by throwing in cordials, and other superfluous and over-learned medicines, the disease is aggravated, and the sick man dies of his doctor. This, however, must be borne in mind. If there occur at the beginning of the eruption either epileptic fits, or coma—as they often do occur with children or young patients—a large blister must be placed at the back of the neck, and a paregoric draught of syrup of poppies must be administered at once. This last must be repeated every night until he recover. The ordinary drink must be warm milk with three parts water, and animal food must be abstained from.

1676

Science and Surgery—
John Hunter
LOGAN CLENDENING

MR. JOHN HUNTER, the surgeon, had been arguing. He stood now with his legs apart, his back to the fire, lifting up his coat-tails to the heat. To one who knew Mr. Hunter there was a glint in his eye which indicated he was losing his rather unstable temper.

The florid, plump, bewildered man of thirty-five who sat before him was staring stubbornly ahead. He had been driven to resist Mr. Hunter's arguments by silence.

The experience indeed had been a most unsettling one. When his father had fallen ill a few weeks before, he had been assured that Mr. Hunter was the most skilful practitioner then in London —it was the early spring of 1788. So, being a man of means, he employed Mr. Hunter in consultation. And Mr. Hunter had failed him, for his father had died, and all that was mortal of him lay upstairs on the wide bed, covered by a sheet.

In the first shock of bereavement Mr. Hunter had been very gentle. He had assisted him downstairs and poured him a glass of tawny port to give him a little control and strength. His loss was great and almost insupportable. It was almost impossible for him to realize that his father's strong and imperious personality was no more, that his wise old voice was for ever stilled and could counsel him no longer, that all the responsibility of the business and the family was now on his own unworthy shoulders. He explained as much, brokenly, to Mr. Hunter and to young Mr. Abernethy, Mr. Hunter's assistant, who was with him. He was, indeed, if ever a man could be expected to be so, an object for pity.

But, suddenly, Mr. Hunter had made a very strange request. It puzzled him. Mr. Hunter had asked permission to open his father's body in order to examine into the cause of death. The effect was unpleasant. Here Mr. Hunter had been touted to him as the cleverest of practitioners, and with what disastrous results! And now it appeared that Mr. Hunter did not even know what the disease was from which his father had died, and proposed to use the body to satisfy his ghoulish curiosity.

The thing revolted him. And he refused. Mr. Hunter had argued. He had at first attempted to reply, but Mr. Hunter seemed always to get round him. So now he sat in stolid silence, and Mr. Hunter warmed his legs before the fire, the dangerous gleam playing in his blue Scotch eyes.

"Then, sir," says Mr. Hunter, evenly, at the last, "you will not permit the examination to be made?"

"It is impossible," responded the helplessly bewildered merchant.

"Then, sir," said Mr. Hunter, breaking into a sea of anger, "I heartily hope that yourself and all your family, nay, all your friends, may die of the same disease, and that no one may be able to afford any assistance."

And having pronounced this dreadful doom upon the poor gentleman, "so saying he departed," concludes young Mr. Abernethy, the veritable chronicler of the anecdote.

It was one of the few instances, we are told, when Mr. Hunter was ever brutal towards his patients or their friends. And most people, I suppose, will feel their sympathy going out towards the unhappily bereaved son rather than to Mr. John Hunter.

But it must be remembered that Mr. Hunter was fighting for the great central sanctity of his life—and in these circumstances a man of his temperament does not suffer fools gladly. That central sanctity was, of course, the right to a free and independent investigation of nature in all her aspects. Mr. Hunter, who bore the same relation to medical London in his day as Samuel Johnson did in that same period to literary London, went through his earthly pilgrimage with the fierce light of that preeminence burning in his countenance. He exercised the privilege of investigating nature where he found her. You might have discovered him lying on his belly near a fish-pond to determine if fish could hear, or in that two-acre garden of his house at Earl's Court on the outskirts of London, up to his armpits in the dissection of a whale brought him from Greenland, while zebras and panthers wandered all around him.[1]

"Cannot you get me a large porpoise for love or money?" he writes Edward Jenner, the discoverer of smallpox vaccination. Jenner, by head and shoulders the greatest medical man of his time, was always faintly patronized by Hunter. Hunter sent him into Gloucester to set up in practice. When Jenner consulted him about the value of vaccination, Hunter wrote him the words which have become the motto of experimental science: "Don't think, try; be patient, be accurate." Hunter and Jenner engaged in a lifelong correspondence—which racily reflects Hunter's restless activities.

"What do you think of examining eels? Their sexes have not yet been found out."

"Have you any eaves where bats go at night? If you have I will put you upon a set of experiments concerning the heat of them at different seasons."

Such was the nature of the suggestions John Hunter showered on his bucolic protégé.

Had you lived in London in 1783 you might have seen John Hunter looking lasciviously at O'Brien, the Irish Giant, who was on exhibition at a raree-show. Mr. Hunter had gone to see the giant as a medical curiosity and had been interested. He wondered what a giant's skeleton looked like. They had dropped into conversation, and Mr. Hunter had remarked that giants did not usually live long and that he would esteem it an especial favour if O'Brien would consent to allow his body to be dissected after death. This suggestion terminated their conversation and acquaintance abruptly, for the giant had a superstitious horror

---

[1] "In the garden of Mr. Hunter, surgeon, at Earl's Court, are seen buffalo, rams, and sheep from Turkey, and a shawl goat from the East Indies, all feeding together in the greatest harmony: besides a prodigious variety of other beasts and birds supposed to be naturally hostile to each other." (*London Morning Post*, August 30, 1793.)

of being dissected and was not particularly pleased at the thought of early death.

Mr. Hunter's particular interest was re-excited when the state of health of the towering prodigy began to decline. The contemporary records state that O'Brien died from alcoholism and tuberculosis, but our present knowledge of his form of giantism makes it probable that he had a tumour of the pituitary gland. Whatever the cause, the symptoms of disruption of his frame were evident even to O'Brien himself. The poor frightened giant found Mr. Hunter's eyes glinting at him from every alleyway. He moved from lodging to lodging to escape him. In every new place he thought for a time he was safe; but inevitably some day he would leave his house and spy that sinister figure peering from a neighbouring doorway. Mr. Hunter set his servant Howison to shadow the quarry. And as the giant was eight feet, four inches tall, the task was not difficult. The gangling monster whinnied with terror whenever little five foot two inch Mr. Hunter hove in view. Whimpering on his death-bed, he left orders that his body should be watched day and night until a leaden coffin had been prepared, and that it was then to be taken in a vessel into the middle of the Irish Channel and sunk. Having thus prepared himself, he died, but he reckoned without John Hunter. The faithful Howison learned the details of the affair and plied one of the watchers with strong drink and found he could be bribed to allow the body to be kidnapped. Fifty pounds was at first demanded, but, finding Mr. Hunter's appetite so keen, the price soared until it came to five hundred pounds. The money had to be borrowed, but it was obtained and the body hustled into a hackney-coach "at dead of night."

The hackney-coach dashed through several streets. Then its pace became slower and it drew up beside a carriage waiting at a curb. The spot was prearranged. It was Mr. Hunter's own carriage. Those glistening eyes at the carriage window were his. He had his quarry at last. The body of the giant was bundled into Mr. Hunter's carriage, and, there, clinging to his eight and a half feet of treasure, Mr. Hunter drove out of the London streets to Earl's Court and boiled his trove in a vat. The bones of the Irish giant do not lie at the bottom of the Irish Channel. They stand articulated in the museum of the Royal College of Surgeons, London.

Yes, John Hunter was a dangerous man when stalking quarry.

A certain Dr. Clarke had a specimen which Hunter coveted. "Come, doctor," he said, "I positively must have that preparation."

"No, John Hunter," was the reply, "you positively shall not."

"You will not give it to me, then?"

"No."

"Will you sell it?"

"No."

"Well, then, take care I don't meet you with it in some dark lane at night, for if I do, I'll murder you to get it."

He did not even spare his own person in this agony of curiosity about nature's secrets. He inoculated himself with syphilis and refused treatment that he might observe the course of the disease in his own person. He wrote a treatise on the subject. Today the chancre, the first site of the entrance of the syphilitic virus into the body and the first manifestation of its activity, is known as the "Hunterian chancre."

"Pray, George," said he to his friend Nicol, the bookseller, "have you got five guineas in your pocket? Because if you have and will lend it to me, you shall go halves."

"Halves in what?"

"Why, halves in a magnificent tiger which is now dying in Castle Street."

"The hedgehogs came," he wrote Jenner in 1778, "with one dead, which was a female, which I made a preparation of. . . . I was told the other day that you was married and to a young lady with a considerable fortune. I hope it is true, for I do not know anybody more deserving of one. What is become of your paper on lead in cider?" The new wife, the hedgehogs, and the lead in the cider all mixed together on an even footing. And then wistfully, as if he wondered whether Jenner would pursue his science now that he had a rich wife: "How do the fossils go on?" And again, even more wistfully: "We had a sale of bad pictures lately. Pictures seem to be rising again. I am told there is the skin of a toad in Berkeley Castle that is of prodigious size. Let me know the truth of it, its dimensions, what bones are still in it, *and if it can be stolen by some invisible being.* I buried two toads, last August was a twelvemonth; I opened the grave last October, and they were well and lively. . . . Have you any queer fish? Amy sends, with little John, their compliments."

And what was the result of all this endless gathering of specimens?

Well, there they are today all in the Hunterian Museum in London. Here is Victor Robinson's eloquent description of it:

"What specimens—thousands upon thousands—dry, in spirits, stuffed,—everything: varieties of the cuticle of different animals, showing how it increases in vascularity in proportion as its sensibility increases; the organs of taste, smell, hearing and sight, exhibited in ascending series. The individual peculiarities of plants and animals, monsters, mummies, the skulls of the five great divisions of the human race, the development of the brain and spinal marrow from the knotted cord of the crustacea upwards through fishes, reptiles and birds, to the brain and spinal cord of the mammalia; teeth, from the beaks of birds to the tusks of boars; specimens showing the effects of various diseases on brains, hearts, lungs, stomachs, intestines, spleens, kidneys—the apotheosis of pathology."

Broad as were his interests in science, they all focused on the processes of disease. If he studied the normal, it was to have a standard for the abnormal. And in his study of disease he found the most valuable method was by means of the post-mortem—the examination of the body after death. Hence his anger before that poor stolid British merchant when we first met him.

"He alone made us gentlemen," said one of his colleagues in surgery. And if he thus raised the social status of surgeons, he did it all the more for pathologists. He put the thing on high ground: a man who opened a dead body was no longer a ghoul, he was a scientist—a student of the order of nature, and, as such, on a plane with every other kind of a student.

There is exactly as much culture to be derived from the study of cirrhotic livers as from the study of the elegies of Tibullus.

The deep influence of Hunter in this respect may be seen in the attitude of his immediate successors. His nephew, Mathew Baillie, published, in 1794, an atlas and text-book on *Morbid Anatomy*. This was the first systematic account of the diseased appearance of the internal organs of the body to appear in print.

One of the plates represents a lung and is an illustration of the disease called "emphysema." The lung was that of Dr. Samuel Johnson: its state accounts for the "heavy form, rolling," and the "puffing" of Macaulay's description. So the Great Cham is dead, and here is dry little Dr. Baillie cutting him up as if he were any other piece of flesh.

Why not?

See the will of Sir Astley Paston Cooper, surgeon to Guy's

Hospital, London. We meet him in another part of this narrative. He lived in the great Hunterian tradition. Do you suppose that surgeons and physicians who ask to examine a body after death are squeamish about their own personal autopsies? Hear what Sir Astley commanded when he thought he was about to die. "Shortly before his death, Sir Astley Cooper expressed a wish that the appearances which should be presented on the inspection of his body might be recorded in the Guy's Hospital Reports. He had particularly alluded to four points, the investigation of which he thought desirable—a cured oblique inguinal hernia; some suspected indications of phthisis in his youth; and an inability to sleep whilst lying on his left side."

These points were accordingly investigated on February 13, 1841, at nine o'clock in the evening, thirty-two hours after Sir Astley's death, in the presence, among others, of Doctor Richard Bright.

For myself, I know exactly how Sir Astley felt. It must have been a bitter disappointment to him to realize that he could not be present at the post-mortem himself and with his own eyes see the explanation of those disarrangements of his body with which he was so familiar. But he had no intention of depriving his friends of that pleasure. I know of no post-mortem I should rather attend than my own.[1]

1933

Experiments Made to Ascertain the Progress and Effects of the Venereal Poison

JOHN HUNTER

To ASCERTAIN several facts relative to the venereal disease, the following experiments were made. They were begun in May 1767.

Two punctures were made on the penis with a lancet dipped in

[1] Or hardly any.

venereal matter from a gonorrhea; one puncture was on the glans, the other on the prepuce.

This was on a Friday; on the Sunday following there was a teasing itching in those parts, which lasted till the Tuesday following. In the mean time, these parts being often examined, there seemed to be a greater redness and moisture than usual, which was imputed to the parts being rubbed. Upon the Tuesday morning the parts of the prepuce where the puncture had been made were redder, thickened, and had formed a speck; by the Tuesday following the speck had increased, and discharged some matter, and there seemed to be a little pouting of the lips of the urethra, also a sensation in it in making water, so that a discharge was expected from it. The speck was now touched with lunar caustic, and afterwards dressed with calomel ointment. On Saturday morning the slough came off, and it was again touched, and another slough came off on the Monday following. The preceding night the glans had itched a good deal, and on Tuesday a white speck was observed where the puncture had been made; this speck, when examined was found to be a pimple full of yellowish matter. This was now touched with the caustic, and dressed as the former. On the Wednesday the sore on the prepuce was yellow, and therefore was again touched with caustic. On the Friday both sloughs came off, and the sore on the prepuce looked red, and its basis was not so hard; but on the Saturday it did not look quite so well, and was touched again, and when that went off it was allowed to heal, as also the other, which left a dent in the glans. This dent on the glans was filled up in some months, but for a considerable time it had a bluish cast.

Four months afterwards the chancre on the prepuce broke out again, and very stimulating applications were tried; but these seemed not to agree with it, and nothing being applied, it healed up. This it did several times afterwards, but always healed up without any application to it. That on the glans never did break out, and herein also it differed from the other.

While the sores remained on the prepuce and glans a swelling took place in one of the glands of the right groin. I had for some time conceived an idea that the most effectual way to put back a bubo was to rub in mercury on that leg and thigh; that thus a current of mercury would pass through the inflamed gland. There was a good opportunity of making the experiment. I had often succeeded in this way, but now wanted to put it more critically to the test. The sores upon the penis were healed before the reduction of the bubo was attempted. A few days after beginning the mercury in this method the gland subsided considerably. It was then left off, for the intention was not to cure it completely at present. The gland some time after began to swell again, and as much mercury was rubbed in as appeared to be sufficient for the entire reduction of the gland; but it was meant to do no more than to cure the gland locally, without giving enough to prevent the constitution from being contaminated.

About two months after the last attack of the bubo, a little sharp pricking pain was felt in one of the tonsils in swallowing anything, and on inspection a small ulcer was found, which was allowed to go on till the nature of it was ascertained, and then recourse was had to mercury. The mercury was thrown in by the same leg and thigh as before, to secure the gland more effectually, although that was not now probably necessary.

As soon as the ulcer was skinned over the mercury was left off, it not being intended to destroy the poison, but to observe what parts it would next affect. About three months after, copper-coloured blotches broke out on the skin, and the former ulcer returned in the tonsil. Mercury was now applied the second time for those effects of the poison upon the constitution, but still only with a view to palliate.

It was left off a second time, and the attention was given to mark where it would break out next; but it returned again in the same parts. It not appearing that any further knowledge was to be procured by only palliating the disease a fourth time in the tonsil, and a third time in the skin, mercury was now taken in a sufficient quantity, and for a proper time, to complete the cure.

The time the experiments took up, from the first insertion to the complete cure, was about three years.

The above case is only uncommon in the mode of contracting the disease, and the particular views with which some parts of the treatment were directed; but as it was meant to prove many things which though not uncommon, as yet not attended to, attention was paid to all the circumstances. It proves many things, and opens a field for further conjectures.

It proves, first, that matter from a gonorrhoea will produce chancres.

It makes it probable that the glans does not admit the venereal irritation so quickly as the prepuce. The chancre on the prepuce infoamed and suppurated in somewhat more than three days, and that on the glans in about ten. This is probably the reason why the glans did not throw off its sloughs so soon.

It renders it highly probable that to apply mercury to the legs and thighs is the best method of resolving a bubo; and therefore also the best method of applying mercury to assist in the cure, even when the bubo suppurates.

It also shows that buboes may be resolved in this way, and yet the constitution not be safe; and therefore that more mercury should be thrown in, especially in cases of easy resolution, than what simply resolves the bubo.

It shows that parts may be contaminated, and may have the poison kept dormant in them while under a course of mercury for other symptoms, but break out afterwards.

It also shows that the poison having originally only contaminated certain parts, when not completely cured, can break out again only in those parts.

1786

Inoculation Against Smallpox

LADY MARY WORTLEY MONTAGU

I AM going to tell you a thing that I am sure will make you wish yourself here. The smallpox, so fatal and so general among us, is here rendered entirely harmless by the invention of ingrafting, which is the term they give it. There is a set of old women who make it their business to perform the operation every autumn, in the month of September, when the great heat is abated. People send to one another to know if any of their family has a mind to have the smallpox; they make parties for this purpose, and when they are met (commonly fifteen or sixteen together), the old woman comes with a nutshell full of the matter of the best sort of small pox and asks what veins you please to have opened. She immediately rips open that you offer to her with a large needle (which gives you no more pain than a common scratch), and puts into the vein as much venom as can lie upon the head of her needle, and after binds up the little wound with a hollow bit of shell; and in this manner opens four or five veins. The Grecians have commonly the superstition of opening one in the middle of the forehead, in each arm, and on the breast to mark the sign of the cross; but this has a very ill effect, all these wounds leaving little scars, and is not done by those that are not superstitious, who choose to have them in the legs, or that part of the arm that is concealed. The children or young patients play together all the rest of the day and are in perfect health to the eighth. Then the fever begins to seize them, and they keep their beds two days, very seldom three. Every year thousands undergo this operation; and the French ambassador says pleasantly that they take the smallpox here by way of diversion, as they take the waters in other countries. There is no example of anyone that has died in it; and you may believe I am very well satisfied of the safety of this experiment, since I intend to try it on my dear little son.

Edition of 1779

An Inquiry Into the Causes and Effects of the Variolae Vaccinae, Known by the Name of the Cow-Pox

EDWARD JENNER

THE deviation of man from the state in which he was originally placed by nature seems to have proved to him a prolific source of diseases. From the love of splendour, from the indulgence of luxury, and from his fondness for amusement he has familiarized himself with a great number of animals, which may not originally have been intended for his associates.

The wolf, disarmed of ferocity, is now pillowed in the lady's lap. The cat, the little tiger of our island, whose natural home is the forest, is equally domesticated and caressed. The cow, the hog, the sheep, and the horse, are all, for a variety of purposes, brought under his care and dominion.

There is a disease to which the horse, from his state of domestication, is frequently subject. The farriers call it the grease. It is an inflammation and swelling in the heel, from which issues matter possessing properties of very peculiar kind, which seems capable of generating a disease in the human body (after it has undergone the modification which I shall presently speak of), which bears so strong a resemblance to the smallpox that I think it highly probable it may be the source of the disease.

In this dairy country a great number of cows are kept, and the office of milking is performed indiscriminately by men and maid servants. One of the former having been appointed to apply dressings to the heels of a horse affected with the grease, and not paying due attention to cleanliness, incautiously bears his part in milking the cows, with some particles of the infectious matter adhering to his fingers. When this is the case, it commonly happens that a disease is communicated to the cows, and from the cows to dairy maids, which spreads through the farm until the most of the cattle and domestics feel its unpleasant consequences. This disease has obtained the name of the cow-pox. It appears on the nipples of the cows in the form of irregular pustules. At their first appearance they are commonly of a palish blue, or rather of a colour somewhat approaching to livid, and are surrounded by an erysipelatous inflammation. These pustules, unless a timely remedy be applied, frequently degenerate into phagedenic ulcers, which prove extremely troublesome. The animals become indisposed, and the secretion of milk is much lessened. Inflamed spots now begin to appear on different parts of the hands of the domestics employed in milking, and sometimes on the wrists, which quickly run on to suppuration, first assuming the appearance of the small vesications produced by a burn. Most commonly they appear about the joints of the fingers and at their extremities; but whatever parts are affected, if the situation will admit, these superficial suppurations put on a circular form, with their edges more elevated than their centre, and of a colour distantly approaching to blue. Absorption takes place, and tumours appear in each axilla. The system becomes affected—the pulse is quickened; and shiverings, succeeded by heat, with general lassitude and pains about the loins and limbs, with vomiting, come on. The head is painful, and the patient is now and then even affected with delirium. These symptoms, varying in their degrees of violence, generally continue from one day to three or four, leaving ulcerated sores about the hands, which, from the sensibility of the parts, are very troublesome, and commonly heal slowly, frequently becoming phagedenic, like those from whence they sprung. The lips, nostrils, eyelids, and other parts of the body are sometimes affected with sores; but these evidently arise from their being heedlessly rubbed or scratched with the patient's infected fingers. No eruptions on the skin have followed the decline of the feverish symptoms in any instance that has come to my inspection, one only excepted, and in this case a very few appeared on the arms: they were very minute, of a vivid red colour, and soon died away without advancing to maturation; so that I cannot determine whether they had any connection with the preceding symptoms.

Thus the disease makes its progress from the horse to the nipple of the cow, and from the cow to the human subject.

Morbid matter of various kinds, when absorbed into the system, may produce effects in some degree similar; but what renders the cow-pox virus so extremely singular is that the person who has been thus affected is forever after secure from the infection of the smallpox; neither exposure to the variolous effluvia, nor the insertion of the matter into the skin, producing this distemper.

In support of so extraordinary a fact, I shall lay before my reader a great number of instances.

Case I. Joseph Merret, now as under gardener to the Earl of Berkeley, lived as a servant with a farmer near this place in the year 1770, and occasionally assisted in milking his master's cows. Several horses belonging to the farm began to have sore heels, which Merret frequently attended. The cows soon became affected with the cow-pox, and soon after several sores appeared on his hands. Swellings and stiffness in each axilla followed, and he was so much indisposed for several days as to be incapable of pursuing his ordinary employment. Previously to the appearance of the distemper among the cows there was no fresh cow brought into the farm, nor any servant employed who was affected with the cow-pox.

In April, 1795, a general inoculation taking place here, Merret was inoculated with his family; so that a period of twenty-five years had elapsed from his having the cow-pox to this time. However, though the variolous matter was repeatedly inserted into his arm, I found it impracticable to infect him with it; an efflorescence only, taking on an erysipelatous look about the centre, appearing on the skin near the punctured parts. During the whole time that his family had the smallpox, one of whom had it very full, he remained in the house with them, but received no injury from exposure to the contagion.

It is necessary to observe that the utmost care was taken to ascertain, with the most scrupulous precision, that no one whose case is here adduced had gone through the smallpox previous to these attempts to produce that disease.

Had these experiments been conducted in a large city, or in a populous neighborhood, some doubts might have been entertained; but here, where population is thin, and where such an event as a person's having had the smallpox is always faithfully recorded, no risk of inaccuracy in this particular can arise.

Case II. Sarah Portlock, of this place, was infected with the cow-pox when a servant at a farmer's in the neighborhood, twenty-seven years ago.

In the year 1792, conceiving herself, from this circumstance, secure from the infection of the smallpox, she nursed one of her own children who had accidentally caught the disease, but no indisposition ensued. During the time she remained in the infected room, variolous matter was inserted into both her arms, but without any further effect than in the preceding case.

Case XVII. The more accurately to observe the progress of the infection I selected a healthy boy, about eight years old, for the purpose of inoculating for the cow-pox. The matter was taken from a sore on the hand of a dairymaid, who was infected by her master's cows, and it was inserted on the 14th day of May, 1796, into the arm of the boy by means of two superficial incisions, barely penetrating the cutis, each about an inch long.

On the seventh day he complained of uneasiness in the axilla and on the ninth he became a little chilly, lost his appetite, and had a slight headache. During the whole of this day he was perceptibly indisposed, and spent the night with some degree of restlessness, but on the day following he was perfectly well.

The appearance of the incisions in their progress to a state of maturation were much the same as when produced in a similar manner by variolous matter. The difference which I perceived was in the state of the limpid fluid arising from the action of the virus, which assumed rather a darker hue, and in that of the

efflorescence spreading round the incisions, which had more of
an erysipelatous look than we commonly perceive when variolous
matter has been made use of in the same manner; but the whole
died away (leaving on the inoculated parts scabs and subsequent
eschars) without giving me or my patient the least trouble.

In order to ascertain whether the boy, after feeling so slight an
affection of the system from the cow-pox virus, was secure from
the contagion of the smallpox, he was inoculated the 1st of July
following with variolous matter, immediately taken from a pustule. Several slight punctures and incisions were made on both
his arms, and the matter was carefully inserted, but no disease
followed. The same appearances were observable on the arms as
we commonly see when a patient has had variolous matter applied,
after having either the cow-pox or smallpox. Several months afterwards he was again inoculated with variolous matter, but no
sensible effect was produced on the constitution.

After the many fruitless attempts to give the smallpox to those
who had had the cow-pox, it did not appear necessary, nor was it
convenient to me, to inoculate the whole of those who had been
the subjects of these late trials; yet I thought it right to see the
effects of variolous matter on some of them, particularly William
Summers, the first of these patients who had been infected with
matter taken from the cow. He was, therefore, inoculated from
a fresh pustule; but, as in the preceding cases, the system did not
feel the effects of it in the smallest degree. I had an opportunity
also of having this boy and William Pead inoculated by my
nephew, Mr. Henry Jenner, whose report to me is as follows:
"I have inoculated Pead and Barge, two of the boys whom you
lately infected with the cow-pox. On the second day the incisions
were inflamed and there was a pale inflammatory stain around
them. On the third day these appearances were still increasing
and their arms itched considerably. On the fourth day the inflammation was evidently subsiding, and on the sixth day it was
scarcely perceptible. No symptoms of indisposition followed.

"To convince myself that the variolous matter made use of was
in a perfect state I at the same time inoculated a patient with some
of it who never had gone through the cow-pox, and it produced
the smallpox in the usual regular manner."

These experiments afforded me much satisfaction; they proved
that the matter, in passing from one human subject to another,

through five gradations, lost none of its original properties, J. Barge being the fifth who received the infection successively from William Summers, the boy to whom it was communicated from the cow. . . .

Although I presume it may not be necessary to produce further testimony in support of my assertion "that the cow-pox protects the human constitution from the infection of the smallpox," yet it affords me considerable satisfaction to say that Lord Somerville, the President of the Board of Agriculture, to whom this paper was shown by Sir Joseph Banks, has found upon inquiry that the statements were confirmed by the concurring testimony of Mr. Dolland, a surgeon, who resides in a dairy country remote from this, in which these observations were made. . . .

1798

The History of the Kine-pox,
Commonly Called
the Cow-pox

WITH AN ACCOUNT OF A SERIES OF INOCULATIONS PERFORMED FOR THE KINE-POX IN MASSACHUSETTS

BENJAMIN WATERHOUSE

IN THE beginning of the year 1799 I received from my friend Dr. Lettsom of London, a copy of Dr. Edward Jenner's "Inquiry into the causes and effects of the variolae vaccinate, or Cow-pox"; a disease totally unknown in this quarter of the world. On perusing this work I was struck with the unspeakable advantages that might accrue to this, and indeed to the human race at large, from the discovery of a mild distemper that would ever after secure the constitution from that terrible scourge, the smallpox.

As the ordinary mode of communicating even medical discoveries in this country is by newspapers, I drew up the following account of the Cow-pox, which was printed in the Columbian Centinal March 12, 1799.

SOMETHING CURIOUS IN THE MEDICAL LINE

Everybody has heard of these distempers accompanied by pocks and pustules, called the small-pox, and chickenpox and the swinepox, but few have ever heard of the cow-pox, or if you like the term better, the cow small-pox; or to° express it in technical language, the variolae vaccinae. There is however such a disease which has been noticed here and there in several parts of England, more particularly in Gloucestershire, for sixty or seventy years past, but has never been an object of medical inquiry until lately.

This variolae vaccinae is very readily communicated to those who milk cows infected with it. This malady appears on the teats of the cows . . . Those who milk the cows thus affected, seldom or ever fail catching the distemper, *if there be cracks, wounds or abrasions of the hands* . . . But what makes this newly discovered disease so very curious, and so extremely important is that every person thus affected is EVER AFTER SECURED FROM THE ORDINARY SMALLPOX, *let him be ever so much exposed to the effluvian of it, or let ever so much ripe matter be inserted into the skin by inoculation.*

Dr. Edward Jenner is the physician in England who has collected and arranged a series of facts and experiments respecting the disease there called the Cow-pox.

Under the serious impression of effecting a public benefit, and conceiving it moreover a duty in my official situation in this University, I sent to England for some of the vaccine, or cow-pox matter for trial. After several fruitless attempts, I obtained some by a short passage from Bristol, and with it I inoculated all the younger part of my family.

The first of my children that I inoculated was a boy of five years old, named Daniel Oliver Waterhouse. I made a slight incision in the usual place for inoculation in the arm, inserted a small portion of the infected thread, and covered it with a sticking plaster. It exhibited no other appearances than what would have arisen from any other extraneous substance, until the sixth day when an increased redness called forth my attention. On the eighth day he complained of pain under the inoculated arm and on the ninth the inoculated part exhibited evident signs of virulency. By the tenth anyone much experienced in the inoculated small-pox would have pronounced the arm infected. The pain and swelling under his arm went on gradually encreasing and by the eleventh day from inoculation his febrile symptoms were pretty strongly marked. The sore in the arm proceeded exactly as Drs. Jenner and Woodville described, and appeared to the eye very like the second plate in Dr. Jenner's elegant publication.

The inoculated part in this boy was surrounded by an efflorescence which extended from his shoulder to his elbow, which made it necessary to apply some remedies to lessen it; but the "symptoms," as they are called, scarcely drew him from his play more than an hour or two; and he went through the disease in so light a manner as hardly even to express any marks of peevishness. A piece of true skin was fairly taken out of the arm by the virus, the part appearing as if eaten out by a caustick, a never failing sign of thorough section of the system by the inoculated small-pox.

Satisfied with the appearances and symptoms in this boy I inoculated another of three years of age with matter taken from his brother's arm, for he had no pustules on his body. He likewise went through the disease in a perfect and very satisfactory manner. The child pursued his amusements with as little interruption as his brother. Then I inoculated a servant boy of about 12 years of age, with some of the infected thread from England. His arm was pretty sore and his symptoms pretty severe. He treated himself rather harshly by exercising unnecessarily in the garden when the weather was extremely hot (Fahrt.. Therm. 96 in the shade!) and then washing his head and upper parts of his body under the pump, and setting, in short, all rules at defiance in my absence. Nevertheless this boy went through the disorder without any other accident than a sore throat and a stiffness of the muscles of the neck. All which soon vanished by the help of a few remedies.

Being obliged to go from home a few days, I requested my colleague Dr. Warren to visit these children. Dr. Danforth as well as some other physicians, came to Boston out of curiosity, and so did several practitioners from the country. I mention this because it gave rise to a groundless report, that one of the children had so bad an arm that I thought it prudent to take the advice of some of my brethren upon it.

From a full matured pustule in my little boy three years old I inoculated his infant sister, already weaned, of one year. At the same time and from the same pustule, I inoculated its nursery maid. They both went through the disease with equal regularity. . . .

Having thus traced the most important facts respecting the causes and effects of the kine-pox up to their source in England, and having confirmed most of them by actual experiment in America, one experiment only remained behind to complete the business. To effect this I wrote the following letter to Dr. Aspinwall, physician to the smallpox hospital in the neighborhood of Boston.

Cambridge, August 2, 1800

Dear Doctor:

You have doubtless heard of the newly discovered disorder, known in England by the name of cow-pox, which so nearly resembles the smallpox, that it is now agreed in Great Britain, that the former will pass for the latter.

I have procured some of the vaccine matter, and therewith inoculated seven of my family. The inoculation has proceeded in six of them exactly as described by Woodville and Jenner; but my desire is to confirm the doctrine by having some of them inoculated by you.

I can obtain variolous matter and inoculate them privately, but I wish to do it in the most open and public way possible. As I have imported a new distemper, I conceive that the public have a right to know exactly every step I take in it. I write this, then to enquire whether you will on philanthropic principles try the experiment of inoculating some of my children who have already undergone the cow-pox. If you accede to my proposal, I shall consider it as an experiment in which we have co-operated for the good of our fellow-citizens, and relate it as such in the pamphlet I mean to publish on the subject.

I am, etc.

B.W.

Hon. William Aspinwall, Esq.
Brookline.

To this letter the doctor returned a polite answer, assuring me of his readiness to give any assistance in his power, to ascertain whether the cow-pox would prevent the small-pox; observing that he had at that time fresh matter that he could depend on, and desiring me to send the children to the hospital for that purpose. Of the three which I offered, the doctor chose to try the experiment on the boy of 12 years of age, whom he inoculated in my presence by two punctures, and with matter taken at that moment from a patient who had it pretty full upon him. He at the same time inserted an infected thread and then put him into the hospital, where was one patient with it in the natural way. On the fourth day, the doctor pronounced the arm to be infected. It became every hour sorer, but in a day or two it died off, and grew well, without producing the slightest trace of a disease; so that the boy was dismissed from the hospital and returned home the twelfth day after the experiment. One fact, in such cases, is worth a thousand arguments.

1800

The Invention of the Stethoscope

RENÉ LAËNNEC

In 1816 I was consulted by a young woman presenting general symptoms of disease of the heart. Owing to her stoutness little information could be gathered by application of the hand and percussion. The patient's age and sex did not permit me to resort to the kind of examination I have just described (i.e., direct application of the ear to the chest). I recalled a well-known acoustic phenomenon, namely, if you place your ear against one end of a wooden beam the scratch of a pin at the other extremity is most distinctly audible. It occurred to me that this physical property might serve a useful purpose in the case with which I was then dealing. Taking a sheaf of paper, I rolled it into a very tight roll, one end of which I placed over the praecordial region, while I put my ear to the other. I was both surprised and gratified at being able to hear the beating of the heart with much greater clearness and distinctness than I had ever done before by direct application of my ear.

I at once saw that this means might become a useful method for studying not only the beating of the heart but likewise all movements capable of producing sound in the thoracic cavity, and that consequently it might serve for the investigation of respiration, the voice, râles, and even possibly the movements of a liquid effused into the pleural cavity or pericardium.

With this conviction, I at once began and have continued to the present time, a series of observations at the Hospital Necker. As a result I have obtained many new and certain signs, most of which are striking, easy of recognition, and calculated perhaps to render the diagnosis of nearly all complaints of the lungs, pleurae, and heart both more certain and more circumstantial than the surgical diagnosis obtained by use of the sound or by introduction of the finger. . . .

Before proceeding with my subject I consider it my duty to record the various attempts that I have made to improve upon the exploring instrument I at present use; these attempts have proved almost entirely vain, and if I mention them it is in the hope that any other investigator seeking to perfect the instrument will strike out a fresh path.

The first instrument employed by me consisted of a cylinder or roll of paper, sixteen lines in diameter and one foot long, made of three quires of paper rolled very tightly round, and held in position with gummed paper and filed smooth at both ends. However tight the roll may be, there will always remain a tube three or four lines in diameter running up the center, because the sheets of paper composing it can never be rolled completely on themselves. This fortuitous circumstance gave rise, as will be seen, to an important observation upon my part: I found that for listening to the voice the tube is an indispensable factor. An entirely solid body is the best instrument that can be used for listening to the heart; such an instrument would indeed suffice also for hearing respiratory sounds and râles; yet these last two phenomena yield greater intensity of sound if a perforated cylinder is used, hollowed out at one end into a kind of funnel one and one half inches in depth.

The densest bodies are not, as analogy would lead us to suppose, the best materials for constructing these instruments. Glass and metals, apart from their weight and the sensation of cold that they impart in winter, are not such good carriers of the heartbeats and the sounds produced by breathing and râles, as are bodies of lesser density. . . .

Substances of medium density, such as paper, wood, and cane, are those which have always appeared to me preferable to all others. This result may be in contradiction with an axiom of physics; nonetheless I consider it to be quite established.

I consequently employ at the present time a wooden cylinder

with a tube three lines [a French line—0.0888 in. or 2.256 mm.] in diameter bored right down its axis; it is divisible into two parts by means of a screw and is thus more portable. One of the parts is hollowed out at its end into a wide funnel-shaped depression one and one half inches deep leading into the central tube. A cylinder made like this is the instrument most suitable for exploring breath sounds and râles. It is converted into a tube of uniform diameter with thick walls all the way, for exploring the voice and the heartbeats, by introducing into the funnel or bell a kind of stopper made of the same wood, fitting it quite closely; this is made fast by means of a small brass tube running through it, entering a certain distance into the tubular space running through the length of the cylinder. This instrument is sufficient for all cases, although, as I have already said, a perfectly solid body might perhaps be better for listening to the beating of the heart.

The dimensions indicated above are not altogether unimportant; if the diameter is larger it is not always possible to apply the stethoscope closely against all points of the chest; if the instrument is longer, it becomes difficult to hold it exactly in place; if it were shorter, the physician would often be obliged to adopt an uncomfortable position, which is to be avoided above all things if he desires to carry out accurate observations.

I shall be careful, when discussing each variety of exploration, to mention the positions which experience has taught me to be most favorable for observation and least tiring for both physician and patient.

Suffice it to say for the moment that in all cases the stethoscope should be held like a pen, and that the hand must be placed quite close to the patient's chest in order to make sure that the instrument is properly applied.

The end of the instrument intended to rest on the patient's chest, that is to say the end provided with the stopper, should be very slightly concave; it is then less liable to wobble, and as this concavity is easily filled by the skin it in no case leaves an empty space even when placed on the flattest part of the chest.

1819
Translated in 1834

Bootlegging Bodies

A HISTORY OF BODY-SNATCHING

ALAN FRANK GUTTMACHER

BODY-SNATCHING was the bootlegging of human dead for purposes of dissection. A consideration of this forgotten trade shows much parallelism between this and the recent bootlegging of a very different commodity. The type of citizenry engaged in it, the methods employed, the gang warfare, the connivance by the police, and the bribery and hypocrisy all find their counterpart in this movement of more than a hundred years ago. . . .

THE RESURRECTIONISTS: PERSONNEL AND METHODS

Body-snatchers, resurrectionists, sack-'em-ups, ghouls or exhumators were of two orders, gentlemen and rascals. The medical students and young anatomists, the gentlemen, were actuated by scientific motives. The rascals, grave-diggers, sextons, rowdies and criminals, found in this business a lucrative, exciting form of employment, which required the occasional and strenuous use of brawn, but little need for brain. They were the professionals.

In the early days of British anatomy, all the body-snatching was done by the gentlemen. It was done secretly and on so small a scale that the fresh graves of unwept, unclaimed criminals and paupers sufficed. Gradually, as the students grew more numerous and as the demand for bodies increased, others entered the field. At first they were recruited entirely from laborers in the grave-yards, and as late as 1789, when Sir Astley Cooper commenced to lecture at St. Thomas', the persons who provided subjects had no distinct denomination and their existence was still unknown to the general public, largely because they were careful to transact their business only at night and, being already associated with the graveyards, were in a position to escape detection. Students, however, still assisted in the procurement of a particularly desired subject. This was the day when splendid anatomic and pathologic museums were peculiarly prized, and any rare specimen was unlikely to remain long beneath the sod, if it ever got that deep. Giants appear to have had a peculiar fascination for the scientists of the period.

A giant, Corney Magrath, in spite of his stature and big frame, died of consumption in Dublin at the age of 23. Robinson, who was professor of anatomy at the University, was very anxious to acquire this rarity, and on the morning of the giant's demise, he thus addressed his class:

> Gentlemen, I have been told that some of you in your zeal have contemplated carrying off the body. I most earnestly beg you not to think of such a thing: but if you should be so carried away with your desire for knowledge that thus against my expressed wish you persist in doing so, I would have you to remember that if you take only the body, there is no law whereby you can be touched, but if you take so much as a rag or a stocking with it, it is a hanging matter.

While the giant was being "waked" in his lodging over a public house, four students in disguise joined the party and ordered up unlimited supplies of whisky, to which they added laudanum; so when those who should have "waked" were sound asleep, the students at a concerted signal were joined by a large reenforcement of their fellows, who carried a large door, on which impromptu bier they placed the body, covered it with their gowns and hastened away in triumph to Trinity.

The next morning, when the theft was discovered, the giant's friends indignantly applied to the provost for a restitution of the body, and Dr. Robinson was sent for. "My dear sir," he said to the provost, "such was the zeal of the young men that they commenced the dissection at once, and it is now far advanced." The provost accordingly compounded liberally with the friends. One of the students was in the square when Dr. Robinson came from the provost, and he observed the old gentleman stopping every now and then on his way to the anatomy room, chuckling to himself, "Divil a knife's in him yet!" The friends, however, were satisfied, and so Robinson was enabled to give a public demonstration on the body of the giant. . . .

In the raising of bodies, strategy and foresight many times had to supplement brute force, and men of intelligence often succeeded when the resurrectionists failed. Such is illustrated by the following incident, in which the distinguished Edinburgh surgeon,

Liston, joined forces with the infamous London resurrectionist, Ben Crouch.

A country lad, whose enormously enlarged head had attracted the attention of many physicians, was buried in an exposed cemetery on the shores of the Firth of Forth, and for weeks thereafter his grave was guarded at night by trustworthy watchers. The agents of the Edinburgh anatomists tried to secure what in the language of the schools was termed a "rare osteological specimen," but all bribes were spurned. After many weeks the contest between the watchers and the resurrectionists was abandoned by the latter, when one evening at dusk, two well dressed gentlemen, smoking their cigars, drove up to the chief hostelry of the village and requested that their horse be taken care of for an hour. The whip-hand gentleman told the stable-boy that he expected a livery servant to bring a parcel for him, which could be put in the box part of their dog-cart. In a short time a man in smart livery came to the stable-yard, deposited a bag under the seat and walked off. Presently, the two gentlemen returned to the inn, ordered out their trap and briskly trotted off. While the unknown gentlemen were trotting home at full speed, the night-watchers of the grave of the hydrocephalic body (it was thought unnecessary to watch graves during the day) were approaching their posts of duty. To their astonishment, they found the grave disturbed, the coffin broken and the body gone. The gentlemen in the dog-cart had, by availing themselves of the twilight, been able to do in thirty minutes a piece of work that had baffled for weeks the most experienced resurrectionists of Scotland. The skeleton now reposes as no. 3,489 in one of England's great anatomic collections, bearing the name of Liston, its donor. . . .

This business, as all others, followed the economic law of supply and demand. The demand for bodies being small, only a few men engaged in the traffic, and the price was less than £2. However, in the course of a few years the students and teachers of anatomy in London multiplied sixfold, so that bodies were at a premium, many of them bringing £14 or more. This naturally attracted many more to the business, and the recruits were from the worst of the populace. The worst and cleverest of the lot soon organized themselves into gangs, and at the beginning of the nineteenth century they operated as unrecognized guilds in London, Edinburgh, Glasgow and Dublin. They invaded every burial-field and graveyard in these metropolises, often going far off into the country when fresh bodies were scarce or were difficult to obtain. They became bolder and bolder in their methods, eventually culminating in murder.

Sir Astley Cooper, the greatest and most active London surgeon of the first quarter of the nineteenth century, was an anatomic enthusiast. Cooper, in 1784, at the age of 16, was apprenticed to Mr. Henry Cline, a surgeon and teacher of anatomy at St. Thomas' Hospital. A fellow student of these days told: "Mr. Cline's class now became so large as to crowd and make the dissecting-room uncomfortable. Astley disliked this, since it hurried our work, and he suggested that we should remove our subjects to Mr. Cline's house, with whom we also resided. The room Astley and I occupied was in the front of the house, with only one window in it. Here we carried on our dissections without interruption for the remainder of the winter." This zeal for dissection remained with Sir Astley (he was knighted because he successfully removed a wen from the scalp of George II) throughout his life, and even after he became the great surgeon of Guy's Hospital he continued daily to dissect at his home. Since most of his span of work coincided exactly with the peak of the resurrection movement (1800 to 1832) he was one of the best authorities on the subject. He, of course, had to deal with the professional resurrectionists and got to know them intimately. He said of them: "They are the lowest dregs of degradation. I do not know that I can describe them better; there is no crime they would not commit, and, as to myself, if they should imagine that I would make a good subject, they really would not have the smallest scruple, if they could do the thing undiscovered, to make a subject of me."

In order that medical teaching should not be wiped out in England, the police were forced to connive with the resurrectionists. . . .

This policy of connivance with the resurrectionists was authorized by the heads of the government, Canning and Peel. This does not mean that the "sack-'em-ups" went about their work unmolested, for they were frequently apprehended by some of the citizenry, and in such a case the hurriedly summoned constables had to arrest them, as much to protect them from the mob as for their punishment. Mobs were easily aroused at even the suspicion of body-snatching.

In Edinburgh, a coach was observed driving along. It contained an empty coffin and two men. The people, suspecting—incorrectly, however—that it was intended to convey a stolen body taken from some churchyard, seized the coach. It was with difficulty that the constables protected the men; the coach they had no power to save. The horses were removed, and with men taking their places in the shafts the coach and coffin were trundled a mile and a half through the streets and dropped over a cliff and smashed. The people, following it to the bottom, kindled the fragments.

In Philadelphia, in 1765, a mob attacked the house of Dr. Shippen, later one of the founders of the medical school of the University of Pennsylvania, because they had been excited by the report that the church burial-ground had been despoiled to furnish material for his private class in anatomy.

The most famous doctors' riot in this country was in New York in 1788. On Sunday, April 13, a number of boys who were playing in the rear of a hospital, noticed a leg which was imprudently hung out of a window to dry. They immediately informed some persons, and a mob soon collected and entered the hospital, and in its fury destroyed a number of anatomic preparations. One or two fresh subjects were also found, all of which were interred the same evening. Several young doctors narrowly escaped the fury of the people and would inevitably have suffered seriously, had not the mayor, the sheriff and some other persons interfered and rescued them by lodging them in the jail. The affair did not stop here.

The New York Packet of April 25 states:

"On the morning following, a number of people collected and were determined to search the houses of the suspected physicians. His Excellency the Governor, His Honor the Chancellor and His Worship the Mayor, went among them and endeavoured to dissuade them from committing unnecessary depredations. They addressed the people pathetically and promised them every satisfaction which the laws of the country could give. This had considerable effect. But in the afternoon the affair assumed a different aspect. A mob went to the gaol and demanded the doctors who were there imprisoned."

Mayor James Duane read the riot act, backed by a handful of militia, and a number of prominent citizens attempted to exert the weight of their dignity to prevent further disorder. John Jay and peppery old Baron Steuben came on the scene, but without a pacifying effect. The mob handled the distinguished citizens in an undignified manner, and poor Baron Steuben was knocked down. He lost his temper and, his military training getting the better of him, called out to the Mayor: "Fire, Duane, fire!" The militia fired, killing seven rioters and wounding many more. On Tuesday morning the militia of General Malcolm's brigade was ordered out for duty day and night, but happily the mob did not again collect, and the peace of the city was once more restored. . . .

When the night workers were caught with their goods, they were severely mauled by the lower classes, and only through great efforts by the police were they saved from the crowd and brought to the safekeeping of the watch-house. The next morning they were taken before the magistrate and committed for a hearing. If any of the party of resurrectionists had escaped, he soon brought information to the schools, or, if all were taken, a friend managed to inform the anatomists. If the men arrested were disliked and not members of one of the regular gangs, they had to care for themselves. However, there was an understanding between the schools and the regular gangs that if the men got into trouble, the teachers would do all they could to get them free at the police examination, and if they were committed, the schools would have to furnish the bail. In case of conviction and imprisonment for a few months, the schools had to support the families of the men, by putting the men on a small salary while they were doing servitude. An item from Sir Astley Cooper's account books reads:

1828		£	s.	d.
Jan. 29	Paid Mr.——, to pay Mr.——, half the expenses for bailing Vaughan from Yarmouth, and going down	14	7	0
May 6	Paid Vaughan's wife	0	6	0
May 29	Ditto Vaughan, for 26 weeks' confinement, at 10s per wk.	13	0	0

In England, the teachers were at the mercy of completely unscrupulous rascals. At the commencement of a new session at the hospitals, when each professor was fully engaged about his particular department and everything augured favorably for a successful academic year, Crouch or Murphy, who were at the head of the resurrectionists of their respective periods in London, were seen flitting about the dissecting room, bowing complacently to the lecturers and either by a proffered smile inviting confidence or perhaps merely by silence leading the anatomic teacher to believe that his school was to be the chosen scene of his traffic during the coming winter. Each was shy in commencing conversation on the matters which brought them together; and, indeed, it generally happened that the topic was broached between the resurrectionist and the superintendent of the dissecting room.

At these meetings, some such dialogue as the following usually occurred:

Well, Mr. Smith, what does Sir Astley mean to stand this season?

Oh, I don't know, Murphy—whatever's fair. What will you take this morning?

Nothing, I thank you, Mr. Smith, but I don't mean to work this season without I get 10 guineas a subject.

Oh, indeed! Well, we don't mean to give more than 8!

Then you may go and tell Sir Astley that he may raise his own subjects; for not one will he get from us.

And so for three weeks or a month, frequently, all conferences with Murphy would end. In the interim, perhaps, some new men would be employed, but it generally happened that their efforts were crushed at the beginning, they being detected by police through information from the old resurrectionists, bribed off or in some other manner hindered from the prosecution of their endeavors. This having failed, Murphy would come again and say, "Come, you can't get on without us—give us £50 down and 9 guineas a body, and we will work for your school and no other." This arrangement was often acceded to, although usually without the slightest expectation that the promise of exclusiveness in the supply would be kept a week after it was made. . . .

BODIES BOUGHT AND SOLD BEFORE BURIAL

The modus operandi of the resurrectionists is interesting. The great bulk of the bodies were exhumed, but a considerable number were obtained before they were even buried. These, of course, were fresher and brought an excellent price. The bodies of those who had met with violent deaths were occasionally stolen, either before or after the coroner's inquest had taken place. The following was the plan pursued on one occasion of this sort:

Patrick, a well known resurrectionist, was strolling in the neighborhood of Sydenham when he heard that the body of a female had been found in the canal and taken to a public house on the preceding evening. Ever alive to business, he at once went to the inn, ordered some beer and soon contrived to enter into conversation with the potboy. From him he learned that the body in the stable was suspected to be that of a pauper who had escaped from the Woolwich workhouse and seemed to be without friends to claim it for burial. He also discovered that his informant, on a previous occasion, had been employed for two nights in watching a body placed there under similar circumstances but had been subsequently so ill repaid by the parish officer for his trouble that he had determined not to sit up with another again. This was sufficient for Patrick. Carefully examining the size and form of the keyhole of the stable door, he left and went on his way to London.

At a late hour on the same evening Patrick returned to Sydenham with a companion, and after prowling about for an hour and a half, proceeded to see whether any of the keys he had brought with him would unlock the door of the stable, which was so placed as to be easily gotten at from the road. To their delight, the first key opened it, and their operations within the stable were soon concluded. Having obtained the prize, they turned down a narrow lane and were soon far away from Sydenham, so that they succeeded in depositing the subject at its destination in London before daybreak. The next afternoon, Patrick was sitting in a room at the Elephant and Castle Inn when a coachman with whom he was slightly acquainted came in and commenced to give him an account of a tremendous disturbance which had occurred that morning at Sydenham, telling him that a coroner's jury had met to act on a corpse, but on going into the stable to inspect it, they had found that the body had disappeared in the course of the night.

The following case is an example of the extraordinary methods now and then adopted by the resurrectionists: An intimate friend of Patrick's was employed in the service of a gentleman whose residence was at a short distance from London. One day this man called on Patrick, in company with a fellow servant and informed him that his master was dead and that he thought something in the way of business might be done with the body, as it was lying in a back parlor, the windows of which opened on to a large lawn. Patrick made several inquiries and, having ascertained the funeral was to take place on the following Sunday, said, in conclusion: "The coffin then will most probably be screwed down on Saturday; if it is, let me know. I will have nothing to do with it until that part of the work is done."

Matters occurred as Patrick anticipated; accordingly, on Saturday night he entered at the back of the premises, and, being admitted to the parlor by the servant, commenced his operations. Unassisted by any light, he drew out all the screws, took off the lid and, having formed an estimate as accurate as the circumstances would allow of the weight of the body, removed it into a box which he had brought with him for the purpose of containing it. Next he placed in the coffin a quantity of earth which the servant had procured from the garden corresponding to the weight of the corpse. The lid was then replaced and was carefully screwed down, the pall was thrown over the coffin, and the box containing the body was passed out of the window to Patrick, who hid it in a toolhouse at some distance from the dwelling. He allowed it to remain in the shed until the morning of the following Monday, when it was removed to one of the private anatomic schools. For this subject Patrick received 15 guineas. Further, being anxious to observe that all went off without interruption, he attended the funeral, which took place in a church adjoining the house. He probably could not help smiling at the allusions from the pulpit to the departed brother reposing so peacefully in the coffin before the altar.

The resurrectionists were always on the alert for a dying person who was friendless. They would know all about his history by the time the dying one was gathered to his fathers, and if possible would personify the person of whom the deceased had spoken in his last moments. Remarkable were the expedients resorted to by these false claimants, and equally remarkable was their success. In Edinburgh, a rascal by the name of Andrew Lees, or Merry-Lees, was the leading spirit in this type of resurrecting. "Of gigantic height, he was thin and gaunt, even to ridiculousness, with a long pale face. His shabby, cast-off clothes no doubt made for some tall person of proportionate girth, hung upon his sharp joints, more as if they had been placed there to dry than to clothe and keep warm." The muscles of his face were exceedingly pliable to any emotional need—tragedy, comedy or farce. When assuming the character of mourner his appearance was exceedingly dismal; his pale face with dropped jaw, set off by the dress of grief and odd manner, far surpassed any theatrical get-up. His approach to the house of death was that of a stranger from the country timidly inquiring for a certain house, on entering which his bleared eyes became suffused with tears. After dwelling on the virtues of his "dear relative," he would at length intimate that he wished to convey the "remains" to the family burial-place in the country and that he and some friends would return with a cart and coffin towards evening. His "friends," all in the same business, were, first, Spune, as he was called, a little man who looked as demure and resigned as a Methodist preacher, he was so saintly. Spune always kept his own counsel, performing his duties in a staid and dignified manner. Mowatt, the second of the group, was a former plasterer. The third, the mock minister or clergyman, was personified by a vagabond who called himself Howard, in the hope of hiding his iniquity under a noble English name. Dressed in a black suit, too seedy for even an impecunious curate, and with a white choker, the "praying Howard" officiated à la mode, improving the occasion by calling on those around the bier to reflect on the uncertainty of life and the need of spiritual regeneration, for man is but a vain shadow. The group of mourners having played their part, the funeral cortège moved toward the suburbs. As soon as night came on, the four remounted the cart and returned to Edinburgh, losing no time in transferring the body to the dissecting room. With cash in hand, they made a night of it. Merry-Lees drank sixteen large glasses of raw whisky daily, and on unusual occasions he was equal to as many pints. These men often employed female accomplices to aid in the deception of the officials of hospitals and other public institutions. In addition, they are believed to have made a great number of purchases in the lower parts of Edinburgh, for not a few drunken, shiftless creatures were willing to sell the bodies of their deceased relatives for a small sum, an arrangement often being made before the soul and body had parted company.

Among other contrivances, the resurrectionists formed partnerships with the lower class of undertaker with whose help they would substitute clay, wood or stone in the coffin in place of the mourned body.

EXHUMATION

As I have pointed out, one of the illegal sources of bodies for dissection was the purchase or theft of them before interment. This was an uncommon method. The commonest method was exhumation. More than 9 of every 10 cadavers seen in the dissecting rooms of Great Britain were "raised" from the grave. The term generally applied to the whole movement, "resurrecting," refers to this method.

The principal sources of supply were the churchyards, the cheap private cemeteries and the public burial-fields of London, Edinburgh, Dublin and Glasgow. When the demand for subjects was still not great, the public burial-fields sufficed. Particularly in Dublin, during the early days, the method of supply of bodies to the medical schools was very simple. Dublin was always remarkable for the number of its pauper inhabitants, since there was a constant influx to the city of the unemployed or vagrant poor from all parts of Ireland who sought work or, when possible, maintenance without work. As they lodged in the densely inhabited and filthy streets of the poorer districts, the death rate was disproportionately high. . . .

When the number of bodies from these potter's fields was no longer sufficient, private graves were despoiled. The sextons of the places robbed generally were in the pay of the resurrection men. They received a piece-work wage, getting so much per body raised, which of course was no small stimulus in maintaining their full cooperation. If the entrance to the cemetery was not too public, the bolt of the gate was left undrawn. The walls of many cemeteries offered a real barrier, since during this reign of terror their tops were lined with broken glass, spikes and loose stones. If the entrance was too public for safety, it was not uncommon to engage a house overlooking the burial place, through which the business could be carried on without suspicion. Sometimes the churchyards a little distance out in the country were used, but this happened only if the recent discovery of pilfered graves in the cities made work in them temporarily hazardous. The most important cause of such discoveries was the quarrels among the resurrection gangs. Certain gangs had a recognized monopoly on certain cemeteries, and if one gang invaded the domain of another, there would be wars of retaliation, with pulling up of coffins, which were then propped against the adjoining wall, and the scattering of grave-clothes, so that the cemetery of the rival gang was effectively "spoilt," which naturally created a great hubbub in the neighborhood. Such excitement would result in a fruitless investigation by the authorities, in lighting of the burial-ground with one or two useless oil lamps and in the establishment of a watchman, who within a few months became the resurrectionists' very humble servant and watched in their behalf. Discovery was occasionally caused by a timid new hand, who became frightened and dropped his burden on the street, so that he might better use his legs.

Business ethics in the trade was nonexistent. The gangs would do anything to spoil the success of their rivals. If a body were bought by one of the teachers from an outside source, the regular men would sometimes break into the dissecting room and cut the body in such a manner as to make it useless for anatomic study. If this could not be done, they would give information to the police that a stolen body was lying in a certain dissecting room. Joshua Brookes, the proprietor of the Great Marlborough Street School, was a victim in this way; a body for which he had paid 16 guineas was taken away from his school through information from such a source, and the police officer who conducted the affair was, as a reward for his efforts, presented with a silver staff purchased by public subscription. Brookes seems to have gotten on very badly with the resurrection men. At one time, because he refused to pay 5 guineas as a douceur at the beginning of the session, two putrid bodies, in a high state of decomposition, were dropped at night close to his school by the men whom he had thus offended. Two young ladies stumbled over the bodies and at once raised such a commotion that, had it not been for the prompt assistance of the police, Brookes would have fared badly at the hands of the mob which soon collected. . . .

An elaborate technic was evolved for carrying out the earthly resurrection. Special tools were required: sharp, curved spades on long handles, scoops on jointed shafts, grappling tongs and crowbars. It was essential that the body-snatchers leave no trace of their work behind to betray them. This was accomplished in two ways. In order to leave the mound untouched, 15 or 20 feet from the head or foot of the grave the "sack-'em-ups" would remove a square of turf 18 or 20 inches in diameter. They would carefully put this aside and then commence to dig. Most graves of the poor were of the same depth, and if the sepulcher was that of a person of importance, the depth of the grave could be estimated by the nature of the soil thrown up to form the mound. In a grave 5 feet deep, the top of the coffin is 4 feet beneath the surface. A rough, slanting tunnel 15 feet in length would therefore be constructed, so as to impinge exactly on the end of the coffin. The coffin being thus reached, the end would be wrenched off as it lay in the tunnel. Then the scalp or feet of the corpse were grasped, and the subject was withdrawn through the narrow aperture. Considerable force was required for this; a jerking movement is said to have been more effective than violent pulling. The tunnel was then refilled and the sod carefully replaced. The mourners, on revisiting the cemetery, would be content and unsuspecting on finding the mound undisturbed. The second method employed by the resurrectionists was to clear away the earth only at the upper third of the grave, taking care to leave the rest of the mound undisturbed. When a third of the coffin was exposed, they inserted a crowbar into the crevice between the end and the lid; in this way, they forced it open. The corpse was removed in the same manner as before. Occasionally, particularly during an epidemic, 3 or 4 coffins would be placed in the same grave. Under such conditions, it was necessary to dig up the whole grave and remove the coffins in succession. The care with which the grave was restored to its status quo ante was the chief source of the resurrectionists' protection, and it was this which largely differentiated the successful from the unsuccessful body-snatcher. Anxious relatives frequently placed a bit of a stick, an oyster shell, a stone or a planted flower at a certain position on the mound, so that if it was moved, they would then know that the grave had been despoiled. The practiced eye of an accomplished resurrectionist noted these markers at once, even in the dark, and they were restored so perfectly to their former position as to deceive the most anxious visitor. The work of the resurrectionist combined most remarkably the necessity for great physical strength, speed of work and extreme care. Speed was second only to care as a protective agent; naturally, the sooner the workers were through, the less chance there was for detection. The job in a shallow grave with loose, soft earth could be done in fifteen minutes; with firmer soil and a deeper grave, it took about an hour. The technic of resurrection was kept a secret by the regulars, of whom there were only ten in London in 1828, in order that their virtual monopoly might not be disturbed by the intru-

sion of new men. At the same time, there were also two hundred
men in London who did resurrecting occasionally as a part time
vocation. Only after body-snatching ceased as a career did all
this technical information come to light.

Ben Crouch, the leader of a gang of four extremely capable
London resurrectionists, in testifying before a committe of parliament in 1828, stated that 23 bodies in four nights was the greatest
number he ever obtained. He added: "When I go to work, I like
to get those of poor people buried from the workhouses; because
instead of working for one subject, you may get three or four,
since they bury several in one grave. I do not think, during the
time I worked for the schools, I got a half dozen of the wealthier
people." Joseph Napier, the writer of "The Diary of a Resurrectionist," was a prominent member of a gang in London in 1810.
His memoranda for the year 1811-1812 are interesting:

To the London schools.......... 305 adults   44 smalls
Exported to Edinburgh......... 37 adults
Bodies unused.................. 18 adults
                             _____
Totals .... 360 adults   44 smalls

A "small" was a body under 3 feet in length; these were sold at
so much per inch and were generally classified as "large small,"
"small" and "foetus." . . .

As soon as the body was raised, it was crammed into an ordinary
sack (thus the name "sack-'em-ups") or an orange basket and laid
aside until as many graves as convenient were opened. They were
then carried by hackney-coach or spring cart into the metropolis
and delivered to the schools the same night, where they were immediately consigned to a cold, damp cellar. On the following or
sometimes on the second morning, the body was placed on the
table of the dissecting rooms. . . .

If a discovery had lately been made and the public newspapers were rife with the description of some scene resulting from
detection, these depredators were afraid to carry on their work in
the ordinary way; then the students used to receive the bodies
at their own houses and ultimately convey them in a hackney-
coach to the dissecting rooms. Though every precaution was
usually adopted, the coachman on these occasions generally became fully aware of the nature of his load and often availed himself of this knowledge to exact a larger remuneration for his

services than he otherwise could claim. An awkward predicament occasionally resulted from the means adopted by the coachman to insure the payment of his exorbitant demands under these circumstances. A pupil who was conveying a body by coach to his hospital from another and better supplied school was astonished on suddenly finding himself in front of the Bow Street police office. The coachman, tapping at the front window, said to his frightened employer within, "Sir, my fare to Webb Street is a guinea, unless you wish to be put down here." The reply, without hesitation, was, "Quite right, my man, drive on." . . .

An interesting and profitable by-product of resurrection was traffic in teeth. Porcelain teeth, though invented in 1776, were not used much until after the first quarter of the nineteenth century. It was common usage to replace extracted teeth with plates and bridges of healthy teeth extracted from corpses. Since the science of filling teeth was crude and inefficient, there was a far greater demand for false teeth than there is now. When the resurrectionists came on a corpse which was too putrid for the dissecting room, they extracted the teeth before reinterring it. In London, there were some paved burial-grounds with subterranean vaults. The resurrectionists, through some ruse, occasionally gained access to them. On such an occasion, Murphy extracted enough teeth in a few hours to net him £60.

METHODS EMPLOYED TO PREVENT
BODY-SNATCHING

Many methods were employed to circumvent the body-snatchers. I have already mentioned the presence of watchers, of grave-markers, of glass, spikes and loose stones on high cemetery walls and of barred gates. These were all futile when opposed by experienced resurrectionists. Spring guns were often set in various directions in the churchyards, but these never answered the purpose for which they were intended. If a resurrectionist proposed to work where these instruments were used and when he was not intimate with the grave-diggers or watchman, he sent women in the course of the day into the grounds, generally at a time when there was a funeral, to note the position of the pegs to which the wires were attached. Having obtained this information, the first object of the party at night would be to feel for one of these; having found it, they carefully followed the wire until they came to the gun, which was then temporarily removed while the grave was opened and was carefully replaced when the grave had been refilled.

However, there were some effectual safeguards, of which only the wealthy could avail themselves. In some burial-grounds, solid stone houses were built in which the bodies were kept for about three weeks (except in winter, when they were kept longer) until they had become putrid and soft and were therefore unfit for dissection. Such a' house is still standing in the burial-ground at Crail. Mort-safes, or strong iron guards, were placed over newly made graves for protection; some of these can be seen at present in the Greyfriars Churchyard, Edinburgh. They resemble strong iron cages, firmly set in a stone base. The time necessary to erect such a contrivance limited its usefulness. The usual wooden coffin was occasionally replaced by an iron one. The latter was usually an insuperable obstacle to the resurrectionists, for although the lids could be readily broken to pieces by a sledge-hammer, the noise which necessarily attended the operation was a sufficient preventive. . . .

MURDER FOR BODIES

The third method of procuring anatomic material was by murder. Considering the persons who supplied the schools with bodies, it is not startling that they occasionally resorted to murder. The first detected crime of this sort occurred in Edinburgh in 1752, and was described in *Scots Magazine*.

Two women, Helen Torrence and Jean Waldie, who were nurse-maids, promised some doctors' apprentices that they would supply them with a subject. They schemed to do so by pretending to sit up at the death-watch of a child, intending after the coffin was made fast to slip something else into the coffin and secure the body. However, they were disappointed in this, for the parents refused to allow them to watch. They were so anxious to keep their promise with the students and then to claim their reward that they decided to murder the child of John Dallas, a chairman in Edinburgh. While the child, a boy of 8 or 9, was alone in the house, they seized him, took him to their own home and there smothered him. Torrence carried the body in her apron to the room of one of the surgeons. The woman were offered 2 shillings in part payment, but they demurred; however, the bargain was closed with an extra tenpence with which to buy a drachm. The facts at length came to light, and they were both hanged for their cruel crime.

This single murder by Torrence and Waldie was soon forgotten. In 1828, Burke and Hare were occupied in a series of murders which have no parallel in medical history, in the number, the ingenuity displayed or the effect which they created.

Burke and Hare were led into murdering as an occupation by the following almost accidental occurrence: Burke and his mistress, Helen McDougal, and Hare and his wife lived together in Edinburgh, where Hare ran a vagrants' boarding-house. An old pensioner named Donald, a harmless, useless old man who was never able to put aside anything for old age, boarded with Hare. He died owing Hare £4, and Hare decided to get this back by selling the body. The parish authorities sent a coffin to the house, and the body was put in it, but Hare and Burke, while left alone, ripped up the lid of the coffin, took out the body, hiding it on the bed and replaced it with Tanner's bark, of which there was much in the yard. They sold the body to Dr. Knox's assistants. The fee they received was £7 10s. This was easy money, and being men of criminal instincts, not mere weaklings led astray, they decided to take up murder as a business, because the wage was high and the labor light.

Their method of murder may be illustrated by their first, that of Abigail Simpson. She was a drunken old hag, who lived on the outskirts of Edinburgh. Hare saw her on the street, thought that she was a likely subject, accosted her, was met in a friendly spirit and took her to his home in Tanner's Court. Here she was plied with liquor, and the crew danced and sang and swore and drank still more. The next morning Abigail was very sick and cried to be taken home to her daughter. Instead, pretending kindness and friendliness, they gave her more whisky and porter, and she again became helplessly drunk. Now was the time. Hare placed his hand over her mouth and nose, and Burke laid himself across her chest. She made no resistance and in ten minutes was dead. As far as is known, this method of murder was original with the copartners, Burke and Hare. It suited their purpose remarkably, for the body of a person killed by smothering after he was rendered nonresistant by drink bore no mark of violence. In fact, even at autopsy, no specific lesion could be found. The men next lifted the body out of the bed, undressed it and bundled it up in a chest. One of the two men afterward informed Dr. Knox's

students that they had another subject for them, and it was arranged that a porter from Surgeons' Square should meet them
behind the castle in the evening. Burke and Hare carried the chest
to the meeting place, and from there the porter assisted them
with it to the rooms. Dr. Knox came in while they were there;
the body was by now cold and stiff. He approved of its freshness
but did not ask any questions. The murderers were paid £10 for
the afternoon's work. This, their first murder, was committed on
Feb. 12, 1828. By November 1, eight and a half months later,
when their business was abruptly closed by their detection, they
had murdered 15 more women, children and men. The same well
planned technic was used in each case. Each murder was a repetition of the one just described, so that I shall make special mention
only of those of Mary Patterson and Daft Jamie.

One of their earlier victims was Mary Patterson, a young
prostitute, who was well known on the streets of Edinburgh;
but the boldness of the murderers did not allow the possibility of
the identification of their subject to deter them. They plied the
girl with drink, as was their custom, and then smothered her.
Apparently without fear of detection, four hours after Mary
Patterson's death, her murderers laid her body in Dr. Knox's
dissecting room and were paid £8. By this time, the corpse was
cold, but not yet very rigid, and presented the appearance of
recent death. Two of the students thought they knew the girl,
and one of them told Burke that she was just like a girl he had
but recently seen in the Canongate. More than that, the girl's hair
was in curlpapers, so that the external appearances suggested that
the body was fresh and had not been buried. The purchasers asked
Burke where he had obtained the body, and he said he had bought
it from an old woman living near Canongate. But this was not all.
Mary Patterson, in life, was an exceedingly good-looking girl.
Her handsome figure and well shaped limbs so attracted the
attention of Dr. Knox that he preserved the body for three months
in alcohol and invited a painter to sketch from it. This tale of
Mary Patterson was thinly disguised by Robert Louis Stevenson
and formed an important part of his story, The Body Snatchers.
At no time, however, did any of the medical men who dealt
with Burke and Hare suspect them of murder; the absence of
external wounds quieted any thoughts that they may have had.

The murder of James Wilson, called Daft Jamie, was even
bolder than that of Mary Patterson. He was a wandering imbecile,

in the psychiatric terminology of 1828, a natural. Daft Jamie
had a kind heart and was a general favorite. Despite the fact that
he was 19 years old, he would never fight to defend himself; a
common sight in Edinburgh was Daft Jamie in full flight before
a group of attackers but half his age and size. He was a queer
half-wit with a statistical turn of mind. He could tell how many
lamps there were in the city and how many days in each month.
He was also a specialist in little conundrums, among his stock
and trade being the following: "In what month of the year do the
ladies talk least?" "The month of February, because there wiz
least days in it!" he would reply. He would ask any one he met:
"Why is a jailer like a musician?" "Because he must take care of
his key." He had left his mother's home eight years before, and
since then had eked out an existence in holes and corners through
the town's pity. He was fond of his drachm, but rarely had
enough coppers to get drunk. He was well known to some of the
medical students, and would talk readily to them, even offering
them a pinch of his "sneeshing mill." This article was a curiosity,
and along with it he carried a brass snuff spoon, in which there
were seven holes; the middle hole he kept for Sunday, and the
others around it for the days of the week.

Jamie was suspicious of no one past boyhood, so one day when
Mrs. Hare accosted him on the street and began to talk to him,
he willingly accepted her invitation to go to her house. When they
arrived, she offered him drink. He refused at first, but finally
drank to drunkenness, and Burke and Hare, who had meanwhile
been summoned, smothered him, not, however, without a long,
hard struggle, for he was strong and not completely under the
influence of the alcohol. His body was then conveyed to Dr.
Knox's rooms, and the firm of Burke and Hare was richer by
£10. No questions were asked by those who received the body,
though it is likely that some of the students recognized it. The
report of the "natural's" disappearance spread rapidly through
the town. The mysterious fate of Daft Jamie took a remarkable
hold on the public mind. It was the talk all over the country,
and when the mystery was solved the effect of this murder far
outweighed all the other crimes put together. The hawkers and
peddlers of the time sold coarsely printed pamphlets containing
biographies of Daft Jamie to which, in some cases, were added the
sympathetic sentiments of crude poets. One leaflet begins with:

The ruffian dogs—the hellish pair—
The villain Burke—the meagre Hare. . . .

The last of their murders, the one which led to their detection, was that of Mary Docherty, an old Irishwoman who had come to Edinburgh in search of her son. Burke, ever on the lookout for "suitable subjects," met the old woman in a grocery store near his home. After inquiry had revealed that her name was Docherty, Burke immediately claimed that his mother's name had been Docherty, which of course it had not, and he at once claimed Irish clanship with the poor unfortunate. This soon won the old woman's good-will, which was reenforced with several "wee" glasses. She then accompanied Burke to his house, where he and Hare "burked" her, by smothering. When they finished their work, they threw the naked body under the bed until they found a tea-crate in which to cram it. In the meantime the body was only partially covered with straw. Burke invited a couple for breakfast who had met the late Mrs. Docherty the previous evening during the round of drunken merrymaking which always preceded one of the murders. The newcomers, named Gray, inquired for the old lady, and Mrs. Hare explained her departure in an evasive fashion. Of course, she knew of her death, for the two women (Helen McDougal and Mrs. Hare) always acted as accomplices until the act of murder was begun. They then discreetly withdrew into the hallway until the victim was lifeless. Breakfast was now served in the room with the corpse. During the meal Burke behaved in a very curious manner, for he held the whisky bottle in his hand, and threw some of the contents under the bed, on the bed and up to the roof of the apartment, at times putting a little on his breast and occasionally taking a sip. In addition, when Mrs. Gray wanted to delve under the bed for some potatoes, which shared this location with the corpse, Burke insisted on doing it himself. This, combined with Burke's queer behavior and Mrs. Hare's evasive answer concerning the whereabouts of the old woman, made Mrs. Gray suspicious. As soon as the others left the room, she lifted the straw, and the first thing she caught hold of was the arm of a dead woman. Her husband came over, and together they identified the corpse as that of the old woman. They immediately left the house, and in a short time the affair was put in the hands of the police. Justice moved speedily. The four principals were incarcerated and indicted. The state had only a dubious case, one based purely on circumstantial evidence, which the excellent talent furnished the prisoners by the Court might have explained away. Therefore, in order to be certain of one conviction, the state offered immunity to the least guilty pair, the two Hares, on the condition that they would turn state's evidence. This they did. Burke was found guilty, but the woman McDougal was freed, since the jury found the libel against her not proved. In passing sentence on Burke, the Lord Chief Justice said:

> In regard to your case, the only doubt that has crossed my mind is whether your body should not be exhibited in chains, in order to deter others from like crimes in the future. But taking into consideration that the public eye would be offended with so dismal an exhibition, I am disposed to agree that your sentence shall be execution in the usual way, but accompanied with the attendant of the punishment of the crime of murder—that your body should be publicly dissected and anatomized. And I trust that, if it is ever customary to preserve skeletons, yours will be preserved in order that posterity may keep in remembrance your atrocious crimes.

Burke made a full written confession before his death. This and the court proceedings were the basis of much of the material on Burke and Hare.

The execution was held in a public square, and was witnessed by twenty-five thousand people. As the trap was sprung, the multitude set up a fearful yell. Dr. Munro, in the afternoon of the day the body was removed to the college, gave a lecture on it, and for this purpose, the upper part of the head was sawed off and the brain exposed. The lecture was popular, in fact so popular that the members of the regular class for which it was intended had to be admitted by ticket. After the reserved seats were thus occupied, students from the other medical classes and faculties completely filled the amphitheater. During the demonstration, a large number of the populace assembled, demanding admission. It was feared that if their request were not granted, the people would tear down the building and seize the partially dissected body. Therefore, on the following day the body of Burke was publicly exhibited. It was placed naked on a black marble table in the anatomic theater. The doors of the anatomy building were thrown open at 10 in the morning, and from that hour until dusk the crowd streamed through the narrow passage in front of the body at the rate of sixty a minute, totalling about twenty-five thousand for the day. . . .

The last case in England of murder to obtain bodies for the dissecting room was in 1831. It was this case, added to that of Burke and Hare, three years before, which finally brought about the passage of the Anatomy Act, which successfully put an end to these foul practices.

On Nov. 5, 1831, two men named Bishop and May called at the dissecting room at King's College, and asked Hill, the porter, if he "wanted anything." On being interrogated as to what they had to dispose of, May replied, "A boy of fourteen." For this body they asked 12 guineas, but ultimately agreed to bring it in for 9. They went off and returned in the afternoon with another man named Williams and the body in a hamper. The appearance of the subject excited Hill's suspicion of foul play, and he at once communicated with Mr. Partridge, the demonstrator in anatomy. A further examination of the body by Mr. Partridge confirmed the porter's suspicions. To delay the men, so that the police might be communicated with, Mr. Partridge produced a £50 note and said that he could not pay until he had changed it. Soon after, police officers appeared on the scene, and the men were given into custody. The body was proved to be that of an Italian boy, named Carlo Ferrari, who obtained his living by showing white mice. The boy's teeth had been extracted, and it was proved that they had been sold by one of the prisoners to Mr. Mills, a dentist, for 12 shillings. The jury found all three prisoners guilty, and they were sentenced to death.

From the subsequent confessions of Bishop and Williams, it was shown that they had enticed the boy to their dwelling in Nova Scotia Gardens; there they drugged him with opium and then let his body into a well, where they kept it until he was suffocated. Bishop and Williams confessed, also, to the murder of a woman named Fanny Pigburn and of a boy, whose name was supposed to be Cunningham. Both of the bodies they sold for dissection.

LEGISLATION TO PROVIDE SUFFICIENT NUMBER OF CADAVERS

As early as 1810 an anatomic society was formed to impress on the government the necessity for an alteration in the law, and among its members were John Abernethy, Charles Bell, Everard

Home, Benjamin Brodie and Astley Cooper. As a result of the efforts of this group, of those of a member of parliament, Henry Warburton, and of those of Thomas Wakley, editor and founder of the *Lancet*, a select committee of parliament was appointed in 1828 to inquire into the study of anatomy as practiced in the United Kingdom and into the best method of obtaining bodies for dissection. The case of Burke and Hare, which occurred shortly after the committee completed its deliberations, caused the chairman, Mr. Warburton, to introduce the anatomy bill into the House of Commons.

The Anatomy Act of 1832 made body-snatching in the British Isles unnecessary, and the resurrectionists immediately ceased to exist.

1935

Part 4

Into Modern Times

THE OLD WORLD ...

Into Modern Times

A. THE OLD WORLD . . .

SYNOPSIS

THE *first selection in our section entitled "Into Modern Times"
describes, in the author's own words, observations made in the
year 1675. It was to be nearly two centuries before the importance
to medicine of these observations, entitled "Very Small Living
Creatures" by Anton van Leeuwenhoek, was to be realized and
the irascible and secretive Dutch burgher's discovery of a new
world of microscopic life was to lead to a modern theory of disease. The work of Vesalius and Harvey built the foundation for
the study of normal body mechanics. That of van Leeuwenhoek,
while only the first step in a progression did, nevertheless, offer
a key which, once properly appreciated, was to result in an understanding of morbid human functioning. The study of this world
of the infinitely small resulted, in the nineteenth century, in the
work of some of the most important men in medicine; men whose
achievements occupy the larger part of this section. Today,
probably most of medical research is similarly concerned.*

*In view of much of the evidence, it may seem surprising that
the connection between microbes and disease required so long to
become apparent. In "On the Mode of Communication of Cholera," John Snow proved that the water in the Broad Street pump
was responsible for a contagion that resulted in cholera for those
who drank it. He had no inkling of the true nature of that contagion although he was convinced that sanitary measures could put
a stop to it. Contamination was the cause of the fantastic death*

*rate from puerperal fever in lying-in hospitals all over the world.
It existed in the cadaveric particles which clung to the hands of
doctors after they had performed dissection. Ignaz Semmelweis,
one of the martyrs of medicine, proved this fact at the lying-in
hospital at Vienna. He showed, too, how cleansing the hands
would end the contagion. His discovery, which was ridiculed and
disbelieved, is the theme of one of the most dramatic selections in
the book, "The Cry and the Covenant" by Morton Thompson.
Semmelweis's priceless contribution to the well-being of mankind
earned for him only official hatred and injustice. He abandoned
one position for another, hoping to obtain recognition. Eventually
he became mentally affected, and died from blood poisoning of
the finger, which he himself had proved identical with puerperal
fever and had probably incurred during one of his last operations.*

*Parenthetically, it should be stated that in his paper "The Con-
tagiousness of Puerperal Fever," published in 1834, Oliver Wendell Holmes had perceived the nature of the physician's role in
carrying childbirth fever from one patient to another, a fact
which had also been observed by others. Holmes's study of the
problem, however, was purely theoretical. It involved him in
controversy but had little effect on the methods of his fellow
physicians. In fact his paper was all but forgotten until after the
work of Semmelweis became known.*

*Parenthetically also, before continuing with a discussion of the
germ theory which is the main theme of the present section, we
present another classic of medical literature, the quiet but moving
account of an operation before either anesthesia or antisepsis: "Rab
and His Friends" by John Brown. The selection owes its position
here to the fact that its author, a well-known doctor of his day,
was first apprenticed to the surgeon John Syme, whose daughter
married Joseph Lister, founder of antisepsis. It has indeed been
suggested that a reading of "Rab" may have helped turn Lister's
mind toward the tragedy of surgical infection.*

*It was Louis Pasteur who, more than any other single individ-
ual, was to be the originator of the germ theory; but before him,
there were, as always in scientific research, many tentative steps
in the right direction. The cause of one of the bitterest controversies in the history of science, was the theory of spontaneous
generation. The problem was this: could animals originate from
sterile matter or must they in every case have ancestors like
themselves? As Pasteur pointed out, many writers of the seven-*

*teenth century had described the spontaneous generation of frogs
from marsh mud and eels in the water of rivers. If the doctrine
were not correct, inquired some investigators, how could maggots
arise in putrefying meat? To this the Italian Physician Francesco
Redi replied that they had been deposited in the meat by flies.
He covered his meat with gauze too fine for the flies' eggs to drop
through, and the maggots grew on the gauze. Later Réamue
pointed out that the worm had not been engendered by the
pollution in the apple but had on the contrary been responsible
for the pollution. These researches dealt with gross objects, and
with the rise of microscopic observation the idea of spontaneous
generation, this time of microbes, was revived, particularly by
Needham and Buffon. In 1765, Spallanzani refuted the arguments
of the generationists by pointing out flaws in the techniques used
in their experiments. He proved that the putrefaction in broth
would not occur if all the little animals in it were killed by
heating and no more were admitted from outside. And putrefaction, as Pasteur pointed out, could be likened to disease.*

*Pasteur first became interested in disease through the problem
of the cause of fermentation. The eminent chemist Leibig was
convinced that this represented a purely chemical change. Pasteur
was able to prove that specific ferments were caused by specific
organisms—that the souring of milk, for example, was caused by
lactic acid bacilli, and that without their presence, milk would
not sour. It was a simple step to the investigation of the souring
of wine and the deterioration of beer. Pasteur was convinced that
there were many specific kinds of microorganisms and that the
presence and reproduction of the wrong kinds was responsible for
the deterioration. His opponents replied that the living organisms were the result and not the cause of the process—that they
were spontaneously generated in fermentation. In a brilliant but
simple crucial experiment, Pasteur demolished them once and for
all, and the issue has not since been of scientific importance.*

*Meanwhile, in 1860, the English Quaker Joseph Lister had
become professor of surgery in the University of Glasgow and
was deeply concerned with the problem of infection in wounds.
The formation of pus and the appearance of blood poisoning were
a mystery, which made any operation, however trivial in itself, a
tragically dangerous venture. Lister knew that in the case of
broken bones where the skin had not been opened, infection did
not appear; while if the skin was broken, the opposite was usually*

the case. *Something in the air, he reasoned, was responsible. He knew also of the work of Semmelweis—the "something" could be killed by proper sterilization. The final results of his thinking came with Pasteur's studies of the diseases of wines—diseases which could be eliminated by the heating process known as "pasteurization." Perhaps the germs that carried the diseases in the wine were similar to the germs causing infection in wounds. The story of his successful experiments, which at a stroke eliminated most of the hazards of infection in operations and entitled him to the position of the greatest surgeon of all time, are described in his own words in, "On the Antiseptic Principle of the Practice of Surgery." Asepsis has replaced antisepsis; the air is no longer considered the important carrying agent that Lister believed; but his contribution remains among the greatest in surgery.*

In Germany too the new idea spread, and almost simultaneously the provincial physician Robert Koch developed the techniques of staining of bacilli, of incubation, pure culturing, etc., which are the foundations of the science of bacteriology. His first major contribution was in the study of the anthrax bacillus. In the little town of Wollstein in benighted Posen, divorced from the stimulus of contact with other researchers and with home made apparatus he had invented, Koch described the entire life history of anthrax and showed how it could exist under unfavorable circumstances for long periods in the form of spores. He originated a method of culturing it in the laboratory, outside the body of an infected animal. Koch was to go on to greater and greater triumphs, which perhaps reached their peak in his discovery that tuberculosis was not due to "bad blood" or "bad heredity," but to a specific organism, the tubercle bacillus. He offered his conclusions on March 24, 1882, in a paper which is reprinted here, "The Etiology of Tuberculosis." It is related that his audience greeted the ending of his oration with profound and utter silence. His opponent Virchow—one of the leaders in modern medicine, the founder of cellular pathology—who had attacked the idea of the specificity of tuberculosis, left the room without attempting a reply. Paul Ehrlich, who was to discover salvarsan and who was also present, wrote later, "That evening remains graven in my memory as the most majestic scientific event in which I have ever participated."[1] It is unfortunate that a later event seriously

[1] See "Robert Koch" by Laurason Brown, N. Y. Academy of Medicine lecture, September, 1932.

marred Koch's record. In 1890, Koch announced that in tuber-culin he had discovered a remedy for tuberculosis. The announce-ment caused almost hysterical rejoicing throughout the world, which was not borne out by subsequent experiment.

Koch's work on anthrax appeared in 1876. Pasteur, who at the time was not fully acquainted with this work, carried the study further in 1877. In 1870 he had shown how microbes were causing the diseases of silkworms and how these diseases could be eradi-cated, thus saving one of the most important industries of France. Now he obtained a pure culture of anthrax and, through a chance observation, made another notable contribution to medi-cine. In his investigation of chicken cholera, he had observed that old cultures which had been permitted to stand for several weeks, when given to chickens would sicken but not kill them. Moreover, such chickens were thus rendered immune and fresh active germs had no effect on them. He determined to use a similar tech-nique with anthrax. In an occasion as dramatic as that of Koch's oration on tuberculosis, Pasteur, in the sheepfolds of Chartres, inoculated fifty sheep with virulent anthrax culture, vaccinated half of them and with superb confidence predicted that the un-vaccinated sheep would all die while the vaccinated ones would all live. As the result of his experiment appeared, he was greeted with cheers—he had been proved completely correct.

Still Pasteur had not used his talents on human disease. But with the background he had established, he now approached one of the most dreadful of human maladies—hydrophobia, or rabies. His success was a direct outgrowth of what he had done before and is not perhaps his greatest scientific triumph. For human interest, however, it is unsurpassed and for that reason we have chosen "Louis Pasteur and the Conquest of Rabies" from the biography by his son-in-law, René Vallery-Radot.

As an interesting sidelight on Pasteur and his work, we present excerpts from his writings under the title "On Experimental Science." Pasteur is often accused of irascibility and even of brutality in his controversies with scientists who in his view failed to recognize the truth. His inherent generosity in the presence of true greatness is shown in "On Claude Bernard and His Work." It was Bernard's early ambition to be a playwright. Instead he became the founder of experimental medicine, which is the artificial production of disease by chemical and physical means. His chief discovery was that the liver has the power of

*converting sugar from food into a substance known as glycogen,
a form of fuel which can be utilized by the body. Hardly less
important were his work on the physiology of digestion, in which
he showed that the work of the stomach was only a preparatory
act; on how the "Vaso-Motor Mechanism" controls the blood
supply; and on the glands of internal secretion. His discoveries
were so numerous and so fundamental that he is usually considered the father of modern physiology.*

*While Pasteur and Koch were searching in their laboratories
for the causes of disease, another struggle, for adequate care of
the sick at the bedside and in the hospitals, was taking place. By
the end of the century the awful situation in the hospitals had
changed entirely, due largely to the efforts of a single woman.*

*The story of Florence Nightingale has been told many times
but never so vividly as in the recent biography by Cecil Woodham-Smith. Her account of the frightful conditions in English
hospitals in the mid-nineteenth century is almost unbelievable
today. "In 1845," she writes, "hospitals were places of degradation
and squalor. 'Hospital smell,' the result of dirt and lack of sanitation, was accepted as unavoidable and was commonly so overpowering that persons entering the wards for the first time were
seized with nausea . . . The patients came from slum tenements
. . . from hovels, from cellars where cholera lurked. Gin and brandy
were smuggled into the wards, and fearful scenes took place,
ending by half-dying creatures attacking each other in frenzy or
writhing in fits." When, therefore, in 1837, Florence Nightingale,
called like Joan of Arc to a service she could not at first define,
decided to enter the field of nursing, the horror of her prim Victorian family was understandable. Nurses were drunkards, nurses
were prostitutes—no respectable woman would think of entering
a hospital. Even Miss Nightingale confessed that the head of a
London hospital had told her that "she had never known a nurse
who was not drunken, and there was immoral conduct practiced
in the very wards." Charles Dickens' portrait of such a nurse in
"Martin Chuzzlewit" is famous, and "Sairey Gamp," described
in the selection which follows, a byword.*

*Yet Florence Nightingale persisted, giving her entire life to the
founding of the nursing profession—a movement which spread
to every part of the world. In the selection used here, Cecil
Woodham-Smith gives a dramatic account of the horrors Florence Nightingale encountered in the Crimea, of her difficulties*

*with lethargic British officialdom, and of her determined struggle
to make conditions bearable for the wounded.*

*In those years while Miss Nightingale was winning her fight
in the Crimea, a child was born in England who became a doctor,
who practiced in Africa during the Boer War and who also saw
the horrors of combat. He is remembered today, however, not
for his doctoring but for his creation of the greatest of fictional
detectives, Sherlock Holmes. A. Conan Doyle also wrote on a
variety of medical subjects, and as our final selection, we offer
his whimsical account of a young doctor's introduction to the
operating theatre, "His First Operation."*

Very Small Living Creatures

ANTON VAN LEEUWENHOEK

In the year 1675 I discovered very small living creatures in rain water, which had stood but few days in a new earthen pot glazed blue within. This invited me to view this water with great attention, especially those little animals appearing to me ten thousand times less than those represented by Monsieur Swammerdam, and by him called water fleas, or water lice, which may be perceived in the water with the naked eye.

The first sort I several times observed to consist of five, six, seven, or eight clear globules without being able to discern any film that held them together, or contained them. When these animalcula or living atoms moved, they put forth two little horns, continually moving. The space between these two horns was flat, though the rest of the body was roundish, sharpening a little toward the end, where they had a tail, near four times the length of the whole body, of the thickness, by my microscope, of a spider's web; at the end of which appeared a globule of the size of one of those which made up the body. These little creatures, if they chanced to light on the least filament or string, or other particle, were entangled therein, extending their body in a long round and endeavoring to disentangle their tail. Their motion of extension and contraction continued awhile; and I have seen several thousands of these poor little creatures, within the space of a grain of gross sand, lie fast clustered together in a few filaments.

I also discovered a second sort, of an oval figure; and I imagined their head to stand on a sharp end. These were a little longer than the former. The inferior part of their body is flat, furnished with several extremely thin feet, which moved very nimbly. The upper part of the body was round, and had within eight, ten, or twelve globules, where they were very clear. These little animals sometimes changed their figure into a perfect round, especially when they came to lie on a dry place. Their body was also very flexible; for as soon as they struck against the smallest fibre or string their body was bent in, which bending presently jerked out again. When I put any of them on a dry place I observed that, changing themselves into a round, their body was raised pyramidal-wise with an extant point in the middle; and having lain thus a little while, with a motion of their feet, they burst asunder, and the globules were presently diffused and dissipated, so that I could not discern the least thing of any film, in which the globules had doubtless been enclosed; and at this time of their bursting asunder I was able to discover more globules than when they were alive.

I observed a third sort of little animal that were twice as long as broad, and to my eye eight times smaller than the first. Yes, I thought I discerned little feet, whereby they moved very briskly, both in round and straight line.

There was a fourth sort, which were so small that I was not able to give them any figure at all. These were a thousand times smaller than the eye of a large louse. These exceeded all the former in celerity. I have often observed them to stand still as it were on a point, and then turn themselves about with that swiftness, as we see a top turn round, the circumference they made being no larger than that of a grain of small sand, and then extending themselves straight forward, and by and by lying in a bending posture. I discovered also several other sorts of animals; these were generally made up of such soft parts, as the former, that they burst asunder as soon as they came to want water.

May 26, it rained hard; the rain growing less, I caused some of that rain water running down from the housetop to be gathered in a clean glass, after it had been washed two or three times with water. And in this I observed some few very small living creatures, and seeing them, I thought they might have been produced in the leaded gutters in some water that had remained there before.

I perceived in pure water, after some days, more of those animals, as also some that were somewhat larger. And I imagined that many thousands of these little creatures do not equal an ordinary grain of sand in bulk; and comparing them with a cheese mite, which may be seen to move with the naked eye, I make the proportion of one of these small water creatures to a cheese mite to be like that of a bee to a horse; for the circumference of one of these little animals in water is not so large as the thickness of a hair in a cheese mite.

In another quantity of rain water, exposed for some days to the air, I observed some thousands of them in a drop of water, which were of the smallest sort that I had seen hitherto. And in some time after I observed, besides the animals already noted, a sort of creature that was eight times as large, of almost a round figure; and as those very small animalcula swam gently among each other, moving as gnats do in the air, so did these larger ones move far more swiftly, tumbling round as it were, and then making a sudden downfall.

In the waters of the river Maese I saw very small creatures of different kinds and colors, and so small that I could very hardly discern their figures; but the number of them was far less than those found in rain water. In the water of a very cold well in the autumn I discovered a very great number of living animals, very small, that were exceedingly clear, and a little larger than the smallest I ever saw. In sea water I observed at first a little blackish animal, looking as if it had been made up of two globules. This creature had a peculiar motion, resembling the skipping of a flea on white paper, so that it might very well be called a water flea; but it was far less than the eye of that little animal, which Dr. Swammerdam calls the water flea. I also discovered little creatures therein that were clear, of the same size with the former animal, but of an oval figure, having a serpentine motion. I further noticed a third sort, which were very slow in their motion; their body was of a mouse color, clear toward the oval point; and before the head and behind the body there stood out a sharp little point anglewise. This sort was a little larger. But there was yet a fourth somewhat longer than oval. Yet of all these sorts there were but a few of each. Some days after viewing this water I saw a hundred where before I had seen but one; but these were of another figure, and not only less, but they were also very clear, and of an oblong oval figure, only with this difference, that their heads ended sharper; and although they were a thousand times smaller than a small grain of sand, yet when they lay out of the water in a dry place they burst in pieces and spread into three or four very little globules, and into some aqueous matter, without any other parts appearing in them.

Having put about one third of an ounce of whole pepper in water, and it having lain about three weeks in the water, to which I had twice added some snow water, the other water being in great part exhaled, I discerned in it with great surprise an incredible number of little animals, of divers kinds, and among the rest, some that were three or four times as long as broad; but their whole thickness did not much exceed the hair of a louse. They had a very pretty motion, often tumbling about and sideways; and when the water was let to run off from them they turned round like a top; at first their body changed into an oval, and afterwards, when the circular motion ceased, they returned to their former length. The second sort of creatures discovered in this water were of a perfect oval figure, and they had no less pleasing or nimble a motion than the former; and these were in far greater numbers. There was a third sort, which exceeded the two former in number, and these had tails like those I had formerly observed in rain water. The fourth sort, which moved through the three former sorts, were incredibly small, so that I judged that if one hundred of them lay one by another they would not equal the length of a grain of coarse sand; and according to this estimate, one million of them could not equal the dimensions of a grain of such coarse sand. There was discovered a fifth sort, which had near the thickness of the former, but almost twice the length.

In snow water, which had been about three years in a glass bottle well stopped, I could discover no living creatures; and having poured some of it into a porcelain teacup, and put therein half an ounce of whole pepper, after some days I observed some animalcula, and those exceedingly small ones, whose body seemed to me twice as long as broad, but they moved very slowly, and often circularly. I observed also a vast multitude of oval-figured animalcula, to the number of eight thousand in a single drop.

Seventeenth Century

On the Mode of Communication of Cholera

JOHN SNOW

THE most terrible outbreak of cholera which ever occurred in this kingdom is probably that which took place in Broad Street, Golden Square, and the adjoining streets, a few weeks ago. Within two hundred and fifty yards of the spot where Cambridge Street joins Broad Street there were upwards of five hundred fatal attacks of cholera in ten days. The mortality in this limited area probably equals any that was ever caused in this country, even by the plague; and it was much more sudden, as the greater number of cases terminated in a few hours. The mortality would undoubtedly have been much greater had it not been for the flight of the population. Persons in furnished lodgings left first, then other lodgers went away, leaving their furniture to be sent for when they could meet with a place to put it in. Many houses were closed altogether, owing to the death of the proprietors; and in a great number of instances the tradesmen who remained had sent away their families; so that in less than six days from the commencement of the outbreak the most afflicted streets were deserted by more than three quarters of their inhabitants.

There were a few cases of cholera in the neighborhood of Broad Street, Golden Square, in the latter part of August; and the so-called outbreak, which commenced in the night between the thirty-first of August and the first of September, was, as in all similar instances, only a violent increase of the malady. As soon as I became acquainted with the situation and extent of this irruption of cholera I suspected some contamination of the water of the much-frequented street pump in Broad Street, near the end of Cambridge Street; but on examining the water, on the evening of the third of September, I found so little impurity in it of an organic nature that I hesitated to come to a conclusion. Further inquiry, however, showed me that there was no other circumstance or agent common to the circumscribed locality in which this sudden increase of cholera occurred, and not extending beyond it, except the water of the above-mentioned pump. I found, moreover, that the water varied, during the next two days, in the amount of organic impurity visible to the naked eye, on close inspection, in the form of small white, flocculent particles; and I concluded that, at the commencement of the outbreak, it might possibly have been still more impure. I requested permission, therefore, to take a list, at the General Register Office, of the deaths from cholera, registered during the week ending the second of September, in the subdistricts of Golden Square, Berwick Street, and St. Ann's, Soho, which was kindly granted. Eighty-nine deaths from cholera were registered during the week in the three subdistricts. Of these, only six occurred in the four first days of the week; four occurred on Thursday, the thirty-first of August; and the remaining seventy-nine on Friday and Saturday. I considered, therefore, that the outbreak commenced on the Thursday; and I made inquiry, in detail, respecting the eighty-three deaths registered as having taken place during the last three days of the week.

On proceeding to the spot, I found that nearly all the deaths had taken place within a short distance of the pump. There were only ten deaths in houses situated decidedly nearer to another street pump. In five of these cases the families of the deceased persons informed me that they always sent to the pump in Broad Street, as they preferred the water to that of the pump which was nearer. In three other cases the deceased were children who went to school near the pump in Broad Street. Two of them were known to drink the water; and the parents of the third think it probable that it did so. The other two deaths, beyond the district which this pump supplies, represent only the amount of mortality from cholera that was occurring before the irruption took place.

With regard to the deaths occurring in the locality belonging to the pump, there were sixty-one instances in which I was informed that the deceased persons used to drink the pump water from Broad Street, either constantly or occasionally. In six instances I could get no information, owing to the death or departure of everyone connected with the deceased individuals; and in six cases I was informed that the deceased persons did not drink the pump water before their illness.

The result of the inquiry, then, was that there had been no particular outbreak or increase of cholera, in this part of London, except among the persons who were in the habit of drinking the water of the above-mentioned pump well.

I had an interview with the Board of Guardians of St. James's parish, on the evening of Thursday, September 7, and represented the above circumstances to them. In consequence of what I said the handle of the pump was removed on the following day. . . .

The additional facts that I have been able to ascertain are in accordance with those above related; and as regards the small number of those attacked, who were believed not to have drunk the water from the Broad Street pump, it must be obvious that there are various ways in which the deceased persons may have taken it without the knowledge of their friends. The water was used for mixing with spirits in all the public houses around. It was used likewise at dining rooms and coffeeshops. The keeper of a coffeeshop in the neighborhood, which was frequented by mechanics, and where the pump water was supplied at dinnertime, informed me (on September 6) that she was already aware of nine of her customers who were dead. The pump water was also sold in various little shops, with a teaspoonful of effervescing powder in it, under the name of sherbet; and it may have been distributed in various other ways with which I am unacquainted. The pump was frequented much more than is usual, even for a London pump in a populous neighborhood.

There are certain circumstances bearing on the subject of this outbreak of cholera which require to be mentioned. The workhouse in Poland Street is more than three fourths surrounded by houses in which deaths from cholera occurred, yet out of five hundred and thirty-five inmates only five died of cholera, the other deaths which took place being those of persons admitted after they were attacked. The workhouse has a pump well on the premises, in addition to the supply from the Grand Junction Waterworks, and the inmates never sent to Broad Street for water. If the mortality in the workhouse had been equal to that in the streets immediately surrounding it on three sides, upwards of one hundred persons would have died.

There is a brewery in Broad Street, near to the pump, and on perceiving that no brewer's men were registered as having died of cholera, I called on Mr. Huggins, the proprietor. He informed me that there were about seventy workmen employed in the brewery, and that none of them had suffered from cholera—at least in a severe form—only two having been indisposed, and that not seriously, at the time the disease prevailed. The men are allowed a certain quantity of malt liquor, and Mr. Huggins believes they do not drink water at all; and he is quite certain that the workmen never obtained water from the pump in the street. There is a deep well in the brewery, in addition to the New River water.

At the percussion-cap manufactory, 37 Broad Street, where, I understand, about two hundred workpeople were employed, two tubs were kept on the premises always supplied with water from the pump in the street, for those to drink who wished; and eighteen of these workpeople died of cholera at their own homes, sixteen men and two women.

All the instances of communication of cholera through the medium of water, above related, have resulted from the contamination of a pump well, or some other limited supply of water; and the outbreaks of cholera connected with the contamination, though sudden and intense, have been limited also; but when the water of a river becomes infected with the cholera evacuations emptied from on board ship, or passing down drains and sewers, the communication of the disease, though generally less sudden and violent, is much more widely extended; more especially when the river water is distributed by the steam engine and pipes connected with waterworks. Cholera may linger in the courts and alleys crowded with the poor, for reasons previously pointed out, but I know of no instance in which it has been generally spread through a town or neighborhood, among all classes of the community, in which the drinking water has not been the medium of its diffusion. Each epidemic of cholera in London has borne a strict relation to the nature of the water supply of its different districts, being modified only by poverty and the crowding and want of cleanliness which always attend it.

THE PREVENTION OF CHOLERA

The measures which are required for the prevention of cholera, and all diseases which are communicated in the same way as cholera, are of a very simple kind. They may be divided into those which may be carried out in the presence of an epidemic, and those which, as they require time, should be taken beforehand.

The measures which should be adopted during the presence of cholera may be enumerated as follows:

1. The strictest cleanliness should be observed by those about the sick. There should be a hand basin, water, and towel in every room where there is a cholera patient, and care should be taken that they are frequently used by the nurse and other attendants, more particularly before touching any food.

2. The soiled bed linen and body linen of the patient should be immersed in water as soon as they are removed, until such time as they can be washed, lest the evacuations should become dry and be wafted about as a fine dust. Articles of bedding and clothing which cannot be washed should be exposed for some time to a temperature of 212° or upwards.

3. Care should be taken that the water employed for drinking and preparing food (whether it come from a pump well or be conveyed in pipes) is not contaminated with the contents of cesspools, house drains, or sewers; or, in the event that water free from suspicion cannot be obtained, it should be well boiled, and, if possible, also filtered.

Works are in progress for supplying a great part of London with water from the Thames, obtained, like that of the Lambeth Company, above Teddington Lock. Although this is not the best possible source for supplying a large town, it is a great improvement on the practice of many of the water companies; and the water, owing to filtration, and especially to its detention in large reservoirs, will probably be quite salubrious: at all events it will be much safer than that of the shallow pump wells of London, which are fed from very polluted sources. It is very desirable that the handles of nearly all the street pumps of London and other large towns should be fastened up, and the water used only for such purposes as watering the streets. A proper supply of water for the shipping in the Thames is much wanted. Water acquires a flat taste by being boiled; but if it is filtered after it becomes cold it gets reaerated, and the flat or vapid taste is entirely removed.

4. When cholera prevails very much in the neighborhood, all the provisions which are brought into the house should be well washed with clean water and exposed to a temperature of 212° F.; or at least they should undergo one of these processes and be purified either by water or by fire. By being careful to wash the hands, and taking due precautions with regard to food, I consider that a person may spend his time among cholera patients without exposing himself to any danger.

5. When a case of cholera or other communicable disease appears among persons living in a crowded room, the healthy should be removed to another apartment, where it is practicable, leaving only those who are useful to wait on the sick.

6. As it would be impossible to clean out coalpits, and establish privies and lavatories in them, or even to provide the means of eating a meal with anything like common decency, the time of working should be divided into periods of four hours instead of eight, so that the pitmen might go home to their meals and be prevented from taking food into the mines.

7. The communicability of cholera ought not to be disguised from the people, under the idea that the knowledge of it would cause a panic or occasion the sick to be deserted.

British people would not desert their friends or relatives in illness, though they should incur danger by attending to them; but the truth is that to look on cholera as a "catching" disease, which one may avoid by a few simple precautions, is a much less discouraging doctrine than that which supposes it to depend on some mysterious state of the atmosphere in which we are all of us immersed and obliged to breathe.

The measures which can be taken beforehand to provide against cholera and other epidemic diseases, which are communicated in a similar way, are:

8. To effect good and perfect drainage.

9. To provide an ample supply of water quite free from contamination with the contents of sewers, cesspools, and house drains, or the refuse of people who navigate the rivers.

10. To provide model lodginghouses for the vagrant class, and sufficient houseroom for the poor generally.

The great benefit of the model lodginghouses arises from the circumstance that the apartments for cooking, eating, and sleeping are distinct, and that all the proper offices which cleanliness and decency require are provided. The very poor who choose to avail themselves of these institutions suffer a rate of mortality as low as that of the most opulent classes. The public washhouses, which enable poor persons to wash the soiled linen of the sick or the healthy without doing it in the midst of the plates and dishes and provisions of the family, are well calculated to prevent the spread of disease.

11. To inculcate habits of personal and domestic cleanliness among the people everywhere.

12. Some attention should undoubtedly be directed to persons, and especially ships, arriving from infected places, in order to segregate the sick from the healthy. In the instance of cholera the supervision would generally not require to be of long duration.

I feel confident, however, that by attending to the above-mentioned precautions, which I consider to be based on a correct knowledge of the cause of cholera, this disease may be rendered extremely rare, if indeed it may not be altogether banished from civilized countries. And the diminution of mortality ought not to stop with cholera.

1824

The Cry and the Covenant

MORTON THOMPSON

For an instant, as he walked with Klein on his first day as provisional assistant, in that silent, purposeful march, both in step, faces grave, the eyes of the patients following respectfully, Ignaz Philipp felt pride full force. His exultance was brief. It was succeeded by embarrassment. He glanced to either side covertly. He had almost strutted. No one had noticed. He contemplated himself with disgust. Klein stopped at a bedside. Ignaz Philipp forgot everything and prepared to assist him. But Klein, ignoring the patient, had stooped and seized something on the floor. He showed Ignaz Philipp a curl of dust.

"You see?" he said triumphantly. "Dust!" . . .

"Order, Dr. Semmelweis. What we must have—what we *shall* have—is order. Dr. Boer had a reputation for keeping this clinic clean. We uphold that reputation. God sends poverty, but not dirt. This is your first day as assistant. See to it that I never again find anything in any ward with which to reproach you."

He walked a little, in silence.

"I want to be able," he continued after a while, "to sit in my office and to know that at any hour of the day or night I may come where I will in the First Division and find every bed exactly the same distance apart, every floor precisely clean, every window entirely gleaming."

"I was noticing the sheets, sir director. On some of the beds they are changed as often as once a week. And yet—"

"On the expenses of this division as a whole and in the matter of laundry charges in particular my budget has been precisely established. I may say that in all my career here the yearly bills have hardly varied more than a few groschen. It is unfortunate that they vary even that much."

"With respect, sir director, because of the discharge, the natural staining, some of them, in fact, are very dirty—"

"They betray the normal consequences of hospital use. Their care conforms to the restrictions of their part in the budget. Naturally we do not expect that anyone should contemplate altering the budget in the slightest particular."

"I regret having mentioned the matter, sir director—"

"It is of no consequence. That is how one learns. I want you to feel free to come to me at any time between one o'clock in the afternoon and three-thirty to discuss any matter that puzzles you. In that way I shall feel you completely understand what it is I desire here. Punctuality, order, regularity, attention to the smallest detail—that is how one gets on, Dr. Semmelweis."

It was true, Ignaz Philipp reflected, that the First Division had a name for precision, for being well-kept, for being administered to near perfection.

"I shall try to be a credit to you, sir director," he said. . . .

Markussovsky was sleeping heavily when Ignaz Philipp rose next morning. He dressed, he let himself out quietly. He walked briskly to the university. As he expected, Kolletschka was already in the dissection room.

"Good morning, sir." Ignaz Philipp looked about the room. "Where is Dr. Lautner?"

"I hope he is sleeping, Naci. How much sleep are you getting lately?"

Ignaz Philipp pointed to a nearby cadaver.

"Not so much as him."

"Still, you are young. When you're old as I am there will still be plenty of time for work."

"They keep dying, sir. They keep on dying."

"I don't think we will ever find the reason here."

"I know. We keep turning the same findings over and over. But the secret must be here. There is no other place to look for it."

"We've examined so many women dead of childbed fever, Naci."

"I can't help it, sir. There's no place else to look. And always—perhaps the next one will give up the secret. Perhaps we're overlooking something. Perhaps if we do enough postmortems we will find it. And it will be something very simple. Something, perhaps, we have been looking at all the time."

"It doesn't do any harm to look, certainly. You're learning a lot of gynaecology, that's certain."

"That's right." He moved to a table and looked at the body. "The same sort of fluid in the thorax—"

Kolletschka nodded sadly.

"A milky, putrid lymph in the lungs—pus around the ovaries—inflammation in the uterus—clots—some gangrene—the peritoneum inflamed—"

"Always, always the same—"

"Blisters of pus and foul-smelling fluid under the skin—"

Ignaz Philipp swallowed.

"Well, there's nothing new here."

"No, Naci. Nor yesterday. Nor— Do you know you've examined more than a hundred bodies now?"

"Not all of them are the same, sir. Some of them are slightly different—"

"Yes, that's true. But all of them—"

"All of them have at least one thing in common. They die. These are women, sir, healthy women. And they walk into the best hospital in the world. And they deliver healthy babies. And then they die. Why do they die? I don't know. How comes this disease? I don't know. But I see them every day. I look on, I observe, I watch them, powerless. But I have not yet reached the point where I can watch them indifferently. And so long as I continue to seek a cause and a remedy I'm not so ashamed at least to look them in the eye, one human being to another."

"Well, we'll keep on hunting, you and I, as long as you please. As for me, one never gets done learning anatomy. Who knows? Perhaps I will discover something too. You come here any time, Naci. I'll always be glad to help."

"You have, sir. You always have. . . ."

As he left the anatomy room and walked hastily to duty in the First Division, Ignaz Philipp marveled, as always, at Kolletschka's patience, his quietness, his warmth, and his affection. He thought with awe of his good fortune in such a friend. . . .

He made his first discovery. He discovered from his statistics that during six years three times as many women died in the First Division as in the adjoining Second Division. He looked up from his papers. A faint hope pulsed in him. His heart beat faster. . . .

Month after frantic month Ignaz Philipp continued frantically to seek a clue to the cause of puerperal fever. In January he came upon a new theory. Authorities blamed male sperm for inoculating women with the fever. He began new research. At the end of January he had proven glumly that only by an incredible coincidence could three times as many men be poisonous to women in the First Clinic as in the Second. The deaths continued. Then they slowed. He grimaced as he watched them decline. Puerperal fever patients were being quietly transferred, undiagnosed, when the death rate in the First Division neared a figure that might disturb the Imperial Court. But there was a limit, he knew, to the number of cases the General Hospital could absorb. "There"— he smiled grimly—"there they have a death rate to consider also."

On the twenty-seventh of February, 1846, obeying almost overwhelming faculty pressure, Klein reluctantly appointed him first assistant. Now, if it was possible, he worked harder than before. There were still theories to explore. There was no lack of learned theories. There was no lack of authorities. One after the other his research rejected such verdicts as summer heat and winter cold, the immorality of the women, the pestilential nature of the timbers and mortar, of the very building which enclosed the maternity hospital. All these things to which childbed fever was learnedly ascribed were common to both divisions. But the First Division's death rate continued invariably higher, and day by day the women continued to sicken, to cry out, to implore him, and to die.

"I have examined every possible cause," he begged Skoda. "You must help me now, for I have exhausted the authorities."

"There are so many hypotheses. So many great men have made them with utter assurance. One of them, my boy, must be right."

"They are not right. Not one. I have tested them all. Not one is right. . . ."

The death rate that October soared so high in the Maternity Hospital that it could no longer be ignored. A commission was appointed to investigate. The commission met in November. A week later it handed down its findings. It blamed the outbreak of puerperal fever on the presence of foreign students. There were then forty-two foreign students studying obstetrics at the university. Their number was cut to twenty. . . .

In France, in England, in Scotland, in Ireland, in America, in Italy, in whatever country there were hospitals, women came to give birth to children. And puerperal fever in this year killed one out of ten, one out of twenty, one out of five, one out of three. And sometimes it killed them all.

Spring came late that year, winter lingered, at Graz travelers groaned about high snow in the Alpine passes. Ignaz Philipp and Markussovsky skirted the high Alps, the stagecoach rumbled southward toward Trieste. For a day they sat quietly. They ignored their fellow passengers. Always they gazed at the changing landscape, sometimes seeing it, sometimes staring blindly.

On the morning of the second day Ignaz Philipp said abruptly, "What I am looking for is in the First Division and nowhere else." His tone was final. His mind was calm and assured. The last doubts had left him. . . .

From Treviso over the road the Romans built the stagecoach rumbled to Venice. In Treviso the red wine foamed but in Venice the Basilica of St. Peter pressed its age upon their mouths and they were silent. They sketched the tombstones of Capasantos and palaces and olive trees. They saw the ocean. They tasted the Adriatic upon their lips, salty, long before they saw its blue, and in the heart of Ignaz Philipp, a boy from Hungary who had seen only the Danube but had often sent his dreams down it, the ocean sent a great pain and humbleness and longing. And in Trieste the steam vessels lay idly, long lines of them, their hawsers languidly adip in the soft waters, like so many great ladies. Here the mountains crowded down to the sea; home they were green and trees browsed on them; here they were stripped, their ribs bared to the blown spume. . . .

The days passed, the halcyon days, the golden days, vivid with great paintings, tumultuous with storied castles, with music, with wine, with unending curious things to explore and admire, with laughing girls and strange tongues and always the Adriatic. The last few days they lay on the warm sands of Lido, simply resting, musing at a blue sky, a galloping of dappled clouds, content to wait for sunset.

It was over at last.

On March 20 he and Markussovsky arrived in Vienna. They

stepped from the stagecoach from warm golden spring into
Austria's bitter winter. The next morning he reported for duty
in the First Division. He was first assistant again.

"Well," said Klein, "this time I shall have perhaps your undi-
vided attention."

"I have always tried to give you that, sir professor."

"Your comments are not necessary. Did you enjoy Venice?
. . . fine . . . are you rested? . . . splendid . . . that will be all."

Ignaz Philipp walked to the door of the office.

"By the way, what was it Kolletschka was working on when
you left?"

"He was experimenting with a stain he had developed for tissue
mounted on microscopic slides—that and some work on lung
tissue."

"I see. Perhaps that's what made him careless. One should devote all one's energies in that to which one is assigned. One hopes
you profit from the lesson."

Cold, bitter cold clamped heavily on Ignaz Philipp's heart. He
stared at Klein. His pulse pounded. He held his breath.

"What"—he licked his lips—"what's the matter with Kolletschka?"

"He's dead. Didn't anyone tell you? Died on the thirteenth of
March. Cadaveric poisoning. Student pricked his finger while
they were dissecting a corpse in class. We have a new provisional
assistant. His name is Fleischer. See that he works. You may go."

He made his rounds mechanically. He led the students through
the wards. He inspected the journal. Kolletschka was dead. He
could think of nothing else. Jakob Kolletschka, aged forty-three,
a true man, a friend, decent, gentle Kolletschka. He shut the
journal. He walked from the First Division into the Second.

"What has happened, Bartsch? What happened to Kolletschka?"

"I'm sorry, Semmelweis. I knew it was going to be terrible for
you. . . ."

"Why didn't you write? Why didn't someone tell me?"

"Professor Skoda said no. Ah, man, you were enjoying yourself
—what good would it have done?"

"Tell me, Bartsch. Tell me what happened."

"It happened in class. He and a student were demonstrating
visceral anatomy. The student was incising. He was clumsy and
Kolletschka moved his hand to help him. The student nicked the
end of his finger."

"And that's all?"

"It bled a little. It was a small nick, nothing much. Kolletschka went on with the lesson. You and I have had such nicks. But the next day he fell ill. He got worse. He was dead within the week. Cadaveric poisoning."

Bartsch looked down. Through the minds of both men rasped the refrain of agony in which men died of cadaveric poisoning. "I thank you, Bartsch." Gentle Jakob. Gentle Jakob suffering. "I'm sorry, Semmelweis. I know you were friends. . . ."

"Thank you . . ." Jakob screaming, Jakob dead, Jakob dying. He finished his duties that day in almost complete silence. He saw the faces of the sick and the agonized. But often the face of Jakob was on the pillow. And often the voice was Kolletschka's.

The next day he rose early and went to the dissecting rooms. He worked alone. Kolletschka was gone. That night with Rokitansky, Hebra, Skoda, he bowed in silence before Frau Kolletschka.

Scrupulously he resumed where he had left off almost a month before. He dissected. He reported at the clinic. He worked harder than before. Each case became his own case, to each woman he fought to give some solace. He looked at them, row after row, each mattress freighted with its weight of misery and fear, and his heart surrendered to them utterly.

They had no money. They were sick. There was no place else for them to go. And each knew she was in a place of deadly peril. Each knew the bed might be her deathbed. Their eyes begged reassurance. They pleaded humbly to be healed, not to die, to have their babies and be released. They woke in fear and they bore in fear and they slept in fear. And that is how they died.

He set himself again to the hopeless task of saving them. He sat with them, he babied them, he fed them, he petted them, he worked with them as he had not dreamed a man could work. And he watched them die. A part of him died with them.

Nothing had changed. In the wards the beds were placed exactly equidistant. The same smells poisoned each breath. The patients were other patients than on his first day nearly two years ago. The faces were different. The bodies were the same. The poverty that brought them was the same poverty. The pregnancies had not changed. The killing went on. The screams and the prayers continued. The deaths had not changed. Nothing had changed.

The frenzied hours had come to nothing. All that he had worked for had come to nothing. He had worked in vain. The days of unending struggle, the nights of study, the weeks of research, the months of raging battle, the sum of his life and his prayers and his unquenchable determination was here in this clinic, this day. Here was the whole sum. And here was the sum of puerperal fever. He had altered nothing.

The killing went on. . . .

In the first ten days following his return to duty the death rate from puerperal fever which had subsided to an incredible 1.92 per cent rose abruptly to 3.60 per cent. He redoubled his dissecting. He rushed back to the wards and flogged himself to greater effort. The women screamed, they looked at him, imploring, he smiled a set smile, his eyes ached with pity, his hands detected the inevitable even as his voice tried to assure them. At the end of April the death rate had risen to 18.27 per cent. He set the figure in his records carefully.

He left the clinic early that evening. He met Bartsch on the steps outside the hospital. For a few blocks their way lay together.

"I can see by your face you've had no luck yet."

"I've had no luck. I've had nothing. Not even hope."

"Ah, well. It's not been a complete loss. All that dissection, all that work, you couldn't help sharpening your surgery and gynaecology."

"And what does it all come to? I know nothing. Against puerperal fever I am as effective as if I had never studied medicine at all."

"So are we all, friend, so are we all. So it has always been. You forget that, I think. Yes, it has always been. And it always will be. You have allowed this to obsess you. You must face the unfortunate reality. It is like death, one of the normal consequences of living. And like death—there is no remedy, no hope, no answer."

"I know. Perhaps it is really hopeless. Perhaps I have always known it. But always there were the women, begging, and always my heart bent down to them. And always there was this to make one hopeful, to tantalize endlessly: Why does the First Division have three times as many deaths and four and five and six and ten times as the Second Division? When everything is the same in both divisions—why?"

"Someday we will know. It will be a perfectly simple, perfectly natural explanation. . . ."

He went to see Skoda . . . Perhaps there was something he could say, some word, which would remain with Skoda, which might inflame that great man so that he would pick up the problem.

"I've seen the latest figures," Skoda said without preamble.

Ignaz Philipp shook his head.

"Yes, sir. They're rising. . . ."

"Be careful, my boy. He may be using his peculiar bookkeeping to get rid of you. You go away—the figures go down. You come back—the death rate mounts. Keep your counsel. Don't be rash. Do your work. Be patient. Those who accept his figures—and his undiagnosed cases, and his cases diagnosed as peritonitis, typhus, and other things—they're all together, all in the same clique with him. Say nothing rash. Be careful. Wait."

"I am doing my best. But the problem is for you, sir. Excuse me, that I blurt it out, but your great mind, your resources, you will solve it, sir. I know it."

"Well, well . . . someday perhaps I will have a look at it . . . And now tell me! What is the latest? What have you found?"

"I will tell you. I will tell you an old story. Tomorrow it will be new. But there will be no change. You are at the hospital. You will admit a healthy woman. A sound, fine woman. This creature of God will come to you in the glory of health, groveling with fear. And you will tell her not to fear. You will use all your art. And she will have her child. And while you look at her, it will strike. There is, incredibly, a fever. There is vomiting. There is diarrhea. There is crunching pain. And now it is all over. In three days this healthy, praying woman is a burning, unrecognizable, insane corruption. And you will watch, helpless. And now she is gone. And we open her up. And we find—"

"Lymphangitis, phlebitis, bilateral pleuritis, pericarditis, peritonitis, meningitis, metastases. . . ."

"Yes, sir. . . ."

"But you keep on trying."

"There's that one clue—that higher rate in the First Clinic. For me it's been a clue that leads nowhere . . . for you, sir, who knows?"

He looked at Skoda searchingly.

"Yes . . . well . . . you must do what you must do, boy. . . . Are you still working in the mornings? Dissecting?"

Ignaz Philipp nodded. He looked down.

"That poor Kolletschka . . . a great loss . . . to you, particularly. . . ."

"I'll never forget him. Nor you, sir."

"And to go—that way. Well, we all have to go—some way. There's no remedy, you know. Still—cadaveric poisoning!"

"I don't know much about it."

"No. No one does."

"Only what happens."

"Only what happens. . . ."

He left Skoda. With his eyes, with his thoughts, he said farewell to him. Tonight he would see Hebra and Rokitansky and perhaps Haller. Perhaps one of them might take over the search . . . There was not much hope. He clung to what hope there was.

He walked now to the graveyard where Kolletschka lay. It was in his mind to say good-by. Walking, he passed the morgue. He paused. He had never seen the death report. This, too, was Kolletschka, of his friend the last sentence.

He turned abruptly and went into the morgue. He entered the department of records.

He opened the file. He turned the pages. He came to the case of Jakob Kolletschka. In the kingdom of God there was the sound of blowing bugles.

He stared at the page, somberly.

He began to read.

The body of Jakob Kolletschka had died of cadaveric poisoning. He read on. The record was plain.

It said:

In the upper extremity the lymphatic system was badly inflamed.

The veins were inflamed and swollen.

The tissues of his lungs were inflamed.

The heart was inflamed.

The inmost lining of his abdomen was inflamed, and the lining of his brain.

And wherever the murder traveled, in the abdomen, the lungs, the veins, the lymph system, the brain, the eye, there was a milky fluid. There was the odor of putrefaction. There was the clear and stinking liquor of death.

The poison had leaped through him, from his fingertip to his left eye. There were swellings there.

The lymphatic system inflamed. . . .

The veins inflamed and swollen. . . .
The record leaped out at him.
Lymphangitis . . . phlebitis . . . bilateral pleurisy . . . pericarditis
. . . peritonitis . . . meningitis . . . and metastases. . . .
He heard a roaring.
He stared at the report.
He looked up. His breathing stopped. His ears rang with a
clamor of Jericho. His eyes were blind with a great light.
He closed the book of records. He left the morgue. He began
to walk. His mind read and reread the records. He saw the very
texture of the paper. He saw the handwriting. He saw every
word. And now carefully, delicately, his mind sifted the last
case of puerperal fever he had dissected. He watched his knife
cutting. He saw the tissues. He reported the findings. He compared them with the record he had just seen. Step by step, fact
by fact, the cases tallied. There was one difference. Jakob Kolletschka had no uterus. In the woman the uterus and the cervix
had been inflamed and the tubes and the ovaries. But the woman
died and Kolletschka died. And the same thing had killed them
both. His mind began slowly and carefully to select case after
case, dead woman after dead woman. The dead were an endless
procession. The cause of death was always the same. The symptoms were identical. The thing that killed Kolletschka killed
the women.
And suddenly he remembered the dead babies, the heaped small
ones, those who had died with symptoms like their dead mothers!
The puzzling small ones, who could not have another small one
like themselves in their uteri, the little boy infants who could
never have a birth disease. And it, too, was clear now. They, too,
had died of that which had killed Kolletschka.
Kolletschka had died following a wound.
But it was not the wound which had killed Kolletschka.
The wound was only a pinprick.
No man could die of such a tiny wound, a wound which shed
perhaps four drops of blood.
What, then, killed Kolletschka?
His mind went back to the dissection.
He pictured the scalpel. He saw it enter the flesh of the cadaver.
It was shiny and clean. He saw the knife after the dissection had
gone on a little time. It was foul-looking, corroded, stained, tar-
nished. Instantly he remembered his final examination in chemistry.

He saw Stauern probe a foul-smelling bone fistula with a silver instrument. He saw the silver emerging, tarnished, black.

"What makes this silver black?"

And he heard himself answering:

"It might be hydrogen sulfide—"

And Stauern:

"It is acetic acid . . ."

It wasn't acetic acid, of course. For if acetic acid had coated the dissection knife, Kolletschka would not have died of it. And hydrogen sulfide would never kill a man unless he choked with it. It wasn't hydrogen sulfide that had killed Jakob Kolletschka and it wasn't acetic acid.

No knife. . . .

No chemical. . . .

What remained?

He saw the knife. He saw the blade, black, coated with cadaveric material.

It was the cadaveric material.

There was no other answer.

The next thought was inexorable.

He saw himself dissecting women. They were dead of puerperal fever. He felt his fingers wet with the pus and the fluids of putrefaction. He saw those hands, partly wiped, entering the bodies of living women. The contagion passed from his fingers to the living tissues, to wounded tissues. He saw the women fever. He heard them scream. He saw them die.

He shook violently. He was remembering. Spurred by pity, he had plunged into dissection after dissection. He had dissected early in the mornings with Kolletschka. During the day he had dissected with the students. The more dissecting he did, the more infection he carried to the patients. And every student who dissected carried infection to the patients.

A new light blinded him. Now also the riddle of the clinics was solved. The First Clinic had a higher death rate than the Second Clinic because in the Second Clinic there were only midwives. And midwives did not do dissections.

Ignaz Philipp Semmelweis had discovered the cause of puerperal fever. . . .

He thought of the hospital. Instantly the discovery washed over him . . . a fever plucked at him to go to the wards, to apply his discovery, to begin immediately the end of the murder. His country was life. His countrymen were the living. He ached with impatience to begin. He knew that in a month after the discovery became known his work would be finished. For the first time in man's long history women would no longer die of puerperal fever. In all the world the women of the world would go to their childbeds in safety. The murder would stop. In a month the discovery could succor the planet. It was absurdly simple. The remedy called for no special equipment. The remedy meant only the slightest change in the routine.

To end puerperal fever: one simply washed one's hands.

A basin must be placed in every ward.

A pitcher of warm water.

A bar of soap.

A supply of towels.

A gray horror swept him. He trembled, thinking of the women he had killed. No more must die. There was no time to lose. He seized his book of records. First, he said to himself, I must be honest. He dipped his quill into the inkpot. He began to write.

The variations in the mortality as they occurred in the divisions can be attributed to the special occupations of the various members of the staff. As an assistant I took special interest in pathological anatomy. I dissected endlessly to discover why these women were dying. The mortality soared. Consequently must I here make my confession that God only knows the number of women whom I have consigned prematurely to the grave. I have occupied myself with the cadaver to an extent reached by few obstetricians. However painful and depressing the recognition may be, there is no advantage in concealment; if the misfortune is not to remain permanent, the truth must be brought home to all concerned. . . .

He closed the book.

It was done now. It was all over.

In a month puerperal fever would be a memory.

He was at the hospital before dawn. He smiled genially. He talked pleasantly to amazed attendants. He walked, exulting, from ward to ward. He walked, shuddering, past the autopsy room. Henceforth he would do no more dissecting.

He chafed to begin. He bit his lips to keep from crying out. He wanted to run through the wards, to rouse the patients, to cry to them all: "It's over, mothers! It's all over! There will be no more puerperal fever!" He mastered himself. The students arrived.

He tried to find words to begin. His eyes filled. They waited, wondering.

"There will be no more puerperal fever," he blurted suddenly. They looked at him in silence. He began again.

"I have found the secret of puerperal fever. Gentlemen—it is all over. Professor Kolletschka—as you know, he died of cadaveric poisoning. The symptoms of which he died and the symptoms of women who die of puerperal fever are identical. There is no difference. I have seen the record. They are exactly the same."

They waited. He plunged on.

"It is we who are the killers. It is the cadaveric particles clinging to our hands which pass into the bodies of the women we examine."

They gaped, waiting.

"Gentlemen," he said, his voice breaking with strain and joy, "from this day on we will all wash our hands!"

The students slumped, disappointed. They began to look at one another significantly. They looked back at him coldly.

"Is it understood? From this time forth no student—no midwife —no one in this division ever again will examine any patient without first washing his hands as he enters the ward."

There was an embarrassed silence.

"May—may one know why, sir doctor?"

He controlled the swift flash of anger. He smiled. They were students, after all. "It's simple, boys. We must wash off those cadaveric particles. That is all. That is absolutely all. Now come. Now let us wash. With us begins the end of puerperal fever."

Some laughed. Some murmured angrily. Some shrugged. They went to the basins. Obediently they washed their hands. When they had finished he was waiting for them.

"Now let me see them."

This was incredible. There was something of a nightmare about this. Slowly, reluctantly, incredulously, they held out their hands. He examined them cheerfully and thoroughly.

"Now come. Let us begin."

He walked to the wards. They followed after him. Rounds began. The tour ended. The students prepared to go to class. One of them stopped.

"I beg your pardon, sir."

"Yes? You want to know more about the discovery, eh? Naturally! Fine! Come to me any time!"

The student stared at him.

"Will it be necessary to submit to that somewhat unusual performance every morning, sir doctor?" he asked, his lips tight.

"Of course. One must be very careful now. Every morning, gentlemen. And every afternoon. In short, every time you examine the patients. You see there's nothing to it. We simply— wash."

The students lingered. They looked at one another uneasily. Another spoke.

· "With respect, sir doctor. Do you not consider this a somewhat humiliating performance?"

Ignaz Philipp stopped smiling. He frowned a moment, thinking. He decided he had not understood.

"Humiliating? To wash your hands?" He smiled. "I'm afraid —my thoughts were wandering—perhaps I didn't understand. You found something objectionable?"

"Some of us are undergraduates, sir doctor. Many of us are already doctors. Will you be pleased to consider—"

"We aren't schoolboys!" a student cried out.

"As you know, sir, the midwives line up every morning in the Second Division to have their fingernails inspected. We aren't midwives, sir, we are students and doctors. It is, to say the least, undignified—"

Ignaz Philipp looked at them open-mouthed.

"But—but I have only asked you to wash your hands—"

"Your hypothesis, sir, with all respect, is still unproven—"

"Are we required to make ourselves ridiculous for the sake of an incredible experiment?"

A vein in his left temple began to swell. It pulsed visibly.

"Enough!" he shouted. His voice rang through the wards. He glared at them, still incredulous. "It is I who am ashamed. I have spoken to you as equals. I speak to you now as your superior. This division is my direct responsibility. I am from this day on, knowing what I know, responsible for every death that occurs in it. I have made my position perfectly plain. I believe puerperal fever can be eliminated by washing the hands. I tell you this. I ask you merely to wash your hands. You will wash your hands. You will do exactly as I say. If you find my requirements unsuitable, you may pursue your studies elsewhere. You may transfer to Berlin, if you like, where one out of three die. Or to Kiel, where one of four die. Or to Jena, where *all* die. You may go where you like. But here—so long as you attend this clinic—until this thing is proven otherwise—you will wash your hands!"

In medicine the age of antisepsis had begun.

Klein came on the second day. As always, rounds began at Bed 1, in the labor room. Ignaz Philipp appeared in the doorway. Klein walked toward the bed. Ignaz Philipp walked quickly to bar his way. With a nod he tactfully indicated the basin. Klein looked.

"What's that for?"

"To wash your hands, sir director," Ignaz Philipp said in a low voice.

Klein drew back. His face reddened.

"Have you lost your senses? Is this some joke, Doctor?"

"I have made a discovery, sir director, which I believe will end puerperal fever. I am positive I have discovered the cause. The remedy is simply washing the hands. It's really not much to ask, is it, sir director?"

Klein looked uncertainly at his hands.

"Why was I not informed? If there is to be any change in the routine of this division I am instantly to be informed. You are aware of that, Doctor?"

"You were not available, sir director. But I am happy to explain —to tell you all the circumstances—"

"If you have discoveries, Dr. Semmelweis, there is a certain, definite, well-known order for their presentation. One makes a report. One presents the report to one's director. One receives the director's permission to proceed."

"I put the report on your desk this morning, sir. I entered the procedure yesterday in the journal."

"But you began before you received permission. I am responsible for this division. I must remind you, you are only first assistant. If you execute unsanctioned ideas, and the patients die, it is I who am responsible. And is it possible, Dr. Semmelweis, that you have forgotten the code of ethics? Is it possible that you are now prepared to experiment on patients?"

Resolutely, his eyes dim with rage, his pulse pounding, Ignaz Philipp kept his voice even. Klein was no student. He was Klein. His dignity was offended. When he understood—

"The patients were hardly in peril, sir. The students and the midwives merely washed their hands."

"Morning rounds is not the time to begin some innovation based on a flight of your imagination. Order must be and will be preserved, Dr. Semmelweis. From now on—"

"Not imagination, sir director. Not imagination, but proof! If you have read the report I submitted, you will recall that I examined the death report of Dr. Kolletschka. I found that his tissues showed the same changes as the tissues of women dead of puerperal fever. That the dissecting knife carried into his body cadaveric particles which—"

"I am familiar with your report. It is not necessary to quote it to me. I am familiar with every comma in it. I pride myself, Dr. Semmelweis, on detail. I suggest you do likewise. I have read the full details of the coincidence. And now, if you please, stand out of my way—"

Ignaz Philipp reddened with rage. He barred Klein's way. His hands clenched.

"Will you accept the responsibility, then, of examining these women with unwashed hands? For I must tell you I intend to report this discovery."

"You have told me nothing of proven medical value."

"I am not fighting for myself now, Dr. Klein. I am fighting for these women. I have shown you plainly a means by which it is, to say the least, extremely probable that we can reduce the death rate in the First Division. I suggest to you, now, that such a reduction will be to your credit. I have found a means of ending puerperal fever. It is not expensive. It does not demand great change in routine. It cannot affect the patients adversely. It is simply washing the hands."

Klein had grown a little pale. He stared at Ignaz Philipp fixedly. Ignaz Philipp waited. Klein licked his thin lips.

"This is most irregular, Dr. Semmelweis. However—"

He walked to the basin.

"With respect, sir director—a most careful washing."

Klein stiffened. He hesitated a moment. Then he began to wash harder.

At the end of May the death rate in the First Division had dropped from 18.26 per cent to 12.24 per cent.

He was beside himself with joy. But soon he frowned.

It was not enough.

Soap and water cleansed the hands. But wash as they would those students who dissected longest still wore on their hands the odor of the death room. The most conscientious students could kill the most patients.

What shall I use? he asked himself. What shall I use against these deadly particles?

Again his memory took him back to chemistry class. Again he heard the professor . . .

"I deduced instantly you had just come from an anatomy lecture. A peculiar odor accompanied you. The odor was chlorine gas—*and chlorine is a most effective agent in destroying contagion and putrid exhalations of all kinds . . .*"

Liquor Chlorina . . . ! He smiled grimly.

That day he ordered a quantity. He made a solution.

"Soap and water," he told the students at evening rounds, "is only partly effective. The odor of decay lingers. That is because the smallest particles are clinging to your hands in tiny crevices. From now on we will wash our hands in this solution."

There were angry murmurs. They turned sullen or exasperated faces upon him.

"Wash," he said. "Wash or leave the class."

They washed. He made the attendants wash in the strong-smelling solution. He made the midwives wash in it. They gritted their teeth. They daggered him with looks of hatred. They washed.

In this time Ignaz Philipp walked the earth in tumult. Night and day became the same to him. He seldom went to bed. Often he slept sitting up, in the labor ward. His vigil was almost unceasing. He watched any person who approached a patient. He looked at the journal twenty times a day. Elation kept his heart pounding. Every hour and every moment was filled with the thunder of discovery. He lived in the wards. With his eyes he embraced every patient, he protected them, his arms were around them. Klein was seldom in the wards now. He did not often attend classes. He busied himself with administration. Ignaz Philipp became the ruler of the First Division. He ruled with iron. He was absolute and unequivocal. He permitted no doubt. Resentment grew. He grew harsher.

"My manner is sometimes unfortunate," he conceded. "I do not mean to hurt your feelings. But these are human lives. Nobody will die of your hurt feelings. Thousands may die of your dirty hands. Wash, gentlemen! Wash!"

"But, sir, in science there is always room for the doubt—for the modification—for truth can be seen in many ways—"

"Here we do not permit doubt. Here there is nothing to discuss—until after you have washed your hands!"

June ended.

The records were summed.

The death rate had dropped from 12.24 per cent to 2.38 per cent.

The wards were quieter now. The screaming had died down. The faces of the women did not implore so much. Here and there in their beds there was even a timid smile. Furtively, hope had begun.

He sat with Skoda, Hebra, and Rokitansky one night. From his pocket he drew the latest figures.

"We know all about you," waved Skoda. "We've heard about it."

"The death rate is dropping. It is dropping steadily."

"That's fine. Now prepare for the letdown. Prepare yourself now for the day when the figures soar again."

"I don't know, Joseph," said Hebra. "It's beginning to look as if he might be getting somewhere."

"Perhaps. Perhaps. All the same it's no harm preparing oneself for what we all have experienced. For the beautiful experiment gone wrong. For—for what usually happens . . . And now let's see those figures, my boy."

He and Hebra scanned Ignaz Philipp's records silently.

"Well," said Skoda at last, "it looks as if you might have something. Don't let your hopes rise too high. Let's see what the end of July brings. Even the Second Division has been known to go epidemic in July."

Ignaz Philipp left. A little worry began to gnaw at the edges of his elation. Skoda's warnings rapped at him louder with each step. Halfway home he turned abruptly and returned to the maternity clinic. He looked over the sleeping wards. He peered into the delivery room. He spoke guardedly to the attendants, to the students on night duty. He looked at them all warily. He glanced at their hands. He saw that the basins were full. He went into the students' sleeping quarters and lay down. There were two deliveries that night. He assumed charge of both of them. The midwives looked at him with disgust. The students gave way

and shrugged. He was oblivious to them. He attended the patients.
The days passed.

Toward the middle of June, Klein summoned him.

"I find that your experiments have become quite costly. Your
use of Liquor Chlorina is costing us at least fifty kreutzer per
patient. You will discontinue using it immediately."

Ignaz Philipp wandered to the wards dazed. He called the head
midwife. He placed her in charge. He went to Skoda. He asked
for the use of his library. He scanned rapidly through chemistry
textbooks. He found the works of the great Justus von Leibig.
He read them for hours. He made a great pile of notes. He left
Skoda. He went to a pharmacy. He bought chemicals.

When he returned to the Lying-in Division it was night. He
went directly to the autopsy room. He mixed a solution. He removed the sheet from a cadaver. It had been prepared for demonstration of deliveries. He plunged his hands into the cavity. He
rubbed them together. He poured over his hands the solution he
had prepared. Then he smelled his fingers. The odor of putrefaction was still strong.

He made another solution. He repeated the experiment. He discarded the solution. He made another. . . .

At about three o'clock in the morning he mixed a solution of
water and chlorinated lime. He plunged his hands into the corpse.
He used the solution. The odor had disappeared.

He set down the proportions of the solution. He estimated the
cost. The total came to less than a kreutzer per patient. He smiled
grimly.

The next morning Liquor Chlorina had been removed from
beside the washbasins. In its stead was a large bottle of chlorinated
lime solution. On Klein's desk lay a full report, together with
costs.

The work went on.

July ended.

The records were summed.

The death rate had sunk from 2.38 per cent to 1.20 per cent.

The news swept the hospital and the university.

Skoda, Hebra, and Rokitansky now began to spread Ignaz
Philipp's doctrine. Haller attempted to compliment Klein.

"I hope, my dear Primarius," Klein said contemptuously, "that
you are not of that number who regard this coincidence with the
respect due a scientific fact. Rest assured, sir, welcome as your

compliments are, your confidence in that young man is misplaced. His results are coincidence, sir. Pure coincidence."

"They appear to be facts, Doctor."

"Oh yes," said Klein. He smiled.

In August the death rate rose a little. It had been 1.20 per cent. Now it was 1.89 per cent.

Suddenly the death rate leaped to 5.25 per cent.

On a day in September Ignaz Philipp entered a ward in time to see four students pass by the basin, stop at a bed, prepare to thrust their unwashed hands into the body of a woman who had just delivered a child.

For an instant he could not move. He was stupefied.

A student pulled back the coverlet.

"Now, Mother, just spread your legs apart—"

The student bent over.

Ignaz Philipp rushed from the end of the ward.

"Gentlemen!" he shouted.

The students whirled.

"You stupid imbeciles! You clod-brained—you irresponsible—are you gone mad? Are you killers?"

They shrank, mortified, their faces burning, the patients listening.

"I don't like being talked to that way," one cried.

"Would you rather I took the sole of my shoe to you? Do you know what you're doing? Do you know what my orders are?"

"Look here, Doctor, with all respect, there are patients here—"

"No thanks to you!"

"Really, Doctor, these patients have gotten well before without any of this childish handwashing in your foul-smelling solutions—"

"You will leave the class. You will report to Professor Haller. You will not return to class. I will not have you."

The others fell silent instantly.

"I am not going to Professor Haller. I am going to another university. Some place where they behave with propriety and respect."

"You will leave instantly. Where you go is a matter of indifference to me. You will not now or ever return to this class. You are dismissed for insubordination and disobedience. That report will follow you wherever you go. And if you take my advice, you will leave medicine. You will cure more patients, resigned, than ever you will as a doctor. Now go."

The student left the ward in silence, passing red-faced between the rows of watching patients.

He paused in the doorway.

"You don't think that's the first time any of us have examined without washing our hands, do you?" he called mockingly. Then he disappeared down the corridor.

Ignaz Philipp turned slowly to the remaining students.

"Is this true?"

"Well, sir doctor, the fact is—"

"Is what he says true?"

They hung their heads.

"I have explained to you—I have told you why cleanliness is necessary—you have seen the results with your own eyes—and you *still* don't wash your hands? You deliberately flout me? You sneak? You evade for the joy of rebellion? You take these women's lives in your hands—for a whim?"

He spoke in a low voice. He could not believe it. His eyes were full of horror.

"How long has this been going on? How often—"

"Not many times, sir doctor."

"Just once or twice—"

"Just to see what would happen—"

"Come," said Ignaz Philipp tiredly. "Come. I will show you what will happen."

He took them into the labor room. In a far bed, behind a screen, a woman was dying of puerperal fever. A great stench rose from about the bed. They stood by the bedside. She no longer saw them. Her eyes were glazed. Her breath left her chest painfully and returned in slow agony.

"Let us sit here, gentlemen. Let us sit here to the last. Let us watch her die."

And so they sat until the woman breathed her last. . . .

In October, in the First Division, there were two hundred and seventy-eight deliveries. The mortality was 3.95 per cent.

"Now," said Skoda, "I am willing to think that perhaps we have found something."

"Wait," said Ignaz Philipp. "You have seen nothing."

In the first week of November, in the First Division, there were no deaths from puerperal fever.

"There's no longer any use in waiting," said Skoda.

"What shall we do?" Rokitansky asked.

"You, Hebra, you and I shall see Klein. He is the one to announce it."

"Then tomorrow, my boy, be on your good behavior," said Rokitansky. "Put him in the best possible mood. Flatter him. Do anything."

"I will do my best," promised Ignaz Philipp.

In the morning, after rounds, he went to Klein's office.

"It is somewhat irregular to come here at this hour," he said humbly.

"The hours from one-thirty to four o'clock each day are at your convenience," said Klein. "You understand my feeling about order."

"I do understand, sir director. You will comprehend then the deep satisfaction that drew me here before the hour. I wish to report, sir, that thanks to your wise and able administration we may yet end this year with a mortality record lower than the Second Division."

Klein looked at him sharply. Ignaz Philipp's face was grave.

"It has been a privilege, sir director, to have worked with such a man as yourself."

"I find your admiration unexpected, Doctor. I would appreciate it even more if your hopes were based on science rather than emotion. The First Division's mortality rate has always been higher than the Second Division's. That is the order of things. It will, therefore, unquestionably always remain so."

"I had not thought about the order of things. You are probably quite right, sir director."

"Give a thought to the order of things, Doctor. Think of it oftener. It will help you."

"I shall, sir director."

"And in future—"

"From one-thirty until four o'clock, sir!"

"Thank you for your compliments. It is not necessary to be impulsive. You may go now."

"Thank you, sir director."

Ignaz Philipp bowed. He walked out humbly.

In the afternoon he watched from a ward as Skoda and Hebra walked toward Klein's office.

He did not see them leave.

In the evening he went quickly to Rokitansky's house. Skoda was there, and Hebra.

"We started with you," said Hebra to Ignaz Philipp. "We reviewed your work as a student, your postgraduate work, your long hours, the amount of work you did without complaint—we went over everything. We told him, God forgive us, how you respected him."

"The best we got from that," said Skoda, "was the response that you were a radical, a troublemaker, a man without order or tact or respect for duly-constituted authority."

"We proceeded to the discovery. We showed him that it had become general knowledge throughout the hospital and university that you had hit upon something that might well be a boon to humanity. We begged him to face the records, to acknowledge the falling death rate, to join in the plan to eliminate puerperal fever."

"It was then," said Skoda, "I offered him full credit for the discovery."

He paused.

"He was shocked," said Skoda. "He was shocked to his very core."

"He looked frightened," said Hebra.

"He considers the whole thing a wild concept, an irresponsible experiment which sooner or later will bring ridicule and contempt upon the whole Lying-in Division."

"He thought we were trying to trap him into being chief target for what he's sure will follow."

"Did you show him the figures?" demanded Ignaz Philipp.

"He said: 'Anything can be done with figures, gentlemen. We are all familiar enough with coincidence.' I asked him point-blank: 'Do you consider these figures a coincidence, Professor?' And he looked at me and blinked and said: 'Do you, sir professor, consider them anything else?'"

In the second week of November a pregnant woman was admitted to the labor ward and assigned to bed Number 1. In the morning Ignaz Philipp appeared with the students for rounds. They washed their hands with soap and water. They next washed with chloride-of-lime solution. They were inspected. They marched then to bed Number 1.

Upon examination she was discovered to be suffering from a carious knee joint. An ulcer had pocketed the region with pus.

The dirty dressing was replaced. They returned to the basins. They washed their hands and disinfected them with chloride-of-lime solution. They went to bed Number 2, and bed Number 3 followed, and so to the end of the ward.

The next day fevers rose in the labor ward. On the second day fevers rose higher. In nine days eleven of the women died.

Again there was no answer.

It appeared that every precaution had been taken.

Other women sickened.

At the end of November, this month which had begun with no mortalities reached 4.47 per cent. Out of two hundred and forty-six patients, eleven had died.

During the first week in December eight more died.

Now there was only one course.

The woman with the caricus knee joint was placed in isolation. Everything that was used about her was kept from other patients. Attendants, midwives, and students were forbidden to touch her.

The deaths stopped.

No other women sickened.

The mortality rate began to fall again.

"It must have been contact with something else or that the very air of the labor room was charged with the putrid matter," Ignaz Philipp decided.

"But isolation stopped it," said Rokitansky.

"Isolation stopped it."

"You know the answer, then," said Skoda.

"Henceforth," Ignaz Philipp told the students next day, "all such cases are to be kept in strict isolation." He entered the order in the journal.

The mortality rate dropped steadily. Day followed day and there were no deaths. December ended. The mortality rate for the First Division was 2.93 per cent. Eight had died out of two hundred and seventy-three.

"Well, Hebra?" said Skoda.

Hebra, editor of the *Vienna Medical Society Journal*, smiled. "I had it written four days ago. And you?"

"I'm going to write to Prague. To Nadherny himself."

"And I," said Rokitansky, "shall put on my top hat and my ribbons and make a formal visit to Haller."

They turned to Ignaz Philipp.

"What are you going to do?"

He stood smiling at them, his eyes full of tears.

"I am going home and thank God for such friends. With Klein —one doesn't expect much. With the students—well, even so not all of them are indifferent. But when the great men of the medical world—when Nadherny—when the others read the great *Vienna Medical Journal*—now, now I am happy. Now I know it is all over. In a month the murder will stop. My friends . . . my very dear friends. . . ."

Skoda wrote that night to von Nadherny, head of the University of Prague.

In the *Vienna Medical Society Journal,* one of the most widely read medical periodicals in the world, Ferdinand Hebra, editor and head of Vienna University's Department of Skin Diseases, wrote for the world to see:

EXPERIENCE OF THE HIGHEST IMPORTANCE

CONCERNING THE ETIOLOGY

OF EPIDEMIC PUERPERAL FEVER

AT THE LYING-IN HOSPITAL

The Editor of this Journal feels it is his duty to communicate to the medical profession . . . the following observations made by Dr. Semmelweis, Assistant in the First Obstetric Clinic in the General Hospital of this city. . . .

Dr. Semmelweis . . . for five years at the hospital . . . thoroughly instructed . . . for the last two years has devoted special attention to the subject of midwifery and has undertaken the task of inquiring into the causes . . . of the prevailing epidemic puerperal processes. . . .

. . . observations aroused in him the thought that in lying-in hospitals . . . the patients might be inoculated by the accoucheur himself . . . and that puerperal fever was in most cases nothing else than cadaveric infection.

In order to test this opinion it was laid down as a rule in the First Obstetric Clinic that everyone, before making an examination of a pregnant woman, must first wash his hands in an aqueous solution of chloride of lime (Chloralis calcis unc. 1, Aqua fontana lib. duas). The result was surprisingly favorable . . . April and May . . . rule not yet in force . . . 100 cases of labor . . . 18 deaths . . . in the following months up to November 26 . . . 47 out of 1547 cases . . . 2.45 per cent.

From this circumstance the problem is perhaps solved, why in schools for midwives the proportion of the prevalent mortality is so favorable in comparison with . . . institutions for the training of medical students. An exception is the Maternité of Paris where, as is well known, postmortem examinations are conducted by the pupil-midwives.

Three distinct facts of experience may perhaps still further confirm the conviction . . . extend still further its scope. Dr. Semmelweis believes that he can prove that:

1. Owing to careless washing some student engaged in dissection caused the loss of several patients in the month of September.

2. In the month of October, owing to frequent examinations of a patient in labor who suffered from a foul-smelling medullary sarcoma of the uterus, when washing was not practiced.

3. Owing to a filthy discharge in an ulcer of the leg in one of the patients, several who were confined at the time were infected.

Thus, therefore, *the conveyance of a foul exudation from a living organism may be one cause which produces the puerperal process.*

In publishing these experiences we invite the directors of all lying-in institutions . . . to contribute the results of their investigations either to support or refute them.

In one of the world's most widely read medical journals in December 1847 this fact was brought out clearly: Puerperal fever is in most cases a cadaveric infection, but it is sometimes an infection by means of putrid exudation or discharge from a living organism. . . .

"You'll be a great man now," said Hebra. "This university will be too small for you. You have done something more than save the living. These women will die and new women will be born and there will never be a woman born who may not owe her life to what you have discovered."

"They were dying," Ignaz Philipp mumbled, embarrassed. "They were screaming and dying. If you had seen them, if you had heard them—you'd have found a way. You couldn't have stood it, either. As long as I live I'll hear them."

"You'll hear a sweeter music henceforth," said Skoda.

"Yes," said Rokitansky, "you'll be St. Ignaz before long."

"See, here we sit in a room, and it spreads through the world. Even as we talk together, it's spreading," said Hebra.

"It's out of Klein's hands. It's out of the university. It's out of Vienna. Presently it belongs to the world."

1949

Rab and His Friends

JOHN BROWN

SIX years have passed,—a long time for a boy and a dog: Bob Ainslie is off to the wars; I am a medical student, and Clerk at Minto House Hospital.

Rab I saw almost every week, on the Wednesday; and we had much pleasant intimacy. I found the way to his heart by frequent scratching of his huge head, and an occasional bone. When I did not notice him he would plant himself straight before me, and stand wagging that bud of a tail, and looking up, with his head a little to the one side. His master I occasionally saw; he used to call me "Maister John," but was laconic as any Spartan.

One fine October afternoon, I was leaving the hospital, when I saw the large gate open, and in walked Rab, with that great and easy saunter of his. He looked as if taking general possession of the place; like the Duke of Wellington entering a subdued city, satiated with victory and peace. After him came Jess, now white with age, with her cart; and in it a woman, carefully wrapped up, —the carrier leading the horse anxiously, and looking back. When he saw me, James (for his name was James Noble) made a curt and grotesque "boo,"ᵃ and said, "Maister John, this is the mistress; she's got a trouble in her breest—some kind o' an income we're thinkin'."

By this time I saw the woman's face; she was sitting on a sack filled with straw, her husband's plaid round her, and his big-coat, with its large white metal buttons, over her feet. I never saw a more unforgettable face—pale, serious, lonely,[1] delicate, sweet, without being what we call fine. She looked sixty, and had on a

[1] It is not easy giving this look by one word; it was expressive of her being so much of her life alone.

mutch, white as snow, with its black ribbon; her silvery smooth hair setting off her dark-grey eyes—eyes such as one sees only twice or thrice in a lifetime, full of suffering, but full also of the overcoming of it; her eyebrows black and delicate, and her mouth firm, patient, and contented, which few mouths ever are.

As I have said, I never saw a more beautiful countenance, or one more subdued to settled quiet. "Ailie," said James, "this is Maister John, the young doctor; Rab's freend, ye ken. We often speak about you, doctor." She smiled, and made a movement, but said nothing; and prepared to come down, putting her plaid aside and rising. Had Solomon, in all his glory, been handing down the Queen of Sheba at his palace gate, he could not have done it more daintily, more tenderly, more like a gentleman, than did James the Howgate carrier, when he lifted down Ailie, his wife. The contrast of his small, swarthy, weatherbeaten, keen, worldly face to hers—pale, subdued, and beautiful—was something wonderful. Rab looked on concerned and puzzled; but ready for anything that might turn up,—were it to strangle the nurse, the porter, or even me. Ailie and he seemed great friends.

"As I was sayin', she's got a kind o' trouble in her breest, doctor; wull ye tak' a look at it?" We walked into the consulting-room, all four; Rab grim and comic, willing to be happy and confidential if cause could be shown, willing also to be quite the reverse, on the same terms. Ailie sat down, undid her open gown and her lawn handkerchief round her neck, and, without a word, showed me her right breast. I looked at and examined it carefully, —she and James watching me, and Rab eyeing all three. What could I say? there it was, that had once been so soft, so shapely, so white, so gracious and bountiful, "so full of all blessed conditions,"—hard as a stone, a centre of horrid pain, making that pale face, with its grey, lucid, reasonable eyes, and its sweet resolved mouth, express the full measure of suffering overcome. Why was that gentle, modest, sweet woman, clean and lovable, condemned by God to bear such a burden?

I got her away to bed. "May Rab and me bide?" said James. "You may; and Rab, if he will behave himself." "I'se warrant he's do that, doctor"; and in slunk the faithful beast. I wish you could have seen him. There are no such dogs now: he belonged to a lost tribe. As I have said, he was brindled, and grey like Aberdeen granite; his hair short, hard, and close, like a lion's; his body thick set, like a little bull—a sort of compressed Hercules of a dog. He

INTO MODERN TIMES   249

must have been ninety pounds' weight, at the least; he had a large blunt head; his muzzle black as night; his mouth blacker than any night, a tooth or two—being all he had—gleaming out of his jaws of darkness. His head was scarred with the records of old wounds, a sort of series of fields of battle all over it; one eye out; one ear cropped as close as was Archbishop Leighton's father's—but for different reasons,—the remaining eye had the power of two; and above it, and in constant communication with it, was a tattered rag of an ear, which was for ever unfurling itself, like an old flag; and then that bud of a tail, about one inch long, if it could in any sense be said to be long, being as broad as long—the mobility, the instantaneousness of that bud was very funny and surprising, and its expressive twinklings and winkings, the inter-communications between the eye, the ear, and it, were of the subtlest and swiftest. Rab had the dignity and simplicity of great size; and having fought his way all along the road to absolute supremacy, he was as mighty in his own line as Julius Caesar or the Duke of Wellington; and he had the gravity[1] of all great fighters.

Next day, my master, the surgeon, examined Ailie. There was no doubt it must kill her, and soon. It could be removed—it might never return—it would give her speedy relief—and she should have it done. She curtsied, looked at James, and said, "When?" "Tomorrow," said the kind surgeon, a man of few words. She and James and Rab and I retired. I noticed that he and she spoke little, but seemed to anticipate everything in each other. The following day, at noon, the students came in, hurrying up the great stair. At the first landing place, on a small well-known black board, was a bit of paper fastened by wafers, and many remains of old wafers beside it. On the paper were the words, "An operation to-day. J. B. Clerk."

Up ran the youths, eager to secure good places: in they crowded, full of interest and talk. "What's the case?" "Which side is it?"

Don't think them heartless; they are neither better nor worse than you or I: they get over their professional horrors, and into their proper work; and in them pity—as an emotion, ending in itself or at best in tears and a long-drawn breath, lessens, while

[1] A Highland game-keeper, when asked why a certain terrier, of singular pluck, was so much graver than the other dogs, said, "Oh, Sir, life's full o' sairiousness to him—he just never can get enuff o' fechtin'."

pity as a motive, is quickened, and gains power and purpose. It is well for poor human nature that it is so.

The operating theatre is crowded; much talk and fun, and all the cordiality and stir of youth. The surgeon with his staff of assistants is there. In comes Ailie: one look at her quiets and abates the eager students. That beautiful old woman is too much for them; they sit down, and are dumb, and gaze at her. These rough boys feel the power of her presence. She walks in quickly, but without haste; dressed in her mutch, her neckerchief, her white dimity shortgown, her black bombazeen petticoat, showing her white worsted stockings and her carpet-shoes. Behind her was James, with Rab. James sat down in the distance, and took that huge and noble head between his knees. Rab looked perplexed and dangerous; forever cocking his ear and dropping it as fast.

Ailie stepped up on a seat, and laid herself on the table, as her friend the surgeon told her; arranged herself, gave a rapid look at James, shut her eyes, rested herself on me, and took my hand. The operation was at once begun; it was necessarily slow; and chloroform—one of God's best gifts to his suffering children— was then unknown. The surgeon did his work. The pale face showed its pain, but was still and silent. Rab's soul was working within him; he saw that something strange was going on,—blood flowing from his mistress, and she suffering; his ragged ear was up, and importunate; he growled and gave now and then a sharp impatient yelp; he would have liked to have done something to that man. But James had him firm, and gave him a glower from time to time and an intimation of a possible kick;—all the better for James, it kept his eye and his mind off Ailie.

It is over: she is dressed, steps gently and decently down from the table, looks for James, then, turning to the surgeon and the students, she curtsies,—and in a low, clear voice, begs their pardon if she has behaved ill. The students—all of us—wept like children; the surgeon wrapped her up carefully,—and, resting on James and me, Ailie went to her room, Rab following. We put her to bed. James took off his heavy shoes, crammed with tackets, heel-capt and toe-capt, and put them carefully under the table, saying, "Maister John, I'm for nane o' yer strynge nurse bodies for Ailie. I'll be her nurse, and on my stockin' soles I'll gang about as canny as pussy." And so he did; and handy and clever, and swift and tender as any woman, was that horny-handed, snell, peremptory little man. Everything she got he gave her: he seldom slept:

and often I saw his small, shrewd eyes out of the darkness, fixed on her. As before, they spoke little.

Rab behaved well, never moving, showing us how meek and gentle he could be, and occasionally, in his sleep, letting us know that he was demolishing some adversary. He took a walk with me every day, generally to the Candlemaker Row; but he was sombre and mild; declined doing battle, though some fit cases offered, and indeed submitted to sundry indignities; and was always very ready to turn, and came faster back, and trotted up the stair with much lightness, and went straight to that door.

Jess, the mare—now white—had been sent, with her weather-worn cart, to Howgate, and had doubtless her own dim and placid meditations and confusions, on the absence of her master and Rab, and her unnatural freedom from the road and her cart.

For some days Ailie did well. The wound healed "by the first intention"; as James said, "Oor Ailie's skin's ower clean to beil." The students came in quiet and anxious, and surrounded her bed. She said she liked to see their young, honest faces. The surgeon dressed her, and spoke to her in his own short kind way, pitying her through his eyes. Rab and James outside the circle,—Rab being now reconciled, and even cordial, and having made up his mind that as yet nobody required worrying, but, as you may suppose, semper paratus.

So far well: but, four days after the operation, my patient had a sudden and long shivering, a "groofin'," as she called it. I saw her soon after; her eyes were too bright, her cheek coloured; she was restless, and ashamed of being so; the balance was lost; mischief had begun. On looking at the wound, a blush of red told the secret: her pulse was rapid, her breathing anxious and quick, she wasn't herself, as she said, and was vexed at her restlessness. We tried what we could. James did everything, was everywhere; never in the way, never out of it; Rab subsided under the table into a dark place, and was motionless, all but his eye, which followed every one. Ailie got worse; began to wander in her mind, gently; was more demonstrative in her ways to James, rapid in her questions, and sharp at times. He was vexed, and said, "She was never that way afore; no, never." For a time she knew her head was wrong, and was always asking our pardon—the dear, gentle old woman: then delirium set in strong, without pause. Her brain gave way, and that terrible spectacle,

"The intellectual power, through words and things,
Went sounding on its dim and perilous way;"

she sang bits of old songs and Psalms, stopping suddenly, mingling
the Psalms of David, and the diviner words of his Son and Lord,
with homely odds and ends and scraps of ballads.

Nothing more touching, or in a sense more strangely beautiful,
did I ever witness. Her tremulous, rapid, affectionate, eager
Scotch voice,—the swift, aimless, bewildered mind, the baffled
utterance, the bright and perilous eye; some wild words, some
household cares, something for James, the names of the dead,
Rab called rapidly and in a "fremyt" voice, and he starting up,
surprised, and slinking off as if he were to blame somehow, or
had been dreaming he heard. Many eager questions and beseech-
ings which James and I could make nothing of, and on which she
seemed to set her all and then sink back ununderstood. It was
very sad, but better than many things that are not called sad.
James hovered about, put out and miserable, but active and exact
as ever; read to her, when there was a lull, short bits from the
Psalms, prose and metre, chanting the latter in his own rude and
serious way, showing great knowledge of the fit words, bearing
up like a man, and doating over her as his "ain Ailie." "Ailie, ma
woman!" "Ma ain bonnie wee dawtie!"

The end was drawing on: the golden bowl was breaking; the
silver cord was fast being loosed—that *animula, blandula, vagula,
hospes, comesque,* was about to flee. The body and the soul—
companions for sixty years—were being sundered, and taking
leave. She was walking, alone, through the valley of that shadow,
into which one day we must all enter,—and yet she was not alone,
for we know whose rod and staff were comforting her.

One night she had fallen quiet, and as we hoped, asleep; her
eyes were shut. We put down the gas, and sat watching her.
Suddenly she sat up in bed, and taking a bed-gown which was
lying on it rolled up, she held it eagerly to her breast,—to the
right side. We could see her eyes bright with a surprising tenderness and joy, bending over this bundle of clothes. She held it as a
woman holds her sucking child; opening out her night-gown
impatiently, and holding it close, and brooding over it, and mur-
muring foolish little words, as over one whom his mother com-
forteth, and who is sucking, and being satisfied. It was pitiful and
strange to see her wasted dying look, keen and yet vague—her

immense love. "Preserve me!" groaned James, giving way. And then she rocked back and forward, as if to make it sleep, hushing it, and wasting on it her infinite fondness. "Wae's me, doctor: I declare she's thinkin' it's that bairn." "What bairn?" "The only bairn we ever had; our wee Mysie, and she's in the Kingdom, forty years and mair." It was plainly true: the pain in the breast, telling its urgent story to a bewildered, ruined brain; it was mis-read and mistaken; it suggested to her the uneasiness of a breast full of milk, and then the child; and so again once more they were together, and she had her ain wee Mysie in her bosom.

This was the close. She sunk rapidly; the delirium left her; but as she whispered, she was clean silly; it was the lightening before the final darkness. After having for some time lain still—her eyes shut, she said "James!" He came close to her, and lifting up her calm, clear, beautiful eyes, she gave him a long look, turned to me kindly but shortly, looked for Rab but could not see him, then turned to her husband again, as if she would never leave off looking, shut her eyes, and composed herself. She lay for some time breathing quick, and passed away so gently, that when we thought she was gone, James, in his old-fashioned way, held the mirror to her face. After a long pause, one small spot of dimness was breathed out; it vanished away, and never returned, leaving the blank clear darkness of the mirror without a stain. "What is our life? It is even a vapour, which appeareth for a little time, and then vanisheth away."

Rab all this time had been full awake and motionless: he came forward beside us: Ailie's hand, which James had held, was hang-ing down; it was soaked with his tears; Rab licked it all over carefully, looked at her, and returned to his place under the table.

James and I sat. I don't know how long, but for some time,— saying nothing: he started up abruptly, and with some noise went to the table, and putting his right fore and middle fingers each into a shoe, pulled them out, and put them on, breaking one of the leather latchets, and muttering in anger, "I never did the like o' that afore!"

I believe he never did; nor after either. "Rab!" he said roughly, and pointing with his thumb to the bottom of the bed. Rab leapt up, and settled himself; his head and eye to the dead face. "Maister John, ye'll wait for me," said the carrier; and disappeared in the darkness, thundering down stairs in his heavy shoes. I ran to a front window; there he was, already round the house, and out at the gate, fleeing like a shadow.

I was afraid about him, and yet not afraid; so I sat down beside Rab, and being wearied, fell asleep. I woke from a sudden noise outside. It was November, and there had been a heavy fall of snow. Rab was in *status quo*; he heard the noise too, and plainly knew it, but never moved. I looked out; and there, at the gate, in the dim morning—for the sun was not up, was Jess and the cart,—a cloud of steam rising from the old mare. I did not see James; he was already at the door, and came up the stairs, and met me. It was less than three hours since he left, and he must have posted out—who knows how?—to Howgate, full nine miles off; yoked Jess, and driven her astonished into town. He had an armful of blankets, and was streaming with perspiration. He nodded to me, spread out on the floor two pairs of old clean blankets, having at their corners, "A.G., 1794," in large letters in red worsted. These were the initials of Alison Graeme, and James may have looked in at her from without—unseen but not unthought of—when he was "wat, wat, and weary," and had walked many a mile over the hills, and seen her sitting, while "a' the lave were sleepin' "; and by the firelight putting her name on the blankets for her ain James's bed. He motioned Rab down, and taking his wife in his arms, laid her in the blankets, and wrapped her carefully and firmly up, leaving the face uncovered; and then lifting her, he nodded again sharply to me, and with a resolved but utterly miserable face, strode along the passage, and down stairs, followed by Rab. I also followed, with a light; but he didn't need it. I went out, holding stupidly the light in my hand in the frosty air; we were soon at the gate. I could have helped him, but I saw he was not to be meddled with, and he was strong, and did not need it. He laid her down as tenderly, as safely, as he had lifted her out ten days before—as tenderly as when he had her first in his arms when she was only "A.G.,"— sorted her, leaving that beautiful sealed face open to the heavens: and then taking Jess by the head, he moved away. He did not notice me, neither did Rab, who presided along behind the cart.

I stood till they passed through the long shadow of the College, and turned up Nicolson Street. I heard the solitary cart sound through the streets, and die away and come again; and I returned, thinking of that company going up Liberton brae, then along Roslin muir, the morning light touching the Pent-

lands and making them like on-looking ghosts; then down the
hill through Auchindinny woods, past "haunted Woodhouselee";
and as daybreak came sweeping up the bleak Lammermuirs, and
fell on his own door, the company would stop, and James would
take the key, and lift Ailie up again, laying her on her own bed,
and, having put Jess up, would return with Rab and shut the door.

James buried his wife, with his neighbours mourning, Rab
inspecting the solemnity from a distance. It was snow, and that
black ragged hole would look strange in the midst of the swelling
spotless cushion of white. James looked after everything; then
rather suddenly fell ill, and took to bed; was insensible when the
doctor came, and soon died. A sort of low fever was prevailing
in the village, and his want of sleep, his exhaustion, and his misery,
made him apt to take it. The grave was not difficult to re-open.
A fresh fall of snow had again made all things white and smooth;
Rab once more looked on and slunk home to the stable.

And what of Rab? I asked for him next week at the new
carrier's who got the goodwill of James's business, and was now
master of Jess and her cart. "How's Rab?" He put me off, and
said rather rudely, "What's your business wi' the dowg?" I was
not to be so put off. "Where's Rab?" He, getting confused and
red, and intermeddling with his hair, said, "Deed, sir, Rab's died."
"Dead! what did he die of?" "Weel, sir," said he, getting redder,
"he didna exactly die; he was killed. I had to brain him wi' a
rack-pin; there was nae doin' wi' him. He lay in the treviss wi'
the mear, and wadna come oot. I tempit him wi' kail and meat,
but he wad tak' naething, and keepit me frae feedin' the beast,
and he was aye gur gurrin', and grup gruppin' me by the legs.
I was laith to mak' awa wi' the auld dowg, but his like wasna
atween this and Thornill,—but 'deed, sir I could do naething
else." I believed him. Fit end for Rab, quick and complete. His
teeth and his friends gone, why should he keep the peace and
be civil?

1859

On the Antiseptic Principle
of the Practice of Surgery

JOSEPH LISTER

IN THE course of an extended investigation into the nature of inflammation, and the healthy and morbid conditions of the blood in relation to it, I arrived several years ago at the conclusion that the essential cause of suppuration in wounds is decomposition, brought about by the influence of the atmosphere upon blood or serum retained within them, and, in the case of contused wounds, upon portions of tissue destroyed by the violence of the injury.

To prevent the occurrence of suppuration with all its attendant risks was an object manifestly desirable, but till lately apparently unattainable, since it seemed hopeless to attempt to exclude the oxygen which was universally regarded as the agent by which putrefaction was effected. But when it had been shown by the researches of Pasteur that the septic properties of the atmosphere depended not on the oxygen, or any gaseous constituent, but on minute organisms suspended in it, which owed their energy to their vitality, it occurred to me that decomposition in the injured part might be avoided without excluding the air, by applying as a dressing some material capable of destroying the life of the floating particles. Upon this principle I have based a practice of which I will now attempt to give a short account.

The material which I have employed is carbolic or phenic acid, a volatile organic compound, which appears to exercise a peculiarly destructive influence upon low forms of life, and hence is the most powerful antiseptic with which we are at present acquainted.

The first class of cases to which I applied it was that of compound fractures, in which the effects of decomposition in the injured part were especially striking and pernicious. The results have been such as to establish conclusively the great principle that all local inflammatory mischief and general febrile disturbances which follow severe injuries are due to the irritating and poisonous influence of decomposing blood or sloughs. For these evils are entirely avoided by the antiseptic treatment, so that limbs which would otherwise be unhesitatingly condemned to amputation may be retained, with confidence of the best results.

In conducting the treatment, the first object must be the destruction of any septic germs which may have been introduced into the wounds, either at the moment of the accident or during the time which has since elapsed. This is done by introducing the acid of full strength into all accessible recesses of the wound by means of a piece of rag held in dressing forceps and dipped into the liquid.* This I did not venture to do in the earlier cases; but experience has shown that the compound which carbolic acid forms with the blood, and also any portions of tissue killed by its caustic action, including even parts of the bone, are disposed of by absorption and organisation, provided they are afterwards kept from decomposing. We are thus enabled to employ the antiseptic treatment efficiently at a period after the occurrence of the injury at which it would otherwise probably fail. Thus I have now under my care, in Glasgow Infirmary, a boy who was admitted with compound fracture of the leg as late as eight and one-half hours after the accident, in whom, nevertheless, all local and constitutional disturbance was avoided by means of carbolic acid, and the bones were soundly united five weeks after his admission.

The next object to be kept in view is to guard effectually against the spreading of decomposition into the wound along the stream of blood and serum which oozes out during the first few days after the accident, when the acid originally applied has been washed out or dissipated by absorption and evaporation. This part of the treatment has been greatly improved during the past few weeks. The method which I have hitherto published consisted in the application of a piece of lint dipped in the acid, overlapping the sound skin to some extent and covered with a tin cap, which was daily raised in order to touch the surface of the lint with the antiseptic. This method certainly succeeded well with wounds of moderate size; and indeed I may say that in all the many cases of this kind which have been so treated by myself or my house-surgeons, not a single failure has occurred. When, however, the wound is very large, the flow of blood and serum is

* The addition of a few drops of water to a considerable quantity of the acid, induces it to assume permanently the liquid form.

so profuse, especially during the first twenty-four hours, that the
antiseptic application cannot prevent the spread of decomposition
into the interior unless it overlaps the sound skin for a very considerable distance, and this was inadmissible by the method described above, on account of the extensive sloughing of the
surface of the cutis which it would involve. This difficulty has,
however, been overcome by employing a paste composed of
common whiting (carbonate of lime), mixed with a solution of
one part of carbolic acid in four parts of boiled linseed oil so as
to form a firm putty. This application contains the acid in too
dilute a form to excoriate the skin, which it may be made to
cover to any extent that may be thought desirable, while its substance serves as a reservoir of the antiseptic material. So long as
any discharge continues, the paste should be changed daily, and,
in order to prevent the chance of mischief occurring during the
process, a piece of rag dipped in the solution of carbolic acid in
oil is put on next the skin, and maintained there permanently, care
being taken to avoid raising it along with the putty. This rag is
always kept in an antiseptic condition from contact with the paste
above it, and destroys any germs which may fall upon it during
the short time that should alone be allowed to pass in the changing
of the dressing. The putty should be in a layer about a quarter
of an inch thick, and may be advantageously applied rolled out
between two pieces of thin calico, which maintain it in the form
of a continuous sheet, which may be wrapped in a moment round
the whole circumference of a limb if this be thought desirable,
while the putty is prevented by the calico from sticking to the
rag which is next the skin. When all discharge has ceased, the use
of the paste is discontinued, but the original rag is left adhering to
the skin till healing by scabbing is supposed to be complete. I have
at present in the hospital a man with severe compound fracture
of both bones of the left leg, caused by direct violence, who,
after the cessation of the sanious discharge under the use of the
paste, without a drop of pus appearing, has been treated for the
last two weeks exactly as if the fracture was a simple one. During
this time the rag, adhering by means of a crust of inspissated
blood collected beneath it, has continued perfectly dry, and it
will be left untouched till the usual period for removing the splints
in a simple fracture, when we may fairly expect to find a sound
cicatrix beneath it.

We cannot, however, always calculate on so perfect a result as this. More or less pus may appear after the lapse of the first week, and the larger the wound, the more likely this is to happen. And here I would desire earnestly to enforce the necessity of persevering with the antiseptic application in spite of the appearance of suppuration, so long as other symptoms are favorable. The surgeon is extremely apt to suppose that any suppuration is an indication that the antiseptic treatment has failed, and that poulticing or water dressing should be resorted to. But such a course would in many cases sacrifice a limb or a life. I cannot, however, expect my professional brethren to follow my advice blindly in such a matter, and therefore I feel it necessary to place before them, as shortly as I can, some pathological principles intimately connected, not only with the point we are immediately considering, but with the whole subject of this paper.

If a perfectly healthy granulating sore be well washed and covered with a plate of clean metal, such as block tin, fitting its surface pretty accurately, and overlapping the surrounding skin an inch or so in every direction and retained in position by adhesive plaster and a bandage, it will be found, on removing it after twenty-four or forty-eight hours, that little or nothing that can be called pus is present, merely a little transparent fluid, while at the same time there is an entire absence of the unpleasant odour invariably perceived when water dressing is changed. Here the clean metallic surface presents no recesses like those of porous lint for the septic germs to develop in, the fluid exuding from the surface of the granulations has flowed away undecomposed, and the result is the absence of suppuration. This simple experiment illustrates the important fact that granulations have no inherent tendency to form pus, but do so only when subjected to preternatural stimulus. Further, it shows that the mere contact of a foreign body does not of itself stimulate granulations to suppurate; whereas the presence of decomposing organic matter does. These truths are even more strikingly exemplified by the fact that I have elsewhere recorded that a piece of dead bone free from decomposition may not only fail to induce the granulations around it to suppurate, but may actually be absorbed by them; whereas a bit of dead bone soaked with putrid pus infallibly induces suppuration in its vicinity. . . .

I left behind me in Glasgow a boy, thirteen years of age, who, between three and four weeks previously, met with a most severe injury to the left arm, which he got entangled in a machine at a fair. There was a wound six inches long and three inches broad, and the skin was very extensively undermined beyond its limits, while the soft parts were generally so much lacerated that a pair of dressing forceps introduced at the wound and pushed directly inwards appeared beneath the skin at the opposite aspect of the limb. From this wound several tags of muscle were hanging, and among them was one consisting of about three inches of the triceps in almost its entire thickness; while the lower fragment of the bone, which was broken high up, was protruding four inches and a half, stripped of muscle, the skin being tucked in under it. Without the assistance of the antiseptic treatment, I should certainly have thought of nothing else but amputation at the shoulder-joint; but, as the radial pulse could be felt and the fingers had sensation, I did not hesitate to try to save the limb and adopted the plan of treatment above described, wrapping the arm from the shoulder to below the elbow in the antiseptic application, the whole interior of the wound, together with the protruding bone, having previously been freely treated with strong carbolic acid. About the tenth day, the discharge, which up to that time had been only sanious and serous, showed a slight admixture of slimy pus; and this increased till (a few days before I left) it amounted to about three drachms in twenty-four hours. But the boy continued as he had been after the second day, free from unfavorable symptoms, with pulse, tongue, appetite, and sleep natural and strength increasing, while the limb remained as it had been from the first, free from swelling, redness, or pain. I, therefore, persevered with the antiseptic dressing; and, before I left, the discharge was already somewhat less, while the bone was becoming firm. I think it likely that, in that boy's case, I should have found merely a superficial sore had I taken off all the dressings at the end of the three weeks; though, considering the extent of the injury, I thought it prudent to let the month expire before disturbing the rag next the skin. But I feel sure that, if I had resorted to ordinary dressing when the pus first appeared, the progress of the case would have been exceedingly different. . . .

Ordinary contused wounds are, of course, amenable to the same treatment as compound fractures, which are a complicated variety of them. I will content myself with mentioning a single instance of this class of cases. In April last, a volunteer was discharging a rifle when it burst, and blew back the thumb with its metacarpal bone, so that it could be bent back as on a hinge at the trapezial joint, which had evidently been opened, while all the soft parts between the metacarpal bones of the thumb and forefinger were torn through. I need not insist before my present audience on the ugly character of such an injury. My house-surgeon, Mr. Hector Cameron, applied carbolic acid to the whole raw surface, and completed the dressing as if for compound fracture. The hand remained free from pain, redness or swelling, and with the exception of a shallow groove, all the wound consolidated without a drop of matter, so that if it had been a clean cut, it would have been regarded as a good example of primary union. The small granulating surface soon healed, and at present a linear cicatrix alone tells of the injury he has sustained, while his thumb has all its movements and his hand a fine grasp.

If the severest forms of contused and lacerated wounds heal thus kindly under the antiseptic treatment, it is obvious that its application to simple incised wounds must be merely a matter of detail. I have devoted a good deal of attention to this class, but I have not as yet pleased myself altogether with any of the methods I have employed. I am, however, prepared to go so far as to say that a solution of carbolic acid in twenty parts of water, while a, mild and cleanly application, may be relied on for destroying any septic germs that may fall upon the wound during the performance of an operation; and also that, for preventing the subsequent introduction of others, the paste above described, applied as for compound fractures, gives excellent results. Thus I have had a case of strangulated inguinal hernia in which it was necessary to take away half a pound of thickened omentum, heal without any deep-seated suppuration or any tenderness of the sac or any fever; and amputations, including one immediately below the knee, have remained absolutely free from constitutional symptoms . . .

There is one point more that I cannot but advert to, viz., the influence of this mode of treatment upon the general healthiness of an hospital. Previously to its introduction the two large wards in which most of my cases of accident and of operation are treated were among the unhealthiest in the whole surgical division of the Glasgow Royal Infirmary, in consequence apparently of those wards being unfavorably placed with reference to the supply of fresh air; and I have felt ashamed when recording the results of my practice, to have so often to allude to hospital gangrene or pyæmia. It was interesting, though melancholy, to observe that whenever all or nearly all the beds contained cases with open sores, these grievous complications were pretty sure to show themselves; so that I came to welcome simple fractures, though in themselves of little interest either for myself or the students, because their presence diminished the proportion of open sores among the patients. But since the antiseptic treatment has been brought into full operation, and wounds and abscesses no longer poison the atmosphere with putrid exhalations, my wards, though in other respects under precisely the same circumstances as before, have completely changed their character; so that during the last nine months not a single instance of pyæmia, hospital gangrene, or erysipelas has occurred in them.

As there appears to be no doubt regarding the cause of this change, the importance of the fact can hardly be exaggerated.

1867

Louis Pasteur and the
Conquest of Rabies

RENÉ VALLERY-RADOT

AMIDST the various researches undertaken in his laboratory, one study was placed by Pasteur above every other, one mystery constantly haunted his mind—that of hydrophobia. When he was received at the Académie Française, Renan, hoping to prove himself a prophet for once, said to him: "Humanity will owe to you deliverance from a horrible disease and also from a sad anomaly: I mean the distrust which we cannot help mingling with the caresses of the animal in whom we see most of nature's smiling benevolence."

The two first mad dogs brought into the laboratory were given to Pasteur, in 1880, by M. Bourrel, an old army veterinary surgeon who had long been trying to find a remedy for hydrophobia. He had invented a preventive measure which consisted in filing down the teeth of dogs, so that they should not bite into the skin; in 1874, he had written that vivisection threw no light on that disease, the laws of which were "impenetrable to science until now." It now occurred to him that, perhaps, the investigators in the laboratory of the Ecole Normale might be more successful than he had been in his kennels in the Rue Fontaine-au-Roi.

One of the two dogs he sent was suffering from what is called *dumb madness*: his jaw hung, half opened and paralyzed, his tongue was covered with foam, and his eyes full of wistful anguish; the other made ferocious darts at anything held out to him, with a rabid fury in his bloodshot eyes, and, in the hallucinations of his delirium, gave vent to haunting, despairing howls.

Much confusion prevailed at that time regarding this disease, its seat, its causes, and its remedy. Three things seemed positive: firstly, that the rabic virus was contained in the saliva of the mad animals; secondly, that it was communicated through bites; and thirdly, that the period of incubation might vary from a few days to several months. Clinical observation was reduced to complete impotence; perhaps experiments might throw some light on the subject. . . .

One day, Pasteur having wished to collect a little saliva from the jaws of a rabid dog, so as to obtain it directly, two of Bourrel's assistants undertook to drag a mad bulldog, foaming at the mouth, from its cage; they seized it by means of a lasso, and stretched it on a table. These two men, thus associated with Pasteur in the same danger, with the same calm heroism, held the struggling, ferocious animal down with their powerful hands, whilst the scientist drew, by means of a glass tube held between his lips, a few drops of the deadly saliva.

But the same uncertainty followed the inoculation of the saliva; the incubation was so slow that weeks and months often elapsed whilst the result of an experiment was being anxiously awaited. Evidently the saliva was not a sure agent for experiments, and if more knowledge was to be obtained, some other means had to be found of obtaining it. . . .

As the number of cases observed became larger, he felt a growing conviction that hydrophobia has its seat in the nervous system, and particularly in the medulla oblongata. "The propagation of the virus in a rabid dog's nervous system can almost be observed in its every stage," writes M. Roux, Pasteur's daily associate in these researches, which he afterwards made the subject of his thesis. "The anguish and fury due to the excitation of the grey cortex of the brain are followed by an alteration of the voice and a difficulty in deglutition. The medulla oblongata and the nerves starting from it are attacked in their turn; finally, the spinal cord itself becomes invaded and paralysis closes the scene."

As long as the virus has not reached the nervous centres, it may sojourn for weeks or months in some point of the body; this explains the slowness of certain incubations, and the fortunate escapes after some bites from rabid dogs. The *a priori* supposition that the virus attacks the nervous centres went very far back; it had served as a basis to a theory enunciated by Dr. Duboué (of Pau), who had, however, not supported it by any experiments. . . .

Pasteur was about to prove that it was possible to succeed by operating in a special manner, according to a rigorous technique, unknown in other laboratories. When the post-mortem examination of a mad dog had revealed no characteristic lesion, the brain was uncovered, and the surface of the medulla oblongata scalded with a glass stick, so as to destroy any external dust or dirt. Then, with a long tube previously put through a flame, a particle of the substance was drawn and deposited in a glass just taken from a stove heated up to 200° C., and mixed with a little water or sterilized broth by means of a glass agitator, also previously put through a flame. The syringe used for inoculation on the rabbit or dog (lying ready on the operating board) had been purified in boiling water.

Most of the animals who received this inoculation under the skin succumbed to hydrophobia; that virulent matter was therefore more successful than the saliva, which was a great result obtained.

"The seat of the rabic virus," wrote Pasteur, "is therefore not in the saliva only: the brain contains it in a degree of virulence at least equal to that of the saliva of rabid animals." But, to Pasteur's eyes, this was but a preliminary step on the long road which stretched before him; it was necessary that all the inoculated animals should contract hydrophobia, and the period of incubation had to be shortened.

It was then that it occurred to Pasteur to inoculate the rabic virus directly on the surface of a dog's brain. He thought that, by placing the virus from the beginning in its true medium, hydrophobia would more surely supervene and the incubation might be shorter. The experiment was attempted: a dog under chloroform was fixed to the operating board, and a small, round portion of the cranium removed by means of a trephine (a surgical instrument somewhat similar to a fret-saw); the tough fibrous membrane called the dura-mater, being thus exposed, was then injected with a small quantity of the prepared virus, which lay in readiness in a Pravaz syringe. The wound was washed with carbolic and the skin stitched together, the whole thing lasting but a few minutes. The dog, on returning to consciousness, seemed quite the same as usual. But, after fourteen days, hydrophobia appeared: rabid fury, characteristic howls, the tearing up and devouring of his bed, delirious hallucination, and finally, paralysis and death.

A method was therefore found by which rabies was contracted surely and swiftly. Trephinings were again performed on chloroformed animals—Pasteur had a great horror of useless sufferings, and always insisted on anæsthesia. In every case, characteristic hydrophobia occurred after inoculation on the brain. The main lines of this complicated question were beginning to be traceable; but other obstacles were in the way. Pasteur could not apply the method he had hitherto used, *i.e.* to isolate, and then to cultivate in an artificial medium, the microbe of hydrophobia, for he failed in detecting this microbe. Yet its existence admitted of no doubt; perhaps it was beyond the limits of human sight. "Since this unknown being is living," thought Pasteur, "we must cultivate it; failing an artificial medium, let us try the brain of living rabbits; it would indeed be an experimental feat!"

As soon as a trephined and inoculated rabbit died paralyzed, a little of his rabic medulla was inoculated to another; each inoculation succeeded another, and the time of incubation became shorter and shorter, until, after a hundred uninterrupted inoculations, it came to be reduced to seven days. But the virus, having reached this degree, the virulence of which was found to be greater than that of the virus of dogs made rabid by an accidental bite, now became fixed; Pasteur had mastered it. He could now predict the exact time when death should occur in each of the inoculated animals; his predictions were verified with surprising accuracy.

Pasteur was not yet satisfied with the immense progress marked by infallible inoculation and the shortened incubation; he now wished to decrease the degrees of virulence—when the attenuation of the virus was once conquered, it might be hoped that dogs could be made refractory to rabies. Pasteur abstracted a fragment of the medulla from a rabbit which had just died of rabies after an inoculation of the fixed virus; this fragment was suspended by a thread in a sterilized phial, the air in which was kept dry by some pieces of caustic potash lying at the bottom of the vessel and which was closed by a cotton-wool plug to prevent the entrance of atmospheric dusts. The temperature of the room where this desiccation took place was maintained at 23° C. As the medulla gradually became dry, its virulence decreased, until, at the end of fourteen days, it had become absolutely extinguished. This now inactive medulla was crushed and mixed with pure water, and injected under the skin of some dogs. The next day they were inoculated with medulla which had been desiccating for thirteen days, and so on, using increased virulence until the medulla was used of a rabbit dead the same day. These dogs might now be bitten by rabid dogs given them as companions for a few minutes, or submitted to the intracranial inoculations of the deadly virus: they resisted both.

Having at last obtained this refractory condition, Pasteur was anxious that his results should be verified by a Commission. The Minister of Public Instruction acceded to this desire, and a Commission was constituted in May, 1884, composed of Messrs. Béclard, Dean of the Faculty of Medicine, Paul Bert, Bouley, Villemin, Vulpian, and Tisserand, Director of the Agricultural Office. The Commission immediately set to work; a rabid dog having succumbed at Alfort on June 1, its carcass was brought to the laboratory of the Ecole Normale, and a fragment of the medulla oblongata was mixed with some sterilized broth. Two dogs, declared by Pasteur to be refractory to rabies, were trephined, and a few drops of the liquid injected into their brains; two other dogs and two rabbits received inoculations at the same time, with the same liquid and in precisely the same manner.

Bouley was taking notes for a report to be presented to the Minister:

"M. Pasteur tells us that, considering the nature of the rabic virus used, the rabbits and the two new dogs will develop rabies within twelve or fifteen days, and that the two refractory dogs will not develop it at all, however long they may be detained under observation."

On May 29, Mme. Pasteur wrote to her children:

"The Commission on rabies met to-day and elected M. Bouley as chairman. Nothing is settled as to commencing experiments. Your father is absorbed in his thoughts, talks little, sleeps little, rises at dawn, and, in one word, continues the life I began with him this day thirty-five years ago."

On June 3, Bourrel sent word that he had a rabid dog in the kennels of the Rue Fontaine-au-Roi; a refractory dog and a new dog were immediately submitted to numerous bites; the latter was violently bitten on the head in several places. The rabid dog, still living the next day and still able to bite, was given two more dogs, one of which was refractory; this dog, and the refractory dog bitten on the 3rd, were allowed to receive the first bites, the Commission having thought that perhaps the saliva might then be more abundant and more dangerous.

On June 6, the rabid dog having died, the Commission proceeded to inoculate the medulla of the animal into six more dogs, by means of trephining. Three of those dogs were refractory; the three others were fresh from the kennels; there were also two rabbits.

On the 10th, Bourrel telegraphed the arrival of another rabid dog, and the same operations were gone through.

"This rabid, furious dog," wrote Pasteur to his son-in-law, "had spent the night lying on his master's bed; his appearance had been suspicious for a day or two. On the morning of the 10th, his voice became rabietic, and his master, who had heard the bark of a rabid dog twenty years ago, was seized with terror, and brought the dog to M. Bourrel, who found that he was indeed in the biting stage of rabies. Fortunately a lingering fidelity had prevented him from attacking his master. . . .

"This morning a rabic condition is beginning to appear on one of the new dogs trephined on June 1, at the same time as two refractory dogs. Let us hope that the other new dog will also develop it and that the two refractory ones will resist."

At the same time that the Commission examined this dog which developed rabies within the exact time indicated by Pasteur, the two rabbits on whom inoculation had been performed at the same time were found to present the first symptoms of rabic paralysis. "This paralysis," noted Bouley, "is revealed by great weakness of the limbs, particularly of the hind quarters; the least shock knocks them over and they experience great difficulty in getting up again." The second new dog on whom inoculation had been performed on June 1 was now also rabid; the refractory dogs were in perfect health. . . .

. . . Pasteur pondered on the means of extinguishing hydrophobia or of merely diminishing its frequency. Could dogs be vaccinated? There are 100,000 dogs in Paris, about 2,500,000 more

in the provinces: vaccination necessitates several preventive inoculations; innumerable kennels would have to be built for the
purpose, to say nothing of the expense of keeping the dogs and
of providing a trained staff capable of performing the difficult
and dangerous operations. And, as M. Nocard truly remarked,
where were rabbits to be found in sufficient number for the vaccine emulsions?

Optional vaccination did not seem more practicable; it could
only be worked on a very restricted scale and was therefore of
very little use in a general way.

The main question was the possibility of preventing hydrophobia from occurring in a human being, previously bitten by a
rabid dog . . .

As to the origin of rabies, it remained unknown and was
erroneously attributed to divers causes. Spontaneity was still
believed in. Bouley himself did not absolutely reject the idea of
it, for he said in 1870: "In the immense majority of cases, this
disease proceeds from contagion; out of 1,000 rabid dogs, 999
at least owe their condition to inoculation by a bite."

Pasteur was anxious to uproot this fallacy, as also another very
serious error, vigorously opposed by Bouley, by M. Nocard, and
by another veterinary surgeon in a *Manual on Rabies*, published
in 1882, and still as tenacious as most prejudices, viz., that the
word hydrophobia is synonymous with rabies. The rabid dog
is *not* hydrophobe, he does *not* abhor water. The word is applicable to rabid human beings, but is false concerning rabid dogs.

Many people in the country, constantly seeing Pasteur's name
associated with the word rabies, fancied that he was a consulting
veterinary surgeon, and pestered him with letters full of questions.
What was to be done to a dog whose manner seemed strange,
though there was no evidence of a suspicious bite? Should he
be shot? "No," answered Pasteur, "shut him up securely, and he
will soon die if he is really mad." Some dog owners hesitated to
destroy a dog manifestly bitten by a mad dog. "It is such a good
dog!" "The law is absolute," answered Pasteur; "every dog bitten
by a mad dog must be destroyed at once." And it irritated him
that village mayors should close their eyes to the non-observance
of the law, and thus contribute to a recrudescence of rabies.

Pasteur wasted his precious time answering all those letters.
On March 28, 1885, he wrote to his friend Jules Vercel—

"Alas! we shall not be able to go to Arbois for Easter; I shall be busy for some time settling down, or rather settling my dogs down at Villeneuve l'Etang. I also have some new experiments on rabies on hand which will take some months. I am demonstrating this year that dogs can be vaccinated, or made refractory to rabies *after* they have been bitten by mad dogs.

"I have not yet dared to treat human beings after bites from rabid dogs; but the time is not far off, and I am much inclined to begin by myself—inoculating myself with rabies, and then arresting the consequences; for I am beginning to feel very sure of my results. . . ."

In May, everything at Villeneuve l'Etang was ready for the reception of sixty dogs. Fifty of them, already made refractory to bites or rabic inoculation, were successively accommodated in the immense kennel, where each had his cell and his experiment number. They had been made refractory by being inoculated with fragments of medulla, which had hung for a fortnight in a phial, and of which the virulence was extinguished, after which further inoculations had been made, gradually increasing in virulence until the highest degree of it had again been reached . . .

On May 29 Pasteur wrote to his son—

"I thought I should have done with rabies by the end of April; I must postpone my hopes till the end of July. Yet I have not remained stationary; but, in these difficult studies, one is far from the goal as long as the last word, the last decisive proof is not acquired. What I aspire to is the possibility of treating a man after a bite with no fear of accidents. . . ."

Two series of experiments were being carried out . . . The first consisted in making dogs refractory to rabies by preventive inoculations; the second in preventing the onset of rabies in dogs bitten or subjected to inoculation . . .

On Monday, July 6, Pasteur saw a little Alsatian boy, Joseph Meister, enter his laboratory, accompanied by his mother. He was only nine years old, and had been bitten two days before by a mad dog at Meissengott, near Schlestadt.

The child, going alone to school by a little by-road, had been attacked by a furious dog and thrown to the ground. Too small to defend himself, he had only thought of covering his face with his hands. A bricklayer, seeing the scene from a distance, arrived, and succeeded in beating the dog off with an iron bar; he picked up the boy, covered with blood and saliva. The dog went back to his master, Théodore Vone, a grocer at Meissengott, whom he bit on the arm. Vone seized a gun and shot the animal, whose stomach was found to be full of hay, straw, pieces of wood, etc. When little Meister's parents heard all these details they went, full of anxiety, to consult Dr. Weber, at Villé, that same evening. After cauterizing the wounds with carbolic, Dr. Weber advised Mme. Meister to start for Paris, where she could relate the facts to one who was not a physician, but who would be the best judge of what could be done in such a serious case. Théodore Vone, anxious on his own and on the child's account, decided to come also.

Pasteur reassured him; his clothes had wiped off the dog's saliva, and his shirt-sleeve was intact. He might safely go back to Alsace, and he promptly did so.

Pasteur's emotion was great at the sight of the fourteen wounds of the little boy, who suffered so much that he could hardly walk. What should he do for this child? could he risk the preventive treatment which had been constantly successful on his dogs? Pasteur was divided between his hopes and his scruples, painful in their acuteness. Before deciding on a course of action, he made arrangements for the comfort of this poor woman and her child, alone in Paris, and gave them an appointment for five o'clock, after the Institute meeting. He did not wish to attempt anything without having seen Vulpian and talked it over with him. Since the Rabies Commission had been constituted, Pasteur had formed a growing esteem for the great judgment of Vulpian, who, in his lectures on the general and comparative physiology of the nervous system, had already mentioned the profit to human clinics to be drawn from experimenting on animals.

His was a most prudent mind, always seeing all the aspects of a problem. The man was worthy of the scientist: he was absolutely straightforward, and of a discreet and active kindness. He was passionately fond of work, and had recourse to it when smitten by a deep sorrow.

Vulpian expressed the opinion that Pasteur's experiments on dogs were sufficiently conclusive to authorize him to foresee the same success in human pathology. Why not try this treatment? added the professor, usually so reserved. Was there any other efficacious treatment against hydrophobia? If at least the cauterizations had been made with a red-hot iron! but what was the good of carbolic acid twelve hours after the accident. If the almost certain danger which threatened the boy were weighed against the chances of snatching him from death, Pasteur would see that it was more than a right, that it was a duty to apply anti-rabic inoculation to little Meister.

This was also the opinion of Dr. Grancher, whom Pasteur consulted. M. Grancher worked at the laboratory; he and Dr. Straus might claim to be the two first French physicians who took up the study of bacteriology; these novel studies fascinated him, and he was drawn to Pasteur by the deepest admiration and by a strong affection, which Pasteur thoroughly reciprocated.

Vulpian and M. Grancher examined little Meister in the evening, and, seeing the number of bites, some of which, on one hand especially, were very deep, they decided on performing the first inoculation immediately; the substance chosen was fourteen days old and had quite lost its virulence: it was to be followed by further inoculations gradually increasing in strength.

It was a very slight operation, a mere injection into the side (by means of a Pravaz syringe) of a few drops of a liquid prepared with some fragments of medulla oblongata. The child, who cried very much before the operation, soon dried his tears when he found the slight prick was all that he had to undergo.

Pasteur had had a bedroom comfortably arranged for the mother and child in the old Rollin College, and the little boy was very happy amidst the various animals—chickens, rabbits, white mice, guinea-pigs, etc.; he begged and easily obtained of Pasteur the life of several of the youngest of them.

"All is going well," Pasteur wrote to his son-in-law on July 11: "the child sleeps well, has a good appetite, and the inoculated matter is absorbed into the system from one day to another without leaving a trace. It is true that I have not yet come to the test inoculations, which will take place on Tuesday, Wednesday and Thursday. If the lad keeps well during the three following weeks, I think the experiment will be safe to succeed. I shall send the child and his mother back to Meissengott (near Schlestadt) in any case on August 1, giving these good people detailed instruction as to the observations they are to record for me. I shall make no statement before the end of the vacation."

But, as the inoculations were becoming more virulent, Pasteur became a prey to anxiety: "My dear children," wrote Mme. Pasteur, "your father has had another bad night; he is dreading the last inoculations on the child. And yet there can be no drawing back now! The boy continues in perfect health."

Renewed hopes were expressed in the following letter from Pasteur—

"My dear René, I think great things are coming to pass. Joseph Meister has just left the laboratory. The three last inoculations have left some pink marks under the skin, gradually widening and not at all tender. There is some action, which is becoming more intense as we approach the final inoculation, which will take place on Thursday, July 16. The lad is very well this morning, and has slept well, though slightly restless; he has a good appetite and no feverishness. He had a slight hysterical attack yesterday."

The letter ended with an affectionate invitation. "Perhaps one of the great medical facts of the century is going to take place; you would regret not having seen it!"

Pasteur was going through a succession of hopes, fears, anguish, and an ardent yearning to snatch little Meister from death; he could no longer work. At night, feverish visions came to him of this child whom he had seen playing in the garden, suffocating in the mad struggles of hydrophobia, like the dying child he had seen at the Hôpital Trousseau in 1880. Vainly his experimental genius assured him that the virus of that most terrible of diseases was about to be vanquished, that humanity was about to be delivered from this dread horror—his human tenderness was stronger than all, his accustomed ready sympathy for the sufferings and anxieties of others was for the nonce centered in "the dear lad."

The treatment lasted ten days; Meister was inoculated twelve times. The virulence of the medulla used was tested by trephinings on rabbits, and proved to be gradually stronger. Pasteur even inoculated on July 16, at 11 A.M., some medulla only one day old, bound to give hydrophobia to rabbits after only seven days' incubation; it was the surest test of the immunity and preservation due to the treatment.

Cured from his wounds, delighted with all he saw, gaily running about as if he had been in his own Alsatian farm, little Meister, whose blue eyes now showed neither fear nor shyness, merrily received the last inoculation; in the evening, after claiming a kiss from "Dear Monsieur Pasteur," as he called him, he went to bed and slept peacefully. Pasteur spent a terrible night of insomnia; in those slow dark hours of night when all vision is distorted, Pasteur, losing sight of the accumulation of experi-

ments which guaranteed his success, imagined that the little boy
would die.

The treatment being now completed, Pasteur left little Meister
to the care of Dr. Grancher (the lad was not to return to Alsace
until July 27) and consented to take a few days' rest. He spent
them with his daughter in a quiet, almost deserted country place
in Burgundy, but without however finding much restfulness in
the beautiful peaceful scenery; he lived in constant expectation
of Dr. Grancher's daily telegram or letter containing news of
Joseph Meister.

By the time he went to the Jura, Pasteur's fears had almost
disappeared. He wrote from Arbois to his son August 3, 1885:·
"Very good news last night of the bitten lad. I am looking forward with great hopes to the time when I can draw a conclusion.
It will be thirty-one days to-morrow since he was bitten."

. . . On his return to Paris, Pasteur found himself obliged to
hasten the organization of a "service" for the preventive treatment of hydrophobia after a bite. The Mayor of Villers-Farlay,
in the Jura, wrote to him that, on October 14, a shepherd had been
cruelly bitten by a rabid dog.

Six little shepherd boys were watching over their sheep in a
meadow; suddenly they saw a large dog passing along the road,
with hanging, foaming jaws.

"A mad dog!" they exclaimed. The dog, seeing the children,
left the road and charged them; they ran away shrieking, but the
eldest of them, J. B. Jupille, fourteen years of age, bravely turned
back in order to protect the flight of his comrades. Armed with
his whip, he confronted the infuriated animal, who flew at him
and seized his left hand. Jupille, wrestling with the dog, succeeded
in kneeling on him, and forcing his jaws open in order to disen-
gage his left hand; in so doing, his right hand was seriously bitten
in its turn; finally, having been able to get hold of the animal by
the neck, Jupille called to his little brother to pick up his whip
which had fallen during the struggle, and securely fastened the
dog's jaws with the lash. He then took his wooden *sabot*, with
which he battered the dog's head, after which, in order to be
sure that it could do no further harm, he dragged the body down
to a little stream in the meadow, and held the head under water
for several minutes. Death being now certain, and all danger
removed from his comrades, Jupille returned to Villers-Farlay.

Whilst the boy's wounds were being bandaged, the dog's carcass was fetched, and a necropsy took place the next day. The two veterinary surgeons who examined the body had not the slightest hesitation in declaring that the dog was rabid.

The Mayor of Villers-Farlay, who had been to see Pasteur during the summer, wrote to tell him that this lad would die a victim of his own courage unless the new treatment intervened. The answer came immediately: Pasteur declared that, after five years' study, he had succeeded in making dogs refractory to rabies, even six or eight days after being bitten; that, he had only once yet applied his method to a human being, but that once with success, in the case of little Meister, and that, if Jupille's family consented, the boy might be sent to him. "I shall keep him near me in a room of my laboratory; he will be watched and need not go to bed; he will merely receive a daily prick, not more painful than a pin-prick."

The family, on hearing this letter, came to an immediate decision; but, between the day when he was bitten and Jupille's arrival in Paris, six whole days had elapsed, whilst in Meister's case there had only been two and a half!

Yet, however great were Pasteur's fears for the life of this tall lad, who seemed quite surprised when congratulated on his courageous conduct, they were not what they had been in the first instance—he felt much greater confidence.

A few days later, on October 26, Pasteur in a statement at the Academy of Sciences described the treatment followed for Meister. Three months and three days had passed, and the child remained perfectly well. Then he spoke of his new attempt. Vulpian rose—

"The Academy will not be surprised," he said, "if, as a member of the Medical and Surgical Section, I ask to be allowed to express the feelings of admiration inspired in me by M. Pasteur's statement. I feel certain that those feelings will be shared by the whole of the medical profession.

"Hydrophobia, that dread disease against which all therapeutic measures had hitherto failed, has at last, found a remedy. M. Pasteur, who has been preceded by no one in this path, has been led by a series of investigations unceasingly carried on for several years, to create a method of treatment, by means of which the development of hydrophobia can *infallibly* be prevented in a patient recently bitten by a rabid dog. I say infallibly, because, after what I have seen in M. Pasteur's laboratory, I do not doubt the constant success of this treatment when it is put into full practice a few days only after a rabic bite. . . . "

As soon as Pasteur's paper was published, people bitten by rabid dogs began to arrive from all sides to the laboratory. The "service" of hydrophobia became the chief business of the day. Every morning was spent by Eugène Viala in preparing the fragments of marrow used for inoculations: in a little room permanently kept at a temperature of 20° to 23° C., stood rows of sterilized flasks, their tubular openings closed by plugs of cotton wool. Each flask contained a rabic marrow, hanging from the stopper by a thread and gradually drying up by the action of some fragments of caustic potash lying at the bottom of the flask. Viala cut those marrows into small pieces by means of scissors previously put through a flame, and placed them in small sterilized glasses; he then added a few drops of veal broth and pounded the mixture with a glass rod. The vaccinal liquid was now ready; each glass was covered with a paper cover, and bore the date of the medulla used, the earliest of which was fourteen days old. For each patient under the treatment from a certain date, there was a whole series of little glasses. . . .

Pasteur took a personal interest in each of his patients, helping those who were poor and illiterate to find suitable lodgings in the great capital. Children especially inspired him with a loving solicitude. But his pity was mingled with terror, when, on November 9, a little girl of ten was brought to him who had been severely bitten on the head by a mountain dog, on October 3, thirty-seven days before! The wound was still suppurating. He said to himself, "This is a hopeless case: hydrophobia is no doubt about to appear immediately; it is much too late for the preventive treatment to have the least chance of success. Should I not, in the scientific interest of the method, refuse to treat this child? If the issue is fatal, all those who have already been treated will be frightened, and many bitten persons, discouraged from coming to the laboratory, may succumb to the disease!" These thoughts rapidly crossed Pasteur's mind. But he found himself unable to resist his compassion for the father and mother, begging him to try and save their child.

After the treatment was over, Louise Pelletier had returned to school, when fits of breathlessness appeared, soon followed by convulsive spasms; she could swallow nothing. Pasteur hastened to her side when these symptoms began, and new inoculations were attempted. On December 2, there was a respite of a few hours, moments of calm which inspired Pasteur with the vain hope that she might yet be saved. This delusion was a short-lived one. Pasteur spent the day by little Louise's bedside, in her parents' rooms in the Rue Dauphine. He could not tear himself away; she herself, full of affection for him, gasped out a desire that he should not go away, that he should stay with her! She felt for his hand between two spasms. Pasteur shared the grief of the father and mother. When all hope had to be abandoned: "I did so wish I could have saved your little one!" he said. And as he came down the staircase, he burst into tears.

He was obliged, a few days later, to preside at the reception of Joseph Bertrand at the Académie Française; his sad feelings little in harmony with the occasion. He read in a mournful and troubled voice the speech he had prepared during his peaceful and happy holidays at Arbois. Henry Houssaye, reporting on this ceremony in the *Journal des Débats*, wrote, "M. Pasteur ended his speech amidst a torrent of applause, he received a veritable ovation. He seemed unaccountably moved. How can M. Pasteur, who has received every mark of admiration, every supreme honour, whose name is consecrated by universal renown, still be touched by anything save the discoveries of his powerful genius?" People did not realize that Pasteur's thoughts were far away from himself and from his brilliant discovery. He was thinking of the child he had been unable to snatch from the jaws of death; his mind was not with the living, but with the dead. . . .

Edition of 1920

On Experimental Science

LOUIS PASTEUR

To will is a great thing, for Action and Work usually follow Will, and almost always Work is accompanied by success. These three things, Will, Work, Success, fill human existence. Will opens the door to success both brilliant and happy; Work passes these doors, and at the end of the journey Success comes to crown one's efforts. And so, if your resolution is firm, your task, be it what it may, is already begun; you have but to walk forward, it will achieve itself. . . .

The cultivation of Science in its highest expression is perhaps even more necessary to the moral condition than to the material prosperity of a nation.

Great discoveries—the manifestations of thought in Art, in Science and in Letters, in a word the disinterested exercise of the mind in every direction and the centres of instruction from which it radiates, introduces into the whole of Society that philosophical or scientific spirit, that spirit of discernment which submits everything to severe reasoning, condemns ignorance and scatters errors and prejudices. They raise the intellectual level and the moral sense, and through them the Divine idea itself is spread abroad and intensified.

Science should not concern itself in any way with the philosophical consequences of its discoveries. If through the development of my experimental studies I come to demonstrate that matter can organize itself of its own accord into a cell or into a living being, I would come here to proclaim it with the legitimate pride of an inventor conscious of having made a great discovery, and I would add, if provoked to do so, "All the worse for those whose doctrines or systems do not fit in with the truth of the natural facts."

It was with similar pride that I defied my opponents to contradict me when I said, "In the present state of science the doctrine of spontaneous generation is a chimera." And I add, with similar independence, "All the worse for those whose philosophical or political ideas are hindered by my studies."

This is not to be taken to mean that, in my beliefs and in the conduct of my life, I only take account of acquired science; if I would, I could not do so, for I should then have to strip myself of a part of myself. There are two men in each one of us: the scientist, he who starts with a clear field and desires to rise to the knowledge of Nature through observation, experimentation and reasoning, and the man of sentiment, the man of belief, the man who mourns his dead children, and who cannot, alas, prove that he will see them again, but who believes that he will, and lives in that hope, the man who will not die like a vibrio, but who feels that the force that is within him cannot die. The two domains are distinct, and woe to him who tries to let them trespass on each other in the so imperfect state of human knowledge.

To his adversaries on the doctrine of fermentation:
What is then your idea of the progress of Science? Science advances one step, then another, and then draws back and meditates before taking a third. Does the impossibility of taking that last step suppress the success acquired by the two others? Would you say to an infant who hesitated before a third step, having ventured on two previous ones: 'Thy former efforts are of no avail; never shalt thou walk'?

You wish to upset what you call my theory, apparently in order to defend another; allow me to tell you by what signs these theories are recognized: the characteristic of erroneous theories is the impossibility of ever seeing new facts; whenever such a fact is discovered, these theories have to be grafted with further hypotheses in order to account for them. True theories, on the contrary, are the expression of actual facts and are characterized by being able to predict new facts, a natural, consequence of those already known. In a word, the characteristic of a true theory is its fruitfulness.

The boldest conceptions, the most legitimate speculations can be embodied but from the day when they are consecrated by observation and experiment. Laboratories and discoveries are correlative terms; if you suppress laboratories, Physical Science will become stricken with barrenness and death; it will become mere powerless information instead of a science of progress and futurity; give it back its laboratories, and life, fecundity and power will reappear. Away from their laboratories, physicists and chemists are but disarmed soldiers on a battlefield.

The deduction from these principles is evident: if the conquests useful to humanity touch your heart—if you remain confounded before the marvels of telegraphy, of anaesthesia, of the daguerreotype, and many other admirable discoveries—if you are jealous of the share your country may boast in these wonders—then, I implore you, take some interest in those sacred dwellings meaningly described as *laboratories*. Ask that they may be multiplied and completed. They are the temples of the future, of riches and of comfort. There humanity grows greater, better, stronger; there she can learn to read the works of Nature, works of progress and universal harmony, while humanity's own works are too often those of barbarism, of fanaticism and of destruction. . . .

Keep your early enthusiasm, dear collaborators, but let it ever be regulated by rigorous examinations and tests. Never advance anything which cannot be proved in a simple and decisive fashion.

Worship the spirit of criticism. If reduced to itself, it is not an awakener of ideas or a stimulant to great things, but, without it, everything is fallible; it always has the last word. What I am now asking you, and you will ask of your pupils later on, is what is most difficult to an inventor.

It is indeed a hard task, when you believe you have found an important scientific fact and are feverishly anxious to publish it, to constrain yourself for days, weeks, years sometimes, to fight with yourself, to try and ruin your own experiments and only to proclaim your discovery after having exhausted all contrary hypotheses.

But when, after so many efforts, you have at last arrived at a certainty, your joy is one of the greatest which can be felt by a human soul, and the thought that you will have contributed to the honour of your country renders that joy still deeper. . . .

I should say that two contrary laws seem to be wrestling with each other nowadays; the one, a law of blood and of death, ever imagining new means of destruction and forcing nations to be constantly ready for the battlefield—the other, a law of peace, work and health, ever evolving new means of delivering man from the scourges which beset him.

The one seeks violent conquests, the other the relief of humanity. The latter places human life above any victory; while the former would sacrifice hundreds and thousands of lives to the ambition of one. The law of which we are the instruments seeks, even in the midst of carnage, to cure the sanguinary ills of the law of war; the treatment inspired by our antiseptic methods may preserve thousands of soldiers. Which of these two laws will ultimately prevail, God alone knows. But we may assert that French Science will have tried, by obeying the law of Humanity, to extend the frontiers of Life.

On Claude Bernard
and His Work

LOUIS PASTEUR

MEAT is an aliment which cannot develop sugar by the digestive process known to us. Now M. Bernard having fed some carnivorous animals during a certain time exclusively with meat, he assured himself, with his precise knowledge of the most perfect means of investigation offered him by chemistry, that the blood which enters the liver by the portal vein and pours into it the nutritive substances prepared and rendered soluble by digestion is absolutely devoid of sugar; whilst the blood which issues from the liver by the hepatic veins is always abundantly provided with it . . . M. Claude Bernard has also thrown full light on the close connection which exists between the secretion of sugar in the liver and the influence of the nervous system. He has demonstrated, with a rare sagacity, that by acting on some determined portion of that system it was possible to suppress or exaggerate at will the production of sugar. He has done more still; he has discovered within the liver the existence of an absolutely new substance which is the natural substance whence this organ draws the sugar that it produces.

A long commentary would be necessary to present this splendid work (*Introduction to the Study of Experimental Medicine*) to the reader; it is a monument raised to honour the method which has constituted Physical and Chemical Science since Galileo and Newton, and which M. Bernard is trying to introduce into physiology and pathology. Nothing so complete, so profound, so luminous has ever been written on the true principles of the difficult art of experimentation . . . This book will exert an immense influence on medical science, its teaching, its progress, its language even.

I have spoken of the man of science. I might have spoken of the man in everyday life, the colleague who has inspired so many with a solid friendship, for I should seek in vain for a weak point in M. Bernard; it is not to be found. His personal distinction, the noble beauty of his physiognomy, his gentle kindness attract at first sight; he has no pedantry, none of a scientist's usual faults, but an antique simplicity, a perfectly natural and unaffected manner, while his conversation is deep and full of ideas. . . .

Comment by Claude Bernard to Henri Sainte Claire Deville:

I have received the article Pasteur has written about me in the *Moniteur*; that article paralyzed the vasomotor nerves of my sympathetic system, and caused me to blush to the roots of my hair. I was so amazed that I don't know what I wrote to Pasteur; but I did not dare to say to him that he had wrongly exaggerated my merits. I know he believes all that he writes, and I am happy and proud of his opinion, because it is that of a scientist and experimentalist of the very first rank. . . .

The Truth Seekers

CLAUDE BERNARD

ARDENT desire for knowledge, and this knowledge really grasped, and yet always flying before them, becomes at once their sole torment and sole happiness. Those who do not know the torment of the unknown cannot have the joy of discovery, which is certainly the liveliest that the mind of man can ever feel. But, by a whim of nature, the joy of discovery, so sought and hoped for, vanishes as soon as found. It is but a flash, whose gleam discovers for us fresh horizons toward which our insatiate curiosity repairs with still more ardor. Thus, even in science itself, the known loses its attraction, while the unknown is always full of charm.

When you meet with a fact opposed to a prevailing theory, you should adhere to the fact and abandon the theory, even when the latter is supported by great authorities and generally adopted.

Put off your imagination as you take off your overcoat when you enter the laboratory; but put it on again, as you do the overcoat, when you leave the laboratory. Before the experiment and between whiles let your imagination wrap you around; put it right away from yourself during the experiment itself, lest it hinder your observing power.

When I am in my laboratory, I begin by shutting the door on materialism and on spiritualism; I observe facts alone, I seek but the scientific conditions under which life manifests itself.

The Etiology of Tuberculosis

ROBERT KOCH

VILLEMIN'S discovery that tuberculosis is transmissible to animals has, as is well known, found varied confirmation, but also apparently well-grounded opposition, so that it remained undecided until a few years ago whether tuberculosis is or is not an infectious disease. Since then, however, inoculations into the anterior ocular chamber, first performed by Cohnheim and Salomonsen, and later by Baumgarten, and furthermore the inhalation experiments done by Tappeiner and others have established the transmissibility of tuberculosis beyond any doubt, and in future tuberculosis must be classed as an infectious disease.

If the number of victims which a disease claims is the measure of its significance, then all diseases, particularly the most dreaded infectious diseases, such as bubonic plague, Asiatic cholera, etc., must rank far behind tuberculosis. Statistics teach that one-seventh of all human beings die of tuberculosis, and that, if one considers only the productive middle-age groups, tuberculosis carries away one-third and often more of these. . . .

In my studies on tuberculosis I first used the known methods without elucidating the nature of the disease. But by reason of several incidental observations I was prompted to abandon these methods and to follow other paths which finally led to positive results.

The aim of the study had to be directed first toward the demonstration of some kind of parasitic forms, which are foreign to the body and which might possibly be interpreted as the cause of the disease. This demonstration became successful, indeed, by means of a certain staining process, which disclosed characteristic and heretofore unknown bacteria in all tuberculous organs. It would take us too far afield to tell of the road by which I arrived at this new process, and I shall therefore immediately give its description.

The objects for study are prepared in the usual fashion for the examination for pathogenic bacteria. They are either spread on the cover-slip, dried and heated, or they are cut in sections after being hardened in alcohol. The cover-slips or sections are put in a staining solution of the following formula: 200 cc. of distilled water are mixed with 1 cc. of a concentrated alcoholic methylene-blue solution, and with repeated shaking 0.2 cc. of a 10 per cent potassium-hydrate solution is added. This mixture should not produce a precipitate even after standing for several days. The objects to be stained remain in it from 20 to 24 hours. By heating the staining solution to 40°C. in a water-bath this time can be shortened to from one-half to one hour. The cover-slips are then covered with a concentrated aqueous solution of vesuvin, which must be filtered each time before use and rinsed after one to two minutes with distilled water. When the cover-slips are removed from the methylene-blue the smear looks dark blue and is much overstained, but upon the treatment with vesuvin the blue color disappears and the specimen appears faintly brown. Under the microscope all constituents of animal tissue, particularly the nuclei and their disintegration products, appear brown, with the tubercle bacilli, however, beautifully blue. With the exception of leprosy bacilli, all other bacteria which I have thus far examined in this respect assume a brown color with this staining method. The color contrast between the brown-stained tissue and the blue tubercle bacilli is so striking, that the latter, which are frequently present only in very small numbers, are nevertheless seen and identified with the greatest certainty. . . .

In several respects the bacteria made visible by this process exhibit a characteristic behavior. They are rod-shaped, and they belong to the group of *bacilli*. They are very thin and one-fourth to one-half as long as the diameter of a red blood-corpuscle, although they may sometimes reach a greater length,—up to the full diameter of an erythrocyte. In shape and size they bear a striking similarity to leprosy bacilli. They are differentiated from the latter by being a bit more slender and by having tapered ends. . . .

As soon as the height of tubercle-development is passed the bacilli become rarer, and occur only in small groups or quite singly, in the margin of the tuberculous focus and side by side with weakly stained and sometimes hardly recognizable bacilli which are presumably dying or dead. Finally, they may disappear completely; but they are but seldom entirely absent and, if so, only in such places in which the tuberculous process has come to a standstill.

If giant cells occur in the tuberculous tissue the bacilli are by predilection within these formations. In very slowly progressing tuberculous processes, the interior of giant cells is usually the only place in which bacilli are to be found. In this case the majority of giant cells enclose one or a few bacilli; and it produces a surprising impression to find repeatedly in large areas of the section groups of giant cells, most of which contain one or two tiny blue rods in the center, and within the wide space enclosed by brown-stained nuclei. . . .

The bacilli are also observable unstained in unprepared specimens. For this it is necessary to take a little material from such places as contain considerable numbers of bacilli, for example, from a gray tubercle from the lung of a guinea pig, dead of inoculation tuberculosis. This material must be examined after the addition of a little distilled water or, preferably, blood-serum, and best in a hollow slide, in order to avoid streaming in the fluid. The bacilli appear then as very fine rods which show only molecular, but not the slightest trace of intrinsic movement.

Under certain conditions to be mentioned later the bacilli form spores even in the animal body. Individual bacilli contain several, usually 2 to 4 spores, oval in shape, and distributed at even intervals along the entire length of the bacillus.

In regard to the occurrence of bacilli in the various tuberculous manifestations in human beings and animals it has been possible to examine the following material thus far:

1. From Human Beings: Eleven cases of miliary tuberculosis: The bacilli never failed of demonstration in miliary tubercles of the lungs. . . .

Twelve cases of caseous bronchitis and pneumonia (in 6 cases cavity-formation): The presence of bacilli was usually limited to the margin of the caseously infiltrated tissue, where several times, however, they were very numerous. . . .

In larger cavities the bacilli occur mixed with other bacteria.

However, they were easily distinguishable because, with the staining-method mentioned, only tubercle bacilli stain blue while other bacteria assume a brown color.

One case of solitary tubercle in the brain, larger than a hazelnut: The caseous part of the tubercle was enclosed by a cellular tissue in which were embedded many giant cells. Most of these did not contain any parasites, but here and there were encountered groups of giant cells, each of which contained one or two bacilli.

Two cases of intestinal tuberculosis: In tuberculous nodules which were grouped around the intestinal ulcers, the bacilli were demonstrable with particular ease. . . .

Three cases of freshly excised scrofulous lymph nodes: In only two of them could bacilli be demonstrated in giant cells.

Four cases of fungoid arthritis: In two cases separate small groups of giant cells contained bacilli.

2. From Animals: Ten cases of Perlsucht with calcified nodules in the lungs, in several cases also in the peritoneum and once on the pericardium. . . .

Three cases in which the lungs of cattle contained, not the well-known calcified nodules with knobby surface, as usually seen in Perlsucht, but smooth-walled, spherical nodes, filled with a thick, cheesy material. . . .

A caseated cervical lymph node from a hog likewise contained the bacilli.

Large amounts of tubercle bacilli were found in the organs of a chicken dead of tuberculosis, both in tubercles in the bone-marrow and in the peculiar large lymph nodes of the intestines, the liver, and the lungs.

Of three monkeys which had died spontaneously of tuberculosis, the lungs, spleen, liver and omentum, all were studded with innumerable nodules. . . .

Of spontaneously diseased animals, nine guinea pigs and seven rabbits were examined; all showed bacilli in the tubercles.

In addition to these cases of spontaneous tuberculosis, I could avail myself of a not inconsiderable number of animals which had been infected by inoculation with the most varied tuberculous materials: as, for instance, with gray and caseated tubercles from human lungs, with sputum from consumptives, with tuberculous masses from spontaneously diseased monkeys, rabbits and guinea pigs, with masses of calcified or caseated lesions from *Perlsucht* in cattle, and finally with material from lesions obtained by animal-passage. The number of animals so infected amounted to 172 guinea pigs, 32 rabbits and 5 cats. In the majority of these cases the demonstration of bacilli had to be limited to the examination of tubercles in the lungs which were always present in large numbers. Here bacilli never failed to be found: frequently they were extraordinarily numerous, and sometimes spore-bearing, but in some preparations only a few yet unmistakable individual forms were observed. . . .

On the basis of my numerous observations I consider it established that, in all tuberculous affections of man and animals, there occur constantly those bacilli which I have designated *tubercle bacilli* and which are distinguishable from all other microorganisms by characteristic properties. However, from the mere coincidental relation of tuberculous affections and bacilli it may not be concluded that these two phenomena have a causal relation, notwithstanding the not inconsiderable degree of likelihood for this assumption that is derivable from the fact that the bacilli occur by preference where tuberculous processes are incipient or progressing, and that they disappear where the disease comes to a standstill.

To prove that tuberculosis is a parasitic disease, that it is caused by the invasion of bacilli and that it is conditioned primarily by the growth and multiplication of the bacilli, it was necessary to isolate the bacilli from the body; to grow them in pure culture until they were freed from any disease-product of the animal organism which might adhere to them; and, by administering the isolated bacilli to animals, to reproduce the same morbid condition which, as known, is obtained by inoculation with spontaneously developed tuberculous material.

Disregarding the many preliminary experiments which served for the solution of this task, here again the finished method will be described. Its principle rests on the use of a solid transparent medium, which retains its solid consistence at incubator temperature. The advantages of this method of pure culture which I have introduced into bacteriology I have explained in detail in an earlier publication. That the really complicated task of growing tubercle bacilli in pure culture was achieved by this method is to me a new proof of its efficiency.

Serum from sheep- or cattle-blood, separated as pure as possible, is put into test-tubes closed with a cotton stopper and heated every day to 58°C. for six subsequent days. It is not always possible to sterilize the serum completely by this process, but in most cases it suffices. Then the serum is heated to 65°C. during several hours, or sufficiently long for it to be just coagulated and solidified. After this treatment it appears as an amber-yellow, completely transparent or only slightly opalescent, solid, jelly-like mass; and after several days at incubator temperature it must not show the slightest development of bacterial colonies. If the heating exceeds 75°C. or if it lasts too long, the serum becomes opaque. In order to obtain a large surface for the preparation of the cultures the serum is solidified in test-tubes slanted as much as possible. For those cultures intended for direct microscopical examination the serum is solidified in flat watch-crystals or in small hollow glass blocks.

Upon this solidified blood-serum, which forms a transparent medium that remains solid at incubator temperature, the tuberculous materials are applied in the following manner:

The simplest case in which the experiment is successful is presented, almost without exception, when an animal which has just died of tuberculosis, or a tuberculous animal which has just been killed for this purpose, is at one's disposal. First, the skin is deflected over the thorax and abdomen with instruments flamed just before use. With similarly prepared scissors and forceps, the ribs are cut in the middle, and the anterior chestwall is removed without opening the abdominal cavity, so that the lungs are to a large extent laid free. Then the instruments are again exchanged for freshly disinfected ones, and single tubercles or particles of them, of the size of a millet-seed, are quickly excised with scissors from the lung tissue, and immediately transferred to the surface of the solidified blood-serum with a platinum wire, which has been melted into a glass rod which must be flamed immediately before use. Of course, the cotton stopper may be removed for only a minimal time. In this manner a number of test-tubes, about six to ten, are implanted with tuberculous material, because, with even the most cautious manipulation, not all test-tubes remain free from accidental contamination . . . The test-tubes, provided with tuberculous substance in the described manner, are kept in the incubator at a constant temperature of 37° or 38°C. In the first week no noticeable alteration occurs. . . .

Cultures that result from a growth of tubercle bacilli do not appear to the naked eye until the second week after the seeding, and ordinarily not until after the tenth day. They come into view as very small points and dry-looking scales. Depending upon whether the tuberculous material was more or less crushed in seeding and whether it was brought into contact with a large surface of the medium by rubbing motions, the colonies surround the explanted bit of tissue in smaller or larger areas.

With the aid of a 30- to 40-times magnification one can perceive the bacterial colonies as soon as toward the end of the first week. They appear as very neat spindle- and usually S-shaped or similarly curved formations, which consist of the well-known most tenuous bacilli when spread on a cover-slip, and stained and examined with high magnifications. Up to a certain degree their growth proceeds for a period of 3 to 4 weeks, as they enlarge to flat scale-like bits, usually not reaching the size of a poppy seed, and lie loosely on the medium, which they never invade or liquefy. Furthermore, the bacillary colony forms such a compact mass that its small scale can easily be removed with a platinum wire from the solidified blood-serum as a whole, and can be crushed only upon the application of a certain pressure. The exceedingly slow growth which can be obtained only at incubator temperature, and the peculiar scale-like dry and firm texture of these bacillary colonies are not met with in any other known bacterial species, so that it is impossible to confuse cultures of tubercle bacilli with those of other bacteria; and, even with but little experience, nothing is simpler than to recognize accidental contaminations of the cultures immediately. . . .

In order to keep such a culture going, it is necessary to transplant it to a new medium some time after the first seeding, approximately after 10 to 14 days. This is done by removing a few scales with the flamed platinum wire and by transferring these into a fresh test-tube of sterilized coagulated blood-serum, where they are crushed on the surface of the medium and spread as widely as possible. Within the same interval there again develop scale-like, dry masses, which coalesce and, depending upon the extent of their seeding, cover a larger or smaller part of the surface of the blood-serum. In this manner are the cultures continued. . . .

Up to this point it was established by my studies that the occurrence of characteristic bacilli is regularly coincidental with tuberculosis and that these bacilli can be obtained and isolated in pure cultures from tuberculous organs. It remained to answer the important question whether the isolated bacilli when again introduced into the animal body are capable of reproducing the morbid process of tuberculosis.

In order to exclude every error in the solution of this question, which contains the principal point in the whole study of the tubercle virus, many different series of experiments were done, which, on account of the significance of the point at issue, will be enumerated.

First, were done experiments involving the simple inoculation of bacilli. . . .

First Experiment: Of six recently bought guinea pigs which were kept in the same cage, four were inoculated on the abdomen with bacillary culture material derived from human lungs with miliary tubercles and grown in five transfers for fifty-four days. Two animals remained uninoculated. In the inoculated animals the inguinal lymph nodes swelled after fourteen days, the site of inoculation changed into an ulcer, and the animals became emaciated. After thirty-two days one of the inoculated animals died, and after thirty-five days the rest were killed. The inoculated guinea pigs, the one that had died spontaneously as well as the three killed ones, showed far-advanced tuberculosis of the spleen, liver and lungs; the inguinal nodes were much swollen and caseated; the bronchial lymph nodes were but little swollen. The two noninoculated animals displayed no trace of tuberculosis in lungs, liver or spleen.

Second Experiment: Of eight guinea pigs, six were inoculated with bacillary culture material, derived from the tuberculous lung of an ape, and cultivated in eight transfers for ninety-five days. Two animals remained uninoculated as controls. The course was exactly the same as in the first experiment. At autopsy the six inoculated animals were found with far-advanced tuberculosis, while the two noninoculated ones were healthy when they were killed, after thirty-two days.

Third Experiment: Of six guinea pigs, five were inoculated with culture material, derived from a *Perlsucht* lung, and seventy-two days old and transferred six times. After thirty-four days all animals were killed. The five inoculated ones were tuberculous, the noninoculated one was healthy.

Fourth Experiment: A number of animals (mice, rats, hedgehogs, hamsters, pigeons, frogs), whose susceptibility to tuberculosis is not known, were inoculated with cultures derived from the tuberculous lung of a monkey which had been cultivated for

113 days outside the animal body. Four field mice, killed 53 days after the inoculation, had numerous tubercles in the spleen, liver and lung; a hamster, killed 53 days after inoculation, showed the same result.

In these four experiments the inoculation of bacillary cultures on the abdomen of the experimental animals had, then, produced exactly the same kind of inoculation tuberculosis as if fresh tuberculous materials had been inoculated.

In the next experiment the inoculum was introduced into the anterior chamber of rabbits' eyes, in order to find out whether, in the so modified inoculation method, the same effect would be obtained by the artificially cultivated tubercle virus as with the natural virus.

Fifth Experiment: Three rabbits were inoculated with a small crumb of a culture (derived from a caseous pneumonia in a human lung and cultivated for 89 days) in the anterior ocular chamber. An intense iritis developed after a few days, and the cornea soon became clouded and discolored to a yellowish-gray. The animals rapidly became emaciated. They were killed after 25 days and their lungs were found studded with countless tubercles.

Sixth Experiment: Of three rabbits, one received an injection of pure blood-serum into the anterior chamber of the eye, and the two others an injection of the same blood-serum, in which however, a small crumb of a culture (originating from a lung with *Perlsucht* and cultivated 91 days) had been suspended. In the latter two rabbits, the same phenomena occurred as in the preceding experiment—rapidly progressing iritis and clouding of the cornea. After 28 days the animals were killed. The first rabbit, injected with pure blood-serum, was completely healthy, while the lungs of the other two were studded with innumerable tubercles.

Seventh Experiment: Of four rabbits, the first received pure blood-serum in the anterior eye chamber; in the case of the second the needle, which contained blood-serum with a bacillary culture (from monkey tuberculosis, cultivated 132 days), was introduced into the anterior chamber of the eye, but the plunger was not moved, so that only a minimal amount of the fluid could get into the aqueous humor. The third and fourth rabbits were injected in the anterior chamber with several drops of the blood-serum with bacillary culture. Iritis and panophthalmitis developed in the latter two animals, and very rapid emaciation followed.

In the case of the second rabbit, on the other hand, the eye remained at first unchanged, but in the course of the second week single whitish-yellow nodules appeared on the iris near the site of the puncture, and there developed, growing out from this center, a typical tuberculosis of the iris. New nodules kept forming on the iris, which became wrinkled, while the cornea clouded slowly and the further changes were obscured to further observation. After 30 days these four animals were killed. The first was entirely healthy; in the second, besides the formerly noted changes in the eye, the lymph nodes near the mandible and beside the root of the ear were swollen and studded with yellowish-white foci. The lungs and the other organs were still free from tuberculosis. The two latter rabbits, again, had countless tubercles in the lungs. . . .

All these facts, taken together, justify the statement that the bacilli present in tuberculous substances are not only coincidental with the tuberculous process, but are the cause of the process, and that we have in the bacilli the real tuberculous virus.

This establishes the possibility of defining the boundaries of the diseases to be understood as tuberculosis, which could not be done with certainty until now. A definite criterion for tuberculosis was lacking. One author would reckon miliary tuberculosis, phthisis, scrofulosis, *Perlsucht*, etc., as tuberculosis; another would hold, perhaps with quite as much right, that all these morbid processes were different. In future it will not be difficult to decide what is tuberculous and what is not tuberculous. The decision will be established, not by the typical structure of the tubercle, nor its avascularity, nor the presence of giant cells, but by the demonstration of tubercle bacilli, whether in the tissues by staining-reactions or by culture on coagulated blood-serum. Taking this criterion as decisive, miliary tuberculosis, caseous pneumonia, caseous bronchitis, intestinal and lymph-node tuberculosis, *Perlsucht* in cattle, spontaneous and infectious tuberculosis in animals, must, according to my investigations, be declared identical. . . .

Since the parasitic nature of tuberculosis is proved, it is still necessary for the completion of its etiology to answer the questions of where the parasites come from and how they enter the body.

In regard to the first question it must be decided whether the infectious materials can propagate only under such conditions as prevail in the animal body or whether they may undergo a development independent of the animal organism, somewhere in free nature, such as, for example, is the case with anthrax bacilli. In several experiments it was found that the tubercle bacilli grow only at temperatures between 30° and 41 °C. Below 30° and above 42° not the slightest growth occurred within three weeks, while anthrax bacilli, for example, grow vigourously at 20° and between 42° and 43 °C. The question mentioned can already be decided on the basis of this fact. In temperate climates there is no opportunity offered outside the animal body for an even temperature of above 30°C. of at least two weeks' duration. It may be concluded that, in their development, tubercle bacilli are dependent exclusively upon the animal organism; that they are true and not occasional parasites; and that they can be derived only from the animal organism.

Also the second question, as to how the parasites enter the body, can be answered. The great majority of all cases of tuberculosis begin in the respiratory tract, and the infectious material leaves its mark first in the lungs or in the bronchial lymph nodes. It is therefore very likely that tubercle bacilli are usually inspired with the air, attached to dust particles. There can hardly be any doubt about the manner by which they get into the air, considering in what excessive numbers tubercle bacilli present in cavity-contents are expectorated by consumptives and scattered everywhere.

In order to gain an opinion about the occurrence of tubercle bacilli in phthisical sputum I have examined repeatedly the sputum of a large series of consumptives and have found that in some of them no bacilli are present, and that, however, in approximately one-half of the cases, extraordinarily numerous bacilli are present, some of them sporogenic. Incidentally, it may be remarked that, in a number of specimens of sputum of persons not diseased with phthisis, tubercle bacilli were never found. Animals inoculated with fresh bacilliferous sputum become tuberculous as certainly as following inoculations with miliary tubercles.

Also, such infectious sputa did not lose their virulence after drying. Four guinea pigs were inoculated with two-weeks-old dried sputum, and four guinea pigs with sputum kept in the same way for 8 weeks; they all became tuberculous in the same manner as following infection with fresh material. It can therefore be assumed that phthisical sputum dried on the floor, clothes, etc., retains for a considerable time its virulence, and that, if it enters the lung in a pulverized state, it can produce tuberculosis there. . . .

In regard to milk from cows with *Perlsucht* it is noteworthy that the extension of the tuberculous process to the mammary gland has been observed not rarely by veterinarians, and it is therefore quite possible that in such cases the tuberculous virus may be mixed directly with the milk.

Still further viewpoints might be mentioned in regard to measures which could serve to limit the disease on the basis of our present knowledge of the etiology of tuberculosis but the discussion here would lead too far. When the conviction that tuberculosis is an exquisite infectious disease has become firmly established among physicians, the question of an adequate campaign against tuberculosis will certainly come under discussion and it will develop by itself.

1882

Translated in 1932

Sairey Gamp

CHARLES DICKENS

Deep in the City, and within the ward of Cheap, stood Mr. Mould's establishment. His Harem, or, in other words, the common sitting-room of Mrs. Mould and family, was at the back, over the little counting-house behind the shop: abutting on a churchyard small and shady. In this domestic chamber Mr. Mould now sat; gazing, a placid man, upon his punch and home. . . .

Mr. Mould looked lovingly at Mrs. Mould, who sat hard by, and was a helpmate to him in his punch as in all other things. Each seraph daughter, too, enjoyed her share of his regards, and smiled upon him in return. So bountiful were Mr. Mould's possessions, and so large his stock in trade, that even there, within his household sanctuary, stood a cumbrous press, whose mahogany maw was filled with shrouds, and winding-sheets, and other furniture of funerals. But, though the Misses Mould had been brought up, as one may say, beneath his eye, it had cast no shadow on their timid infancy or blooming youth. Sporting behind the scenes of death and burial from cradlehood, the Misses Mould knew better. Hatbands, to them, were but so many yards of silk or crape; the final robe but such a quantity of linen. The Misses Mould could idealise a player's habit, or a court-lady's petticoat, or even an act of parliament. But they were not to be taken in by palls. They made them sometimes. . . .

A knock was heard at the room-door.

"That's Tacker, *I* know," said Mrs. Mould, "by the wheezing he makes. Who that hears him now, would suppose he'd ever had wind enough to carry the feathers on his head! Come in, Tacker."

"Beg your pardon, ma'am," said Tacker, looking in a little way. . . .

"Mrs. Gamp's below, and wants to speak to you."

"Tell Mrs. Gamp to come upstairs," said Mould. "Now, Mrs. Gamp, what's *your* news?"

The lady in question was by this time in the door-way, curtsey-ing to Mrs. Mould. At the same moment a peculiar fragrance was borne upon the breeze, as if a passing fairy had hiccoughed, and had previously been to a wine-vault.

Mrs. Gamp made no response to Mr. Mould, but curtsied to Mrs. Mould again, and held up her hands and eyes, as in a devout thanksgiving that she looked so well. She was neatly, but not gaudily attired. . . .

"There are some happy creeturs," Mrs. Gamp observed, "as time runs back-ards with, and you are one, Mrs. Mould; not that he need do nothing except use you in his most owldacious way for years to come, I'm sure; for young you are and will be. I says to Mrs. Harris," Mrs. Gamp continued, "only t' other day; the last Monday evening fortnight as ever dawned upon this Piljian's Projiss of a mortal wale; I says to Mrs. Harris when she says to me, 'Years and our trials, Mrs. Gamp, sets marks upon us all.'— 'Say not the words, Mrs. Harris, if you and me is to be continual friends, for sech is not the case. Mrs. Mould,' I says, making so free, I will confess, as use the name," (she curtsied here), " 'is one of them that goes agen the obserwation straight; and never, Mrs. Harris, whilst I've a drop of breath to draw, will I set by, and not stand up, don't think it.' 'I ast your pardon, ma'am—,' says Mrs. Harris, 'and I humbly grant your grace; for if ever a woman lived as would see her feller-creeturs into fits to serve her friends, well do I know that woman's name is Sairey Gamp.'"

"Oh! Fie, fie! Nonsense, Mrs. Gamp," replied the undertaker. "My dear—" aloud again—"Mrs. Gamp can drink a glass of rum, I dare say. Sit down, Mrs. Gamp, sit down."

Mrs. Gamp took the chair that was nearest the door, and casting
up her eyes towards the ceiling, feigned to be wholly insensible
to the fact of a glass of rum being in preparation, until it was
placed in her hand by one of the young ladies, when she exhibited
the greatest surprise.

"A thing," she said, "as hardly ever, Mrs. Mould, occurs with
me unless it is when I am indisposged, and find my half-a-pint of
porter settling heavy on the chest. Mrs. Harris often and often says
to me, 'Sairey Gamp,' she says, 'you raly do amaze me!'
'Mrs. Harris,' I says to her, 'why so? Give it a name, I beg.'"
"'Telling the truth then, ma'am,' says Mrs. Harris, 'and sham-
ing him as shall be nameless betwixt you and me, never did I
think till I know'd you, as any woman could sick-nurse and
monthly likeways, on the little that you takes to drink.' 'Mrs.
Harris,' I says to her, 'none on us knows what we can do till
we tries; and wunst, when me and Gamp kept 'ouse, I thought
so too. But now,' I says, 'my half-a-pint of porter fully satisfies;
perwisin', Mrs. Harris, that it is brought reg'lar, and draw'd
mild. Whether I sicks or monthlies, ma'am, I hope I does my
duty, but I am but a poor woman, and I earns my living hard;
therefore I do require it, which I makes confession, to be brought
reg'lar and draw'd mild.'"

The precise connection between these observations and the
glass of rum, did not appear; for Mrs. Gamp proposing as a
toast 'The best of lucks to all!' took off the dram in quite a
scientific manner, without any further remarks.

"And what's your news, Mrs. Gamp?" asked Mould again, as
that lady wiped her lips upon her shawl, and nibbled a corner off
a soft biscuit, which she appeared to carry in her pocket as a
provision against contingent drams. "How's Mr. Chuffey?"

"Mr. Chuffey, sir," she replied, "is jest as usual; he an't no
better and he an't no worse. I take it very kind in the gentleman
to have wrote up to you and said, 'let Mrs. Gamp take care of
him till I come home'; but ev'rythink he does is kind. There an't
a many like him. If there was, we shouldn't want no churches."

"What do you want to speak to me about, Mrs. Gamp?" said
Mould, coming to the point.

"Jest this, sir," Mrs. Gamp returned, "with thanks to you for
asking. There is a gent, sir, at the Bull in Holborn, as has been took
ill there, and is bad abed. They have a day nurse as was recommended from Bartholomew's; and well I knows her, Mr. Mould,
her name bein' Mrs. Prig, the best of creeturs. But she is other-

ways engaged at night, and they are in wants of night-watching; consequent she says to them, having reposed the greatest friendliness in me for twenty year, 'The soberest person going, and the best of blessings in a sick room, is Mrs. Gamp. Send a boy to Kingsgate Street,' she says, 'and snap her up at any price, for Mrs. Gamp is worth her weight and more in goldian guineas.' My landlord brings the message down to me, and says, 'bein' in a light place where you are, and this job promising so well, why not unite the two?' 'No, sir,' I says, 'not unbeknown to Mr. Mould, and therefore do not think it. But I will go to Mr. Mould,' I says, 'and ast him, if you like.' " Here she looked sideways at the undertaker, and came to a stop.

"Night-watching, eh?" said Mould, rubbing his chin.

"From eight o'clock till eight, sir. I will not deceive you," Mrs. Gamp rejoined.

"And then go back, eh?" said Mould.

"Quite free then, sir, to attend to Mr. Chuffey. His ways bein' quiet, and his hours early, he'd be abed, sir, nearly all the time. I will not deny," said Mrs. Gamp with meekness, "that I am but a poor woman, and that the money is a object; but do not let that act upon you, Mr. Mould. Rich folks may ride on camels, but it an't so easy for 'em to see out of a needle's eye. This is my comfort, and I hope I knows it."

"Well, Mrs. Gamp," observed Mould, "I don't see any particular objection to your earning an honest penny under such circumstances. I should keep it quiet, I think, Mrs. Gamp. I wouldn't mention it to Mr. Chuzzlewit on his return, for instance, unless it were necessary, or he asked you point-blank."

"The very words was on my lips, sir," Mrs. Gamp rejoined. 'Suppoging that the gent should die, I hope I might take the liberty of saying as I know'd some one in the undertaking line, and yet give no offence to you, sir?'

"Certainly, Mrs. Gamp," said Mould, with much condescension. "You may casually remark, in such a case, that we do the thing pleasantly and in a great variety of styles, and are generally considered to make it as agreeable as possible to the feelings of the survivors. But don't obtrude it, don't obtrude it. Easy, easy! My dear, you may as well give Mrs. Gamp a card or two, if you please."

Mrs. Gamp received them, and scenting no more rum in the wind (for the bottle was locked up again) rose to take her departure.

"Wishing ev'ry happiness to this happy family," said Mrs. Gamp, "with all my heart. Good arternoon, Mrs. Mould! If I was Mr. Mould, I should be jealous of you, ma'am; and I'm sure, if I was you, I should be jealous of Mr. Mould."

"Tut, tut! Bah, bah! Go along, Mrs. Gamp!" cried the delighted undertaker.

"I'll tell you what, my dear," he observed, when Mrs. Gamp had at last withdrawn, and shut the door, "that's a ve-ry shrewd woman. That's a woman whose intellect is immensely superior to her station in life. That's a woman who observes and reflects in an uncommon manner. She's the sort of woman now," said Mould, drawing his silk handkerchief over his head again, and composing himself for a nap, "one would almost feel disposed to bury for nothing: and do it neatly, too!"

Mrs. Mould and her daughters fully concurred in these remarks; the subject of which had by this time reached the street, where she experienced so much inconvenience from the air, that she was obliged to stand under an archway for a short time, to recover herself. Even after this precaution, she walked so unsteadily as to attract the compassionate regards of divers kind-hearted boys, who took the liveliest interest in her disorder; and in their simple language, bade her be of good cheer, for she was "only a little screwed.". . .

She went to her private lodgings in Kingsgate Street, for a bundle of robes and wrappings comfortable in the night season; and then repaired to the Bull in Holborn, which she reached as the clocks were striking eight.

As she turned into the yard, she stopped; for the landlord, landlady, and head-chambermaid, were all on the threshold together, talking earnestly with a young gentleman who seemed to have just come or to be just going away. The first words that struck upon Mrs. Gamp's ear obviously bore reference to the patient; and it being expedient that all good attendants should know as much as possible about the case on which their skill is brought to bear, Mrs. Gamp listened as a matter of duty.

"No better, then?" observed the gentleman.

"Worse!" said the landlord.

"Much worse," added the landlady.

"Oh! a deal badder," cried the chambermaid from the background, opening her eyes very wide, and shaking her head.

"Poor fellow!" said the gentleman, "I am sorry to hear it. The worst of it is, that I have no idea what friends or relations he has, or where they live, except that it certainly is not in London."

Mrs. Gamp felt the necessity of advancing, bundle in hand, and introducing herself.

"The night-nurse," she observed, "from Kingsgate Street, well beknown to Mrs. Prig, the day-nurse, and the best of creeturs. How is the poor dear gentleman, to-night? If he an't no better yet, still that is what must be expected and prepared for. It an't the fust time by a many score, ma'am," dropping a curtesy to the landlady, "that Mrs. Prig and me has nussed together, turn and turn about, one off, one on. We knows each other's ways, and often gives relief when others failed. Our charges is but low, sir": Mrs. Gamp addressed herself to John on this head: "considerin' the nater of our painful dooty. If they wos made accordin' to our wishes, they would be easy paid."

Regarding herself as having now delivered her inauguration address, Mrs. Gamp curtsied all round, and signified her wish to be conducted to the scene of her official duties. The chambermaid led her, through a variety of intricate passages, to the top of the house; and pointing at length to a solitary door at the end of a gallery, informed her that yonder was the chamber where the patient lay. That done, she hurried off with all the speed she could make.

Mrs. Gamp traversed the gallery in a great heat from having carried her large bundle up so many stairs, and tapped at the door, which was immediately opened by Mrs. Prig, bonneted and shawled and all impatience to be gone. Mrs. Prig was of the Gamp build, but not so fat; and her voice was deeper and more like a man's. She had also a beard.

"I began to think you warn't coming!" Mrs. Prig observed, in some displeasure.

"I shall be made good to-morrow night," said Mrs. Gamp, "honourable. I had to go and fetch my things." She had begun to make signs of inquiry in reference to the position of the patient and his over-hearing them—for there was a screen before the door—when Mrs. Prig settled that point easily.

"Oh!" she said aloud, "he's quiet, but his wits is gone. It an't no matter wot you say."

"Anythin' to tell afore you goes, my dear?" asked Mrs. Gamp, setting her bundle down inside the door, and looking affectionately at her partner.

"The pickled salmon," Mrs. Prig replied, "is quite delicious. I can partick'ler recommend it. Don't have nothink to say to the cold meat, for it tastes of the stable. The drinks is all good."

Mrs. Gamp expressed herself much gratified.

"The physic and the things is on the drawers and mankleshelf," said Mrs. Prig, cursorily. "He took his last slime draught at seven. The easy-chair an't soft enough. You'll want his piller."

Mrs. Gamp thanked her for these hints, and giving her a friendly good-night, held the door open until she had disappeared at the other end of the gallery. Having thus performed the hospitable duty of seeing her safely off, she shut it, locked it on the inside, took up her bundle, walked round the screen, and entered on her occupation at the sick chamber.

"A little dull, but not so bad as might be," Mrs. Gamp remarked. "I'm glad to see a parapidge, in case of fire, and lots of roofs and chimley-pots to walk upon."

It will be seen from these remarks that Mrs. Gamp was looking out of window. When she had exhausted the prospect, she tried the easy-chair, which she indignantly declared was "harder than a brick-badge." Next she pursued her researches among the physic-bottles, glasses, jugs, and tea-cups: and when she had entirely satisfied her curiosity on all these subjects of investigation, she untied her bonnet-strings and strolled up to the bedside to take a look at the patient.

A young man—dark and not ill-looking—with long black hair, that seemed the blacker for the whiteness of the bedclothes. His eyes were partly open, and he never ceased to roll his head from side to side upon the pillow, keeping his body almost quiet. He did not utter words; but every now and then gave vent to an expression of impatience or fatigue, sometimes of surprise; and still his restless head—oh, weary, weary hour!—went to and fro without a moment's intermission.

Mrs. Gamp solaced herself with a pinch of snuff, and stood looking at him with her head inclined a little sideways, as a connoisseur might gaze upon a doubtful work of art. By degrees, a horrible remembrance of one branch of her calling took possession of the woman; and stooping down, she pinned his wandering arms against his sides, to see how he would look if laid out as a dead man. Hideous as it may appear, her fingers itched to compose his limbs in that last marble attitude.

"Ah!" said Mrs. Gamp, walking away from the bed, "he'd make a lovely corpse."

She now proceeded to unpack her bundle; lighted a candle with the aid of a fire-box on the drawers; filled a small kettle, as a preliminary to refreshing herself with a cup of tea in the course of the night; laid what she called "a little bit of fire," for the same philanthropic purpose; and also set forth a small tea-board, that nothing might be wanting for her comfortable enjoyment. These preparations occupied so long, that when they were brought to a conclusion it was high time to think about supper; so she rang the bell and ordered it.

"I think, young woman," said Mrs. Gamp to the assistant-chambermaid, in a tone expressive of weakness, "that I could pick a little bit of pickled salmon, with a nice little sprig of fennel, and a sprinkling of white pepper. I takes new bread, my dear, with jest a little pat of fresh butter, and a mossel of cheese. In case there should be such a thing as a cowcumber in the 'ouse, will you be so kind as bring it, for I'm rather partial to 'em, and they does a world of good in a sick room. If they draws the Brighton Old Tipper here, I takes *that* ale at night, my love; it bein' considered wakeful by the doctors. And whatever you do, young woman, don't bring more than a shilling's-worth of gin-and-water warm when I rings the bell a second time: for that is always my allowance, and I never takes a drop beyond!"

Having preferred these moderate requests, Mrs. Gamp observed that she would stand at the door until the order was executed, to the end that the patient might not be disturbed by her opening it a second time; and therefore she would thank the young woman to "look sharp."

A tray was brought with everything upon it, even to the cucumber; and Mrs. Gamp accordingly sat down to eat and drink in high good-humour. The extent to which she availed herself of the vinegar, and supped up that refreshing fluid with the blade of her knife, can scarcely be expressed in narrative.

"Ah!" sighed Mrs. Gamp, as she meditated over the warm shilling's-worth, "what a blessed thing it is—living in a wale—to be contented! What a blessed thing it is to make sick people happy in their beds, and never mind one's-self as long as one can do a service! I don't believe a finer cowcumber was ever grow'd. I'm sure I never see one!"

She moralised in the same vein until her glass was empty, and then administered the patient's medicine, by the simple process of

clutching his windpipe to make him gasp, and immediately pouring it down his throat.

"I a'most forgot the piller, I declare!" said Mrs. Gamp, drawing
it away. "There! Now he's comfortable as he can be, *I'm* sure!
I must try to make myself as much so as I can."

With this view, she went about the construction of an extempo-
raneous bed in the easy-chair, with the addition of the next easy
one for her feet. Having formed the best couch that the circumstances admitted of, she took out of her bundle a yellow night-
cap, of prodigious size, in shape resembling a cabbage; which
article of dress she fixed and tied on with the utmost care, previously divesting herself of a row of bald old curls that could
scarcely be called false, they were so very innocent of anything
approaching to deception. From the same repository she brought
forth a night-jacket, in which she also attired herself. Finally, she
produced a watchman's coat, which she tied around her neck
by the sleeves, so that she became two people; and looked, behind,
as if she were in the act of being embraced by one of the old
patrol.

All these arrangements made, she lighted the rush-light, coiled
herself up on her couch, and went to sleep. Ghostly and dark the
room became, and full of lowering shadows. The distant noises in
the streets were gradually hushed; the house was quiet as a sepul-
chre; the dead of night was coffined in the silent city.

Oh, weary, weary hour! Oh, haggard mind, groping darkly
through the past; incapable of detaching itself from the miserable
present; dragging its heavy chain of care through imaginary feasts
and revels, and scenes of awful pomp; seeking but a moment's
rest among the long-forgotten haunts of childhood, and the resorts
of yesterday; and dimly finding fear and horror everywhere! Oh,
weary, weary hour! What were the wanderings of Cain, to these?

Still, without a moment's interval, the burning head tossed to
and fro. Still, from time to time, fatigue, impatience, suffering,
and surprise, found utterance upon that rack, and plainly too,
though never once in words. At length, in the solemn hour of
midnight, he began to talk; waiting awfully for answers sometimes; as though invisible companions were about his bed; and so
replying to their speech and questioning again.

Mrs. Gamp awoke, and sat up in her bed: presenting on the
wall the shadow of a gigantic night constable, struggling with a
prisoner.

"Come! Hold your tongue!" she cried, in sharp reproof. "Don't make none of that noise here."

There was no alteration in the face, or in the incessant motion of the head, but he talked on wildly.

"Ah!" said Mrs. Gamp, coming out of the chair with an impatient shiver; "I thought I was asleepin' too pleasant to last! The devil's in the night, I think, it's turned so chilly!"

"Don't drink so much!" cried the sick man. "You'll ruin us all. Don't you see how the fountain sinks? Look at the mark where the sparkling water was just now!"

"Sparkling water, indeed!" said Mrs. Gamp. "I'll have a sparkling cup o' tea, I think. I wish you'd hold your noise!"

He burst into a laugh, which, being prolonged, fell off into a dismal wail. Checking himself, with fierce inconstancy he began to count, fast.

"One—two—three—four—five—six."

"One, two, buckle my shoe," said Mrs. Gamp, who was now on her knees, lighting the fire, "three, four, shut the door,—I wish you'd shut your mouth, young man—five, six, picking up sticks. If I'd got a few handy, I should have the kettle biling all the sooner."

Awaiting this desirable consummation, she sat down so close to the fender (which was a high one) that her nose rested upon it; and for some time she drowsily amused herself by sliding that feature backwards and forwards along the brass top, as far as she could, without changing her position to do it. She maintained, all the while, a running commentary upon the wanderings of the man in bed.

"That makes five hundred and twenty-one men, all dressed alike, and with the same distortion on their faces, that have passed in at the window, and out at the door," he cried, anxiously. "Look there! Five hundred and twenty-two—twenty-three—twenty-four. Do you see them?"

"Ah! *I* see 'em," said Mrs. Gamp; "all the whole kit of 'em numbered like hackney-coaches, ain't they?"

"Touch me! Let me be sure of this. Touch me!"

"You'll take your next draught when I've made the kettle bile," retorted Mrs. Gamp, composedly, "and you'll be touched then. You'll be touched up, too, if you don't take it quiet."

"Five hundred and twenty-eight, five hundred and twenty-nine, five hundred and thirty,—look here!"

"What's the matter now?" said Mrs. Gamp.

"They're coming four abreast, each man with his arm entwined in the next man's, and his hand upon his shoulder. What's that upon the arm of every man, and on the flag?"

"Spiders, p'raps," said Mrs. Gamp.

"Crape! Black crape! Good God! why do they wear it outside?"

"Would you have 'em carry black crape in their insides?" Mrs. Gamp retorted. "Hold your noise, hold your noise."

The fire beginning by this time to impart a grateful warmth, Mrs. Gamp became silent; gradually rubbed her nose more and more slowly along the top of the fender; and fell into a heavy doze. She was awakened by the room ringing (as she fancied) with a name she knew—

"Chuzzlewit!"

The sound was so distinct and real, and so full of agonised entreaty, that Mrs. Gamp jumped up in terror, and ran to the door. She expected to find the passage filled with people, come to tell her that the house in the City had taken fire. But the place was empty: not a soul was there. She opened the window, and looked out. Dark, dull, dingy, and desolate house-tops. As she passed to her seat again, she glanced at the patient. Just the same; but silent. Mrs. Gamp was so warm now, that she threw off the watchman's coat, and fanned herself.

"It seemed to make the wery bottles ring," she said. "What could I have been dreaming of? That dratted Chuffey, I'll be bound."

The supposition was probable enough. At any rate, a pinch of snuff, and the song of the steaming kettle, quite restored the tone of Mrs. Gamp's nerves, which were none of the weakest. She brewed her tea; made some buttered toast; and sat down at the tea-board, with her face to the fire.

When once again, in a tone more terrible than that which had vibrated in her slumbering ear, these words were shrieked out—

"Chuzzlewit! Jonas! No!"

Mrs. Gamp dropped the cup she was in the act of raising to her lips, and turned round with a start that made her little tea-board leap. The cry had come from the bed.

It was bright morning the next time Mrs. Gamp looked out of the window, and the sun was rising cheerfully. Lighter and lighter grew the sky, and noisier the streets; and high into the summer air uprose the smoke of newly-kindled fires, until the busy day was broad-awake.

Mrs. Prig relieved punctually, having passed a good night at her other patient's. Mr. Westlock came at the same time, but he was not admitted, the disorder being infectious. The doctor came too. The doctor shook his head. It was all he could do, under the circumstances, and he did it well.

"What sort of a night, nurse?"

"Restless, sir," said Mrs. Gamp.

"Talk much?"

"Middling, sir," said Mrs. Gamp.

"Nothing to the purpose, I suppose?"

"Oh bless you no, sir. Only jargon."

"Well!" said the doctor, "we must keep him quiet; keep the room cool: give him his draughts regularly; and see that he's carefully looked to. That's all!"

"And as long as Mrs. Prig and me waits upon him, sir, no fear of that," said Mrs. Gamp.

"I suppose," observed Mrs. Prig, when they had curtsied the doctor out: "there's nothin' new?"

"Nothin' at all, my dear," said Mrs. Gamp. "He's rather wearin' in his talk from making up a lot of names; elseways you needn't mind him."

"Oh, I shan't mind him," Mrs. Prig returned. "I have somethin' else to think of."

"I pays my debts to-night, you know, my dear, and comes afore my time," said Mrs. Gamp. "But, Betsey Prig": speaking with great feeling, and laying her hand upon her arm: "try the cowcumbers, God bless you!"

From "Martin Chuzzlewit", 1843

Florence Nightingale

CECIL WOODHAM-SMITH

To THE British people the invincibility of the British Army was an article of faith. Waterloo was a recent memory, and it was taken for granted that the nation which had beaten Napoleon could not be defeated. But since Waterloo forty years of economy had run their course, and the army which had won Wellington's victories had ceased to exist. In 1852 the artillery of the British Army consisted of forty field-pieces, many officially described as defective. In 1854, when the army was mobilizing for the Crimea, volunteers had to be drafted into the battalions selected for active service to raise their numbers to the regulation 850. The staff of the supply departments had been reduced to a few clerks, who were overwhelmed by the demands of mobilization. Before the Army sailed, the processes by which the troops were to receive food and clothing, to be maintained in health and cared for when wounded or sick, had already fallen into confusion. . . .

But in the spring of 1854, confidence was complete. The Guards were a magnificent body of fighting men as they marched through London to embark. The crowds which cheered them did not know that behind these splendid troops, the flower of the British Army, were no reserves. They were doomed to perish, and when they perished, their ranks were filled with raw recruits made "pretty perfect in drill in sixty days."

The first operation was not to be in the Crimea. The British Army was to relieve Silistria, in Roumania, then a Turkish province, where the Russians were besieging the Turks. A base was established at Scutari, a large village on the Asian shore of the Bosphorus, and in June, 1854 the British Army disembarked at Varna, in Bulgaria. Nothing was accomplished. A cholera epidemic broke out; the army became an army of invalids, and the Turks raised the siege of Silistria on their own account. The Allies then proceeded to the true objective of the war, the destruction of the great naval base recently constructed by the Russians at Sebastopol.

Though the plan of a descent on Sebastopol was an open secret and had been discussed in the Press, it had never been officially intimated to the supply departments; consequently no preparations had been made. When the British Army embarked at Varna for the Crimea, there were not enough transports to take both the army and its equipment across the Black Sea. Thirty thousand men were crammed in, but pack animals, tents, cooking equipment, hospital marquees, regimental medicine chests, bedding, and stores had all to be left behind. Twenty-one wagons only were brought for 30,000 men going into action. On September 14 the army disembarked at a cove with the sinister name of Calamita Bay. "My God," exclaimed Dr. Alexander, 1st class Staff Surgeon of the Light Division, "they have landed this army without any kind of hospital transport, litters or carts or anything." Cholera still raged, and over 1000 cholera cases were sent back to Scutari.

A week later, the British and the French won the hard-fought battle of the Alma, and the wounded paid the price of the abandonment of the army's hospital equipment. There were no bandages, no splints, no chloroform, no morphia. The wounded lay on the ground or on straw mixed with manure in a farmyard. Amputations were performed without anesthetics; the victims sat on tubs or lay on old doors; the surgeons worked by moonlight because there were no candles or lamps. And another 1000 cholera cases were sent back to Scutari.

Of this the British public knew nothing. Nor did they know what awaited the wounded and the sick when they reached the base at Scutari. At Scutari were enormous barracks, the headquarters of the Turkish artillery. These barracks and the hospital attached had been handed over to the British, and the British authorities assumed that the hospital, known as the General Hospital, would be adequate. The unexpected disaster of the cholera epidemic produced total disorganization. The first 1000 cholera cases sent back after the landing at Calamita Bay filled the hospital to overflowing; drugs, sanitary conveniences, bedding, doctors were insufficient. While Dr. Menzies, senior Medical Officer, was struggling with the crisis, he was notified that many hundreds of battle casualties from the Alma and another 1000 cholera cases were on their way. Since the General Hospital was filled, he was ordered to convert the artillery barracks into a hospital. It was an impossible task. The vast building was bare, filthy, and dilapidated. There was no labor to clean it; there was no hospital equipment to put in it.

Meanwhile the sick and wounded were enduring a ghastly journey across the Black Sea. They were conveyed in "hospital ships" which figured well on paper but in fact were ordinary transports equipped "with some medicines and medical appliances." They were packed far beyond their capacity. One, the *Kangaroo*, fitted to receive 250 sick, received between 1200 and 1500. Cholera cases, battle casualties, were crammed in together. Too weak to move, too weak to reach the sanitary conveniences, they fell on each other as the ship rolled and were soon lying in heaps of filth. Men with amputations were flung about the deck screaming with pain.

When the men arrived at the Barrack Hospital, there were no beds. They lay on the floor wrapped in the blankets saturated with blood and ordure in which they had been lying since they left the battlefield. No food could be given them because there was no kitchen. No one could attend to them because there were not sufficient doctors. Some of them lay without even a drink of water all that night and through the next day. There were no cups or buckets to bring water in. There were no chairs or tables. There was not an operating table. The men, half naked, lay in long lines on the bare filthy floors of the huge dilapidated rooms. . . .

England rang with the story of Scutari because with the British Army was the first war correspondent, William Howard Russell of *The Times*.

"By God, Sir, I'd as soon see the devil," said General Pennefather to Russell when they met in the Crimea; but Pennefather did not order Russell home. . . .

Russell was an Irishman with an Irishman's capacity for indignation, and in dispatches published on October 9, 12, and 13 he furiously described the sufferings of the sick and wounded. "It is with feelings of surprise and anger that the public will learn that no sufficient preparations have been made for the care of the wounded. Not only are there not sufficient surgeons . . . not only are there no dressers and nurses . . . there is not even linen to make bandages. . . . Can it be said that the battle of the Alma has been an event to take the world by surprise? Yet . . . there is no preparation for the commonest surgical operations! Not only are the men kept, in some cases for a week, without the hand of a medical man coming near their wounds, . . . but now . . . it is found that the commonest appliances of a workhouse sick ward are wanting, and that the men must die through the medical staff of the British Army having forgotten that old rags are necessary for the dressing of wounds. . . ."

The country seethed with rage. Russell's statement that British arrangements compared unfavorably with those of the French was intolerable, and the next day a letter in *The Times* demanded angrily, "Why have we no Sisters of Charity?"

It was read by Sidney Herbert, who in December, 1852 had been appointed Secretary at War, and was now responsible for the treatment of the sick and wounded. . . . He wrote to the British Ambassador at Constantinople, Lord Stratford de Redcliffe giving him *carte blanche* to purchase anything he considered necessary for the hospitals, and on October 15 he wrote to Miss Nightingale inviting her to go to Scutari in command of a party of nurses. She would go with the Government's sanction and at the Government's expense.

She had already acted on her own account and, without consulting the Herberts, had arranged to sail for Constantinople with a party of nurses in three days' time. She had hesitated to approach them, embarrassed by the attacks being made on Sidney Herbert; but when her plans were completed, she called at 49 Belgrave Square on the morning of Saturday, October 14. The Herberts had gone to Bournemouth for the week-end.

On Saturday afternoon Miss Nightingale wrote to Liz Herbert: "My dearest I went to Belgrave Square this morning for the chance of catching you, or Mr. Herbert even, had he been in Town. A small private expedition of nurses has been organized for Scutari and I have been asked to command it. . . ."

This letter crossed one written by Sidney Herbert at Bournemouth on the Sunday, in which he formally asked her to take charge of an official scheme for introducing female nurses into the hospitals of the British Army. . . .

The terms of this letter were accepted by Miss Nightingale and considered by her to be her charter. They make it clear that from the inception of her mission she was to be an administrator.

It was not as an angel of mercy that she was asked to go to Scutari—relieving the sufferings of the troops was scarcely mentioned. The consideration of overwhelming importance was the opportunity offered to advance the cause of nursing. Were nurses capable of being employed with success to nurse men under such conditions? The eyes of the nation were fixed on Scutari. If the nurses acquitted themselves creditably, never again would they be despised. "If this succeeds," Sidney Herbert had written, "an enormous amount of good will have been done now . . . a prejudice will have been broken through and a precedent established which will multiply the good to all time. . . ."

The number of nurses in the party was fixed at forty. She was doubtful of her ability to control more than twenty, but Sidney Herbert insisted that twenty would not be a sufficiently large number to make the experiment impressive. He would have preferred an even larger number than forty. On Wednesday, October 18, Sidney Herbert, supported by the Duke of Newcastle, placed Miss Nightingale's appointment before the Cabinet. The appointment was unanimously approved, and next day she received a formal confirmation written and signed by Sidney Herbert as Secretary at War. She was appointed "Superintendent of the Female Nursing Establishment of the English General Hospitals in Turkey. . . ."

With the assistance of Manning it was arranged that ten Roman Catholic nuns, five from a convent in Bermondsey and five from an orphanage in Norwood, should join the party, and it was conceded that they should be completely under Miss Nightingale's control. If she were to weld this heterogeneous, undisciplined collection of women into an efficient instrument, she must have absolute and unquestioned authority; her word must be law; a nun or a sister nursing for Miss Nightingale must take her nursing orders from Miss Nightingale and not from her mother superior; and the mother superior must take her nursing orders from Miss Nightingale and not from the bishop.

Miss Nightingale refused to admit "ladies," as such, into her party. All must be nurses; all must eat the same food, have the same accommodation, wear the same uniform, except the nuns and sisters, who were allowed to wear their habits. And the uniform was extremely ugly. . . .

On October 27 the party sailed in the *Vectis*. She was a horrible ship, built for carrying fast mails from Marseilles to Malta, infested with huge cockroaches and so notorious for her discomfort that the Government had difficulty in manning her. Miss Nightingale, a wretchedly bad sailor, was prostrated by sea sickness. On the second day out the *Vectis* ran into a gale. The guns with which she was armed had to be jettisoned; the stewards' cabin and the galley were washed overboard. Miss Nightingale suffered so severely that when Malta was reached she was too weak to go ashore.

On November 3, still in atrocious weather, the *Vectis*, "blustering, storming, shrieking," wrote Miss Nightingale, rushed up the Bosphorus, and anchored off Seraglio Point next day. Constantinople, in the pouring rain, looked like a washed-out daguerreotype. On the opposite shore stood the enormous Barrack Hospital. Everyone was on deck eager to see their goal. "Oh, Miss Nightingale," said one of the party, "when we land don't let there be any red tape delays, let us get straight to nursing the poor fellows!" Miss Nightingale, gazing at the gigantic pile, replied: "The strongest will be wanted at the wash tub."

At breakfast-time the *Vectis* anchored, and during the morning Lord Stratford, the British Ambassador at Constantinople, sent across Lord Napier, the Secretary of the Embassy. Lord Napier found Miss Nightingale, exhausted from the effects of prolonged sea sickness, stretched on a sofa. Fourteen years later he recalled their first meeting: ". . . I was sent by Lord Stratford to salute and welcome you on your first arrival at Scutari . . . and found you stretched on the sofa where I believe you never lay down again. I thought *then* that it would be a great happiness to serve you."

The nurses were to go to the hospital at once, for wounded were expected from the battle of Balaclava, fought on October 25. Painted caïques, the gondola-like boats of the Bosphorus, were procured, the nurses were lowered into them with their carpetbags and umbrellas, and the party was rowed across to Scutari. . . .

The nurses disembarked, climbed the slope, and passed through the enormous gateway of the Barrack Hospital, that gateway over which Miss Nightingale said should have been written. "Abandon hope all ye who enter here." Dr. Menzies and Major Sillery, the Military Commandant, were waiting to receive them. That night Lord Stratford wrote to the Duke of Newcastle: "Miss Nightingale and her brigade of nurses are actually established at Scutari under the same roof with the gallant and suffering objects of their compassion."

From the European shore of the Bosphorus, from the magnificent house where the British Ambassador lived, the great quadrangle of the Turkish Barracks glimmered golden, magnificent as a giant's palace, but at close quarters romance vanished. Vast echoing corridors with floors of broken tiles and walls streaming damp, empty of any kind of furniture, stretched for miles. Later Miss Nightingale calculated there were four miles of beds. Everything was filthy; everything was dilapidated. The form of the building was a hollow square with towers at each corner. One side had been gutted in a fire and could not be used. The courtyard in the center was a sea of mud littered with refuse. Within the vast ramifications of the barracks were a depot for troops, a canteen where spirits were sold, and a stable for cavalry horses. Deep in the cellars were dark and noisome dens where more than 200 women, who had been allowed by an oversight to accompany the army, drank, starved, gave birth to infants, carried on their trade as prostitutes, and died of cholera. "But it is not a building, it's a town!" exclaimed a new arrival.

To reach the Barrack Hospital meant martyrdom for wounded men. There was no pier, and the rickety landing-stage could only be used by small boats. The men were taken out of the sick transports and lowered into caïques or rowing-boats; after landing they were jolted on stretchers over rough ground up a precipitous slope.

Although so near Constantinople the situation was isolated. The only communication with Constantinople was by boat, and the Bosphorus was swept by sudden storms which cut off all communication for three or four days at a time. At Scutari were the principal cemeteries of Constantinople, but no markets or shops, only a "profusion of tombs, fountains and weeping willows"— and ample opportunities for drunkenness and vice. As soon as the British Army occupied Scutari, a horde of Jews, Greeks, and Armenians descended. Tents, booths, ramshackle sheds used as drinking shops and brothels sprang up round the barracks, and spirits of the worst quality were drunk by the troops in enormous quantities. Regiments sent to Scutari rapidly deteriorated, and on one night, out of 2400 troops stationed in the barracks, 1400 were reported drunk.

These were obvious drawbacks, but the vast building hid a more fatal secret. Sanitary defects made it a pest house, and the majority of the men who died there died not of wounds or sickness with which they arrived but of disease they contracted as a result of being in the hospital.

The catastrophe which destroyed the British Army was a catastrophe of sickness, not of losses in battle. There were two different sicknesses. The troops on the heights before Sebastopol fell sick of diseases resulting from starvation and exposure. When they were brought down to Scutari and entered the Barrack Hospital, they died of fevers resulting from the unsanitary construction of the Barrack Hospital assisted by insufficient food, filth, and overcrowding. The second sickness was the more fatal. When the war was over, it was found that the mortality in each regiment depended on the number of men which that regiment had been able to send to Scutari.

When Miss Nightingale entered the Barrack Hospital on November 5, 1854, there were ominous signs of approaching disaster, but the catastrophe had not yet occurred. Food, drugs, medical necessities had already run short, the Barrack Hospital was without equipment, and in the Crimea supply was breaking down. Winter was swiftly advancing, and each week the number of sick sent to Scutari steadily increased.

There were men in the Crimea, there were men in Scutari, there were men at home in England who saw the tragedy approach. They were powerless. The system under which the health of the British Army was administered defeated them. The exactions, the imbecilities of the system killed energy and efficiency, crushed initiative, removed responsibility, and were the death of common sense.

Three departments were responsible for maintaining the health of the British Army and for the organization of its hospitals. The Commissariat, the Purveyor's Department, and the Medical Department. They were departments which during forty years of economy had been cut down nearer and still nearer the bone. In 1853, Dr. Andrew Smith, the Director-General of the British Army Medical Service, received 1200 pounds sterling a year and had only twelve clerks to execute the entire administration of his department. The Purveyor's Department had been reduced to a staff of four, and at the outbreak of war it was extremely difficult to find anyone with sufficient experience to send out as a Purveyor-in-Chief. Mr. Ward, "poor old Ward," the Purveyor at Scutari, was over seventy years of age, a veteran not only of the Peninsula but of Walcheren. His staff consisted of two inexperienced clerks and three boys who also acted as messengers. . . .

The method by which the hospitals were supplied was confused. The Commissariat were the caterers, bankers, carriers, and store-keepers of the army. They bought and delivered the standard daily rations of the men whether they were on duty or in hospital. The bread and the meat used in the hospitals, the fuel burned there were supplied by the Commissariat. But the Commissariat did not supply food for men too ill to eat their normal rations. At this point the Purveyor stepped in. All invalid foods, known as "medical comforts," sago, rice, milk, arrowroot, port wine, were supplied by the Purveyor. But though these comforts were supplied to the hospital by the Purveyor, he did not obtain them: all the Purveyor's contracts were made by the Commissariat. The Purveyor never dealt directly with his merchant and had no power over him. If goods were unsatisfactory, the Purveyor could only complain to the Commissariat. . . .

Relations between the doctors and the Purveyor were even more obscure. A doctor might order a man a special diet, but it depended on the Purveyor whether the patient received it or not. Having made a requisition on the Purveyor, the doctor was powerless. . . .

Though the system placed executive power in the hands of the Commissariat and the Purveyor, it was only a limited power. Certain goods only might be supplied.

The result was the extraordinary shortages. When the sick and wounded came down to Scutari from the Crimea, they were in the majority of cases without forks, spoons, knives, or shirts. The regulations of the British Army laid down that each soldier should bring his pack into hospital with him, and his pack contained a change of clothing and utensils for eating. These articles were consequently not on the Purveyor's warrant. But most of the men who came down to Scutari had abandoned their packs after Calamita Bay, or on the march from the Alma to Balaclava, at the orders of their officers. Nevertheless, the Purveyor refused to consider any requisitions on him for these articles.

Officials were trained not to make trouble, not to spend money, never to risk responsibility; and at Scutari, grossly overworked as they were, they were placed in a situation which demanded courage and resource. The system, while it discouraged action, was enormously prolific of forms, requisitions, dockets, cross-checks, authorizations, and reports. In the hospitals at Scutari every requisition, however trifling, had to be checked and counter-signed by two doctors, one of them a senior officer. No medical officer was permitted to use his discretion. . . .

The Barrack Hospital was the fatal fruit of the system. When the General Hospital was unexpectedly filled with cholera cases and Dr. Menzies was abruptly notified that the casualties from the Alma and a further large number of cholera cases were on their way, he was instructed to turn the Turkish Barracks into a hospital. The preparation and equipment of a hospital formed no part of his duties, his task being to instruct the Purveyor. He sent for "poor old Ward" and told him to prepare the Turkish Barracks for the reception of wounded. He had then, in accordance with the rules of the service, performed his duty. How Mr. Ward was to conjure hospital equipment at a moment's notice out of the drink-shops, brothels, and tombs of Scutari, how he was to collect labor to clean the vast filthy building when no labor existed nearer than Constantinople, was not Dr. Menzies' concern. Mr. Ward also knew the correct procedure. He had no authority to expend sums of money in purchasing goods in the open market, and in any case many of the articles required were not on his warrant. He requisitioned the Commissariat on the proper forms, the Commissariat wrote on the forms "None in store," and the matter was closed. The wounded arrived and were placed in the building without food, bedding, or medical attention. At a later date Dr. Menzies instructed the Purveyor to issue the men shirts. This was not done, and the men continued to lie naked. Dr. Menzies was asked by the Roebuck Committee why he had not seen to it that his order was carried out. He replied that it was no part of his duty to see that an order was executed. Having issued the instruction correctly and placed it on record, his duty was done. "Their heads," wrote Miss Nightingale in 1855, "are so flattened between the boards of Army discipline that they remain old children all their lives. . . ."

The doctors at Scutari received the news of Miss Nightingale's appointment with disgust. They were understaffed, overworked; it was the last straw that a youngish Society lady should be foisted on them with a pack of nurses. Of all Government follies, this was the worst. However, they had no choice but to submit; open opposition would be dangerous, for Miss Nightingale was known to have powerful backing, to be the intimate friend of Sidney Herbert and on friendly terms with half the Cabinet. . . .

However, on November 5 Miss Nightingale and her party were welcomed into the Barrack Hospital with every appearance of flattering attention and escorted into the hospital with compliments and expressions of goodwill. When they saw their quarters, the picture abruptly changed. Six rooms, one of which was a kitchen and another a closet ten feet square, had been allotted to a party of forty persons. The same space had previously been allotted to three doctors and, in another part of the hospital, was occupied solely by a major. The rooms were damp, filthy and unfurnished except for a few chairs. There were no tables; there was no food. Miss Nightingale made no comment, and the officials withdrew. It was a warning, a caution against placing reliance on the flowery promises, the resounding compliments of Stratford Canning, first Viscount Stratford de Redcliffe.

Lord Stratford had been British Ambassador to Constantinople three times and associated with Turkey since 1807. His influence was immense; he was virtually a dictator; his latest "reign" at Constantinople had lasted, with a two years' intermission, for sixteen years. The Turks called him "the great Elchi," the great ambassador. Physically he was extremely handsome, and he prided himself on his presence—"the thin rigid lips, the majesty of brow of a Canning." He lived magnificently and traveled with twenty-five servants and seventy tons of plate . . . In his magnificent palace on the Bosphorus he lived for two years with, said Miss Nightingale, "the British Army perishing within sight of his windows," and during those two years he visited the hospitals only once, when she "dragged" him there for a visit of only one and a half hours. . . .

That night, as Miss Nightingale was calculating how she could cram her party of forty into five small rooms and a kitchen, Lord Stratford wrote a flowery letter to the Duke of Newcastle complimenting her on the "accomplishments" she brought into the field of charity and venturing to hope that "much comfort may be derived by the sick and wounded from that attractive source."

Fourteen nurses were to sleep in one room, ten nuns in another; Miss Nightingale and Mrs. Bracebridge shared the closet; Mr. Bracebridge and the courier-interpreter slept in the office; Mrs. Clark, who was to be cook, and her assistant must go to bed in the kitchen. There was one more room upstairs, and the eight Sellonites must sleep there. They went upstairs, and hurried back. The room was still occupied—by the dead body of a Russian general. Mr. Bracebridge fetched two men to remove the corpse while the sisters waited. The room was not cleaned, and there was nothing to clean it with; it was days before they could get a broom, and meanwhile the deceased general's white hairs littered the floor. There was no furniture, no food, no means of cooking food, no beds. Most of the party prepared to sleep on so-called Turkish "divans," raised wooden platforms running round the rooms on which the Turks placed bedding; there was, however, no bedding. While the nurses and sisters unpacked, Miss Nightingale went down into the hospital and managed to procure tin basins of milk-less tea. As the party drank it, she told them what she had discovered.

The hospital was totally lacking in equipment. It was hopeless to ask for furniture. There was no furniture. There was not even an operating table. There were no medical supplies. There were not even the ordinary necessities of life. For the present the nurses must use their tin basins for everything, washing, eating, and drinking.

They must be prepared to go short of water. The allowance was limited to a pint a head a day for washing and drinking, including tea, and it was necessary to line up in one of the corridors where there was a fountain to obtain it. Tomorrow the situation would become worse; a battle at Balaclava had been fought on October 25, and transports loaded with sick and wounded were expected.

The party had to go to bed in darkness, for the shortage of lamps and candles was acute. Sisters and nurses lying on the hard divans tried to console themselves by thinking how much greater were the sufferings of the wounded in the sick transports. The rooms were alive with fleas, and rats scurried beneath the divans all night long. The spirits of all, wrote Sister Margaret Goodman, sank.

The doctors ignored Miss Nightingale. She was to be frozen out, and only one doctor would use her nurses and her supplies. Mr. Macdonald told the Hospitals Commission: "Nurses were offered by Miss Nightingale and not accepted"; and he experienced similar difficulty himself. He had *The Times* fund to spend; the urgency of the need for supplies was tragically evident, but he had the greatest difficulty in "squeezing out" of the doctors an admission of what was needed. The medical authorities drew together in a close defensive phalanx. Admit failure! Accept help for the army from civilians, from *The Times* under whose attacks the army authorities were smarting! From a high Society miss who happened to be on dining terms with the Cabinet! Their experience of army methods, of confidential reports, told them that the man who consorted with Miss Nightingale or who supplied his wards through *The Times* fund would be a marked man.

She realized that before she could accomplish anything she must win the confidence of the doctors. She determined not to offer her nurses and her stores again, but to wait until the doctors asked her for help. She would demonstrate that she and her party wished neither to interfere nor attract attention, that they were prepared to be completely subservient to the authority of the doctors.

It was a policy which demanded self-control; the party were to stand by, see troops suffer, and do nothing until officially in-

structed. Though Miss Nightingale could accept the hard fact that
the experiment on which she had embarked could never succeed
against official opposition, yet she inevitably came into conflict
with her nurses.

A day passed, and some stores arrived. She made them sort old
linen, count packages of provisions. The hardships of life continued. They stood in the corridor to get their pint of water. They
ate out of the tin bowls, wiped them with paper, washed their
faces and hands in them, wiped them again and drank tea from
them. Discomfort would have been ignored if the sufferings of the
wounded had been relieved, but they were not relieved. The cries
of the men were unanswered while old linen was counted and
mended—this was not what they had left England to accomplish. They blamed Miss Nightingale.

On Sunday, November 6, the ships bringing the wounded from
Balaclava began to unload at Scutari. As on other occasions the
arrangements were inadequate, and the men suffered frightfully;
they were brought up to the hospital on stretchers carried by
Turks, who rolled their bleeding burdens about, put the stretchers
down with a bump when they needed a rest, and on several
occasions threw the patient off. Screams of pain were the accompaniment to the unhappy procession, and Sister Margaret
Goodman recorded the case of a soldier who died as a result.

Still Miss Nightingale would not allow her nurses to throw
themselves into the work of attending on these miserable victims.
She allocated twenty-eight nurses to the Barrack Hospital and
ten to the General Hospital a quarter of a mile away. All were
to sleep in the Barrack Hospital, and all were to wait. No nurse
was to enter a ward except at the invitation of a doctor. However
piteous the state of the wounded, the doctor must give the order
for attention. She sent her nurses to church to sit through an
admirable sermon by the chief Chaplain, Mr. Sabin. If the
doctors did not choose to employ the nurses, then the nurses must
remain idle.

She was also determined to send no nurse into the wards until
she knew that nurse could be relied on. The reliability of the nurse
was as important to the success of the experiment as the cooperation of the doctors, and for nearly a week the party were kept
shut up in their detestable quarters making shirts, pillows, stump-
rests, and slings and being observed by her penetrating eye. The

time, sighed one of the English Sisters of Mercy, seemed extremely long. . . .

Miss Nightingale herself rigidly obeyed regulations. On a later
occasion she was sitting by the bedside of a man critically ill and
found his feet stone cold. She told an orderly to fetch a hot-
water bottle. The man refused, saying he had been told to do
nothing for a patient without directions from a medical officer.
She accepted the correction, found a doctor, and obtained a
requisition in proper form. For weeks she stood by in silence
while the skill of highly efficient nurses was wasted. . . .

She was first able to get a footing in the hospital through the
kitchen. A state of starvation existed in the Barrack Hospital.
According to regulations a private soldier in hospital was placed
on what was known as a whole diet, a half-diet, or a spoon diet,
the first representing the man's ordinary rations cooked for him
by the hospital, the second about half his rations, and the third
liquid food. In addition he was supposed to receive "extra diet,"
wine, milk, butter, arrowroot, jelly, milk puddings, eggs, etc.,
as prescribed by the surgeon attending him and procured through
the Purveyor.

But to cook anything at the Barrack Hospital was practically
impossible. The sole provision for cooking was thirteen Turkish
coppers each holding about 450 pints. There was only one
kitchen. There were no kettles, no saucepans; the only fuel was
green wood. The tea was made in the coppers in which the meat
had just been boiled, water was short, the coppers were not
cleaned, and the tea was undrinkable. The meat for each ward was
issued to the orderly for the ward, who stood in line to receive
it from the Purveyor's Department. The Purveyor was understaffed, and when the hospital had 2500 patients one clerk did all
the issues, and the orderlies had to wait an hour or more. When
the orderly had the meat, he tied it up, put some distinguishing
marks on it, and dropped it into the pot. Some of the articles
used by the orderlies to distinguish their meat included red rags,
buttons, old nails, reeking pairs of surgical scissors, and odd bits
of uniform. The water did not generally boil; the fires smoked
abominably. When the cook considered that sufficient time had
been taken up in cooking, the orderlies threw buckets of water on
the fires to put them out, and the contents of the coppers were
distributed, the cook standing by to see that each man got his
own joint; the joints which had been dropped in last were some-

times almost raw. The orderly then carried the meat into the ward and divided it up, usually on his bed, and never less than twenty minutes could elapse between taking it out of the pot and serving it. Not only were the dinners always cold, but the meat was issued with bone and gristle weighed in, and some men got portions which were all bone. Those who could eat meat usually tore it with their fingers—there were almost no forks, spoons, or knives. Men on a spoon diet got the water in which the meat had been cooked, as soup. There were no vegetables only, sometimes, dried peas. . . .

The food was almost uneatable by men in rude health; as a diet for cholera and dysentery cases it produced agonies. The torture endured by the men when the pangs of hunger were superimposed on diarrhea was frightful. "I have never seen suffering greater," wrote one observer.

The day after Miss Nightingale arrived she began to cook "extras." She had bought arrowroot, wine and beef essences, and portable stoves in Marseilles. On the 6 of November, with the doctors' permission, she provided pails of hot arrowroot and port wine for the Balaclava survivors, and within a week the kitchen belonging to her quarters had become an extra diet kitchen, where food from her own stores was cooked. For five months this kitchen was the only means of supplying invalid food in the Barrack Hospital. She strictly observed official routine, nothing being supplied from the kitchen without a requisition signed by a doctor. No nurse was permitted to give a patient any nourishment without a doctor's written directions.

Cooking was all she had managed to accomplish when, on November 9, the situation completely changed. A flood of sick poured into Scutari on such a scale that a crisis of terrible urgency arose, and prejudices and resentments were for the moment forgotten.

It was the opening of the catastrophe. The destruction of the British Army had begun. These were the first of the stream of men suffering from dysentery, from scurvy, from starvation and exposure who were to pour down on Scutari all through the terrible winter. Over in the Crimea on the heights above Sebastopol the army was marooned, as completely as if on a lighthouse. Thousands of men possessed only what they stood up in. After the landing at Calamita Bay and after the battle of the Alma, when the troops were riddled with cholera and the heat was intense, the men had, by their officers' orders, abandoned their packs . . .

Balaclava had become a nightmare of filth. Lord Raglan had been attracted by its extraordinary harbor, a land-locked lagoon, calm, clear, and almost tideless, so deep that a large vessel could anchor close inshore. But Balaclava was a fishing village of only 500 inhabitants, a single street of white vine-wreathed houses clinging to a precipitous ravine. No steps were taken to inspect Balaclava before it was occupied or to keep it in a sanitary condition. The army which marched in was stricken with cholera, and within a few days the narrow street had become a disgusting quagmire. Piles of arms and legs amputated after the battle of Balaclava, with the sleeves and trousers still on them, had been thrown into the harbor and could be seen dimly through the water. Bodies of dead men rose suddenly and horribly out of the mud to the surface. Anchor chains and cables were fouled by limbs and trunks. The surface of the once translucent water was covered with brightly colored scum, and the whole village smelled of sulphuretted hydrogen.

On November 5 the Russians had attacked at Inkerman, on the heights above Sebastopol. In a grim battle fought in swirling fog the British were victorious. But victory was not reassuring. The British troops were exhausted; their commanders were shaken by the revelation of Russian strength. It was evident that Sebastopol would not fall until the spring. . . .

The weather changed rapidly, icy winds blew—and the troops on the heights above Sebastopol had no fuel. Every bush, every stunted tree was consumed, and the men clawed roots out of the sodden earth to gain a little warmth. As it grew colder, they had to live without shelter, without clothing, drenched by incessant driving rain, to sleep in mud, to eat hard dried peas and raw salt meat. The percentage of sickness rose and rose, and the miserable victims began to pour down on Scutari. The authorities were overwhelmed. The first transports were not even expected. Through an oversight, notification that they had sailed was received only half an hour before the sick and wounded began to land. . . .

It was Miss Nightingale's opportunity—at last the doctors turned to her. Her nurses dropped their sorting of linen and began with desperate haste to seam up great bags and stuff them with straw. These were laid down not only in the wards but in the corridors, a line of stuffed sacks on each side with just room to pass between them.

Day after day the sick poured in until the enormous building was entirely filled. The wards were full; the corridors were lined with men lying on the bare boards because the supply of bags stuffed with straw had given out. Chaos reigned. The doctors were unable even to examine each man. Mr. Sabin, the head Chaplain, was told that men were a fortnight in the Barrack Hospital without seeing a surgeon. Yet the doctors, especially the older men, worked "like lions" and were frequently on their feet for twenty-four hours at a time. . . .

The filth became indescribable. The men in the corridors lay on unwashed rotten floors crawling with vermin. As the Rev. Sidney Godolphin Osborne knelt to take down dying messages, his paper became covered thickly with lice. There were no pillows, no blankets; the men lay, with their heads on their boots, wrapped in the blanket or greatcoat stiff with blood and filth which had been their sole covering perhaps for more than a week. There were no screens or operating tables. Amputations had to be performed in the wards in full sight of the patients. Mr. Osborne describes the amputation of a thigh "done upon boards put on two trestles. I assisted . . . during the latter part of the operation the man's position became such from want of a table he was supported by my arm underneath, a surgeon on the other side grasping my wrist." One of Miss Nightingale's first acts was to procure a screen from Constantinople so that men might be spared the sight of the suffering they themselves were doomed to undergo.

She estimated that in the hospital at this time there were more than one thousand men suffering from acute diarrhea and only twenty chamber pots. The privies in the towers of the Barrack Hospital had been allowed to become useless; the water pipes which flushed them had been stopped up when the Barracks were used for troops, and when the building was converted into a hospital they had never been unstopped. Mr. Augustus Stafford said there was liquid filth which floated over the floor an inch deep and came out of the privy itself into the ante-room . . . By the end of the second week in November the atmosphere in the Barrack Hospital was so frightful that it gave Mr. Stafford the prevailing disease of diarrhea in five minutes. The stench from the hospital could be smelled *outside* the walls.

A change came over the men, said Mr. Macdonald. The classi-

fication between wounded and sick was broken down. The
wounded who had been well before began to catch fevers, "gradually all signs of cheerfulness disappeared, they drew their blankets over their heads and were buried in silence."

Fate had worse in store. On the night of November 14 it was
noticed that the sea in the Bosphorus was running abnormally
high, and there was a strange thrumming wind. Within a few
days news came that the Crimea had been devastated by the worst
hurricane within the memory of man. Tents were reduced to
shreds, horses blown helplessly for miles, buildings destroyed,
trees uprooted. The marquees which formed the regimental field
hospitals vanished, and men were left half buried in mud without
coverings of any kind. Most serious of all, every vessel in Balaclava harbor was destroyed, amongst them a large ship, the *Prince*,
which had entered the harbor the previous day loaded with warm
winter clothing and stores for the troops.

The hurricane rendered the situation of the army desperate.
Such few stores and such little forage as it possessed were destroyed. Winter began in earnest with storms of sleet and winds
that cut like a knife as they howled across the bleak plateau.
Dysentery, diarrhea, rheumatic fever increased by leaps and
bounds. More and more shiploads of sick inundated Scutari. The
men came down starved and in rags. "They were without their
shoes and their shirts had been thrown away in utter disgust at
their filthiness or torn in shreds . . . they were swarming with
vermin; their trousers were all torn; their coats ragged . . . sometimes they came down without any coats at all," said Mr. Macdonald in his evidence before the Roebuck Committee. The men
told the nurses to keep away because they were so filthy, "My
own mother could not touch me," said one man to Sister Margaret
Goodman. By the end of November the administration of the
hospital had collapsed. . . .

And then in the misery, the confusion, a light began to break.
Gradually it dawned on harassed doctors and overworked officials
that there was one person in Scutari who could take action—who
had money and the authority to spend it—Miss Nightingale.

She had a very large sum at her disposal derived from various
sources and amounting to over £30,000, of which £7000 had
been collected by her personally; and Constantinople was one of
the great markets of the world. During the first horrors of November, the gathering catastrophe of December, it became known

that whatever was wanted, from a milk pudding to a water-bed, the thing to do was to "go to Miss Nightingale."

Each day she ascertained what comforts were lacking in the Purveyor's Store, what articles supply was short of, what requisitions had been made which had not been met. Mr. Macdonald then went into Constantinople and bought the goods, which were placed in her store and issued by her upon requisition in the official form by a medical officer. Nothing, with the exception of letter-paper and pencils, was ever given out without an official requisition duly signed. Gradually, Mr. Macdonald told the Roebuck Committee, the doctors ceased to be suspicious and their jealousy disappeared.

In one urgent work she met no opposition. Just as it was no one's business to clean the lavatories, so it was no one's business to clean the wards. The first commission Mr. Macdonald executed for Miss Nightingale was the purchase of 200 hard scrubbing-brushes and sacking for washing the floors. She insisted on the huge wooden tubs in the wards being emptied, standing quietly and obstinately by the side of each one, sometimes for an hour at a time, never scolding or raising her voice, until the orderlies gave way and the tub was emptied.

Her next step was to wash the men's clothes. Mr. Macdonald stated that for five weeks after he arrived at Scutari no washing was done at all. The Purveyor had been instructed to make a laundry contract and had done so with a Greek, who was quite unable to fulfill his obligations; he either failed to wash at all or washed in cold water, and shirts came back as filthy as they were sent, still crawling with lice. The men said they preferred their own lice to other people's and refused to part with their shirts, stuffing them, filthy and vermin-ridden, under their blankets. The total amount of washing satisfactorily accomplished for the vast hospital was seven shirts. Miss Nightingale made arrangements to rent a house outside the barracks and have the washing done by soldiers' wives. She consulted Dr. Menzies, telling him she wished to have boilers put in by the Engineers Corps. "Oh, but that is putting you to a great deal of trouble," said Dr. Menzies. "I should think the Purveyor would be able to make arrangements." The boilers were installed and the cost paid out of *The Times* fund. . . .

For a time she tried to work with Lady Stratford. On November 7, two days after her arrival, she wrote to Lord Stratford asking for sheets, shirts, and portable stoves for cooking "extras." He sent her Lady Stratford instead. Lady Stratford would not come across to Scutari (she had been in the Barrack Hospital once and the stench had made her sick), nor did she send linen and stoves, but she offered to get anything that was required in Constantinople. Miss Nightingale asked her to obtain twelve wagons to bring heavy goods up to the Barrack Hospital. Next day she looked out and saw drawn up before her quarters seven glass and gilt coaches and five other vehicles, which she had to pay off out of her own private funds. "This lark of the Ambassadress's," she wrote, "cost Miss Nightingale 500 piastres."

By the end of December Miss Nightingale was in fact purveying the hospital. During a period of two months she supplied, on requisition of Medical Officers, about 6000 shirts, 2000 socks, and 500 pairs of drawers. She supplied nightcaps, slippers, plates, tin cups, knives, forks, spoons "in proportion." She procured trays, tables, forms, clocks, operating tables, scrubbers, towels, soap, and screens. She caused an entire regiment which had only tropical clothing to be re-fitted with warm clothing purchased by Mr. Macdonald in the markets of Constantinople when Supply had declared such clothing unprocurable in the time—Supply was compelled to get all its goods from England. "I am a kind of General Dealer," she wrote to Sidney Herbert on January 4, 1855, "in socks, shirts, knives and forks, wooden spoons, tin baths, tables and forms, cabbages and carrots, operating tables, towels and soap, small tooth combs, precipitate for destroying lice, scissors, bed pans, and stump pillows."

Before Sebastopol conditions grew steadily worse. The stores lost in the hurricane were not replaced. Men, sick or well, lay in a foot of water in the mud covered only by a single blanket. Every root had been burned, and the men had to eat their food raw: meat stiff with salt and dried peas. Tea was withdrawn and green coffee, needing roasting and pounding, was issued instead, because good results had been obtained from the use of green coffee in the Caffre War. There was no bread. As the percentage of sick climbed and climbed, double turns of duty were thrown on the survivors. Men were in the trenches before Sebastopol for thirty-six hours at a stretch, never dry, never warmed, never fed. The sick were brought down to Balaclava strapped to mule-litters lent by the French—there was no British transport of any kind— naked, emaciated, and filthy. They were universally suffering

from diarrhea, and strapped to the mules they could not relieve
themselves. After waiting hours without food or shelter in the icy
wind or driving sleet at Balaclava, they were piled on to the decks
of the sick transports and brought down to Scutari. And the
catastrophe had not yet reached its height.

At the beginning of December, when the Barrack Hospital was
filled to overflowing, a letter from Lord Raglan announced the
arrival of a further 500 sick and wounded. It was impossible to
cram any additional cases into the existing wards and corridors,
and Miss Nightingale, supported by Dr. McGrigor, pressed to
have put in order the wing of the hospital which had been damaged by fire before the British occupation; it consisted of two
wards and a corridor and would accommodate nearly 1000 extra
cases. But the cost would be considerable, and no one in the
hospital had the necessary authority to put the work in hand. She
had been repeatedly assured by Sidney Herbert that Lord Stratford had *carte blanche*; now she applied to him, and Lady Stratford came across to Scutari escorted by a couple of *attachés*.
Preferring not to come inside the hospital, she held conferences
with the Purveyor and Major Sillery in the courtyard, and 125
Turkish workmen were engaged to repair the wards. After a few
days a dispute about the rate of wages arose, and the Turkish
workmen struck. Miss Nightingale wrote to Lord Stratford, who
denied the slightest knowledge of the business; Lady Stratford
withdrew; worried Major Sillery had neither money nor authority. On this Miss Nightingale took matters into her own hands.
She engaged on her own responsibility not 125 but 200 workmen,
and paid for them partly out of her own pocket and partly out of
The Times fund. The wards were repaired and cleaned in time
to receive the wounded.

Not only did she repair the wards; she equipped them. The
Purveyor could provide nothing. "Orderlies were wanting, utensils were wanting, even water was wanting," she wrote to Sidney
Herbert on December 12, 1854. "I supplied all the utensils, including knives and forks, spoons, cans, towels, etc. . . . and was
able to send on the instant arrowroot in huge milk pails (two
bottles of port wine in each) for 500 men." The number of sick
and wounded finally received was 800. One of the men described
his sensations when he, at last got off the filthy sick transport and
was received by Miss Nightingale and her nurses with clean bedding and warm food—"we felt we were in heaven," he said . . .

Miss Nightingale . . . never for a moment lost sight of the fact that the object of her mission was to prove the value of women as nurses. But, unhappily, no difficulties with doctors or purveyors were as wearing or as discouraging as her difficulties with her nurses. Reluctance to accept her authority and obey her instructions was constant from the beginning to the end of her mission, and many of her nurses heartily disliked her.

However, she had managed to establish herself, and now her nurses were fully occupied. . . .

In January, 1855 the sufferings of the British Army before Sebastopol began to reach a fearful climax. William Howard Russell described the wounded arriving at Balaclava, strapped to the mules lent by the French: "They formed one of the most ghastly processions that ever poet imagined. . . . With closed eyes, open mouths and ghastly attenuated faces, they were borne along two by two, the thin stream of breath visible in the frosty air alone showing that they were alive. One figure was a horror, a corpse, stone dead, strapped upright in its seat . . . no doubt the man had died on his way down to the harbour. . . . Another man I saw with raw flesh and skin hanging from his fingers, the raw bones of which protruded into the cold, undressed and uncovered."

Still no stores had reached the army. What had happened to them, the Roebuck Committee demanded later? Huge quantities of warm clothing, of preserved foods, of medical comforts and surgical supplies had been sent out—where did they all go? It was never discovered. The Roebuck Committee found it impossible not to suspect dishonesty, but Miss Nightingale reached a different conclusion. Large quantities unquestionably vanished in the Turkish Customs House, a "bottomless pit whence nothing ever issues of all that is thrown in," but she declared all the same that stores were available all the time the men were suffering, never reaching them through the "regulations of the service." She cites a number of instances in her *Notes on Matters affecting the Health, Efficiency and Hospital Administration of the British Army*. In January, 1855, when the army before Sebastopol was being ravaged by scurvy, a shipload of cabbages was thrown into the harbor at Balaclava on the ground that it was not consigned to anyone. This happened not once but several times. During November, December, and January 1854-55, when green coffee was being issued to the men, there were 173,000 rations of tea in store at Balaclava; 20,000 lb. of lime juice arrived for the troops on December 10, 1854, but none was issued until February. Why? Because no order existed for the inclusion of tea and lime juice in the daily ration.

Again, at the end of December there were blankets enough in store, says Miss Nightingale, to have given a third one to every man. But the men lay on the muddy ground with nothing under them and nothing over them since their blankets had been lost in battle or destroyed in the hurricane, because the regulations did not entitle them to replacement. At Scutari the Hospitals Commission recorded in January, 1855: "Goods have been refused although they were, to our personal knowledge, lying in abundance in the store of the Purveyor. This was done because they had not been examined by the Board of Survey." Miss Nightingale wrote to Sidney Herbert in March of that year. "The *Eagle* has now been arrived three weeks, and no use whatever has been made of her stores. Cumming says they have not yet been 'sat on.' In February when the men were lying naked in the bitter cold Mr. Wreford, the Purveyor, admitted to the Hospitals Commission that he had received a large quantity of shirts a fortnight ago, but he had done nothing with them, did not even know the quantity as he had not yet had a 'board'. . . ."

In January, 1855 there were 12,000 men in hospital and only 11,000 in the camp before Sebastopol; and still the shiploads came pouring down. It was, Miss Nightingale wrote, "calamity unparalleled in the history of calamity."

In this emergency she became supreme. She was the rock to which everyone clung, even the Purveyors. She described "Messrs. Wreford, Ward and Reade, veterans of the Spanish War, coming to me for a moment's solace, trembling under responsibility and afraid of informality." "Nursing," she wrote on January 4 to Sidney Herbert, "is the least of the functions into which I have been forced."

Her calmness, her resource, her power to take action raised her to the position of a goddess. The men adored her. "If she were at our head," they said, "we should be in Sebastopol next week." The doctors came to be absolutely dependent on her, and Colonel Sterling wrote home: "Miss Nightingale now queens it with absolute power. . . ."

In spite of the improvements in the Barrack Hospital, something was horribly wrong. The wards were cleaner, the lavatories unstopped, the food adequate, but still the mortality climbed. The disaster was about to enter its second phase. At the end of December an epidemic broke out described variously as "Asiatic cholera" or "famine fever," similar to cholera brought over by starving Irish immigrants after the Irish potato famine, and by Miss Nightingale simply as "gaol fever." By the middle of January the epidemic was serious—four surgeons died in three weeks, and three nurses and poor old Ward, the Purveyor, and his wife died. The officers on their rounds began to be afraid to go into the wards; they could do nothing for the unfortunates perishing within; they knocked on the door and an orderly shouted "All right, sir," from inside.

The snow ceased, and faint warmth came to the bleak plateau before Sebastopol on which the British Army was encamped. The number of men sent down by sick transports stopped rising. The percentage of sick was still disastrously, tragically high, but it was stationary.

But in the Barrack Hospital the mortality figures continued to rise. Sister Margaret Goodman saw an *araba*, a rough Turkish tumbril, heaped with what she took to be the carcasses of beasts. They were the naked, emaciated bodies of dead British soldiers. A large square hole of no great depth was dug by Turks, the bodies were tossed into this until they came level with the top; then a layer of earth was shoveled over all, and the Turks stamped it down. They then drove off. The British were unable to bury their dead. A fatigue party could not be mustered whose strength was equal to the task of digging a pit.

In England fury succeeded fury. A great storm of rage, humiliation, and despair had been gathering through the terrible winter of 1854-55. For the first time in history, through reading the despatches of Russell, the public had realized "with what majesty the British soldier fights." And these heroes were dead. The men who had stormed the heights at Alma, charged with the Light Brigade at Balaclava, fought the grim battle against overwhelming odds in the fog at Inkerman had perished of hunger and neglect. Even the horses which had taken part in the Charge of the Light Brigade had starved to death. . . .

At the end of February, Lord Panmure sent out a Sanitary Commission to investigate the sanitary state of the buildings used as hospitals and of the camps both at Scutari and in the Crimea . . . The Sanitary Commission landed at Constantinople at the beginning of March and began work instantly. Their discoveries were hair-raising. They described the sanitary defects of the Barrack Hospital as "murderous." Beneath the magnificent structure were sewers of the worst possible construction, mere cess-pools, choked, inefficient, and grossly over-loaded. The whole vast building stood in a sea of decaying filth. The very walls, constructed of porous plaster, were soaked in it. Every breeze, every puff of air, blew poisonous gas through the pipes of numerous open privies into the corridors and wards where the sick were lying. "It is impossible," Miss Nightingale told the Royal Commission of 1857, "to describe the state of the atmosphere of the Barrack Hospital at night. I have been well acquainted with the dwellings of the worst parts of most of the great cities of Europe, but have never been in any atmosphere which I could compare with it." Nurses had noticed that certain beds were fatal. Every man put in these beds quickly died. They proved to be near the doors of the privies, where the poisonous gases were worst. The water supply was contaminated and totally insufficient. The Commissioners had the channel opened through which the water flowed, and the water supply for the greater part of the hospital was found to be passing through the decaying carcass of a dead horse. The storage of water was in tanks in the courtyard, and these had been built next temporary privies, erected to cope with the needs of men suffering from the prevalent diarrhea. The privies were open and without any means of flushing or cleaning. The courtyard and precincts of the hospital were filthy. The Commissioners ordered them to be cleared, and during the first fortnight of this work 556 handcarts and large baskets full of rubbish were removed and 24 dead animals and 2 dead horses buried. The Commission began to flush and cleanse the sewers, to limewash the walls and free them from vermin, to tear out the wooden shelves known as Turkish divans which ran round the wards and harbored the rats for which the Barrack Hospital was notorious. The effect was instant. At last the rate of mortality began to fall. In the Crimea spring came with a rush; the bleak plateau before Sebastopol was bathed in sunlight and carpeted with crocuses and hyacinths. The road to Balaclava became passable, the men's rations improved, and the survivors of the fearful winter lost their unnatural silence and began once more to curse and swear. . . .

1951

Medical Education

THOMAS HENRY HUXLEY

WHAT is the object of medical education? It is to enable the practitioner, on the one hand, to prevent disease by his knowledge of hygiene; on the other hand, to divine its nature, and to alleviate and cure it, by his knowledge of pathology, therapeutics and practical medicine. That is his business in life, and if he has not a thorough and practical knowledge of the conditions of health, of the causes which tend to the establishment of disease, of the meaning of symptoms, and of the uses of medicine and operative appliances, he is incompetent, even if he were the best anatomist, or physiologist, or chemist, that ever took a gold medal or even a prize certificate.

This is one great truth respecting medical education. Another is, that all practice in medicine is based upon theory of some sort or other; and therefore, that it is desirable to have such theory in the closest possible accordance with fact. The veriest empiric who gives a drug in one case because he has seen it do good in another of apparently the same sort, acts upon the theory that similarity of superficial symptoms means similarity of lesions; which, by the way, is perhaps as wild a hypothesis as could be invented. To understand the nature of disease we must understand health, and the understanding of the healthy body means the having a knowledge of its structure and of the way in which its manifold actions are performed, which is what is technically termed human anatomy and human physiology. The physiologist again must needs possess an acquaintance with physics and chemistry, inasmuch as physiology is, to a great extent, applied physics and chemistry. For ordinary purposes a limited amount of such knowledge is all that is needful; but for the pursuit of the higher branches of physiology no knowledge of these branches of science can be too extensive, or too profound.

1876

His First Operation

A. CONAN DOYLE

It was the first day of the winter session, and the third year's man was walking with the first year's man. Twelve o'clock was just booming out from the Tron Church.

"Let me see," said the third year's man. "You have never seen an operation?"

"Never."

"Then this way, please. This is Rutherford's historic bar. A glass of sherry, please, for this gentleman. You are rather sensitive, are you not?"

"My nerves are not very strong, I am afraid."

"Hum! Another glass of sherry for this gentleman. We are going to an operation now, you know."

The novice squared his shoulders and made a gallant attempt to look unconcerned.

"Nothing very bad—eh?"

"Well, yes—pretty bad."

"An—an amputation?"

"No; it's a bigger affair than that."

"I think—I think they must be expecting me at home."

"There's no sense in funking. If you don't go to-day, you must to-morrow. Better get it over at once. Feel pretty fit?"

"Oh, yes; all right!" The smile was not a success.

"One more glass of sherry, then. Now come on or we shall be late. I want you to be well in front."

"Surely that is not necessary."

"Oh, it is far better! What a drove of students! There are plenty of new men among them. You can tell them easily enough, can't you? If they were going down to be operated upon themselves, they could not look whiter."

"I don't think I should look as white."

"Well, I was just the same myself. But the feeling soon wears off. You see a fellow with a face like plaster, and before the week is out he is eating his lunch in the dissecting rooms. I'll tell you all about the case when we get to the theatre."

The students were pouring down the sloping street which led to the infirmary—each with his little sheaf of note-books in his hand. There were pale, frightened lads, fresh from the high schools, and callous old chronics, whose generation had passed on and left them. They swept in an unbroken, tumultuous stream from the university gate to the hospital. The figures and gait of the men were young, but there was little youth in most of their faces. Some looked as if they ate too little—a few as if they drank too much. Tall and short, tweed-coated and black, round-shouldered, bespectacled, and slim, they crowded with clatter of feet and rattle of sticks through the hospital gate. Now and again they thickened into two lines, as the carriage of a surgeon of the staff rolled over the cobblestones between.

"There's going to be a crowd at Archer's," whispered the senior man with suppressed excitement. "It is grand to see him at work. I've seen him jab all round the aorta until it made me jumpy to watch him. This way, and mind the whitewash."

They passed under an archway and down a long, stone-flagged corridor, with drab-coloured doors on either side, each marked with a number. Some of them were ajar, and the novice glanced into them with tingling nerves. He was reassured to catch a glimpse of cheery fires, lines of white-counterpaned beds, and a profusion of coloured texts upon the wall. The corridor opened upon a small hall, with a fringe of poorly clad people seated all round upon benches. A young man, with a pair of scissors stuck like a flower in his buttonhole and a note-book in his hand, was passing from one to the other, whispering and writing.

"Anything good?" asked the third year's man.

"You should have been here yesterday," said the out-patient clerk, glancing up. "We had a regular field day. A popliteal aneurism, a Colles' fracture, a spina bifida, a tropical abscess, and an elephantiasis. How's that for a single haul?"

"I'm sorry I missed it. But they'll come again, I suppose. What's up with the old gentleman?"

A broken workman was sitting in the shadow, rocking himself slowly to and fro, and groaning. A woman beside him was trying to console him, patting his shoulder with a hand which was spotted over with curious little white blisters.

"It's a fine carbuncle," said the clerk, with the air of a connoisseur who describes his orchids to one who can appreciate them. "It's on his back and the passage is draughty, so we must not look at it, must we, daddy? Pemphigus," he added carelessly, pointing to the woman's disfigured hands. "Would you care to stop and take out a metacarpal?"

"No, thank you. We are due at Archer's. Come on!" and they rejoined the throng which was hurrying to the theatre of the famous surgeon.

The tiers of horseshoe benches rising from the floor to the ceiling were already packed, and the novice as he entered saw vague curving lines of faces in front of him, and heard the deep buzz of a hundred voices, and sounds of laughter from somewhere up above him. His companion spied an opening on the second bench, and they both squeezed into it.

"This is grand!" the senior man whispered. "You'll have a rare view of it all."

Only a single row of heads intervened between them and the operating table. It was of unpainted deal, plain, strong, and scrupulously clean. A sheet of brown water-proofing covered half of it, and beneath stood a large tin tray full of sawdust. On the further side, in front of the window, there was a board which was strewed with glittering instruments—forceps, tenacula, saws, canulas, and trocars. A line of knives, with long, thin, delicate blades, lay at one side. Two young men lounged in front of this, one threading needles, the other doing something to a brass coffee-pot-like thing which hissed out puffs of steam.

"That's Peterson," whispered the senior, "the big, bald man in the front row. He's the skin-grafting man, you know. And that's Anthony Browne, who took a larynx out successfully last winter. And there's Murphy, the pathologist, and Stoddart, the eye-man. You'll come to know them all soon."

"Who are the two men at the table?"

"Nobody—dressers. One has charge of the instruments and the other of the puffing Billy. It's Lister's antiseptic spray, you know, and Archer's one of the carbolic-acid men. Hayes is the leader of the cleanliness-and-cold-water school, and they all hate each other like poison."

A flutter of interest passed through the closely packed benches as a woman in petticoat and bodice was led in by two nurses. A red woolen shawl was draped over her head and round her neck. The face which looked out from it was that of a woman in the prime of her years, but drawn with suffering, and of a peculiar beeswax tint. Her head drooped as she walked, and one of the nurses, with her arm round her waist, was whispering consolation in her ear. She gave a quick side-glance at the instrument table as she passed, but the nurses turned her away from it.

"What ails her?" asked the novice.

"Cancer of the parotid. It's the devil of a case; extends right away back behind the carotids. There's hardly a man but Archer would dare to follow it. Ah, here he is himself!"

As he spoke, a small, brisk, iron-grey man came striding into the room, rubbing his hands together as he walked. He had a clean-shaven face, of the naval officer type, with large, bright eyes, and a firm, straight mouth. Behind him came his big house-surgeon, with his gleaming *pince-nez*, and a trail of dressers, who grouped themselves into the corners of the room.

"Gentlemen," cried the surgeon in a voice as hard and brisk as his manner, "we have here an interesting case of tumour of the parotid, originally cartilaginous but now assuming malignant characteristics, and therefore requiring excision. On to the table, nurse! Thank you! Chloroform, clerk! Thank you! You can take the shawl off, nurse."

The woman lay back upon the water-proofed pillow, and her murderous tumour lay revealed. In itself. it was a pretty thing— ivory white, with a mesh of blue veins, and curving gently from jaw to chest. But the lean, yellow face and the stringy throat were in horrible contrast with the plumpness and sleekness of this monstrous growth. The surgeon placed a hand on each side of it and pressed it slowly backwards and forwards.

"Adherent at one place, gentlemen," he cried. "The growth involves the carotids and jugulars, and passes behind the ramus of the jaw, whither we must be prepared to follow it. It is impossible to say how deep our dissection may carry us. Carbolic tray. Thank you! Dressings of carbolic gauze, if you please! Push the chloroform, Mr. Johnson. Have the small saw ready in case it is necessary to remove the jaw."

The patient was moaning gently under the towel which had been placed over her face. She tried to raise her arms and to draw up her knees, but two dressers restrained her. The heavy air was full of the penetrating smells of carbolic acid and of chloroform. A muffled cry came from under the towel, and then a snatch of a song, sung in a high, quavering, monotonous voice:

> "He says, says he,
> If you fly with me

You'll be mistress of the ice-cream van.

You'll be mistress of the——"

It mumbled off into a drone and stopped. The surgeon came across, still rubbing his hands, and spoke to an elderly man in front of the novice.

"Narrow squeak for the Government," he said.

"Oh, ten is enough."

"They won't have ten long. They'd do better to resign before they are driven to it."

"Oh, I should fight it out."

"What's the use. They can't get past the committee even if they get a vote in the House. I was talking to——"

"Patient's ready, sir," said the dresser.

"Talking to McDonald—but I'll tell you about it presently." He walked back to the patient, who was breathing in long, heavy gasps. "I propose," said he, passing his hand over the tumour in an almost caressing fashion, "to make a free incision over the posterior border, and to take another forward at right angles to the lower end of it. Might I trouble you for a medium knife, Mr. Johnson?"

The novice, with eyes which were dilating with horror, saw the surgeon pick up the long, gleaming knife, dip it into a tin basin, and balance it in his fingers as an artist might his brush. Then he saw him pinch up the skin above the tumour with his left hand. At the sight his nerves, which had already been tried once or twice that day, gave way utterly. His head swam round, and he felt that in another instant he might faint. He dared not look at the patient. He dug his thumbs into his ears lest some scream should come to haunt him, and he fixed his eyes rigidly upon the wooden ledge in front of him. One glance, one cry, would, he knew, break down the shred of self-possession which he still retained. He tried to think of cricket, of green fields and rippling water, of his sisters at home—of anything rather than of what was going on so near him.

And yet somehow, even with his ears stopped up, sounds seemed to penerate to him and to carry their own tale. He heard, or thought that he heard, the long hissing of the carbolic engine. Then he was conscious of some movement among the dressers. Were there groans, too, breaking in upon him, and some other sound, some fluid sound, which was more dreadfully suggestive still? His mind would keep building up every step of the operation, and fancy made it more ghastly than fact could have been. His nerves tingled and quivered. Minute by minute the giddiness grew more marked, the numb, sickly feeling at his heart more distressing. And then suddenly, with a groan, his head pitching forward, and his brow cracking sharply upon the narrow wooden shelf in front of him, he lay in a dead faint.

When he came to himself, he was lying in the empty theatre, with his collar and shirt undone. The third year's man was dabbing a wet sponge over his face, and a couple of grinning dressers were looking on.

"All right," cried the novice, sitting up and rubbing his eyes. "I'm sorry to have made an ass of myself."

"Well, so I should think," said his companion. "What on earth did you faint about?"

"I couldn't help it. It was that operation."

"What operation?"

"Why, that cancer."

There was a pause, and then the three students burst out laughing. "Why, you juggins!" cried the senior man, "there never was an operation at all! They found the patient didn't stand the chloroform well, and so the whole thing was off. Archer has been giving us one of his racy lectures, and you fainted just in the middle of his favourite story."

1894

Into Modern Times

... *AND THE NEW*

Into Modern Times

. . . *AND THE NEW*

SYNOPSIS

WHILE *medicine in Europe evolved from witchcraft into science, explorers and adventurers sailed the seven seas in quest of new lands. They sailed on ships ridden with rats, pervaded by filth. They lived on dried meat and mouldy potatoes. Fresh vegetables or fruits were a rarity. It was small wonder, therefore, that so many of them died of scurvy, smallpox or cholera. The story of these voyages and their consequences is told by Karl Vogel in his graphic "Medicine in the Days of Sail." Professor Vogel takes us from the days when Columbus sailed and scurvy was rampant, to more recent times when the steerage quarters of the Western Ocean Packets reeked with humanity, crawled with vermin and were frequently swept by plagues of smallpox and cholera. The New World was populated by ships like these.*

Our first American selection is from the pen of the protean Ben Franklin. His "Observations" deal with the invention of bifocal glasses and the effects of lead poisoning on the human system. Franklin died in 1790. At that time a nineteen year old boy in Danville in the backwoods of Kentucky was preparing himself for the medical career which was to make him "the leading surgeon of the Kentucky frontier." In "A Backwoods Galahad," James Thomas Flexner, son of Simon Flexner, tells the astonishing story of this remarkable man. Ephraim McDowell made one of the great contributions to surgical history. He was the first to perform a successful operation on an ovarian tumor,

339

refuting dire predictions by contemporary surgeons of certain death. As Flexner says, he showed that "the abdominal cavity could be cut into with impunity" and so opened the way to the millions of appendicitis, gall stone and ovarian operations of the future.

McDowell was one of the few enlightened American doctors of the period. For an idea of what many a patient received in the way of treatment, we refer to "New World Remedies." The best that could be said of some of these remedies—such as the administering of chicken broth to a sufferer from cholera morbus—was that at least they could do no harm.

While McDowell was struggling to save the lives of pioneers on the Kentucky frontier, a young woman named Dorothea Lynde Dix was preparing for another fight in Massachusetts. It was a fight to improve the conditions of those with disordered minds, who at the time were doomed to a life of hell on earth. Her impassioned account of visits to the abodes of the pauper insane, her plea to the Massachusetts legislature for improvement of conditions was an historical event in the annals of the country. In France, forty years before, Philippe Pinel had described the chaos which had greeted his entrance into the Asylum de Bicêtre. Pinel analyzed and recorded the conditions of his patients and urged the advantages of "The Proper Treatment of the Insane." Yet while in France something had been done to ameliorate conditions, his words had not been heard in America. The fact is all too apparent in the horrifying picture drawn in "Memorial to the Legislature of Massachusetts." Dorothea Dix was to go on to expose conditions in numerous other states. She became the authority on the subject. Her life parallels that of Florence Nightingale.

We now come to what is perhaps the greatest single contribution of America to medicine, the discovery of anesthesia, related in "The Death of Pain" by James Thomas Flexner. As Flexner points out: "A strange story this. The story of a discovery . . . of overwhelming importance knocking continually at the doors of the scientific great, begging to be taken in until at last, like the angel of an old fable, it knocked at the humbler doorways of the inconspicuous and found a home." Here also is the tragic aftermath, the bitter controversy over credit for the discovery, ending in insanity, suicide and death through apoplexy of three of the four men principally involved.

(The above episode is taken from Mr. Flexner's excellent book "Doctors on Horseback," which is recommended to the reader especially for its story of William Beaumont, whom chance placed in the way of first learning the elementary principles of human digestion. In a primitive trading post in Michigan, he was called on to attend a young French-Canadian, Alexis St. Martin, who had accidentally received a shotgun charge in the stomach. St. Martin recovered but an opening remained below his left nipple which communicated with an opening in his stomach. Beaumont was able to look directly into the cavity, thus becoming practically an eyewitness of the stomach at work. By a series of experiments, among which he inserted food into the stomach attached to a string, he described the gastric juice, showed that its important acid was hydrochloric acid, and refuted many errors relating to digestion. His relations with the unwilling subject of his experiments were stormy in the extreme; but they enabled him, almost by accident, to make a unique contribution to physiology.)

It was that omniscient and honorable gentleman, Dr. Oliver Wendell Holmes, who suggested that the name "anesthesia" be applied to the discovery described in "The Death of Pain," and whose prestige resulted in its adoption. Holmes did not originate the word itself, which had often been used in the eighteenth century. He was the great man of his profession, and of course one of the leading literary lights of his day. No physician's library was complete without at least one of his books. His medical writings were filled with wit and humor as well as with profound common sense. From his papers we have selected one of his addresses to new-fledged doctors, "The Young Practitioner." It is as fresh and lively as the day it was delivered, and may well induce the reader to examine the whole book of Holmes' "Medical Essays," from which it is taken.

The qualities of sympathy, humanity and willingness to serve which a first-rate doctor must possess, have been illustrated repeatedly in these pages—from the time of Hippocrates to that of McDowell. It is seen perhaps most vividly in the life of the country doctor. If Hertzler, "The Horse and Buggy Doctor," had known Holmes, "The Autocrat of the Breakfast Table," they would certainly have become close friends. Both had the wonderful quality of humor, the warm and understanding way of stating their ideas which appeal to all humanity. In the selection from

Hertzler's well-known book here reprinted, those qualities are represented at their peak.

From the country roads of the middle west the reader is carried to the White House in the dramatic medical adventure entitled "The Surgical Operation on President Cleveland in 1893," by W. W. Keen. A nation in political and financial crisis, a leader on whom the entire responsibility rested who suddenly was found to be suffering from a malignant growth of the jaw, are the elements in this true thriller by one of the greatest surgeons of the past generation.

We are at the turn of the century. Since Vesalius, medicine has grown from sickly infancy to powerful manhood. But the charlatan we have always with us. To emphasize the fact, we present "Peruna and the Bracers," one of a notable series of articles which was in part responsible for stirring up public opinion to a point where the pure food and drug laws of the country were enacted for better protection of the ignorant and unwary.

Medicine at Sea
in the Days of Sail

KARL VOGEL

THE professional students of human behavior—those enviable persons whose agreeable occupation it is to reflect upon the weaknesses and hidden motives of other people—sometimes apply to certain quite admirable kinds of reading matter the slightly supercilious designation of "escape literature." The fairy tales of childhood, the cowboy and Tarzan thrillers of adolescence, and the murder mysteries and "boy-meets-girl" fiction of maturer years, all open the portals into a bright world of make-believe in which cares are momentarily forgotten and we can grow in self-importance by subconsciously identifying ourselves with imaginary heroes—supermen and women of surpassing strength, intelligence, and beauty. The sagas of the sea, authentic or fictitious, rank high in the category of such emollients to harassed egos. . . .

It seems a pity to dim the colors of these romantic fancies, but as a matter of fact their actual background was pretty drab and grim. Life at sea in the early days of sail was hideously uncomfortable, and the magnificent hardihood of those who braved it was only too often inspired by nothing more praiseworthy than the profit motive—the hope of riches to be gained by trade, or by the more brutal outrages of plunder and depredation. . . .

One cannot get a better idea of what his life seemed like to the early sailor than from a remarkable seventeenth-century manuscript which has only recently come to light and been transcribed from the original by Basil Lubbock. It is the journal, hundreds of pages long and most engaging in its phraseology, kept for many years by an ordinary seaman, Edward Barlow by name. . . .

On his way to "Lisborne" in 1661, food and water ran short, and Barlow says:

We were now forced to go to one quart of "befraiage" to one man a day, which "befraiage" was made of sour wine and stinking water, which was very hard with us; and the weather being hot and always eating salt victuals, I could not get my belly full, which made me often repent of my going to sea. . . . And I was always thinking that beggars had a far better life of it and lived better than I did, for they seldom missed of their bellies full of better victuals than we could get; and also at night to lie quiet and out of danger in a good barn full of straw, nobody disturbing them and might lie as long as they pleased; but it was quite contrary with us, for we seldom in a month got our belly full of victuals, and that of such salt as many beggars would think scorn to eat; and at night when we went to take our rest, we were not to lie still above four hours; and many times when it blew hard we were not sure to lie one hour, yea often we were called up before we had slept one half hour and forced to go up into the main top or the fore top to take in our topsails, half awake and half asleep, with one shoe on and the other shoe off, not having time to put it on; always sleeping in our clothes for readiness; and in stormy weather when the ship rolled and tumbled as though some great millstone were rolling up one hill and down another we had much ado to hold ourselves fast by the small ropes from falling by the board; and being gotten up into the tops there we must haul and pull to make fast the sail, seeing nothing but air above us and water beneath us, and that so raging as though every wave would make a grave for us; and many times the nights so dark we could not see one another, and blowing so hard that we could not hear one another speak, being close to one another; and thundering and lightening as though Heaven and earth would come together, it being usual in those countries, with showers of rain so hard it will wet a man "dunge wet" before he can go the length of the ship.

In the "spacious days" of Queen Elizabeth, when Drake, Raleigh, Hawkins, Frobisher, Gilbert, and the others were roaming and raiding the world in her service, the treatment of the sailors was inhumanly bad, and the crews that singed the Spanish King's beard by smashing the Invincible Armada, the proudest fleet the world till then had seen, were wretchedly clothed, half-starved, and riddled with infection. Under the Stuarts conditions were no better, and just seven years after the *Mayflower* had sailed from Plymouth we find Admiral Mervyn writing to Buckingham that the seamen were sickening so fast that the King would shortly have more ships than men, and lamenting:

> . . . the more than miserable condition of the men, who have neither shoes, stockings nor rags to cover their nakedness. All the ships are so infectious that I fear if we hold the sea one month we shall not bring enough men home to moor the ships. You may think I make it worse, but I vow to God I cannot deliver it in words . . . The poor men bear all as patiently as they can. . . .

The ships of that time were resplendent with gilded carving and streamed silken banners from every spar, but there was no thought for the sick or wounded sailor. When the ship went into action he was bundled out of the way into the dank and dismal cable tier or was stretched on the foul and stinking ballast. If he survived the medical science of the day and was landed disabled there was little or no provision for his care, though in 1590 a sort of mutual benefit fund called the Chatham Chest was established and supported by taking sixpence a month from the meager pay of every man and boy in the navy. There was a further deduction of twopence for the ship's surgeon, but the health of the soul was seemingly esteemed twice as highly as that of the body for double this amount was abstracted for the benefit of the chaplain. It was not until the Commonwealth that there were any effective measures for looking after the sick and wounded; hospital ships were added to the fleet, naval hospitals were founded on shore, and the beginning of a pension system was instituted.

Overcrowding and bad food were the great sources of disease and operated in a vicious circle. The complement of the famous *Henri Grace à Dieu* of Henry VIII which was about the size of an American thirty-six gun frigate, was seven hundred men or more, and the *Mary Rose* of the same period, a vessel of only six hundred tons, hád five or six hundred men crowded into her. Some centuries later crews of three hundred, and one hundred and eighty respectively would have been considered correct for ships of this size. . . .

The diet was so restricted in variety and so deficient in the essentials for well-balanced nutrition that it is no wonder scurvy and other diseases were so prevalent. The regulation ration for the middle of the seventeenth century was as follows: In addition to a gallon of beer and a pound of biscuit daily, on Sundays and Tuesdays two pounds of salt beef; on Mondays and Thursdays one pound of salt pork and one pint of peas, or if pork was lacking óne pound and a half of beef instead; on Wednesdays, Fridays and Saturdays one-eighth part of a "sized" fish, one-eighth of a pound of butter and one quarter of a pound of cheese. The standard fish sizes were twenty-four inches for cod, twenty-two inches for haberdine, and a one-half-sized stock fish was supposed to measure sixteen inches. Even more serious than the limited variety of the foodstuffs was the fact that through imperfect means of preservation and the outrageous dishonesty of the contractors they were nearly always more or less decomposed and wholly unfit for human consumption, but if condemned and returned they were often enough repacked and sent to other ships. A contemporary commentator remarks: "I must needs say that here hath been found very ill dealing; and that not only in the provision of flesh . . . but in the rottenness of the cheese, in the frowsiness and foul condition of the butter, and in the badness of the salted fish . . . and as for the beer it was for the most part very undrinkable."

In the merchant service where the individual commander had some discretion and authority the conditions were not necessarily so bad. Captain Luke Foxe of Hull was one of the long list of those who sought fame and fortune by attempting to tap the treasures of the East by way of the icy northwest passage, and was evidently quite pleased with the superior quality of his commissariat, and also of his medical supplies, for he records that when he set out in 1631 he

. . . was victualled compleatly for 18 moneths. . . . I had excellent fat Beefe, strong Beere, good wheaten Bread, good Island Ling, Butter and Cheese of the best, admirable Sacke and Aqua Vitae, Pease, Oat-meale, Wheat-meale, Oyle, Spice,

Suger, Fruit and Rice, with Chyrurgerie, as Sirrups, Iulips, Condits, Trechissis, antidotes, balsoms, gummes, unguents, implaisters, oyles, potions, suppositors, and purging Pils; and if I had wanted Instruments, my Chyrurgion had enough.

Salt beef and pork, green and moldy, and hardtack crawling with weevils remained the staples of the seaman's nutriment until comparatively recent times, and even our frigates of the War of 1812 were fitted out with only the following provisions: Beef, pork, molasses, rice, butter, cheese, vinegar, beans, rum, flour, Indian meal, bread, potatoes, and salt fish. . . .

At about the period of our Revolution three naval surgeons, James Lind, Thomas Trotter, and Sir Gilbert Blane, and also the famous explorer Captain James Cook, changed the whole complexion of the seaman's life by introducing reforms that were so important and so beneficial that the names of these great sanitarians should be written high in every hall of fame. Scurvy, due to the faulty diet, deficient as we now understand in vitamins, was conquered by Lind's demonstration of the value of fresh vegetables and especially the citrus fruits, a doctrine long known but till then never consistently applied. The frightful epidemics of typhus and typhoid—then significantly called ship fever or gaol fever—smallpox, tropical fevers or calentures, and dysentery or the bloody flux, were greatly reduced by the enforcement of systematic regulations making for cleanliness and general sanitation. Methods of ventilation were devised, newly drafted men were medically examined and scrubbed before they were allowed to enter healthy ships, soap was issued to the crews and they were obliged to keep their bodies and clothing clean. A space on each ship called the sick bay was set aside for hospital purposes, though originally its location was not definite and varied according to the convenience of the moment. In 1800 at the instance of Lord St. Vincent the Admiralty ordered that no sick were to be kept below the upper deck of any line-of-battle ship, and that the sick berth was to be established under the forecastle on the starboard side with a roundhouse [latrine] enclosed for the use of the invalids. Ambulant patients were treated at regular clinics held twice a day at the foremast by the assistant surgeons and their stewards or loblolly boys. By way of contrast to the severe discipline and savage floggings that were so frequent it is a truly pleasant thing to read of the consideration the captain and other officers appear to have shown in contributing from their tables whatever was available in the way of wines, fresh meat, or other additions to the regular ship's supplies for those in the sick bay. Captain Basil Hall states that after the carver in the gun-room has helped his messmates he generally turns to the surgeon and says: "Doctor, what shall I send to the sick?"

Scurvy was the greatest single enemy of the early seaman and nearly always was present to some extent on ships engaged in long voyages. Its symptoms were horrible and loathsome, particularly under the existing conditions where no nursing care was possible, as may be seen from the typical description given by William Hutchinson, later a famous captain, who endured its miseries for three months while serving as a forecastle man in a ship on its way to the East Indies in 1738. After a gradual onset of increasing weakness which finally became so extreme that he lost the use of his hands and feet so that he could not even crawl up the ladder to the deck he says:

> I thus struggled with the disease 'till it increased so that my armpits and hams grew black, and I pined away to a weak helpless condition, with my teeth all loose, and my upper and lower gums swelled and clotted together like a jelly, and they bled to that degree that I was obliged to lie with my mouth hanging over the side of my hammock, to let the blood run out and to keep it from clotting so as to choak me; 'till after a seven months passage we arrived in Pullicat Road; from whence we got fresh provisions, and sent for men to carry the ship to Madras, where what remained of the sick were got on shore to sick quarters; and where with fresh provisions and fomentations of herbs I got well and returned on board in eighteen days.

During an engagement the decks were sanded to make them less slippery from blood, and the petty officers and many of the men themselves carried tourniquets with which to check the hemorrhage from limbs shattered by shot or caused by the even more ghastly injuries due to flying splinters. The hopelessly wounded were thrown overboard at once, otherwise the victim had to make his way or be assisted by his messmates down the steep ladders to the cockpit, a dark space below the waterline, normally the midshipmen's berth but now used as an operating room. Here by dim lantern light the surgeon and his mates took each man rigidly in his turn, working at top speed on patients whose courage—with a tot of rum—was their only anesthetic. Conservative surgery was unknown, and would have been impossible. An arm or leg, if a hasty inspection showed that it was at all badly wounded was amputated as a matter of course—for abdominal and thoracic injuries little could be done except to probe for foreign bodies and apply a dressing. Skull fractures were trephined and usually ended in brain abscess. Tetanus and infection were responsible for many deaths, but the ultimate results following even dreadfully severe operations were sometimes surprisingly good. William Burd, Surgeon of the *Niger*, gives a detailed account of an amputation at the shoulder joint for a compound comminuted gunshot fracture of the head of the humerus, performed at sea, which is harrowing to read, for one cannot forget that it was done on a fully conscious patient. The assisting French surgeon, a prisoner of war, whose responsibility it was to control the subclavian artery by digital compression lost his nerve, and as Burd says "forsook him" at the most critical moment, but Burd succeeded in completing the operation "without the loss of so much blood as might have been expected," and three and a half months later the patient was discharged perfectly well.

Incongruous as it seems, lack of fresh air, or perhaps better said, the presence of extremely foul air, was responsible for much discomfort and disease on shipboard. It might appear that the one place above all others where one would be sure to enjoy the pure breath of heaven most abundantly would be on a sailing ship in the middle of the ocean, and it is true that while he remained on deck the sailor had plenty of it, and often indeed too much, but as soon as he stepped below he entered an atmosphere usually either too cold and too damp or too hot and too damp, and always sickeningly offensive to the sense of smell. The latter quality was sometimes developed to an extreme point, and it has been stated, for example, that in 1739 the ships in the squadron anchored at Spithead "stunk to such a degree" that they infected each other and the men became so dangerously ill that they had to be put ashore. Lind gives a description of the conditions on the *Panther* which reveals what an abode of misery and generator of stenches the sick bay could be. During the voyage home forty men died of scurvy and there were usually ninety patients huddled in a place with no provision whatever for ventilation. The atmosphere was so suffocating that the sick were stifled for want of air, and the surgeon when visiting them could hardly breathe or remain for any length of time without going often on deck, or reviving himself with spirit of hartshorn or a glass of wine. The dampness was particularly bad in new vessels for the timber was often unseasoned or had been treated with brine to make it more durable, and it took many months before they dried out and were free from mildew. Large ships were worse in this respect than small, and some were notoriously bad, like the *Arrogant*, of which it was said that the decks and beams were remarkable for their moisture which seemed to exhale from the timbers, and one of her officers has noted that he "observed the damp vapor on his bed-cloaths every morning like a heavy dew." In addition there was the moisture produced by the wet clothing of the men which in bad weather never had a chance to dry, and to make matters still worse there was the routine flooding of the decks. A passion for snowy decks has ever been an obsession with executive officers, and seamen of all ages have had to suffer the affliction of holystoning. The scrubbing and the sluicing of the lower decks with water was particularly objectionable if done after sunset so that they remained wet for hours, and many surgeons protested against this practice. Some officers advocated dry holystoning, which obviated the floods of water but filled the air with dust.

Hundreds of unwashed men had to sleep so crowded together that their hammocks touched—fourteen to eighteen inches was the regulation space for each—and the sick bay contributed its share of noisomeness, particularly after an engagement when there would be many infected wounds, or if there was an epidemic on board. The ballast was likely to be wet and malodorous, and the bilges reeked with stagnant and polluted water which generated gases so noxious that when the ship's well was to be cleaned a lighted candle had to be lowered first to see if it was safe for a man to enter without danger of asphyxiation. The earlier efforts at ventilation were limited to the use of wind sails, great conical tubes of canvas intended to convey a current of fresh air down the hatches, and the occasional resort to fires in pots or small stoves that were moved from place to place to create an upward draft and to dry out the ship. Really effective measures were not developed until the middle of the eighteenth century when various types of windmills and other mechanical ventilators were introduced. One form which acted like gigantic bellows was invented by a clergyman, Dr. Hales, and continued in use for over fifty years. The improvement in health that followed was remarkable, and the Earl of Halifax is credited with the statement that for every twelve men dying on unventilated ships there was but one death on those which used the new appliances.

A favorite sanitary measure was washing the inside of the ship with boiling vinegar; but the greatest reliance was placed on fumigation. For this purpose everything seems to have been used that could make a bad smell—pitch, brimstone, tarry old rope, condemned tobacco, tar, charcoal, asafetida, niter, or common salt mixed with vitriolic acid, and gunpowder dampened with vinegar. This was also sometimes flashed from pistols, on the theory that the shock of the explosion would "disperse the infectious matter from the timbers of the ship." Vinegar was vaporized by plunging a red-hot loggerhead or an iron ball into a bucketful, or by heating over a lamp. Trotter was not much impressed by a special device designed for the latter use, saying that "the smell of the vapor is very agreeable but I would say no more for it. It ought to be trusted, like lavender water on the handkerchief of a belle or a beau."

Providing a sufficient supply of drinking water and keeping it in usable condition has always been one of the major problems on long voyages. Commonly of unsatisfactory quality to begin with and stored in wooden casks, it soon became foul; was often the cause of epidemics, and complaints regarding it are frequent, long, and loud: "The water was so putrid, thick and stinking that often I have held my nose with my hand while I drank it strained through my pocket handkerchief, and we were so short of this necessary article that our consumption was limited to two pints a day for all purposes." This was not the wail of a disgruntled foremast hand but was written by an Admiral of the British Navy, in referring to a time as comparatively recent as the Trafalgar period.

To prevent the slimy vegetable growth that coated the inside of the casks and pervaded the water different expedients were resorted to, such as charring the casks, soaking them first in sea water, or adding various preservatives. Among these were alum and cream of tartar, but the most widely used was quicklime in the proportion of about a pound to each water butt. This was effective in preventing putrefaction but added a disagreeable taste and unpleasant quality, though one medical writer says that it was not injurious to health, but "on the contrary friendly to the bowels." Still, various procedures were suggested to precipitate the lime before use, such as by the addition of magnesia, which was too expensive, or by devices for generating carbon dioxide in the cask, which were much too complicated for use on shipboard. Another method of sweetening offensive water was by means of an apparatus invented by Lieutenant Osbridge of the British Navy. The water was raised several feet by a pump fixed to the scuttle butt and then caused to be exposed to the air in a finely divided state by being allowed to fall through a series of perforated metal disks placed horizontally at intervals in a long cylinder. This worked very well, and Trotter says that no ship should go to sea without it.

It was not until the early part of the last century that the whole difficulty was solved very simply by the substitution of iron tanks for the wooden casks . . . In iron tanks the water kept indefinitely without alteration. The change from wooden to iron containers was begun shortly after the turn of the century and after it had been effected throughout the service there was a great improvement in the seamen's health.

Owing to the difficulty of keeping water in a drinkable condition, for centuries the traditional beverage of the sailor was beer, and it was customary to say that bread, beef, and beer were the backbone of the British Navy. The allowance was the handsome amount of a gallon a day, but through the dishonesty of grafting contractors it was often miserable in quality and speedily spoiled, so that epidemics of intestinal disorders were common and the frightful mortality from disease on the ships of Elizabeth and her successors is supposed to have been in large part due to this cause. Lord Howard of Effingham, the Admiral in command of the fleet that defeated the Spanish Armada, protested that though the beer had been condemned as unfit for use it was still being issued to the men, and added the rather mild comment that "nothing doth displease the seamen more than sour beer." Their displeasure must have been further increased if it was true as Sir Walter Raleigh complained, that often it was kept in casks that had previously been used for oil or fish. The evil was perennial, for a hundred and fifty years later we find Admiral Hawke whose fleet was blockading Brest sending to the official at Plym-

outh who was responsible for supplies the terse admonition:
"The beer brewed at your port is so excessively bad that it
employs the whole time of the squadron in surveying it and
throwing it overboard."

In later times wine or spirits were substituted for the beer, a
pint of the former or one half pint of rum or brandy being issued
in its place. The earlier practice of serving rum undiluted was
found to have its drawbacks, and it became the custom to mix it
with three or four parts of water before giving it to the men,
usually in two daily portions. This improvement is due to Admiral Vernon, who in 1740 called for a report on the matter
from his captains and surgeons and then put in force their
unanimous recommendation that the rum be watered. Unexpected
manifestations of human ingenuity are often quite delightful, and
there was a rather pleasing directness in the habit of choosing the
men designated to serve the beverage from the size of their
thumbs. This was because in doling out the precious balm the
thirsty sailor's cup was most advantageously grasped with the
outstretched thumb inside, and the amount saved by this short
measurement went to swell the residue which was the perquisite
of those in charge of the distribution. The admiral was known
to the sailors as Old Grog because of the huge cloak of grogram
cloth he used to sport in stormy weather, and his invention has
been called grog ever since. In the American Navy the rum
allowance originally was also one half pint, and the frigates that
won the victories of 1812 were provided with the impressive
amount of eight thousand five hundred gallons of the cheering
fluid when setting out on a twelve-month's cruise. Existing figures
of the cost of fitting out a vessel of this type show that the yearly
estimate for all the provisions was a little over twenty-eight
thousand dollars, and as the rum was quoted at one dollar a gallon
the outlay for this one item made up not far from one third of
the entire sum. It is instructive to note that the corresponding
figure for all medical and surgical supplies was only two thousand
five hundred dollars. . . .

In the mercantile marine of later times the captain with the aid
of the ship's medicine chest had to fulfil the functions of physician
and surgeon, and sometimes of accoucheur as well, in addition
to his more strictly nautical duties. With the well-known ingenuity of the sailor, and thanks to the force of character which
alone could make it possible for him to maintain his position as

the supreme ruler of his little floating world, the emergencies that arose seem to have been dealt with fairly well. The masters of sailing ships were often astonishingly young and one cannot but wonder at the self-reliance with which they faced their complex responsibilities. Captain Nathaniel Brown Palmer was only twenty-one when in 1821 he took the tiny sailing sloop *Hero* from Stonington to the Antarctic and was the first to explore the region known by his name until later cartographers changed it to Graham Land, and Captain Isaiah West of New Bedford commanded a whaler at twenty-two. A well-known surgeon has told me of an incident early in the career of his father, who after a life of active seafaring is still in good health in his home in Scotland at the age of eighty-four. When only twenty-three, while in Calcutta, he was appointed first mate of the *Indian Empire,* a full-rigged ship of two thousand tons. Soon after sailing the captain who had long been ailing died, and the young mate succeeded to the command. Some of the tanks had been filled with tainted water so that an outbreak of cholera developed on board, but in spite of the fact that a large proportion of the crew were disabled and eight of them succumbed to the disease, the youthful captain brought his ship safely home to Dundee. Imagine his anxiety as sailor after sailor sickened and he wondered when, if ever, the pestilence would cease. One is reminded of Joseph Conrad's trials when he received his first command, described by him as fiction in one of his finest stories, but actually based on his own experience. Appointed to the bark *Otago* to replace the captain who had died at sea, he set sail from Bangkok for Melbourne, the ship was becalmed in the torrid gulf of Siam, and the crew began to come down with tropical malaria until all except Conrad and the ship's cook were incapacitated. Then came the calamity of discovering that the former captain who apparently was of unsound mind had disposed of the reserve stock of quinine which should have been in the medicine chest, and refilled the bottles with an inert substitute. Nevertheless, Conrad succeeded in working the ship, filled with helpless invalids, as far as Singapore, where he shipped a new crew and then completed the voyage to Australia.

A chapter of sailing-ship history that remains to be written concerns the heroism of the women on shipboard who sometimes in addition to the perils of the sea willingly faced those of bringing a child into the world with no possibility of medical aid.

British captains, as well as those aristocrats of the ocean the New England skippers, not infrequently took their wives with them on long voyages, often as the only woman on board. A friend of mine, Captain B—— first saw the light of day off the Horn, and every one of his five brothers and sisters was also born at sea in widely different parts of the globe. He is of the fourth generation of a famous line of Maine shipmasters and was only nineteen when he was made captain of the *Herbert Black* of Searsport, and at twenty-three was given command of the *Bangalore*, a splendidly built fifteen-hundred-ton three skysail ship engaged in the Australian and Hawaiian trade. During his days at sea his medical and surgical experiences were many and various and calculated to tax the resources of a trained medical man, such as saving the life of his mate after fourteen days of intestinal obstruction and successfully conducting a confinement during the height of a violent gale. His brother who had preceded him in the command of the *Herbert Black*, a small bark of five hundred and fifty-four tons, was only twenty-five when in that vessel he performed a feat of seamanship such as has seldom been equaled. While rounding the Horn his rudder was lost, but he managed to construct and ship a substitute, getting his material by cutting up a spare topmast. At that time beriberi was common on ships touching the west coast of South and Central America; the disease appeared on board and his mate, second mate, and four of the eight remaining members of the crew died of it. In spite of this he navigated his leaking ship with a jury rudder and a sick and dying crew to Barbados, the few left alive so weakened that on his arrival there help had to be summoned from shore to take the sail off the ship.

The ship's medicine chest usually included a booklet of instructions, and sometimes to simplify the difficult arts of diagnosis and treatment different diseases were numbered to correspond with the bottles containing suitable remedies in each case. A favorite tale, perhaps as apocryphal as most salt-water yarns, is of an ingenious captain, who having decided that his patient presented symptom complex No. 9 and finding this bottle empty, rose to the situation by administering equal doses of No. 3 and No. 6. Most of the time the problems were not difficult. Job-like the sailor is a martyr to boils and these were the commonest surgical condition, while constipation was the most prevalent medical complaint, but was kept in subjection by the enormous quantities of

Epsom salts which formed the most important component of the stock of drugs.

These medical counselors to the captain are often interesting and remarkable. One of them which is called *Cox's Companion to the Sea Medicine Chest* seems to have been a great favorite for it had already run through thirty-three editions in England when it was published in New York in 1851. It must have presented the baffled amateur practitioner with a rather mystifying array of therapeutic possibilities, for it belongs to the machine-gun era of prescribing and about two hundred different drugs are discussed. Many of these are herbs or other vegetable remedies with such animalistic names as snake-root, worm-grass, skunk-cabbage, cranesbill, cowhage, bearberry, dogwood, and dozens of others that have long since passed into the limbo of forgotten things. Several pages are devoted to the resuscitation of the apparently drowned, chief reliance being placed on insufflation of the lungs with bellows, either through the nostril or preferably by passing a curved tin tube attached to the nozzle into the patient's larynx, a feat that if successfully performed would command sincerest admiration. Two life-giving procedures warmly recommended by earlier authorities had apparently been discarded by this time for they are not mentioned. One consisted in having the operator apply his mouth to that of the patient and so blow air into his lungs—if he first chewed garlic the effect was considered to be more reviving—and the other was the introduction of tobacco smoke into the bowel. A generation later another book which also ran through many editions was *The Ship Captain's Medical Guide*, and as its author Dr. Leach was Physician to the Dreadnought Seaman's Hospital of London it is thoroughly practical and the treatments and other procedures advised are not beyond the resources or abilities of the average ship's officer. It is somewhat remarkable, however, that although there is a good deal of matter relating to the management of venereal diseases, which are said to be "the bane of the mercantile marine service," there is not one single word of warning about the necessity of taking precautions to prevent the transmission of infection to others. A *Handbook for the Ship's Medicine Chest* prepared under the auspices of the United States Marine Hospital Service was—and still is—widely circulated in the American merchant marine. This is a wholly admirable manual, and the 1900 edition issued while sailing ships were still making long voyages gives well-selected

lists of medicines and drugs, and is written with regard to simplicity in medication and due emphasis on antisepsis and the prevention of contagion.

Shortly after the War of 1812 had demonstrated the efficiency
of the American Navy a new phase developed in maritime history
which gave the young republic a supremacy on the Atlantic
which was to endure for many years. The lure of the new land
of promise attracted the enterprising or the discontented of the
Old World and an ever-increasing stream of emigration began to
cross the ocean. To meet this demand, in 1816, the Black Ball
Line of packet ships was established, soon followed by numerous
others, and these Western Ocean Packets as they were called
rapidly acquired the domination of the passenger trade between
English and American ports. While the Continent contributed
its share, the majority of the emigrants at this time were English,
Irish, and Scottish, and the records show that between 1815 and
1854 over four million passengers left the British Isles, and of
these nearly two and a half million sailed during the eight years
preceding the latter date. The earlier packet ships were small,
of about five hundred tons, but as the traffic grew they increased.
in capacity up to three times that size or more, but all designed
for speed, heavily sparred, and well adapted to cope with the
gales of the North Atlantic. Beating against the prevailing west-
erlies was slow work, and the average passage to the States took
forty days. In the other direction better time was possible, the
average being twenty-three days, but phenomenally quick cross-
ings were not infrequent and several records of less than fourteen
days are well authenticated. These were the halcyon days of sail,
and though steamship lines began to be established about 1840,
for many years the swift sailing-ships not infrequently made
better passages than the power-driven vessels. When Charles
Dickens astonished the literary world by visiting this country in
1842 he came in the Cunarder *Britannia*, but for the return
journey he chose the sailing packet *George Washington* and had
the satisfaction of arriving a day ahead of the steamer. . . .

Lubbock quotes an old packet captain as having written:

> Men, women and children were tumbled into the 'tween
> decks together, dirty, saucy, ignorant and breeding the most
> loathsome of creeping things. The stench below decks, aggra-
> vated by the seasickness and the ship's poor equipment for

the work, placed us far below the civilization of the dark ages. It was not uncommon in mid-winter to be fifty or sixty days making the homeward passage. In gales, which were frequent, hatches had to be battened down and men, women and children screamed all night in terror. Ship fever, smallpox, and other diseases were common, and it is a wonder that so many survived the voyage as really did.

The passage rates fluctuated somewhat from year to year. In 1842 they were five pounds, but in 1851 when the emigrant traffic was at its height they fell to three pounds ten shillings from Liverpool to New York, and even less to Quebec. This comprised only the passage, and the passenger had to provide for all his needs except fire for cooking and drinking water, and before going aboard was obliged to show that he had an adequate supply of provisions. On the Black X Line for example, the requirement was a suitable amount of flour, biscuit, potatoes, tea, sugar and treacle, two hams, a tin pot, frying-pan, mug, teapot, knife, fork, and spoon. On one of the larger vessels the space assigned to the steerage was about seventy feet long by thirty wide, with six feet between decks. Here several hundred people had to accommodate themselves in rough bunks of unplaned lumber, six feet wide divided by partitions into three sleeping places, arranged in three tiers one above the other. The alleyways, only about three feet wide, were jammed full of the piles of provisions and other belongings, over which it was necessary to crawl on all fours, and when, as was often the case during wet weather, no one was allowed on deck the crowding and lack of ventilation must have been unspeakable. Small port-holes admitted a little light but could almost never be opened and when the hatches had to be kept closed the conditions can hardly be imagined. Cooking had to be done, weather permitting, at galley fires on deck in the waist of the ship. This region was a veritable farmyard, with pens of live stock for the use of the cabin passengers, sheep, pigs, chickens, ducks, and geese, as well as cows and goats carried to supply milk, and what little space was left was reduced by the ship's long boat, spare spars and topmasts, and other nautical gear.

Under these conditions illness was inevitable and when epidemics occurred the mortality was frightful. In 1853 one ship arrived in New York with sixty cases of cholera on board, one hundred deaths having already taken place during the voyage, and eight other ships in the course of the same year reported from fifteen to eighty deaths each, and at about the same time on one vessel to the terror of an unusually rough crossing was added the horror of an outbreak of smallpox with sixty deaths. Rather oddly, it was the ship's carpenter who had charge of the emigrants, and it was his duty to keep them in order, suppress brawling, and guard against the everpresent danger of fire. When as was the case on some ships, no doctor was carried, it was he who doled out from the ship's medicine chest any remedies required and he was also the official dentist. It speaks well for the stoutness of the timber of which the American Ship of State was gradually being built that despite all these outrageous violations of every principle of sanitary science most of the steerage passengers seemed to survive, and it is stated that the births usually outnumbered the deaths. . . .

A highly specialized form of life at sea is represented by the whaling industry, for it was truly an industry as opposed to the carrying trade of the other branches of the mercantile marine. It was predominantly an American activity, and at the height of its development in the middle of the last century when it was estimated that the whaling fleet of the entire world numbered about nine hundred vessels, over seven hundred of these hailed from ports in the United States. Officered by men who were supreme masters of seamanship, the whale ships, slow but seaworthy, roamed the seven seas, making voyages that were measured in years, while their crews partly composed of inexperienced landsmen, led a life which E. P. Hohman says, "at its best was hard, and at its worst represented perhaps the lowest condition to which free American labor has ever fallen." Economy in operation was pushed to the utmost and the food and living conditions were commonly so bad that scurvy ravaged the forecastles of the whalers long after it had become practically extinct in all other ships. Whaling vessels of any size belonging to other nations regularly carried a surgeon, but not so in the fleets sent out from the thrifty New England towns. The risk of accidents was everpresent in this the most dangerous form of big-game hunting, and stove boats, smashed by the jaws or flukes of a wounded whale, treacherous loops of flying line, or the razor edged blubber spades and knives used in the work of cutting in and trying out were the frequent cause of terrible and often fatal injuries. Any surgical aid required had to be furnished by the captain, and as surgical instruments were seldom carried he had to do the best he could with whatever means came to hand, often displaying a remarkable degree of courage and resourcefulness. These qualities were strikingly exhibited by Captain James Huntting of Southampton, a giant six feet six inches tall and weighing two hundred and fifty pounds, when the flying whale line kinked in the boat and a man was caught and jerked overboard by the running whale and dragged with frightful speed until finally released by his limbs giving way to the strain. When rescued and brought on board, in the words of an eyewitness:

> . . . it was found that a portion of the hand including four fingers had been torn away, and the foot sawed through at the ankle, leaving only the great tendon and the heel suspended to the lacerated stump. From the knee downward the muscular flesh had been rasped away by the line, leaving the protruding bone enveloped in a tangled mat of tendons and bleeding arteries. Saved from drowning, the man seemed likely to meet a more cruel death, unless some one had the nerve to perform the necessary amputation. At that time the New Bedford ships were the only ones that carried surgical instruments to meet such a case. But Captain Jim was not the man to let any one perish on slight provocation. He had his carving knife, carpenter's saw and a fish-hook. The injury was so frightful and the poor fellow's groans and cries so touching, that several of the crew fainted in their endeavors to aid the captain in the operation, and others sickened and turned away from the sight. Unaided, the captain then lashed his screaming patient to the carpenter's bench, amputated the leg and dressed the hand as best he could.

The heroism of both patient and operator was rewarded, for the man survived and ultimately reached the United States, to be for many years, as the narrator piously concludes, "another living monument of God's mercy," and he adds: "In my opinion Captain Jim suffered the most in that operation because he couldn't scream to let off his feelings."

In the earlier years even a supply of drugs was not regularly provided, but later a medicine chest with its book of directions was made part of the routine equipment, and another charge of one or two dollars was added to the already long list of items deducted from the whaleman's "lay." The medical relief afforded was not complicated by any refinements of diagnosis, for as one veteran captain says:

> Symptoms don't count in our simple practice. We open our attack with a dose of Glauber or horse salts, which takes such a strong hold on the patient that he is bound to confess we are doing something for him. It may happen that the patient grows worse, and a dose of castor oil to work off the salts is our next resource. He takes hope in the moving evidences of the medicine; and the more he endures the more he hopes. Should oil fail us, the ulterior of our modern healing art is to administer a rousing dose of calomel, with the intention that this shall work off salts, oil, and itself. In severe cases we repeat the entire course, and either kill or cure.

One medically interesting aspect of the whaleman's life that has not received the consideration it perhaps deserves is the influence such an unnatural existence may have had on the psychology of those subjected to it. The perils, the hardships, and the enforced close confinement in crowded quarters with exasperating and often quarrelsome associates during the long intervals of appalling monotony when whales were scarce must have had a deteriorating effect on morale and mental reactions, so that under such stress inferior personalities already near the border line to start with could easily give way, and possibly this explains to some extent the sadistic brutality and cruelty that were not infrequent. Captain Ahab's insane obsession in *Moby Dick* at once comes to mind, and one writer, C. B. Hawes, reproduces extracts from several whaling logs which indicate a definite strain of melancholia in the captains who wrote them. He believes that much information of interest to psychiatrists is to be found in the old manuscript records of life at sea, and expresses the conviction, reached after reading hundreds of log-books and sea journals, that the whalers had on board a disproportionate number of the mentally deranged as compared with the general run of seafaring men. It is a plausible suggestion and might repay investigation by students of abnormal psychology.

We find ourselves ending as we began, oddly enough and quite without intention, with an allusion to the lore of the psychologist. Perhaps this is as it should be, for after all no study of human endeavor can be significant without a consideration of the driving force behind it, and never has man's spirit vindicated itself more triumphantly than in the epic of his activities at sea. If the picture that has been presented of the existence of the early sailor seems unduly full of shadows, it must not be forgotten that somber colors are necessarily inherent in any depiction of medical conditions in former days, and that we have been viewing life at sea from its darkest aspect. That it had its brighter facets is undeniable; the very hardships stimulated manhood and bred a sturdy race of human beings whose courage and endurance will forever be an inspiration. From the earliest days the mariner has symbolized fortitude and daring, and even Rome's most polished poet felt this when he exclaimed, two thousand years ago: "Stout oak and triple bronze must have encased the heart of him who first entrusted his frail bark to the savage sea."

> Illi robur et aes triplex
>   Circa pectus erat, qui fragilem truci
> Commisit pelago ratem
>   Primus.

Horace, Odes, III, 9.

1938

Observations

BENJAMIN FRANKLIN

LEAD POISONING

To Benjamin Vaughan

DEAR FRIEND,

I recollect, that, when I had the great pleasure of seeing you at Southampton, now a 12month since, we had some conversation on the bad effects of lead taken inwardly; and that at your request I promis'd to send you in writing a particular account of several facts I then mention'd to you, of which you thought some good use might be made. I now sit down to fulfil that promise.

The first thing I remember of this kind was a general discourse in Boston, when I was a boy, of a complaint from North Carolina against New England rum, that it poison'd their people, giving them the dry bellyach, with a loss of the use of their limbs. The distilleries being examin'd on the occasion, it was found that several of them used leaden still-heads and worms, and the physicians were of opinion, that the mischief was occasioned by that use of lead. The legislature of Massachusetts thereupon pass'd an Act, prohibiting under severe penalties the use of such still-heads and worms thereafter. Inclos'd I send you a copy of the Act, taken from my printed law-book.

In 1724, being in London, I went to work in the printing-house of Mr. Palmer, Bartholomew Close, as a compositor. I there found a practice, I had never seen before, of drying a case of types (which are wet in distribution) by placing it sloping before the fire. I found this had the additional advantage, when the types were not only dry'd but heated, of being comfortable to the hands working over them in cold weather. I therefore sometimes heated my case when the types did not want drying. But an old workman, observing it, advis'd me not to do so, telling me I might lose the use of my hands by it, as two of our companions had nearly done, one of whom that us'd to earn his guinea a week, could not then make more than ten shillings, and the other, who had the dangles, but seven and sixpence. This, with a kind of obscure pain, that I had sometimes felt, as it were in the bones of my hand when working over the types made very hot, induced me to omit the practice. But talking afterwards with Mr. James, a letter-founder in the same Close, and asking him if his people, who work'd over the little furnaces of melted metal, were not subject to that disorder; he made light of any danger from the effluvia, but ascribed it to particles of the metal swallow'd with their food by slovenly workmen, who went to their meals after handling the metal, without well washing their fingers, so that some of the metalline particles were taken off by their bread and eaten with it. This appeared to have some reason in it. But the pain I had experienc'd made me still afraid of those effluvia.

Being in Derbyshire at some of the furnaces for smelting of lead ore, I was told, that the smoke of those furnaces was pernicious to the neighbouring grass and other vegetables; but I do not recollect to have heard any thing of the effect of such vegetables eaten by animals. It may be well to make the enquiry.

In America I have often observ'd, that on the roofs of our shingled houses, where moss is apt to grow in northern exposures, if there be any thing on the roof painted with white lead, such as balusters, or frames of dormant windows, etc., there is constantly a streak on the shingles from such paint down to the eaves, on which no moss will grow, but the wood remains constantly

clean and free from it. We seldom drink rain water that falls on
our houses; and if we did, perhaps the small quantity of lead,
descending from such paint, might not be sufficient to produce
any sensible ill effect on our bodies. But I have been told of a case
in Europe, I forgot the place, where a whole family was afflicted
with what we call the dry bellyach, or *Colica Pictonum*, by drinking rain-water. It was at a country-seat, which, being situated too
high to have the advantage of a well, was supply'd with water
from a tank, which received the water from the leaded roofs.
This had been drunk several years without mischief; but some
young trees planted near the house growing up above the roof,
and shedding their leaves upon it, it was suppos'd that an acid in
those leaves had corroded the lead they cover'd and furnish'd the
water of that year with its baneful particles and qualities.

When I was in Paris with Sir John Pringle in 1767, he visited
La Charité, a hospital particularly famous for the cure of that
malady, and brought from thence a pamphlet containing a list of
the names of persons, specifying their professions or trades, who
had been cured there. I had the curiosity to examine that list, and
found that all the patients were of trades, that, some way or other,
use or work in lead; such as plumbers, glaziers, painters, etc.,
excepting only two kinds, stonecutters and soldiers. These I could
not reconcile to my notion, that lead was the cause of that disorder. But on my mentioning this difficulty to a physician of that
hospital, he inform'd me that the stonecutters are continually
using melted lead to fix the ends of iron balustrades in stone; and
that the soldiers had been employ'd by painters, as labourers, in
grinding of colours.

This, my dear friend, is all I can at present recollect on the
subject. You will see by it, that the opinion of this mischievous
effect from lead is at least above sixty years old; and you will
observe with concern how long a useful truth may be known and
exist, before it is generally receiv'd and practis'd on.

                                                                1786

BIFOCAL SPECTACLES

To George Whatley

By Mr. Dollond's saying, that my double spectacles can only
serve particular eyes, I doubt he has not been rightly informed of
their construction. I imagine it will be found pretty generally true,

that the same convexity of glass, through which a man sees clearest and best at the distance proper for reading, is not the best for greater distances. I therefore had formerly two pairs of spectacles, which I shifted occasionally, as in travelling I sometimes read, and often wanted to regard the prospects. Finding this change troublesome, and not always sufficiently ready, I had the glasses cut, and half of each kind associated in the same circle.

By this means, as I wear my spectacles constantly, I have only to move my eyes up or down, as I want to see distinctly far or near, the proper glasses being always ready. This I find more particularly convenient since my being in France, the glasses that serve me best at table to see what I eat, not being the best to see the faces of those on the other side of the table who speak to me; and when one's ears are not well accustomed to the sounds of a language, a sight of the movements in the features of him that speaks helps to explain; so that I understand French better by the help of my spectacles.

1785

A Backwoods Galahad:
Ephraim McDowell

JAMES THOMAS FLEXNER

AT THE sound of hoofs the door flew open, disgorging a flood of people. A huddled crowd in a forest clearing, they stared over the hill. Behind them a cabin smoked, its black walls varied by white stripes where the logs were chinked with lime. The crowd waited silently while the hoofbeats grew louder on the frozen earth, and then a rider appeared over the crest of the slope. He was so tall that his legs almost touched the ground. As he approached, the knot of people moved forward to meet him, and a dozen hands reached out to hold his mount.

"You're Dr. McDowell?"

The newcomer nodded. In the gap between his coonskin cap and his fur collar nothing was visible but tiny, brilliant eyes and a huge nose blue with cold. After he had dismounted with the slow movements of fatigue, he painstakingly distinguished the people before him. Then he stepped aside with the two local doctors.

They treated him deferentially, for this man of thirty-eight had during the ten years since 1799 been the leading surgeon of the Kentucky frontier. Ephraim McDowell's name was known in every forest settlement where the language spoken was English, not the guttural accents of Algonquin tribes. Whenever a pioneer required an operation that was beyond the skill of the rural doctors, word was sent to Danville by pony express, by courier, or by some traveler going that way, and McDowell hastily crammed his instruments and drugs into worn saddle bags. The sixty-mile trip he had taken through the wilderness to treat Mrs. Thomas Crawford was a routine matter; often he rode a hundred.

Reconstructing what occurred after McDowell reached her cabin is like the task of an archæologist who must piece together scattered fragments into the statue they once formed. McDowell left three separate brief accounts of the events that were to make him immortal. By combining them with facts we know about the frontier and statements by McDowell's contemporaries, we can rebuild an image which, even if occasionally inexact, will resemble the truth more closely than the uncombined fragments could ever do.

The two local doctors told McDowell that Mrs. Crawford was pregnant; she knew the symptoms well for she was already the mother of five children. Although the ninth and tenth months brought the most terrible labor pains, there were no signs of a birth. By the time the doctors were consulted, she was so big they were convinced she would have twins. When all their skill failed to bring on a delivery, they had called McDowell.

He preceded his colleagues into the cabin. A short, tremendous woman who lay in a box bed filled with willow boughs attempted a smile of greeting, but a spasm of pain pulled her mouth tight. McDowell sat down beside her, asked a few questions, and then launched forth, as was his custom, into a discussion of politics, repeating the news so precious in isolated settlements. While he talked, he began his examination, his hands moving with extreme gentleness over her tortured frame. Suddenly the words died on his lips. He walked to one side with his colleagues and, after a hurried exposition, asked to be left alone with Mrs. Crawford. When all had filed out, he told her that he brought her bad news.

She was not with child; she had a tumor of the ovaries. But perhaps there was some hope.

As dusk faded into night beyond the window of oiled paper, the surgeon and his pain-racked patient held a dialogue that will be famous as long as medical history is written. The little room that housed a whole family was lighted by one candle and an open fire over which heavy iron kettles simmered. The flames became brighter in the growing dimness, the flickering more distinct, while the tall doctor, overflowing a home-made chair, told Mrs. Crawford the truth and gave her a heroic choice.

McDowell has left a short account of their conversation. He explained that he had studied in Edinburgh with some of the world's greatest surgeons, who had taught him that women with ovarian tumors must invariably die; they could promise a patient nothing but two years of gradually increasing misery unless God worked a miracle. However, beneath the pessimism of the professors, there was an undertone of self-communion; they wondered whether ovarian tumors might not be cured by cutting out the diseased part. The operation would be similar to spaying, and animals recovered from being spayed. But no sooner was this suggestion made in the halls of the medical great than it was taken back again, McDowell told Mrs. Crawford. Surgery, as he supposed she knew, was practically limited to dressing wounds and amputating limbs; operators did not dare invade the great cavities of the body. He explained that "John Bell, Hunter, Hey, A. Wood, four of the first and most eminent surgeons in England and Scotland, had uniformly declared in their lectures that such was the danger of peritoneal inflammation that opening the abdomen to extract the tumor was inevitable death." They believed that once the inner wall of the abdomen was exposed to the atmosphere, nothing could protect it from infection.

During the hundred years in which excising tumors had been discussed, no surgeon had ever dared hazard an operation. And so the patients had always died in long-drawn-out agony. McDowell could not understand, he said, why no one had ever made the test. He believed that a patient would be likely to recover even as animals did, but supposing it was a fifty-to-one chance— was not even that desperate gamble better than no chance at all? Perhaps the doctors were thinking more of themselves than of their patients, of how their reputations would be destroyed by a failure.

McDowell knew that if he operated and if Mrs. Crawford died, as all medical authority said she must, no doctor would disagree with a coroner's jury that found him guilty of murder. And even should he escape criminal prosecution, the practice he had built up over many years would be wiped out at one blow; who would dare trust again to a surgeon so reckless and mad?

"If you think you are prepared to die," he none the less told his patient, "I will take the lump from you if you will come to Danville."

A woman like Mrs. Crawford could never look heroic. Short, her naturally heavy body distorted by a tremendous tumor, her face marred by features too large and a long mouth too firmly set, she was a figure for pity, not romance. Yet there must have been a strange look in her gray eyes as she spoke quietly.

"I will go with you."

It seemed a mad scheme to make Mrs. Crawford ride sixty miles through the wilderness in mid-winter, but McDowell's examination had shown that she was strong enough, and there was nothing else to do. Only in his own home, where his drugs, instruments, and trained assistants were at hand, could he give her the care that would be essential to the success of an operation so hazardous that no one had ever tried it before.

The next day Mrs. Crawford was helped from bed and onto the quietest horse that could be borrowed; her huge tumor pressed against the pommel of the saddle, but that was unavoidable. Mrs. Baker, a neighboring housewife, accompanied her, since her husband had to care for the farm. He stood in the doorway of his log cabin surrounded by his sniveling children and watched the little cavalcade move slowly away. It took them minutes to arrive at the crest of the rise, and then they were gone. He gathered the children together and returned to the cabin, certain he would never see his wife again.

When the three riders passed through the near-by village, the faces of the settlers who crowded to the doors showed pity for Mrs. Crawford, but only hostility for the tall doctor who was sacrificing her to his foolishness and pride. The instant the houses were left behind, the forest locked over their heads, a braided canopy of glass, for every branch was sheathed with ice. They rode through gleaming vistas of silence, and although they moved continually, they did not seem to advance, so unchanging was the wilderness. Only the increasing agony of the tumor, which, as McDowell tells us, chafed against the pommel, testified to miles traversed. At night they sought lodgings in some cluster of log cabins that appeared beside the trail. Always the settlers received Mrs. Crawford with sympathy and her doctor with suppressed indignation. Long before he reached Danville, McDowell must have begun to expect trouble from the mob.

At last the sixty miles were behind them. They rode down the main street of a hamlet boasting less than a hundred houses and stopped before one of the finest. Standing at the doorway under the fanlight was the doctor's wife, a tall, graceful woman who received Mrs. Crawford with the expert kindness of long usage, and put her to bed.

When the surgeon's nephew and partner, Dr. James McDowell, heard what his uncle intended to do, he was horrified. Well educated in Philadelphia, he knew that Mrs. Crawford would certainly die, dragging their reputations and their practice to oblivion with her. He argued with his uncle. He washed his hands of such madness several times a day, only to return to the attack a few hours later.

The proposed operation soon became the only topic of conversation in the tiny community of Danville, which had for a long time known no such excitement. Naturally, McDowell's less successful medical rivals did not fail to point out that the butchery he planned was contrary to all medical canons and certain to end fatally. At first the popular murmur ran on the note of gossip, but soon the pitch heightened, the voices became emotional, and men began to say that McDowell must be stopped, either by the law or by the people if need be.

He had decided to operate on Christmas Day, when the prayers of all the world, rising up to God, would create a propitious atmosphere. In the meantime, he engaged in intensive preparation. Anxious to have Mrs. Crawford as strong as possible, he saw to her every comfort and fed her on a planned diet. He studied the plates of the abdomen in his medical books and tried to re-enact in his mind every dissection he had ever made. Since James McDowell had refused to take part in the experiment, he was forced to rely for assistance entirely on his apprentice, Charles McKinny. Each day he rehearsed the youngster, going over and over the operation in pantomime to be sure there would be no slip.

Christmas Day dawned with a ringing of bells. No sooner had Dr. McDowell arisen than his nephew came to him, his face tight with determination. He had struggled with himself all night, he said, and decided at last that, since a life was at stake, it was his duty to help if he could. McDowell must have gone about his preparations with a lighter heart; such trained assistance might make a vast difference.

As Mrs. Crawford walked into the operating-room, the streets were quiet, for everyone was at church. One of the ministers, an exhorter famous for snatching brands from the mouth of hell, chose the operation as the subject of his sermon. He told his congregation of pioneers, who were used to being a law unto themselves, that, although only God had a right to deal out life and death, Dr. McDowell was preparing to destroy one of God's creatures.

The chamber where Mrs. Crawford found herself had no resemblance to the operating-theater of a modern hospital. It was a room like any other in the house, bare except for a plain wooden table onto which Mrs. Crawford was strapped. Since ether had not yet been discovered, she could be given no stronger anæsthetic than a few opium pills; naturally she had to be fastened down. Devoid of white uniforms and gauze masks, the surgeons waited in their ordinary clothes, their coats off and their sleeves rolled up to avoid the blood. The instruments did not repose in steam sterilizers, for antiseptic methods lay far in the future. The knives and forceps had been washed like table silver and laid on an ordinary linen cover.

McDowell tells us that he bared the patient's swollen abdomen, marked with a pen the course of the incision, and handed the knife to his nephew; if James were to share the possible danger, he must share the possible credit too. Seeing the gleaming blade poised over her body, Mrs. Crawford closed her eyes and started to sing a hymn. When the knife bit deep, her voice quavered but the tune continued to fill the little room.

After his nephew had completed the incision, McDowell started on the serious part of the operation. His hand never shook, but his face burned red and he sweated at every pore in the icy chamber. Whenever Mrs. Crawford's voice, attempting hymn after hymn, shook with unusual agony, he whispered tender and soothing words, as he might to a frightened child.

Suddenly the silence of the street gave way to a confused murmur; church was out. More than a hundred people gathered in front of the house, some curious, some sympathetic, but the most vocal screaming with righteous indignation. In the room where Mrs. Crawford lay, her anguished hymns were drowned out by loud shouts of male voices calling for the operation to stop. James McDowell's inwards must have rocked queasily to think what might happen if Mrs. Crawford died. He searched her prostrate body for some symptoms of approaching death, but the suffering woman, her knuckles white where they clenched the table, sang bravely on.

According to McDowell's daughter, the mob swung a rope over a tree so that they might not lose any time in hanging the surgeon when Mrs. Crawford died. As the long minutes passed with no news from the silent house at which all eyes stared, the ringleaders could control their excitement no longer; they dashed for the door and tried to smash it in. But the sheriff, assisted by the more sober citizens, intervened; for a moment there was a struggle outside the surgeon's house. If McDowell heard the uproar, he gave no sign as he proceeded with the operation he later described as follows:

"I made an incision about three inches from the musculus rectus abdominis, on the left side, continuing the same nine inches in length, parallel with the fibers of the above-named muscle, extending into the cavity of the abdomen, the parietes [walls] of which were a good deal contused, which we ascribed to the resting of the tumor on the horn of the saddle during her journey. The tumor then appeared in full view, but was so large that we could not take it away entire. We put a strong ligature around the Fallopian tube near the uterus, and then cut open the tumor, which was the ovarium and fimbrious part of the Fallopian tube very much enlarged. We took out fifteen pounds of dirty, gelatinous-looking substance, after which we cut through the Fallopian tube and extracted the sac, which weighed seven pounds and one-half. As soon as the external opening was made the intestines rushed out upon the table, and so completely was the abdomen filled by the tumor that they could not be replaced during the operation, which was terminated in about twenty-five minutes. We then turned her upon her left side, so as to permit the blood to escape, after which we closed the external opening with the interrupted suture [a series of stitches placed a short distance apart], leaving out, at the lower end of the incision, the ligature which surrounded the Fallopian tube. Between every two stitches we put a strip of adhesive plaster, which, by keeping the parts in contact, hastened the healing of the incision. We then applied the usual dressings. . . ."

The sound of hymns, which had been getting weaker and weaker, stopped at last. Ephraim and his assistants carried the half-unconscious patient to her bed. When the mob learnt that the operation was over and that Mrs. Crawford lived, there was silence for a moment, and then the air was riven by a cheer.

Actually the real danger was yet to come; would Mrs. Crawford develop peritonitis, that deadly infection of the abdominal wall? Dr. McDowell put her on the depleting diet then thought essential for combating fevers, and waited. When he came into her room five days later, he was horrified to see her standing up and making her bed. At his grave reproof, she laughingly replied that she had never been able to lie still. By means of persuasions, dire warnings, and threats he induced her to remain an invalid for twenty-five days, but at the end of that time she insisted on riding back to the neglected household tasks that had been worrying her more and more. With renewed energy she threw herself into the active life of a pioneer, moving on a short time later to a frontier outpost in Indiana, where there was new land to conquer from the forest. She remained in excellent health until her death at the age of seventy-nine.

McDowell's operation was one of the most important in the history of surgery. Although ovarian tumors are so common a malady that some specialists now treat more than a hundred a year, his cure for this otherwise fatal condition was only the lesser part of his discovery. More significant still was his demonstration that the abdominal cavity could be cut into with impunity. Indeed, his operation was a forerunner of a major part of modern surgery; its success combined with the revival of Cæsarian sections to destroy a false taboo and blaze the way for other surgeons who invaded the uterus, the spleen, the kidneys, the gallbladder, and the liver. Every operation for appendicitis or gallstones is a lineal descendant of one daring experiment made in the wilderness of Kentucky.

McDowell was not the first physician who, when confronted with a woman dying of an ovarian tumor, considered the possibility of cutting it out. As early as 1685, Théodore Schorkopoff wrote that the extirpation of the infected ovary might bring a permanent cure were it not so dangerous. Twenty-seven years later Eherenfried Schlenker made a similar observation, and from

then on the suggestion was made again and again. In 1787 the
great English surgeon John Hunter asked: "Why should not a
woman suffer spaying without danger as other animals do?" but
he saved his reputation for sanity by adding in another lecture
that an ovarian tumor was incurable "and that a patient will have
the best chance of living longest who does the least to get rid of
it." It is hard to understand why, since women were almost certain to die anyhow, someone did not take the risk of operating
during the one hundred and twenty-four years that separated
Schorkopoff from McDowell; but such was the case. When a
surgeon was confronted with a fatally stricken patient, he would
call in a committee of distinguished colleagues and, after a long
and learned discussion, decide not to commit murder by using
the only possible means to save the sufferer.

It was no accident that the all-important step which broke this
deadlock was taken in the wilderness. Since McDowell did not
add any new theoretical conception to surgery, he did not need
the inspiration of distinguished colleagues; indeed, they would
have got in his way by insisting, with all the prestige of fame
behind them, that he was mad. McDowell's greatness lay in his
skill as an operator, and in the courage and self-reliance that
prompted him to dare what no physician had ever dared before....

When McDowell sent Mrs. Crawford home cured, he was
aware that the fight against ovarian tumors had only begun.
A doctor with no reputation in the centers of civilization had
operated successfully on one patient, but perhaps his success
was the result of chance, and even if it were not, who would
believe a single voice crying from the wilderness against the
accepted teaching of centuries? In doubt himself and conscious
of the opposition he would have to face, McDowell waited
seven years before announcing his discovery. "Although the
termination of the case was most flattering," he wrote, "I was
more ready to attribute it to accident than to any skill or judgment of my own, but it emboldened me to undertake similar
cases; and not until I had operated three times, all of which were
successful, did I publish anything on the subject."

In 1813 he cured one Negro woman, in 1816 another. Then
he undertook a more difficult task. For days a blank sheet of
paper lay before him while a goose-quill wilted in his hand.

Undoubtedly his literary-minded wife was called in to help, but her talent ran to flowers, not tumors. Although they struggled interminably to get the unadorned facts down, the result was neither elegant nor detailed. The completed paper gave no history of the origin of Mrs. Crawford's condition, on the all-important questions of diagnosis and after-treatment it was hazy to say the least, and the description of the actual operation, which we have already quoted, was not voluminous. He was even more sketchy concerning the other two cases.

McDowell sent one copy of his paper to his old master, John Bell, in Edinburgh, and another to Dr. Philip Syng Physick. "The father of American surgery" was too knowing to be taken in by a nonentity's crude description of the impossible; after glancing through it scornfully, Physick refused to have the paper published. McDowell then sent it to Dr. Thomas C. James, the professor of midwifery at the University of Pennsylvania, who took the trouble to read it carefully and published it in 1817 in his journal, *The Eclectic Repertory*.

Most surgeons paid no attention whatsoever to McDowell's "nonsense," and the two who did, wrote articles for the same journal blaming the inadequacy of McDowell's account for the deaths of patients on whom they had not dared operate. It was unfortunate, Dr. Ezra Michener of the Philadelphia Dispensatory commented, that cases as interesting as McDowell's "should come before the public in such a manner as to frustrate their intention of being useful . . . Few persons will be likely to venture their reputations on such uncertain data."

We can imagine the scorn of Dr. McDowell, who had ventured his reputation on no data at all, for these city practitioners who demanded to be spoon-fed. During September 1819 he answered his critics in a letter to Dr. James: "I thought my statement sufficiently explicit to warrant any surgeon's performing the operation when necessary, without hazarding the odium of making an experiment; and I think my description of the mode of operating, and of the anatomy of the parts concerned, clear enough to enable any good anatomist, possessing the judgment requisite for a surgeon, to operate with safety. I hope no operator of any other description may ever attempt it. It is my most ardent wish that this operation may remain, to the mechanical surgeon, forever incomprehensible. Such have been the *bane* of the science; intruding themselves into the ranks of the profession, with no other qualification but boldness in undertaking, ignorance of their responsibility, and indifference to the lives of their patients; proceeding according to the special dictates of some author, as mechanical as themselves, they cut and tear with fearless indifference, utterly incapable of exercising any judgment of their own in cases of emergency; and sometimes, without even possessing the slightest knowledge of the parts concerned. The preposterous and impious attempts of such pretenders, can seldom fail to prove destructive to the patient, and disgraceful to the science. It is by such this noble science has been degraded in the minds of many to the rank of an art."

McDowell then went on to report two more ovariotomies he had performed since his previous article. One patient had recovered and the other had died of peritonitis, his only fatality in five operations. Although his letter was published in *The Eclectic Repertory* for October 1819, it did not embolden any other surgeon to follow him. Women who might have been cured continued to die in agony . . . He had heard nothing about the paper he had sent to John Bell in Edinburgh, and his practice was falling off at home. Whenever he rode down the street, the Negroes dived into their houses and threw the bolts behind them. One evening, his granddaughter tells us, he met a huge colored man on a solitary part of the road. The man fled, but at McDowell's command to halt fell on his knees and, rolling white eyeballs to heaven, burst into shrill prayer. As the surgeon reined up beside him, he crossed himself without stopping, his hand flying like the shuttle of a loom. McDowell dismounted and shook him until he stopped screaming. "Why are you afraid of me?" he asked. "My master," the Negro answered, "he say Dr. McDowell am next to the devil; Dr. McDowell goes around cutting people open and killing them. . . ."

It would, however, be wrong to think of McDowell sinking into insignificance and poverty; many frontiersmen stuck by him to the end. In 1822 he was called several hundred miles to Hermitage, Tennessee, where he removed an ovarian tumor from the wife of John Overton, Andrew Jackson's wealthy backer. His aide in this operation was Old Hickory himself, who handed him the instruments and put him up in his house; the two men of action got on famously. McDowell asked five hundred dollars, but Overton sent him a check for fifteen hundred. When the doctor returned it, pointing out the error, Overton replied the operation was worth at least that. According to Samuel David Gross, the great surgeon and medical biographer of the next generation, this fee was the largest paid in America until that time.

About then, McDowell accepted as a private pupil a second nephew, Joseph Nashe McDowell. This preternaturally cadaverous young man looked as if he had pared his own flesh down so that he might study his bones; he was an enthusiastic anatomist. In fact, enthusiasm was his principal attribute; he was never happy unless his tiny, sunken eyes gleamed with baleful fire and his high-pitched voice was screaming in bombast. . . .

McDowell's daughter, Mary, had grown into a plump and rosy young lady. Whenever the emaciated Joseph saw her eyes resting on him, he leapt into a paroxysm of boasting: not only would he be the greatest doctor in the United States, he would be the greatest general as well and drive the dirty Spaniards from the continent. Although Mary laughed, he was not discouraged. Following her everywhere, he wooed her so violently that she appealed to her father. McDowell's gentle remonstrances, however, merely drove Joseph into a heroic fury. Mary loved him, he insisted; McDowell was trying to come between them. The surgeon lost his temper too, and the scene ended with Joseph stamping out of the house, shouting that he would show McDowell who was the better man.

Joseph went to Lexington, Kentucky, to study medicine at Transylvania University, then the medical center of the west. Soon it became common gossip there that McDowell had stolen the credit for discovering ovariotomy from his dead nephew and partner, Dr. James McDowell, who had done the operation against his advice. Joseph even went so far as to consult Mrs. Crawford and magnify her story that James had made the first incision into a statement that he had carried out the entire operation while his uncle assisted. The scandal mounted until McDowell was forced to issue a defensive statement accompanied by affidavits from Mrs. Crawford and others who had been present. However, the rumor continued to circulate. . . .

Not until McDowell's fortunes had reached a low ebb did the copy of his first paper which he had sent to John Bell make its appearance in England. On its arrival at Edinburgh seven years before, Bell had been dying in Italy; the paper fell into the hands of his successor, John Lizars, who kept it hidden away until he was able to publish it as an incidental part of the history leading up to an operation of his own. He did not even bother to spell

McDowell's name correctly, and he entitled the article in which the American's epoch-making discovery was included "Observations on the Extirpation of Ovaria, with Cases, by John Lizars."

Lizars recounted his one case at three times the length McDowell had used for three, and he summoned all his literary skill to make the narrative as moving as possible. He introduces us to a young binder of shoes whose husband beat her so cruelly that she was forced to leave him. When a year later a swelling developed in her abdomen, she ascribed it to the beatings, but the hospital to which she went accused her of bearing an illegitimate child. From time to time other doctors "cruelly taunted her with being pregnant." Then Lizars describes how he came to the rescue: he told her she had an ovarian tumor and that he would save her by cutting it out. Although he dwells at great length on his courage in overriding the advice of distinguished colleagues, he gives McDowell's successful cases only passing credit for influencing him to operate.

The amphitheater was filled with students, three venerable surgeons were in attendance, when Lizars prepared to introduce ovariotomy to the civilized world. Conscious that history recorded his every gesture, he made the incision under a hundred admiring eyes, but when he had laid the abdomen open, bewilderment took the place of self-confidence on his features. With growing dismay he examined the patient, and then he called over the other three surgeons. After each in turn had peered gravely into the wound, the four looked at each other blankly, for, alas, there was no tumor whatsoever to be seen; the swelling was caused by a pathological fatness of the intestines. Sadly Lizars sewed his patient up again. However, as she regained strength after the operation, his self-esteem returned; was he not the first reputable doctor to demonstrate that the abdomen could be cut into with impunity? Proudly he wrote the case up and published it in the *Edinburgh Medical Journal* of October 1824. . . .

Although McDowell was helped by the sturdy constitutions which all pioneers were forced to develop, he must have been a brilliant surgeon. The abdominal cavity is particularly sensitive to the type of handling it receives. If the normal flow of fluid is not disturbed, it is almost immune to infection, but once this delicate balance is upset by an inexpert hand, nothing but antisepsis, which had not then been discovered, can save the patient from peritonitis.

Ovariotomy remained so dangerous in hands other than

McDowell's that it was frowned upon by medical faculties all over the world until long after his death . . . Forty years after McDowell had cured Mrs. Crawford, Dr. Washington Atlee was denounced by the entire profession for proposing to do an ovariotomy in Philadelphia, still the medical capital of America. One professor called from the rostrum for the police to intervene, and an eminent surgeon visited the patient to tell her she would be dead in twenty-four hours. She recovered. Professor Meigs thereupon wrote that the operation was not justified by any amount of success. "Dr. Atlee's coolness in cutting open a woman's belly does not, I should think, entitle him to judge more clearly than I as to the morals of such surgery." Meigs wanted the operation forbidden by statute. . . .

While the controversy that was to outlive him raged, McDowell quietly attended his patients in Danville, excising ovarian tumors whenever they appeared in his practice. Although in 1825 he was given an honorary degree by the University of Maryland, the only degree he ever received, he was accorded less praise than censure for carrying out an operation most doctors felt should not be attempted. He remained successful as a lithotomist—Dr. Gross says he cut thirty-two times for bladder stones without a death—but his popularity continued to decline, and the calumny of which he was the object reached amazing proportions.

Once when he was away attending a distant case, his wife came down with an acute illness. Of necessity McDowell's rival, Dr. Anthony Hunn, was called in. Hunn took one look at the ailing lady, threw the prescription McDowell had left her out of the window, and announced that she had been poisoned. Immediately it was whispered that her husband had tried to murder her and, but for Dr. Hunn's timely intervention, would have succeeded. As the story passed from mouth to mouth, accompanied by the click of a spindle or the creak of rockers, it grew until gossip authoritatively stated that the bright-eyed young apprentice who accompanied McDowell everywhere was a girl in man's clothing. The surgeon had tried to kill his wife so that he might marry this paramour. From then on, a contemporary account tells us, he was "the object of the utmost contempt in the neighborhood."

But McDowell had saved enough during his prosperous years to buy a plantation and slaves to work it in the true Southern style. During his middle fifties he retired there and, although sometimes called away to attend a particularly difficult case, lived

the life of a country gentleman. He named his plantation Cambus-
kenneth after an abbey he had seen during his rambles in Scotland; this brief season in the Old World, not the adventures of
the wilderness, seems to have supplied the romance of his life. . . .

One evening during June 1830 McDowell went into his garden
and ate freely of strawberries fresh from the vine. On his return
to the house, his stomach was gripped by the most excruciating
pain. Telling his wife to summon the family physician, he explained between paralyzing spasms that he must have eaten a
deadly insect or some poisonous egg that clung to a berry. A
servant, sent flying to the village, soon returned with the doctor.
Realizing that McDowell was seriously ill, he asked for a consultation and treated the great surgeon for inflammation of the
stomach. But medicine was helpless; after sinking steadily for
two weeks, McDowell died.

His famous operation had paved the way for the cure of appendicitis. He probably died of a ruptured appendix.

1937

New World Remedies

MEDICAL DIRECTIONS IN THE VIRGINIA
ALMANACK—1787

January—Let no blood, and use no Physic, unless there be a
necessity. Eat often, and avoid too much sleep.

February—Be sparing in Physick, and let not blood without
necessity, and be careful of catching cold.

March—The latter end of this month you may purge and bleed,
though not absolutely necessary if you are in perfect health.

April—It is now a good time to cleanse yourself in order to
prepare for the summer season. Abstain from much wine, or
other strong liquors. They will cause a ferment in your blood,
and ruin your constitution.

May—The blood and humours being now in motion, avoid eating
salt or stale meats; fat people must avoid excess of liquors.

June—Cooling sallads, such as lettuce, purslane etc. will prevent
too much perspiration, and throw off feverish disorders. Beware
of sudden cold after heat.

July—Forbear superfluous drinking. Use cold herbs. Shun boiled salts and strong meats, and abstain from physick.

August—Use moderate diet, forbear to sleep soon after meals, for that brings on head-achs, agues, etc. and take great care of sudden cold after heat.

September—Be not out late of nights, or in foggy weather, and keep out of the damp air . . . Drink not too free . . .

October—Avoid the dew and fogs, and be not out late of night. Take no physick unless there is an absolute necessity of it.

November—The best physick this and the next month is good exercise, warm clothes, and wholesome diet. But if any distemper afflicts you, finish your physick this month, and so rest till March.

December—Keep yourself warm by exercise, and be temperate . . . Take no physick, and be careful of catching cold.

REMEDIES FROM THE NANTUCKET INQUIRER—1821

For Consumption or Cough

Two quarts strong ale, one of white honey, two ounces of leaves of longwort (Polmonora officinalis) put in an earthern pot covered closely, and boiled down one half. Strain the liquor, bottle it, cork the bottles closely and keep them in a cool place.

Inhaling the smoke of rosin, while burning, or the steam of tar while boiling have also very powerful effects in strengthening weak and decaying lungs.

Cholera Morbus

At this season of the year when so many valuable lives are lost or put in jeopardy by this terrific disease, take a half grown chicken, strip him of his feathers and intrails as quickly as possible after killing him, and while he is yet warm put him into a gallon of boiling water and continue the boiling half an hour. Take off the liquor and give to the patient.

REMEDIES OF DR. RICHARD CARTER OF
KENTUCKY—1825

Receipt the 41st:

Fill a twenty-five gallon still with elecampane roots and water, distill it and preserve the proceeds, then fill the still with spikenard roots and water, and still it in the same way, and in like manner preserve this, then fill the still with horehound, and treat it likewise, after which clean the still, and put back all the liquid that has been extracted from all those herbs and roots above mentioned, and add five gallons of good whiskey, run it off as you would in making whiskey and save it as long as there appears to be any strength in it. Then put it in a cag, and to every gallon add half a gallon of honey, a table spoonful of refined nitre, a table spoonful of dried pulverised Indian turnip, and a pint of middling strong lie made of the ashes of dry cow dung.

Then get a peck of pollepody, a peck of cinquefoil, and a peck of white plantain; put these into a pot and boil them well in water, strain it, add three gallons of cider to it, boil it down to three gallons, and to every gallon of this add a quart of the above sirop. This medicine may either be taken in a little wine and water, or new milk. We give from half a tablespoonful, to a wine glass full, three times a day, during which time the patient must not eat anything high seasoned, strong nor sweet, and he should be very careful that he does not take cold or even heat his blood. It is best to commence with small doses at first, and increase the dose as the patient's strength increases. This medicine is not at all dangerous unless you give too much for the patient's strength. If this medicine causes the patient to sweat, produces a soreness in the breast, or increases the cough, you may know that it is too strong, and consequently it must be weakened with honey until those symptoms abate. This is good to break any fever, and is excellent in the last stages of the consumption, phthisic, and the cold plague. If the cough is very hard add to every dose a tea spoonful of sweet or linseed oil.

The herbs and roots that you are herein directed to distill, will not produce as well in the heat of summer, as they will in the spring or fall, so by these directions, you may know how to regulate it so as to get all the strength and should not run it too far.

REMEDY—FOR THE GOUT, RHEUMATISMS, CRAMPS, INFIRMITIES OF THE SINEWS, JOINTS ETC.

Take a young fat dog and kill him, scald and clean him as you would a pig, then extract his guts through a hole previously made in his side, and substitute in the place thereof, two handfuls of nettles, two ounces of brimstone, one dozen hen eggs, four ounces of turpentine, a handful of tanzy, a pint of red fishing worms, and about three fourths of a pound of tobacco, cut up fine; mix all those ingredients well together before deposited in

the dog's belly, and then sew up the whole, then roast him well
before a hot fire, save the oil, annoint the joints, and weak parts
before the fire as hot as you can bear it, being careful not to get
wet or expose yourself to damp or night air, or even heating
yourself, or in fact should you not expose yourself in any way.

TESTIMONY OF CURE OF MRS. SARAH LASURE
"attested by seven citizens good and true"

I DO CERTIFY, That in the year of our Lord 1810 that I was
taken with the dropsy, and became very low. I sent for a Doctor,
and mended a little, but never left me, but still grew worse for
two years . . . and my feet and legs swelled to that degree that
they bursted and run a great deal . . . When I commenced taking
medicine of Doctor Carter I was about fifty years of age, and
since that I have had a fine daughter . . . I do certify that I also
had a daughter who had a white swelling in her leg, which was
hollow from the knee to the ancle, and out of which came
sixteen pieces of bone, and this same Doctor Carter attended on
her and she has got nearly well, so that it don't hinder at all
from walking.

This Woman, aged fifty years,
The dropsy had, as it appears;
Who was laid low and almost gone,
Until her legs did burst and run.

While at the point of death she lay,
Without the hope of the next day;
Then by God's blessing and my skill,
She was restored, sound and well.

Observe the means which I did give,
Has almost made the dying live;
And from affliction now has free'd,
And made this aged woman breed.

ON DR. RICHARD CARTER

BY MADGE E. PICKARD AND R. CARLYLE BULEY

Dr. Carter was at his best on the ennui or hypo. This dread
disease manifested itself by feelings of dullness, fear, indefinite
pains, and lack of desire to attend to any business. When one

had it, he "felt disposed to be retired," to tell his troubles, and to feel that he was afflicted with any disease which anyone else had. Carter did not diagnose this affliction as a real disorder unconnected with any other, for it made its appearance only when the "system was released from any cause; such as hard drink, colds, fevers, dropsies, gouts, night air, loss of sleep, incessant studying, loss of friends, and scolding companions." He reasoned that the body and mind were so inseparably connected that one could not suffer without the other's participating. The idea that the complaint was entirely of the mind was erroneous. "My opinion of the hypo is, that it is very hard to exterminate, when it has once taken good hold, it becomes ingratiated, and is in a measure second nature." Like the hypo, but operating only on the female sex, was the hysterics (hi-sterics to Dr. Carter and his pioneer patients).

When affected with hypo or hysterics some persons insisted they were teapots; others thought that they were town clocks, that their legs and feet were made of glass, that they were actually dying or else already dead. One man insisted that he had died at twelve o'clock the night before and was brought to only after his neighbors came in and reflected that no doubt he had gone to hell, 'for if he is not gone there I see not what use there is for such a place.' An old gentleman who went to bed in a room with a small boy tried the next morning to get into the boy's pantaloons instead of his own. When he failed he fell to the floor, awakened the household with a terrible roar, and went into the agonies of death. When help arrived and he was asked what the trouble was, he yelled, "What's the matter? Why can't you see what's the matter? I'm swelled as big as an ox. I can not get my big toe into my pantaloons." Then there was the old woman who tried in vain to keep her head warm, though "she wore a cap, three handkerchiefs, and a boulster of feathers on it." This same old woman proclaimed that she was able to "travel a small path the darkest night that ever came by the aid of nine lighted candles which came out of thin air and stuck to the back of her head."

A patient whose system and nerves were somewhat weakened by the fevers got the idea that his belly was full of young ducks, which he said he could hear and feel plainly. When his doctor was unable to dissuade him from this notion another was called in for consultation. The latter conceded that the patient had a case and stated that he could cure him with a purge. Having procured some young ducks, he placed them in the proper receptacle so that the patient was satisfied that he had delivered himself of them. The sick man was then curious to know how the ducks could have accumulated in his belly. The doctor explained that no doubt the patient "had eat a great many eggs in his time, which had collected and hatched; which explanation entirely satisfied the patient, and in a short time he was as well as ever he was in his life; but never could be prevailed on to eat another egg." Dr. Carter once heard of a man "who became so desperately in love with a young woman, that on her denying him, (although he had ever been considered a prudent man, and managed his estate well) yet he became so extravagant, as to patiently sit for three months on a goose egg. If this was not the hypo, it was very much like it, if not worse."

One of the worst cases of hypo recorded was that of an old urine doctor who, feeling bad, set aside a specimen to be examined after it had settled. While he was out of the office a woman "who imagined from circumstances that she was in a state of pregnancy" decided this would be a good time to find out. "She therefore discharged the phial of its contents, and filled it up with her own water.—When the doctor returned (not suspecting any thing of what had transpired,) his consternation was inexpressible to find from the appearance of the urine, that he was in a state of pregnancy, and found (from) the organization and structure of his system he saw no chance of delivery. He became almost frantic at the discovery, and nothing saved him absolute dispair, but the discovery of the real facts, as they transpired."

In a somewhat similar mistake the embarrassing situation was solved by a bit of mental hygiene. "The gentleman concluded that it was a fact, that he was in a state of pregnancy, and would soon go to shut-eye town. But it happened that this gentleman, for a particular purpose, stepped out and placed himself against an old stump, and just at the critical moment, out jumped a rabbit from the stump, which he owned for his child, but it being rather fleet for the old man, it escaped, and he returned to the house with great joy, &c."

A complete cure of the hysterics, or hypo, Dr. Carter thought, was very seldom obtained, particularly after it became deeply rooted in the system. Blood-letting was in certain cases recommended, also foot-baths, injections, and dosages of calomel and alloes. Some radical cases called for stomach blisters, "frictions nearly all over the skin; give a strong camomile tea to drink, wine, bark and steel; riding on horse back; cheerful company and interesting engagements." Pills made of asafoetida, "rusian caster," and opium were likewise helpful. Sometimes instant relief was obtained by "the vitriolic ether given from thirty to fifty drops in a cup of some kind of drink. Gold filings given in doses (night and morning in honey) about as much as would lay on the point of a penknife" had been known "to cure a person who had been too weak to work for three years. Or take bear's gall and put in rum and drink as a bitter, is excellent for this disorder; and when the choaking is bad, a tea spoonful of wheat flour mixed in water and drank, will stop it; or chew orange peels and swallow your spittle. . . ."

Above all, one should ever keep in mind that "The cure of diseases is never to be attempted . . . by violent methods, but rather by degrees and gentle means," waiting for a suitable opportunity. "If any application is likely to do more hurt than good, it should be abandoned." Perhaps, if abandoned soon enough, Dr. Carter's system would truly conform to his own quoted description of it:

> My medicine, though made of herbs, doth wond'rous
>   cures perform,
> And yet each one may practice it without producing harm.

1945

Memorial to the Legislature
of Massachusetts

DOROTHEA LYNDE DIX

GENTLEMEN,

I RESPECTFULLY ask to present this Memorial, believing that the *cause*, which actuates to and sanctions so unusual a movement, presents no equivocal claim to public consideration and sympathy. Surrendering to calm and deep convictions of duty my habitual views of what is womanly and becoming, I proceed briefly to explain what has conducted me before you unsolicited and unsustained, trusting, while I do so, that the memorialist will be speedily forgotten in the memorial.

About two years since leisure afforded opportunity, and duty prompted me to visit several prisons and alms-houses in the vicinity of this metropolis. I found, near Boston, in the Jails and Asylums for the poor, a numerous class brought into unsuitable connexion with criminals and the general mass of Paupers. I refer to Idiots and Insane persons, dwelling in circumstances not only adverse to their own physical and moral improvement, but productive of extreme disadvantages to all other persons brought into association with them. I applied myself diligently to trace the causes of these evils, and sought to supply remedies. As one obstacle was surmounted, fresh difficulties appeared. Every new investigation has given depth to the conviction that it is only by decided, prompt, and vigorous legislation the evils to which I refer, and which I shall proceed more fully to illustrate, can be remedied. I shall be obliged to speak with great plainness, and to reveal many things revolting to the taste, and from which my woman's nature shrinks with peculiar sensitiveness. But truth is the highest consideration. *I tell what I have seen*—painful and shocking as the details often are—that from them you may feel more deeply the imperative obligation which lies upon you to prevent the possibility of a repetition or continuance of such outrages upon humanity. If I inflict pain upon you, and move you to horror, it is to acquaint you with sufferings which you have the power to alleviate, and make you hasten to the relief of the victims of legalized barbarity.

I come to present the strong claims of suffering humanity. I come to place before the Legislature of Massachusetts the condition of the miserable, the desolate, the outcast. I come as the advocate of helpless, forgotten, insane and idiotic men and women; of beings, sunk to a condition from which the most unconcerned would start with real horror; of beings wretched in our Prisons, and more wretched in our Alms-Houses. And I cannot suppose it needful to employ earnest persuasion, or stubborn argument, in order to arrest and fix attention upon a subject, only the more strongly pressing in its claims, because it is revolting and disgusting in its details.

I must confine myself to few examples, but am ready to furnish other and more complete details, if required. If my pictures are displeasing, coarse, and severe, my subjects, it must be recollected, offer no tranquil, refined, or composing features. The condition of human beings, reduced to the extremest states of degradation and misery, cannot be exhibited in softened language, or adorn a polished page.

I proceed, Gentlemen, briefly to call your attention to the *present* state of Insane Persons confined within this Commonwealth, in *cages, closets, cellars, stalls, pens! Chained, naked, beaten with rods*, and *lashed* into obedience! . . . I give a few illustrations; but description fades before reality.

Danvers. November; visited the almshouse; a large building, much out of repair; understand a new one is in contemplation. Here are from fifty-six to sixty inmates; one idiotic; three insane; one of the latter in close confinement at all times.

Long before reaching the house, wild shouts, snatches of rude songs, imprecations, and obscene language, fell upon the ear, proceeding from the occupant of a low building, rather remote from the principal building to which my course was directed. Found the mistress, and was conducted to the place, which was called "*the home*" of the *forlorn* maniac, a young woman, exhibiting a condition of neglect and misery blotting out the faintest idea of comfort, and outraging every sentiment of decency. She had been, I learnt, "a respectable person; industrious and worthy; disappointments and trials shook her mind, and finally laid prostrate reason and self-control; she became a maniac for life! She had been at Worcester Hospital for a considerable time, and had been returned as incurable." The mistress told me she understood that, while there, she was "comfortable and decent." Alas! what a change was here exhibited! She had passed from one degree of violence and degradation to another, in swift progress; there she stood, clinging to, or beating upon, the bars of her caged apartment, the contracted size of which afforded space only for increasing accumulations of filth, a *foul* spectacle; there she stood with naked arms and dishevelled hair; the unwashed frame invested with fragments of unclean garments, the air so extremely offensive, though ventilation was afforded on all sides save one, that it was not possible to remain beyond a few moments without retreating for recovery to the outward air. Irritation of body, produced by utter filth and exposure, incited her to the horrid process of tearing off her skin by inches; her face, neck, and person, were thus disfigured to hideousness; she held up a fragment just rent off; to my exclamation of horror, the mistress replied, "oh, we can't help it; half the skin is off sometimes; we can do nothing with her; and it makes no difference what she eats, for she consumes her own filth as readily as the food which is brought her."

It is now January; a fortnight since, two visitors reported that most wretched outcast as "wallowing in dirty straw, in a place yet more dirty, and without clothing, without fire. Worse cared for than the brutes, and wholly lost to consciousness of decency!" Is the whole story told? What was seen, is; what is reported is not. These gross exposures are not for the pained sight of one alone; all, all, coarse, brutal men, wondering, neglected children, old and young, each and all, witness this lowest, foulest state of miserable humanity. And who protects her, that worse than Paria outcast, from other wrongs and blacker outrages? I do not *know* that such *have been*. I do know that they are to be dreaded, and that they are not guarded against.

Some may say these things cannot be remedied; these furious maniacs are not to be raised from these base conditions. I *know* they are; could give *many* examples; let *one* suffice. A young woman, a pauper, in a distant town, *Sandisfield*, was for years a raging maniac. A cage, chains, and *the whip*, were the agents for controlling her, united with harsh tones and profane language. Annually, with others (the town's poor) she was put up at auction, and bid off at the lowest price which was declared for her. One year, not long past, an old man came forward in the number of applicants for the poor wretch; he was taunted and ridiculed; "what would he and his old wife do with such a mere beast?" "My wife says yes," replied he, "and I shall take her." She was given to his charge; he conveyed her home; she was washed, neatly dressed, and placed in a decent bed-room, furnished for comfort and opening into the kitchen. How altered her condition! As yet *the chains* were not off. The first week she was somewhat restless, at times violent, but the quiet kind ways of the old people wrought a change; she received her food decently; forsook acts of violence, and no longer uttered blasphemous or indecent language; after a week, the chain was lengthened, and she was received as a companion into the kitchen. Soon she engaged in trivial employments. "After a fortnight," said the old man, "I knocked off the chains and made her a free woman." She is at times excited, but not violently; they are careful of her diet; they keep her very clean; she calls them "father" and "mother." Go

there now and you will find her "clothed," and though not perfectly in her "right mind," so far restored as to be a safe and
comfortable inmate.

Newburyport. Visited the almshouse in June last; eighty inmates; seven insane, one idiotic. Commodious and neat house;
several of the partially insane apparently very comfortable; two
very improperly situated, namely, an insane man, not considered
incurable, in an out-building, whose room opened upon what
was called "the dead room," affording in lieu of companionship
with the living, a contemplation of corpses! The other subject was
a woman in a *cellar*: I desired to see her; much reluctance was
shown. I pressed the request; the Master of the House stated that
she was *in the cellar*; that she was *dangerous to be approached*;
that "she had lately attacked his wife;" and *was often naked*. I
persisted; "if you will not go with me, give me the keys and I
will go alone." Thus importuned, the outer doors were opened.
I descended the stairs from within; a strange, unnatural noise
seemed to proceed from beneath our feet; at the moment I did not
much regard it. My conductor proceeded to remove a padlock,
while my eye explored the wide space in quest of the poor
woman. All for a moment was still. But judge my horror and
amazement, when a door to a closet *beneath* the *staircase* was
opened, revealing in the imperfect light a female apparently
wasted to a skeleton, partially wrapped in blankets, furnished for
the narrow bed on which she was sitting; her countenance furrowed, not by age, but suffering, was the image of distress; in that
contracted space, unlighted, unventilated, she poured forth the
wailings of despair: mournfully she extended her arms and appealed to me, "why am I consigned to hell? dark—dark—I used
to pray, I used to read the Bible—I have done no crime in my
heart; I had friends, why have all forsaken me!—my God! my
God! why hast *thou* forsaken me!" Those groans, those wailings
come up daily, mingling, with how many others, a perpetual and
sad memorial. When the good Lord shall require an account of
our stewardship, what shall all and each answer!

Perhaps it will be inquired how long, how many days or hours
was she imprisoned in these confined limits? *For years!* In
another part of the cellar were other small closets, only better,
because higher through the entire length, into one of which she
by turns was transferred, so as to afford opportunity for fresh
whitewashing, &c.

Saugus. December 24; thermometer below zero; drove to the poorhouse; was conducted to the master's family-room by himself; walls garnished with handcuffs and chains, not less than five pair of the former; did not inquire how or on whom applied; thirteen pauper inmates; one insane man; one woman insane; one idiotic man; asked to see them; the two men were shortly led in; appeared pretty decent and comfortable. Requested to see the other insane subject; was denied decidedly; urged the request, and finally secured a reluctant assent. Was led through an outer passage into a lower room, occupied by the paupers; crowded; not neat; ascended a rather low flight of stairs upon an open entry, through the floor of which was introduced a stove pipe, carried along a *few feet*, about six inches above the floor, through which it was reconveyed below. From this entry opens a room of moderate size, having a sashed-window; floor, I think, painted; apartment *entirely* unfurnished; no chair, table, nor bed; neither, what is seldom missing, a bundle of straw or lock of hay; cold, very cold; the first movement of my conductor was to throw open a window, a measure imperatively necessary for those who entered. *On the floor* sat a woman, her limbs immovably contracted, so that the knees were brought upward to the chin; the face was concealed; the head rested on the folded arms; for clothing she appeared to have been furnished with *fragments* of many discharged garments; these were folded about her, yet they little benefitted her, if one might judge by the constant shuddering which almost convulsed her poor crippled frame. Woeful was this scene; language is feeble to record the misery she was suffering and had suffered! In reply to my inquiry if she could not change her position, I was answered by the master in the negative, and told that the contraction of limbs was occasioned by "neglect and exposure in former years," but *since she had been crazy*, and before she fell under the charge, as I inferred, of her present *guardians*. Poor wretch! she, like many others, was an example of what humanity becomes when the temple of reason falls in ruins, leaving the mortal part to injury and neglect, and showing how much can be endured of privation, exposure, and disease, without extinguishing the lamp of life.

Passing out, the man pointed to a something, revealed to more than one sense, which he called "her bed; and we throw some blankets over her at night." Possibly this is done; others, like myself, might be pardoned a doubt, if they could have seen all I saw, and heard abroad all I heard. The *bed*, so called, was about *three* feet long, and from a half to three-quarters of a yard wide; of old ticking or tow cloth was the case; the contents might have been a *full handful* of hay or straw. My attendant's exclamations on my leaving the house were emphatic, and can hardly be repeated.

The above case recalls another of equal neglect or abuse. Asking my way to the almshouse in Berkeley, which had been repeatedly spoken of as greatly neglected, I was answered as to the direction, and informed that there were "plenty of insane people and idiots there." "Well taken care of?" "Oh, well enough for such sort of creatures?" "Any violently insane?" "Yes; my sister's son is there, a real tiger. I kept him here at my house awhile, but it was too much trouble to go on; so I carried him there." "Is he comfortably provided for?" "Well enough." "Has he decent clothes?" "Good enough; wouldn't wear them if he had more." "Food?" "Good enough; good enough for him." "One more question, has he the comfort of a fire?" "Fire! fire, indeed! what does a crazy man need of fire? red-hot iron wants fire as much as he!" And such are sincerely the ideas of not a few persons in regard to the actual wants of the insane. Less regarded than the lowest brutes! no wonder they sink even lower.

Ipswich. Have visited the prison there several times; visited the almshouse once. In the latter are several cases of insanity; three especially distressing, situated in a miserable out-building, detached from the family-house, and confined in stalls or pens; three individuals, one of which is apparently very insensible to the deplorable circumstances which surround him, and perhaps not likely to comprehend privations or benefits. Not so the person directly opposite to him, who looks up wildly, anxiously by turns, through those strong bars. Cheerless sight! strange companionship for the mind flitting and coming by turns to some perception of persons and things. He too is one of the returned incurables. His history is a sad one; I have not had all the particulars, but it shows distinctly, what the most prosperous and affluent may come to be. I understand his connexions are excellent and respectable; his natural abilities in youth were superior; he removed from Essex county to Albany, and was established there as the editor of a popular newspaper, in course of time he was chosen a senator for that section of the state, and of course was a Judge in the Court of Errors.

Vicissitudes followed, and insanity closed the scene. He was conveyed to Worcester; after a considerable period, either to give place to some new patient, or because the County objected to the continued expense, he being declared incurable, was removed to Salem jail; thence to Ipswich jail; associated with the prisoners there, partaking the same food, and clad in like apparel. After a time the town complained of the expense of keeping him in jail; it was cheaper in the almshouse; to the almshouse he was conveyed, and there perhaps must abide. How sad a fate! I found him in a quiet state; though at times was told that he is greatly excited; what wonder, with such a companion before him; such cruel scenes within! I perceived in him some little confusion as I paused before the stall, against the bars of which he was leaning; he was not so lost to propriety but that a little disorder of the bed-clothes, &c. embarrassed him. I passed on, but he asked, in a moment, earnestly, "Is the lady gone—gone quite away?" I returned; he gazed a moment without answering my inquiry if he wished to see me? "And have you too lost all your dear friends?" Perhaps my mourning apparel excited his inquiry. "Not all." "Have you any dear father and mother to love you?" and then he sighed and then laughed and traversed the limited stall. Immediately adjacent to this stall was one occupied by a *simple* girl, who was "put there to be out of harm's way." A cruel lot! for this privation of a sound mind. A madman on the one hand, not so much separated as to secure decency, another almost opposite, and no screen! I do not know how it is argued, that mad persons and idiots may be dealt with as if no spark of recollection ever lights up the mind; the observation and experience of those, who have had charge of Hospitals, show opposite conclusions.

Violence and severity do but exasperate the Insane: the only availing influence is kindness and firmness. It is amazing what these will produce. How many examples might illustrate this position: I refer to one recently exhibited in Barre. The town Paupers are disposed of annually to some family who, for a stipulated sum agree to take charge of them. One of them, a young woman, was shown to me well clothed, neat, quiet, and employed at needle-work. Is it possible that this is the same being who, but last year, was a raving madwoman, exhibiting every degree of violence in action and speech; a very tigress wrought to fury; caged, chained, beaten, loaded with injuries, and exhibiting the passions which an iron rule might be expected to stimulate and sustain. It is the same person; another family hold her in charge who better understand human nature and human influences; she is no longer chained, caged, and beaten; but if excited, a pair of mittens drawn over the hands secures from mischief. Where will she be next year, after the annual sale?

It is not the insane subject alone who illustrates the power of the all prevailing law of kindness. A poor idiotic young man, a year or two since, used to follow me at times through the prison as I was distributing books and papers: at first he appeared totally stupid, but cheerful expressions, a smile, a trifling gift, seemed gradually to light up the void temple of the intellect, and by slow degrees some faint images of thought passed before the mental vision. He would ask for books, though he could not read. I indulged his fancy and he would appear to experience delight in examining them; and kept them with a singular care. If I read the Bible, he was reverently, wonderingly attentive; if I talked, he listened with a half-conscious aspect. One morning I passed more hurriedly than usual, and did not speak particularly to him. "Me, me, me a book." I returned; "good morning, Jemmy; so you will have a book today? well, keep it carefully." Suddenly turning aside he took the bread brought for his breakfast, and passing it with a hurried earnestness through the bars of his iron door— "Here's bread, a'nt you hungry?" Never may I forget the tone and grateful affectionate aspect of that poor idiot. How much might we do to bring back or restore the mind, if we but knew how to touch the instrument with a skilful hand! . . .

Sudbury. First week in September last I directed my way to the poor-farm there. Approaching, as I supposed, that place, all uncertainty vanished, as to which, of several dwellings in view, the course should be directed. The terrible screams and imprecations, impure language and amazing blasphemies, of a maniac, now, as often heretofore, indicated the place sought after. I know not how to proceed! the English language affords no combinations fit for describing the condition of the unhappy wretch there confined. In a stall, built under a woodshed on the road, was a naked man, defiled with filth, furiously tossing through the bars and about the cage, portions of straw (the only furnishing of his prison) already trampled to chaff. The mass of filth within, diffused wide abroad the most noisome stench. I have never witnessed paroxysms of madness so appalling; it seemed as if the ancient doctrine of the possession of demons was here illustrated.

I hastened to the house overwhelmed with horror. The mistress informed me that ten days since he had been brought from Worcester Hospital, where the town did not choose any longer to meet the expenses of maintaining him; that he had been "dreadful noisy and dangerous to go near," ever since; it was hard work to give him food at any rate, for what was not immediately dashed at those who carried it, was cast down upon the festering mass within. "He's a dreadful care; worse than all the people and work on the farm beside." Have you any other insane persons? "Yes; this man's sister has been crazy here for several years; she does nothing but take on about him; and may-be she'll grow as bad as he." I went into the adjoining room to see this unhappy creature; in a low chair, wearing an air of deepest despondence, sat a female no longer young; her hair fell uncombed upon her shoulders; her whole air revealed woe, unmitigated woe! She regarded me coldly and uneasily; I spoke a few words of sympathy and kindness; she fixed her gaze for a few moments steadily upon me, then grasping my hand, and bursting into a passionate flood of tears, repeatedly kissed it, exclaiming in a voice broken by sobs, "O, my poor brother, my poor brother; hark, hear him! hear him!" then relapsing into apathetic calmness, she neither spoke nor moved, but the tears again flowed fast, as I went away. I avoided passing the maniac's cage; but there, with strange curiosity and eager exclamations, were gathered, at a safe distance, the children of the establishment, little boys and girls, receiving their early lessons in hardness of heart and vice; but the demoralizing influences were not confined to children.

The same day revealed two scenes of extreme exposure and unjustifiable neglect, such as I could not have supposed the whole New-England States could furnish. . . .

Groton. A few rods removed from the poorhouse is a wooden building upon the road-side, constructed of heavy board and plank; it contains one room, unfurnished, except so far as a bundle of straw constitutes furnishing. There is no window, save an opening half the size of a sash, and closed by a board shutter; in one corner is some brick-work surrounding an iron stove, which in cold weather serves for warming the room. The occupant of this dreary abode is a young man, who has been declared incurably insane. He can move a measured distance in his prison; that is, so far as a strong, heavy chain, depending from an *iron collar which invests his neck*, permits. In fine weather, and it was pleasant when I was there in June last, the door is thrown open, at once giving admission to light and air, and affording some little variety to the solitary in watching the passers-by. But that portion of the year which allows of open doors is not the chiefest part; and it may be conceived, without drafting much on the imagination, what is the condition of one who, for days, and weeks, and months, sits in darkness and alone, without employment, without object. It may be supposed that paroxysms of frenzy are often exhibited, and that the tranquil state is rare in comparison with that which incites to violence. This I was told is the fact.

I may here remark that severe measures, in enforcing rule, have in many places been openly revealed. I have not seen chastisement administered by stripes, and in but few instances have I seen the *rods* and *whips*, but I have seen blows inflicted, both passionately and repeatedly.

I have been asked if I have investigated the causes of insanity? I have not; but I have been told that this most calamitous overthrow of reason, often is the result of a life of sin; it is sometimes, but rarely, added, they must take the consequences; they deserve no better care! Shall man be more just than God; he who causes his sun, and refreshing rains, and life-giving influence, to fall alike on the good and the evil? Is not the total wreck of reason, a state of distraction, and the loss of all that makes life cherished, a retribution sufficiently heavy, without adding to consequences so appalling, every indignity that can bring still lower the wretched sufferer? Have pity upon those who, while they were supposed to lie hid in secret sins, "have been scattered under *a dark veil of forgetfulness*; over whom is spread a heavy night, and who unto themselves are more grievous than the darkness." . . .

Bolton. Late in December, 1842; thermometer 4° above zero; visited the almshouse; neat and comfortable establishment; two insane women, one in the house associated with the family, the other *"out of doors."* The day following was expected a young man from Worcester Hospital, incurably insane; fears were expressed of finding him "dreadful hard to manage." I asked to see the subject who was "out of doors;" and following the mistress of the house through the deep snow, shuddering and benumbed by the piercing cold, several hundred yards, we came in rear of the barn to a small building, which might have afforded a degree of comfortable shelter, but it did not. About two thirds of the interior was filled with wood and peat; the other third was divided into two parts, one about six feet square contained a cylinder stove, in which was no fire, the rusty pipe seeming to threaten, in its decay, either suffocation by smoke, which by and by we nearly realized, or conflagration of the building, together with destruction of its poor crazy inmate. My companion uttered an exclamation at finding no fire, and busied herself to light one, while I explored, as the deficient light permitted, the cage which occupied the undescribed portion of the building. "Oh, I'm so cold, so cold," was uttered in plaintive tones by a woman within the cage; "oh, so cold, so cold!" And well might she be cold; the stout, hardy, driver of the sleigh had declared 'twas too hard for a man to stand the wind and snow that day, yet here was a woman caged and imprisoned without fire or clothes, not naked indeed, for one thin cotton garment partly covered her, and part of a blanket was gathered about the shoulders; there she stood, shivering in that dreary place, the grey locks falling in disorder about the face gave a wild expression to the pallid features; untended and comfortless, she might call aloud, none could hear; she might die, and there be none to close the eye. But death would have been a blessing here. "Well, you shall have a fire, Axey; I've been so busy getting ready for the funeral!" One of the paupers lay dead. "Oh, I want some clothes," rejoined the lunatic; "I'm so cold." "Well, Axey, you shall have some as soon as the children come from school; I've had so much to do." "I want to go out, do let me out!" "Yes, as soon as I get time," answered the respondent. "Why do you keep her here?" I asked, "she appears harmless and quiet." "Well, I mean to take her up to the house pretty soon; the people that used to have care here, kept her shut up all the year; but it *is* cold here, and we take her to the house in hard weather; the only danger is her running away; I've been meaning to, this good while." The poor creature listened eagerly, "oh, I won't run away, do take me out!" "Well, I will in a few days." Now the smoke from the kindling fire became so dense that a new anxiety struck the captive; "oh, I shall smother, I'm afraid; don't fill that up, I'm afraid." Pretty soon I moved to go away; "stop, did you walk?" "No." "Did you ride?" "Yes." "Do take me with you, do, I'm so cold. Do you know my sisters? they live in this town; I want to see them so much; do let me go!" and shivering with eagerness to get out, as with the biting cold, she rapidly tried the bars of the cage.

The mistress seemed a kind person; her tones and manner to

the lunatic were kind; but how difficult to unite all the cares of her household, and neglect none! Here was not wilful abuse, but great, very great, suffering through undesigned negligence. We need an Asylum for this class, the incurable, where conflicting duties shall not admit of such examples of privations and misery.

One is continually amazed at the tenacity of life in these persons. In conditions that wring the heart to behold, it is hard to comprehend that days rather than years should not conclude the measure of their griefs and miseries. Picture her condition! place yourselves in that dreary cage, remote from the inhabited dwelling, alone by day and by night, without fire, without clothes, *except when remembered;* without object or employment; weeks and months passing on in drear succession, not a blank, but with keen life to suffering; with kindred, but deserted by them; and you shall not lose the memory of that time when they loved you, and you in turn loved them, but now no act or voice of kindness makes sunshine in the heart. Has fancy realized this to you? It *may* be the state of some of those you cherish! Who shall be sure his own hearth-stone shall not be desolate? nay, who shall say his own mountain stands strong, his lamp of reason shall not go out in darkness! To how many has this become a heart-rending reality! If for selfish ends only, should not effectual Legislation here interpose? . . .

Newton. It was a cold morning in October last, that I visited the almshouse. The building itself is ill adapted for the purposes to which it is appropriated; the town, I understand, have in consideration a more advantageous location, and propose to erect more commodious dwellings. The mistress of the house informed me that they had several insane inmates, some of them very bad. In reply to my request to see them, she objected "that they were not fit—that they were not cleaned—that they were very crazy," &c. Urging my request more decidedly, she said they should be got ready, if I would wait. Still no order was given which would hasten my object. I renewed the subject, when, with manifest unwillingness, she called to a colored man, a cripple, who with several others of the poor were employed in the yard, to go and get a woman up—naming her. I waited some time at the kitchen door to see what all this was to produce. The man slowly proceeded to the remote part of the wood-shed where, part being divided from the open space, were two small rooms, in the outer of which he slept and lived, as I understood; there was his furni-

ture; and there his charge! Opening into this room only, was the
second, which was occupied by a woman not old, and furiously
mad: it contained a wooden bunk filled with filthy straw, the
room itself a counterpart to the lodging place; inexpressibly
disgusting and loathsome was all: but the inmate herself was even
more horribly repelling; she rushed out, as far as the chains
would allow, almost in a state of nudity, exposed to a dozen
persons, and vociferating at the top of her voice; pouring forth
such a flood of indecent language as might corrupt even Newgate.
I entreated the man, who still was there, to go out and close the
door. He refused; that was *his place*! Sick, horror-struck, and
almost incapable of retreating, I gained the outward air, and
hastened to see the other subject, to remove from a scene so outraging all decency and humanity. In the apartment over that last
described was a crazy man, I was told. I ascended the stairs in
the wood-shed, and passing through a small room stood at the
entrance of the one occupied; occupied with what? The furniture
was a wooden box or bunk containing straw, and something I
was told was a man, I could not tell, as likely it might have been
a wild animal, half buried in the offensive mass that made his
bed; his countenance concealed by long tangled hair and un-
shorn beard. He lay sleeping. Filth, neglect and misery reigned
there. I begged he might not be roused. If sleep could visit a
wretch so forlorn, how merciless to break the slumber! Protruding from the foot of the box was ———, nay, it could not be the
feet; yet from these stumps, these maimed members were swinging chains, fastened to the side of the building. I descended; the
master of the house briefly stated the history of these two victims
of wretchedness. The old man had been crazy above twenty
years. As, till within a late period, the town had owned no farm
for the poor, this man with others had been annually put up at
auction. I hope there is nothing offensive in the idea of these
annual sales of old men and women, the sick, the infirm, and the
helpless, the middle-aged and children; why should we not *sell*
people as well as otherwise blot out human rights, it is only being
consistent, surely not worse than chaining and caging naked
Lunatics upon public roads, or burying them in closets and
cellars? But, as I was saying, the crazy man was annually sold to
some new master, and a few winters since, being kept in an out-
house, the people within being warmed and clothed, "did not
reckon how cold it was," and so his feet froze. Were chains now

the more necessary? he cannot run. But he might *crawl* forth, and in his transports of frenzy "do some damage."

That young woman; her lot is most appalling! who shall dare describe it! who shall have courage or hardihood to write her history? That young woman was the child of respectable, hard-working parents. The girl became insane; the father, a farmer with small means, from a narrow income had placed her at the State Hospital. There, said my informer, she remained as long as he could by any means pay her expenses. Then, then only, he resigned her to the care of the town, to those who are, in the eye of the law, the guardians of the poor and needy; she was placed with the other town-paupers, and given in charge to a man. I assert boldly, as truly, that I have given but a *faint representation* of what she was, and what was her condition as I saw her last autumn. Written language is weak to declare it.

Could we in fancy place ourselves in the situation of some of these poor wretches, bereft of reason, deserted of friends, hopeless; troubles without, and more dreary troubles within, overwhelming the wreck of the mind as "a wide breaking in of the waters,"—how should we, as the terrible illusion was cast off, not only offer the thank-offering of prayer, that so mighty a destruction had not overwhelmed our mental nature, but as an offering more acceptable devote ourselves to alleviate that state from which we are so mercifully spared.

It may not appear much more credible than the fact above stated, that a few months since, a young woman in a state of complete insanity, was confined entirely naked in a pen or stall in a barn; there, unfurnished with clothes, without bed, and without fire, she was left—but not alone; profligate men and idle boys had access to the den, whenever curiosity or vulgarity prompted. She is now removed into the house with other paupers; and for this humanizing benefit she was indebted to the remonstrances, in the first instance, *of an insane man!*

Another town now owns a poorhouse, which I visited, and am glad to testify to the present comfortable state of the inmates; but there the only provision the house affords for an insane person, should one, as is not improbable, be conveyed there, is a closet in the cellar, formed by the arch upon which the chimney rests; this has a close door, not only securing the prisoner, but excluding what of light and pure air might else find admission.

Abuses assuredly cannot always or altogether be guarded

against; but if in the civil and social relations all shall have "done what they could," no ampler justification will be demanded at the Great Tribunal.

Of the dangers and mischiefs sometimes following the location of insane persons in our almhouses, I will record but one more example. In Worcester, has for several years resided a young woman, a lunatic pauper of decent life and respectable family. I have seen her as she usually appeared, listless and silent, almost or quite sunk into a state of dementia, sitting one amidst the family, "but not of them." A few weeks since, revisiting that almshouse, judge my horror and amazement to see her negligently bearing in her arms a young infant, of which I was told she was the unconscious parent! Who was the father, none could or would declare. Disqualified for the performance of maternal cares and duties, regarding the helpless little creature with a perplexed, or indifferent gaze, she sat a silent, but O how eloquent, a pleader for the protection of others of her neglected and outraged sex! Details of that black story would not strengthen the cause; needs it a weightier plea, than the sight of that forlorn creature and her wailing infant? Poor little child, more than orphan from birth, in this unfriendly world! a demented Mother—a Father, on whom the sun might blush or refuse to shine!

Men of Massachusetts, I beg, I implore, I demand, pity and protection, for these of my suffering, outraged sex!—Fathers, Husbands, Brothers, I would supplicate you for this boon——but what do I say? I dishonor you, divest you at once of Christianity and humanity—does this appeal imply distrust. If it comes burthened with a doubt of your righteousness in this Legislation, then blot it out; while I declare confidence in your honor, not less than your humanity. Here you will put away the cold, calculating spirit of selfishness and self-seeking; lay off the armor of local strife and political opposition; here and now, for once, forgetful of the earthly and perishable, come up to these halls and consecrate them with one heart and one mind to works of righteousness and just judgment. Become the benefactors of your race, the just guardians of the solemn rights you hold in trust. Raise up the fallen; succor the desolate; restore the outcast; defend the helpless; and for your eternal and great reward, receive the benediction. . . . "Well done, good and faithful servants, become rulers over many things!"

1843

The Death of Pain

JAMES THOMAS FLEXNER

Down all the long centuries of history whenever a knife cut living flesh the result was agony. Then suddenly, within four years, a magic sleep was discovered two separate times on a new continent, once by a rural Georgia practitioner in his twenties, and once by a dentist not yet out of Harvard Medical School.

A strange story this. The story of a discovery waiting for half a century almost found, a discovery of overwhelming importance knocking continually at the doors of the scientific great, begging to be taken in, only to be turned away until at last, like the angel of an old fable, it knocked at the humbler doorways of the inconspicuous and found a home. And astoundingly this great boon to mankind was a scourge to its inventors; of the four men who claimed the discovery in the great ether controversy that raged during the last half of the nineteenth century, two died hopelessly mad, one by his own hand, and a third starved, had a series of nervous breakdowns, and was finally killed by a stroke due to the pamphlet of one of his opponents. Only the fourth lived to an old age, and even he was embittered by a sense of injustice.

Before the discovery of anaesthesia, even as simple an operation as setting a dislocated leg turned the operating-room into a medieval torture chamber. The patient was stretched on a rack, his body attached to one set of pulleys, the offending leg to another, while muscular assistants tugged with all their force. As the heavy ropes inched tighter, the patient's muscles stretched until the sinews seemed about to tear. Despite all that opiates could do, perspiration of agony started out on his forehead. No longer able to stifle his screams, he struggled convulsively, vainly trying to escape from the tension that was inexorable as death. Surely the agony must stop now, surely no human being would submit another to such torture, but the surgeon stands helplessly by, for a long distance still intervenes between the ball of the leg-bone and its socket. The pull becomes stronger, the heavy men sweating at the ropes, until the pain passes human endurance, and

the patient loses consciousness. Then the surgeon, who has been
watching with a stern face of unavailing pity, springs into action.
Taking advantage of the relaxation insensibility brings, he dexterously twists the head of the bone into its socket. Finally the
torn and tortured sufferer is carried to his bed to recover from
the operation as best he may. . . .

The first step towards modern anaesthesia, and one that covered almost the whole distance, was made by Sir Humphrey Davy
during his experiments with laughing gas. In 1799 he wrote: "As
nitrous oxide in its extensive operation seems capable of destroying physical pain, it may probably be used with advantage in
surgical operations in which no great effusion of blood takes
place." It is difficult to understand how this suggestion, so succinctly put in a book often consulted by men of science, could
remain unacted upon for forty-three years. Yet such was the
case. . . .

Besides pointing out the possible anaesthetic qualities of laughing gas, Sir Humphrey Davy showed that its inhalation produced
a most delightful drunkenness. The second part of his lecture was
not forgotten. It became a routine diversion in medical schools
to inhale the gas, have wonderful visions, and, when the effect
wore off, laugh at the ridiculous antics of your friends who were
still under the influence. Immediately the Yankee genius found
a way to turn the amusing properties of the gas to profit. Those
were the palmy days of traveling showmen, for the United States
was fringed with an ever-widening fan of pioneers whose settlements offered them no amusements whatsoever. Soon there set
out over the land a little horde of chemical lecturers . . . In the
winter of 1841, such a "Lyceum lecturer" approached Jefferson,
Georgia. . . .

That night the gayer young men of the town, most of whom
went to the village academy, gathered as was their custom in the
office of the local practitioner, Dr. Crawford W. Long. The
physician was a tall and handsome young man of twenty-six, with
a high forehead, blue eyes, and a large aquiline nose; he was the
center of every frolic and a terror with the young ladies. Since
he had been attending a patient in the country, he had not known
of the lecturer's visit, and he was heartbroken to hear what he
had missed . . . His friends described to him how the showman
had harangued his audience from the tail of his cart and concluded
his act by first inhaling laughing gas himself and then requesting
the townspeople to do so. . . .

"You're supposed to be a doctor and know something about chemistry," Long's friends concluded. "Make us some gas and we'll go on a fine tear."

While a medical student in Philadelphia, Long had attended a chemical lecture during which the more up-to-date urban show-man had induced drunkenness not with laughing gas but with ether . . . He did not have any laughing gas, he explained to his friends in Jefferson, but he knew that ether would do just as well. Reaching into the cupboard, he brought out a bottle he always kept on hand. Ether was a common drug used for nervous ailments in minute quantities because it tasted so strong.

"The company," he told the Georgia State Medical Society many years later, "were anxious to witness its effects, the ether was introduced, and all present in turn inhaled. They were so much pleased with its effects that they afterwards frequently used it and induced others to do the same, and the practice soon became quite fashionable in the county and some of the contiguous counties. On numerous occasions I inhaled ether for its exhilarating properties." It is amusing to see peering from behind these respectable words the laughing face of a high old time. . . .

During the ether jags at his office in Jefferson, [he] was the life of the party, but at the same time he was using his eyes and his mind. He noticed that, when his friends were intoxicated, they received without wincing falls and blows that should have produced pain. When he asked them about it afterwards, they assured him they had felt nothing. Sometimes he found bruises on his own body that he could not remember having received. All this seemed strange to him. He wondered about it, and one day he made the inference that thousands in the same situation had never made; he saw that ether was the death of pain.

At about this time James Venables, a dashing lad of twenty-one who went to the village academy and was very fond of inhaling ether, began to be bothered by two little tumors on the back of his neck. He was an intimate of Long's circle, and one evening, as that senate of good fellows sported in the doctor's office, he complained of his affliction. After a quick examination, Long said that the tumors would have to be cut out, and when Venables blanched at this statement, reached for his knife and jokingly offered to cut them out at once. But the patient made excuses— he did not feel very well that day—and for a long time afterwards he procrastinated until the boys teased him about being afraid.

Early on the morning of March 30, 1842, before the village academy opened, Long called on his friend. He had lain awake all night, worrying about the possibility of using ether to stop pain, and finally he had decided to make the test. Excitedly he suggested that if Venables would inhale the gas while the tumors were being removed, he would probably not be hurt. The idea was a strange one, but the doctor was able to back it up with so many incidents Venables remembered, when their friends had fallen and felt nothing, that he agreed at last to let Long try it on one tumor. The operation was scheduled for that afternoon as soon as school was over. Several of Venables' classmates begged to be allowed to see the experiment, and Long, who was always good-natured, agreed, but he insisted that the principal of the academy be invited as well to lend the proceedings an air of respectability. . . .

After the village academy let out that March afternoon, three of the scholars accompanied their principal down the main street of the little town. . . .

The office into which Long showed his friends had no resemblance to the doctor's offices of today. There was a table, a few hard chairs, and a sofa on which young Venables nervously lay down. Long reached for the bottle which had been their companion in so many sprees, poured ether on a towel as he had done a hundred times, but this time his hand must have trembled a little for he realized that he was making an important experiment. The spectators, gathered in a knot at the back of the room, watched in frowning attention as with one hand he held the towel over his patient's mouth and nose, permitting him to breathe a little air as well as the drug, while with the other hand he felt his pulse. From time to time he pricked his friend with a pin, and when Venables did not feel the prick, he reached for his knife and removed the tumor. The entire operation took about five minutes. When the towel was removed from his face, Venables, after a moment of suspense, returned satisfactorily to life; he had to be shown the tumor to be convinced it was out. The relaxed tension set everybody joking and laughing. They discussed the operation for a while, going over it point by point as you might an exciting baseball game, and then went home to gossip with their families and friends about what had happened. . . .

If Long had immediately sent an account of his experiment to a medical journal and if the editor had condescended to publish so unorthodox and revolutionary a claim coming from an insignificant yokel in his twenties, the great ether war would never have been waged, for there could have been no doubt that Crawford W. Long was the discoverer. But this young man, who was so dashing with the girls, was a cautious and careful scientist. He had studied under Dr. George B. Wood, that enemy of premature publication, and he realized that an experiment done only once and without controls of any sort proves very little.

He soon learnt the need of certain proof. Although the youngsters from the Jefferson Academy and many of the simple people believed what he had done, the more distinguished doctors of the region, who had years and experience on their side, thought his claims ridiculous and were certain that he would kill a patient sooner or later. Their pompous pronouncements terrified even the people who had at first believed, until in a few months Long was changed from a hero into an object of terror. When he rode, jauntily as ever, through the lanes of Georgia that were now alive with spring, farm children scuttled indoors at his approach, while pious old crones reached for the Bible to protect themselves. Even the farmers working in the fields did not wave back when he waved. Word had gone round that this handsome, seemingly innocent young man could put people to sleep and carve them· without their knowledge. Grave elders called on Long to warn him to stop his reckless madness before it was too late; they pointed out that if one of his patients died under ether he might be lynched. Sick people became afraid to come to him, and his practice dwindled. . . .

Long showed an inquiring spirit from the very first. When he removed Venable's second tumor, he experimented by stopping the ether before he began cutting, for he believed that, if ether were to be used in lengthy operations, it might be dangerous for the patient to continue inhaling the whole time. Since his friend's tumor had formed adhesions to the adjoining parts, the excision took a good' many minutes, and towards the end, Venables showed slight signs of suffering. "Since that time," Long told the Georgie State Medical Society, "I have invariably desired patients, when practicable, to continue the inhalation during the time of the operation."

Faced with a rising gale of criticism, Long reacted in the manner of a true scientist; he tried to find possible flaws in his proof that ether killed pain. Perhaps Venables' nerves had been deadened not by ether but by suggestion. The medical great were at that time busily squabbling as to whether patients could be thrown into hypnotic trances before operations and thus made insensible; perhaps Long had inadvertently mesmerized his friend. The way to eliminate this possibility, he decided, was to use ether on many people, since not all individuals could be mesmerized.

It could also be argued, he knew, that a few persons were immune to pain and that his patients were among these. To prove that this was not the explanation, when he amputated two fingers from a Negro boy, he did one operation with ether and one without. The poor child slept satisfyingly under the drug and screamed satisfyingly when deprived of it. Some time later, Long cut three tumors from the same patient in one day, the second with ether, the first and third without, and he was delighted to find that the pain came only when he expected it. . . .

One winter evening four and a half years after he had operated on Venables, Long rode up to his house after a busy day. He dismounted wearily and handed his horse's reins to the colored boy. Soon he was settled before the fire, slippers on feet that ached from the riding boots. He allowed his thoughts to wander nebulous as the nebulous flicker of flame until a prick of conscience arose in the back of his mind and fought forward against the inertia of exhausted nerves. His spare hours were few and he was behind on his reading of the *Medical Examiner*, the journal that kept him up to date. Sighing, he found the December number and returned to the fire, but he could hardly keep his tired mind on the words he read. Suddenly he sat upright. His eyes had struck the following headline: "Insensibility during Surgical Operations Produced by Inhalation."

The article said that "a certain Dr. Morton, a practicing dentist in Boston," had secured a patent for a substance which he asserted would prevent pain. The preparation, it was reported, smelt of ether and was probably an ethereal solution of some narcotic substance. . . .

In great excitement Long called his wife, showed her the article, and then sat down to compose a letter to the editor of the *Medical Examiner*, saying that ether was enough by itself to produce insensibility, and that he had used it for several years. But he had hardly written a few lines when there was a knock on the door, and a frantic man rushed in, crying that his wife was "taken very bad" and begging the doctor to come at once.

Although as his horse stumbled over frozen mud in a hundred

country lanes he composed his letter to the editor again and again
in his mind, seeing the words against bare trees, gray hills, and
deserted stubbly fields; although as he knocked at the ramshackle
doors of distant farms strong phrases pounded through his mind
and struggled with the swell of heat as the doors opened; although he thought of little else for the next four or five days, he
could not find a minute to write another word. And then the
postman brought the January *Medical Examiner*.

This issue gave an entirely different picture. The substance
used was announced as pure ether and its usefulness accepted as
a fact. There was even an indignant communication saying that
Morton's discovery had been anticipated by another dentist named
Wells. Long must have noticed that Wells' first experiment was
two years after his own, yet he merely tore up the beginning of
his letter; there was no further need to point out that pure
ether, without any admixture of narcotics, sufficed to deaden pain.
Although more than ever there was need to claim the credit
for the discovery if he were not to be cheated of his due, he did
nothing about bringing his experiments before the world during
three more years.

Many scholars have speculated on the reason for Long's delay.
They have usually regarded as ridiculous his statement that he
was waiting to see if some other doctor would make a claim
even prior to his, but this is not so ridiculous as it may seem. It
must have been very difficult for a simple country practitioner
only thirty-one years old to believe as he went his routine
rounds, purging babies and delivering farmers' wives, that he
really was a great man, that a simple experiment which had grown
naturally from his carousals with the gay boys of the village could
revolutionize the medical world. . . .

But was his cause just; was he really the discoverer of anaesthesia? Such distinguished physicians as Dr. William H. Welch
and Sir William Osler say: "No." Although they admit that Long
was the first man to use ether as an anaesthetic, they insist that
the credit for the discovery should go to William Thomas Green
Morton, the Boston dentist.

Almost three years after Long's first operation on Venables,
an obscure dentist in Hartford, Connecticut, sat in his office reading the *Hartford Courant*. Dr. Horace Wells was a young man
of twenty-nine, with a round, soft, handsome face and bushy

side-whiskers. Turning the pages idly, he reached the following advertisement:

"A grand exhibition of the effects produced by inhaling NITROUS OXIDE, EXHILARATING, OR LAUGHING GAS! will be given at Union Hall this (Tuesday) evening, December 10, 1844. . . ."

Dr. Wells called to his wife and suggested that they go to the show. Had he foreseen the future, perhaps he would have stayed at home, for this seemingly innocent evening's entertainment brought him not only immortality, but madness, and prison, and death at last by his own hand.

When night came he was sitting next his wife in Union Hall. Having delivered a short lecture on laughing gas, Dr. Gardner Q. Colton administered some to himself from a rubber bag through a wooden faucet similar to those used on cider barrels. Then he declaimed most wonderfully, his words glowing in the air. Finally he stopped short, put his hand to his head, and announced solemnly: "The effect is now nearly gone."

Dr. Colton invited volunteers to come on the stage, and Wells filed up with the others. After watching those before him go through ridiculous antics, he sniffed the gas himself and behaved rather foolishly, his wife thought. He had returned to his seat before Sam Cooley inhaled from the spigot. The brawny drug clerk broke into a cross between an Irish jig and a Hopi war dance, but when he noticed that a little man in the front row was laughing at him, his high spirits turned into fury. Leaping from the stage, he made for the man, who fled in terror. Although smaller than Cooley, the fugitive was fast and shifty; it was a good race that brought the audience to its feet. For an instant, the pursued was cornered at the end of the hall, but he doubled like a rabbit, vaulted a settee, and sprinted down the center aisle. When Cooley struck his leg in following over the hurdle, he did not seem to notice. On the straight stretch, he almost over-hauled his quarry and his hands reached out to clutch; then the gas-madness left him. He stopped, looked about him with a foolish smile, and amid shouts of applause slid into a seat near Wells. Presently the dentist saw him roll up one of his trousers and gaze in a puzzled way at the bloody leg which had struck the settee.

Wells used to tell in later years how he fidgeted on the edge of his chair until the lecture was over, and then rushed to

Cooley. "How did you hurt your leg, Sam?" he asked, trying
to hold his voice calm, not to seem excited.

When Cooley told him that he did not know, that he must have
hit his shin against something while under the influence of the
gas but had felt nothing, Wells turned and tried to charge through
the crowd to the stage. Would these people never get out of the
way? Reaching Dr. Colton at last, he talked so excitedly that
the lecturer could not understand what this young man with
the flushed face wanted. But at last Wells managed to make Dr.
Colton agree to give him gas the next morning when he was to
have a tooth pulled. . . .

The next·morning Dr. Colton administered gas to him while
a fellow-dentist pulled a deeply rooted molar. Wells awoke with
his famous remark: "A new era in tooth-pulling!"

There was no hesitancy in Wells's nature; he went at things
slapdash, in a rush of inspiration, and if they did not pan out
immediately he was likely to drop them altogether. His single
experiment having been successful, he at once began the manufacture of laughing gas, and in a short time he had administered
it to fifteen patients, but only with varying success. Since the
gas worked sometimes, he did not bother to discover why it did
not work always. When Dr. E. E. Marcy suggested to him that
ether might be preferable to gas since it was easier to handle and
had the same exhilarating effect, he allowed himself to be put off
by his next informant who told him that it was unpleasant to
take and less safe.

Still in the full tide of enthusiasm, he hurried to Boston and
through Dr. William Thomas Green Morton, a former dental
partner who was now studying medicine, arranged to give a
demonstration of painless tooth-pulling before one of the classes
of the famous surgeon, Dr. John Collins Warren, at the Massachusetts General Hospital. Unfortunately, Wells had been taught
to give only the exhilarating dose of gas Dr. Colton used in his
lectures; he had never taken the time to find out that more was
needed to produce certain anaesthesia. Since on this occasion he
failed to administer enough, the patient not only felt pain but
was very vocal about it. His agonized screams filled the lecture
hall. The students laughed and jeered at the "humbug" who had
promised not to hurt him, and Wells returned to Hartford as
precipitously as he had come, convinced there was nothing to the
great discovery he had been so enthusiastic about a few hours

before. Dropping all interest in laughing gas, he absorbed himself in arranging a panórama of natural history for the city hall in Hartford, and in selling patented shower baths. However, the excitement of great hope followed by abject failure brought on an illness from which he never completely recovered.

Luck had been against him. When Wells administered his gas, it worked perfectly half the time; had it only worked the day he demonstrated before Dr. Warren's class, he would undoubtedly have been hailed as the discoverer of anaesthesia for the same reasons Morton was. As it happened, Wells's demonstration merely fertilized the mind of the man who was to be his triumphant rival.

Morton had been born at Charlton, Massachusetts, on August 9, 1819, the son of a well-to-do farmer and shopkeeper. So great was the father's ambition for his son that, when William was only eight, he sold one farm and moved to another in order to be nearer the village school. From the first the boy wanted to be a doctor; he dosed his playmates with pills made of bread and leaves. But after he had almost killed his baby sister by pushing some weird compound down her throat as she lay asleep in her cradle, his parents were forced to disbar their infant practitioner for malpractice. . . .

Morton . . . resolved to become a dentist. During the first half of the nineteenth century, the care of teeth was a very backward art. Every physician had to be a dentist too, but he was expected to do no more than pull teeth and fit in an occasional set of false ones if he could make or procure them. Although in the larger cities a few men specialized in dentistry, most of them were ignorant charlatans who knew only what they had been able to learn by their own efforts. When they pulled teeth, for instance, they were satisfied to twist off the crown and leave the roots to fester. . . .

After practicing in a small town for two years, Morton formed a partnership with Wells and set up an office in Boston. Now a city practitioner, he soon became conscious of ignorance . . . he paid Dr. N. C. Keep five hundred dollars for the use of his laboratory. The young man had the practical gift which is a part of the American genius; although he knew no mechanics and practically no medicine, he soon worked out a superior way of putting in false teeth. He had learnt the lesson of secretiveness from his colleagues, and it never occurred to him, as it would

have to a physician, that he should give his discovery to the
world. Instead, he told Wells that they would no longer have
difficulty getting patients since they now had their own specialty
to offer.

Jubilantly the two young partners advertised their new
method in the papers, promising your money back if you were
not satisfied, and waited for a rush of business. Sure enough,
hundreds of people began to shuffle up their stairs that had been
silent so long, but most of them shuffled down again in a few
minutes. Morton's system required the removal of the evil-
smelling roots that had been left in patients' jaws by incompetent
dentists, and the process was so painful that practically no one
would submit to it. Even the few who remained had to be
treated at a low price that left no profit. Wells, incapable of
waiting for anything, resigned from the partnership in disappointment and returned to his native Hartford.

However, this failure brought home to both young men
what a vast fortune could be made by alleviating pain. We have
seen the slapdash rush of inspiration by which Wells sought to
reach this end; Morton's was a more roundabout way . . . He
tried every method he could think of. He got some of his
patients drunk on brandy, and when that failed, on champagne;
others he drugged with opium in vast doses. . . .

Like so many men who are afraid to face the world alone,
Morton fell in love early with a girl even younger than he.
Elizabeth Whitman was only sixteen and a student in Miss Porter's
school at Farmington, Connecticut. During the year before her
graduation, she remembered, "Dr. Morton had paid me attentions
which were not well received by my family, he being regarded
as a poor young man with an undesirable profession. I thought
him very handsome, however, and he was very much in love
with me, coming regularly from Boston to visit me."

By promising to give up dentistry and become a doctor, he
finally won the consent of Miss Whitman's parents. . . .

In 1843 he married, but he could not forget his scientific researches even on his honeymoon. He brought a skeleton along
in a bag and sometimes when his bride awoke on the pillow
next to his she discovered that he had the bones out and was
busily studying anatomy. For Morton had decided that he must
know more about the human body before he could deaden pain.

He had apprenticed himself to a physician who was also a distinguished chemist, Dr. Charles T. Jackson.

Jackson told him what was at the time common knowledge, that ether applied to the outside of a sore tooth lessens sensitivity. Having tried it with reasonable success, Morton wondered how the effects of the drug could be made more general. Perhaps he could have the patient take a bath in it, but that, he had to admit, was a little impracticable. When Jackson said that riotous medical students inhaled ether for their amusement, Morton rushed to the library to discover what effect such inhalation had. He was deeply disappointed to read that ether administered in large enough quantities to produce stupefaction was dangerous to human life. Of course, the books might be wrong, but Morton could think of no experiment to prove them so, that might not also prove fatal to the experimenter. For hours he sat in his laboratory with the ether bottle beside him, staring at the colorless liquid and wondering. Once he had a sudden paroxysm of courage. Quickly, before he had time to change his mind, he poured a few drops in his handkerchief. His arm trembled convulsively as he lifted the handkerchief to his nose. But the amount of ether he had dared inhale was so small that the only result was a fiendish headache. . . .

The next winter he matriculated at the Harvard Medical School, and his dental practice occupied all the time he could spare from his studies. He became so famous for mechanical ingenuity that he was in demand as a plastic surgeon too . . . Morton also established a factory where false teeth were manufactured by the mass-production method Henry Ford was to find so useful later on. Dr. Rice tells us that the receipts from this as well as his practice and his private dental pupils came as high as $20,000 a year.

Early in 1845 he sponsored the demonstration of laughing gas Wells had rushed up from Hartford to give. Pitilessly ragged concerning that disastrous failure by his fellow-students at the Harvard Medical School, the lanky dentist postponed his experiments on the inhalation of ether for yet another year.

While studying medicine, Morton taught dentistry. In the spring of 1846, Thomas R. Spear, Jr., a gay lad who had become one of his apprentices, told him how much he had enjoyed getting drunk on ether at Lexington Academy. Excitedly, Morton asked Spear innumerable questions, repeating them over and over to make sure he had heard aright.

After several sleepless nights, Morton grimly set out for his
country place at West Needham. Under one arm he carried a
glass bell-jar, under the other a bottle of ether. His heart failed
him when the family spaniel greeted him with a wagging tail
and yelps of delight. But he told himself that science was important and that the discovery would make him rich. Taking
two witnesses with him, he led the trusting beast far from the
house to the banks of a deserted lake. The dog cringed but submitted when Morton put his head in the bell-jar that had ether
in the bottom. Instantly, he wilted down in his master's hands.
With a beating heart of dread, Morton removed the jar and
waited to see if his pet would revive. He pinched and poked the
dog to no purpose. For three awful minutes the animal lay there
breathing convulsively; then he emitted an ear-splitting yelp
and with one bound leapt ten feet into the water, or so it seemed
to Morton's excited imagination. . . .

As Morton approached step by step nearer his goal, a new
apprehension assailed him; perhaps someone would guess what
he was doing and beat him to the discovery. From now on, all
his subtlety was employed to avoid such a mishap. Afraid that
his own druggist would suspect if he asked him for any more
ether, he sent his apprentices across the town to purchase a demi-
john under an assumed name. . . .

Morton summoned all his eloquence to persuade his pupils
to inhale the ether themselves. Spear finally agreed, but instead of
going to sleep as the spaniel had done, he became pugnacious and
offered to fight the company. He had to be held down in his
chair. However, when he came to, he "expressed himself delighted
with his sensations." Hearing what fun it was, the other student
agreed to inhale, but only if the sportive Spear were banished
from the room; he wanted no practical jokes. The ether also made
him violent. Later Morton blamed these results on impurities in
the drug, but at the moment he was discouraged, telling his
partner that he "feared there was so much difference in the
qualities of ether that in so delicate a matter there would be great
difficulty in bringing about any generally useful and reliable results." His nervousness affected his companions; when he offered
Spear five dollars to inhale again, the young man, who had gone
on ether jags often and thought them pleasant, hesitated, consulted his family, and finally refused to take the risk.

Disconsolate, Morton fled the hot weather to the country, but in a month he was back in town with a new idea. Thinking that ether might work better if inhaled through some apparatus, he determined to borrow the India rubber bag from which Jackson administered laughing gas. And perhaps his preceptor might be able to suggest some appliance that would be still better. Morton realized that consulting him was a dangerous business; he knew that Jackson had publicly claimed the discovery of the telegraph because once in a conversation with Morse he had given the real inventor some hints upon which he himself had never acted. However, Morton was sure that he was wily enough to get the information he wanted without letting Jackson know why he wanted it.

Although no two witnesses agree concerning what happened when Morton called on his preceptor, by comparing conflicting stories we may reconstruct the scene with reasonable accuracy. Wrapping subtlety around him like a conspirator's cloak, Morton asked, in as bored a voice as he could affect, for the gas bag. After he had taken it from the closet, Jackson laughingly remarked: "Well, doctor, you seem to be all equipped minus the gas."

Morton managed to laugh too and, his face alternately red and white, said there would be no need of having any gas if the person whose tooth he pulled was made to believe there was gas in the bag. With too much detail and emphasis, he told a long story of a man who died because he was made to believe he was bleeding to death, while in reality it was nothing but water that trickled over his leg.

"You'd better not try any trick like that," Dr. Jackson said, "or you'll be set down as a greater humbug than poor Wells was with his nitrous oxide." And then, horror of horrors, he suggested the use of sulphuric ether.

"Sulphuric ether?" cried Morton. "What is it? Is it a gas? Show it to me." The two medical students who were listening to the conversation filed in their memories Morton's admission that he had never heard of ether until Jackson told him of it.

The subject having been brought up, Morton inquired about the different forms of the drug, a subject he had never understood, and learnt that highly rectified sulphuric ether was the kind to use. Saying he had something better than a gas bag for the inhalation of ether, Jackson gave his pupil a flask with a tube inserted in it.

Morton left the laboratory in an agony of apprehension; he had let Jackson get so near the truth he was afraid his preceptor would take the final step before he did. He hurried into a drug store, bought highly rectified sulphuric ether, and ran home. Desperation gave him the courage that for almost two years he had lacked.

"I procured the ether from Burnett's," he wrote, "and taking the tube and flask, I shut myself up in my room, seated myself in the operating-chair, and commenced inhaling. I found the ether so strong that it partially suffocated me, but produced no desired effect. I then saturated my handkerchief and inhaled from that. I looked at my watch and soon lost consciousness. As I recovered I felt a numbness in my limbs, with a sensation like nightmare, and would have given the world for someone to come and arouse me. I thought for a moment I should die in that state, and the world would only pity and ridicule my folly. At length I felt a slight tingling in the end of my third finger, and made an effort to touch it with my thumb, but without success. At a second effort, I touched it, but there seemed to be no sensation. I gradually raised my arm and pinched my thigh, but I could see that sensation was imperfect. I attempted to rise from my chair, but fell back. Gradually I regained power over my limbs and full consciousness. I immediately looked at my watch and found that I had been insensible between seven and eight minutes."

Morton rushed out into his office screaming: "I've found it! I've found it!" He danced round the room with explosive joy, laughing, slapping his pupils on the back. All his doubts and hesitations were destroyed at last. Eagerly he waited for some patient to come on whom he might demonstrate his discovery.

Towards evening fate sent him Eben Frost, a burly young man with a very swollen face whose bicuspid pained him terribly. He explained that he had postponed for days coming to the dentist because he was afraid pulling the tooth would pain him even more. He blanched at the sight of the doctor's instruments and he begged to be mesmerized so he would feel nothing.

Telling Frost he knew a better trick than mesmerism, Morton poured some colorless liquid on a handkerchief. "Just breathe this."

Frost struggled against the heavy drug and then lay still. With a trembling hand his partner held the lamp while Morton reached into the patient's mouth and pulled the tooth. During the painful operation, Frost did not stir. That was all right, but after the handkerchief was removed he did not stir either. The two men leaned over him, one with the lamp in his hand and the other still clutching the bloody tooth. Was Frost asleep or in a fatal coma? Silence descended in choking waves, time stood still as the two men leaned over their victim, motionless as he. They were drawn upright by a groan; was it a death rattle or the return of life? For a moment the dentists waited in heightened anxiety, and then the limp man began to swear. Never had profanity sounded so grateful to human ears. Morton and his partner gazed at Frost with the delighted stare of lovers as he spat blood and awoke to see his tooth lying on the floor.

There was a general jubilation. The patient remained with the doctors, repeating over and over for their enchanted ears the tale of how he had felt nothing until he came alive to see his tooth lying on the floor. Before he left, Morton carefully made him sign an affidavit attesting what had happened. . . .

Morton asked the same Dr. Warren who had permitted Wells to demonstrate laughing gas whether he might not administer his secret preparation during a surgical operation at the Massachusetts General Hospital. That Dr. Warren considered this proposal without first determining the nature of the substance to be used, seems remarkably courageous if not foolhardy . . . In any case, after ten days of suspense Morton received a letter inviting him "to be present on Friday morning at ten o'clock to administer to a patient who is then to be operated upon the preparation which you have invented to diminish the sensibility to pain." As the day approached, Morton's old apprehensions descended upon him with redoubled force; they have been described by Dr. Rice, who wrote his biography of Morton under his subject's critical eye.

Morton had learnt that when he administered ether the effects were not uniform, and he realized that, if Dr. Warren's patient got drunk and violent, he would be laughed out of the amphitheater as Wells had been; he would become a public fool for all Boston to point at. . . . He sped out to ask Dr. A. A. Gould, the distinguished naturalist, if he could think of a better apparatus with which to administer the drug. Although Dr. Gould obligingly sketched an appliance with valves to keep the patient from breathing back into the globe, he advised against the use of anything untried during the crucial experiment. But Morton's nerves cried for action; he took the sketch to an instrument-maker.

When the hour of the experiment approached, the new apparatus was still uncompleted. In an agony of apprehension, Morton stood over the instrument-maker, pleading, suggesting, getting in the way. Finally he snatched the appliance from the man's hands and started to run towards the hospital. When he had covered only a few blocks, he remembered that he wanted to take Frost with him to testify, if worst came to worst, that he had succeeded before. Turning, he sprinted towards Frost's house.

In the meantime, a large audience awaited him in the amphitheater of the Massachusetts General Hospital. Boston's most distinguished surgeons sat in the front seats; behind them rows of medical students stretched to where the mummies and skeletons of the medical museum reposed in glass cases against the wall. At the dot of ten, the time when the demonstration was supposed to start, a young man of twenty was brought in and placed on the operating-table. Then Dr. Warren arose, clad in all the majesty of years of fame, to announce that a "test of some preparation was to be made for which the astonishing claim had been made that it would render the person operated upon free from pain." There was a sound of incredulous whispering which grew louder as Dr. Warren stood there scowling, swinging his watch around on its gold chain, impatiently eyeing the door for Morton to appear.

After fifteen minutes, Dr. Warren put his watch back in his pocket with a determined gesture. "As Dr. Morton has not arrived," witnesses remember that he said, "I presume he is otherwise engaged." The tension relaxed in a derisive laugh, and Dr. Warren ordered that the patient be prepared for the operation. Just as he picked up his knife, there was a sound of tumultuous footsteps in the hall. Morton hurried through the door, out of breath and very pale, followed by a very red and flustered Frost.

Dr. Warren stared at the couple disapprovingly. "Well, sir," he told Morton, "your patient is ready."

Having stammered an apology for being late, Morton walked over to the patient, who, he was relieved to see, was male, young, and sturdy-looking. Now that the crisis had come, he felt surprisingly deliberate. Taking the patient by the hand, he assured him he would partially relieve, if not entirely prevent, all pain.

He pointed out Eben Frost, who was perspiring in a corner, as one of his successful cases. "Are you afraid?" he asked.

"No," the patient replied. "I feel confident and will do precisely as you tell me."

Morton adjusted his apparatus and commenced administering the drug. For one awful moment, the man showed signs of becoming violent; then he fell into a deep slumber. The confused rustle of feet and voices lapsed into silence while the spectators leaned forward, motionless as the skeletons and mummies behind them. Morton's low voice filled the hall when he told Dr. Warren: "Your patient is ready, sir."

The operation was for a congenital tumor of the neck, extending along the jaw to the mouth and embracing the margin of the tongue. As Dr. Warren gathered in his hand the veins under the patient's skin, the famous surgeons in the front row were on their knees, leaning over to get a better view. Behind them not a medical student moved a muscle. The patient neither winced nor made a sound at the sharp stab of the knife; only towards the end of the operation, when the veins were being isolated, did he move his limbs a little and murmur deliriously. After the tumor had been removed, the wound sewed up, and the blood washed from his face, he was allowed to regain consciousness. Dr. Warren asked: "Did you feel any pain?"

At first the patient was dazed and did not seem to know what was being said to him. When at last he understood, he answered: "No. It didn't hurt at all, although my neck did feel for a minute as if someone were scraping it with a hoe."

Turning to the audience, Dr. Warren drew himself up to his full dignity. "Gentlemen," he said, "this is no humbug."

Morton's difficulties were not over. Although he succeeded whenever the Massachusetts General Hospital allowed him to administer ether, they suddenly stopped calling on him. "The surgeons," he was told, "thought it their duty to decline the use of the preparation until informed what it was." Planning to patent his discovery, Morton found himself in a quandary; if he admitted the drug was ether he might lose his exclusive right, and if he kept the secret he would certainly alienate his only professional patrons. The newspapers which had carried accounts of his successes brought him comfort no longer, for they were suddenly full of articles by physicians that derided his claims as ridiculous. He felt himself alone, deserted by the world in what should have been his moment of triumph. When Jackson dropped in to say he wanted five hundred dollars for the advice he had given, Morton was so anxious to have at least one well-known person associated with his discovery that he agreed to take out the patent in both their names and give Jackson ten percent of the proceeds. The application renamed ether "Morton's Letheon"; it was Oliver Wendell Holmes who coined the term "anaesthesia."

After the papers were safely filed in Washington, Morton divulged his secret to the surgeons at the Massachusetts General Hospital. Dr. Bigelow thereupon wrote up the discovery for the *Boston Medical and Surgical Journal*; despite his distinguished reputation, his article elicited violent criticism like that Long read in Georgia . . . In addition to such professional objections there were religious objections. . . .

Against a storm of criticism, Morton worked unsparingly to perfect his invention and build up an organization of salesmen to distribute it all over the world. According to his lawyer, for three months he "hardly knew a full night's rest or a regular meal"; he was forced to abandon his dental practice completely to assistants. He offered ether free to charitable institutions, and published a periodical in which he combined attacks on his critics with persuasive sales talk. When he tried to sell rights to the army and navy for use in the Mexican War, the dentists' calumnious circular, which had been distributed in Washington, barred his way. "The chief of bureau," the Secretary of the Navy wrote, "reports that the article may be of some service for the use of large hospitals, but does not think it expedient for the Department to undergo any expense for its introduction into the general service, in which the Department concurs." The army's reply was similar. . . .

The general acceptance of anaesthesia put the army and navy doctors in a difficult position; they had no legal right to use the drug, and yet it seemed impossible inhumanity not to do so. Reluctantly, they violated the patent. This emboldened the myriad physicians who were annoyed by paying tribute for a common drug like ether, and soon no one bothered with Morton's claims. His agents all over Europe and America demanded their salaries and their fares home, while physicians who had bought licenses insisted they should be reimbursed, since they had received no privileges others did not have. In the meantime, Morton had run up a huge debt for the manufacture of inhaling apparatus which became worthless when a sponge proved to be more effective. Instead of putting money in Morton's pocket, his discovery was draining it out.

He consulted his friends at the Massachusetts General Hospital. Since they had never enjoyed being involved with a patent medicine, they suggested that he forego his rights under the patent and appeal to the United States government for compensation. They gave him a thousand dollars in a silver casket, and in order to start him off correctly drew up a petition to Congress which many leading Boston doctors signed. However, no sooner had Morton presented the petition than two rival claimants appeared in Washington; Wells and Jackson both insisted they were the real discoverers of anaesthesia.

Wells wrote the *Hartford Courant* that his experiments with laughing gas had given him priority. However, he did not seem deeply interested even yet, for he sailed abroad almost immediately to buy cheap reproductions of Louvre pictures which he hoped to sell at a huge profit to the new rich of the West. In Paris, he came under the influence of a dominant American dentist who persuaded him to notify the French learned societies that he was the discoverer. Soon he was swept away by the excitement of being a great benefactor of mankind; he attended meetings, made emotional appeals, accused Morton of stealing his idea. He could hardly sleep at night, his mind was so busy throwing up images of glory. When he sailed back to America to press his claims there, the fire in his brain was already burning dangerously high.

One gentle spring evening a prostitute was strolling up Broadway in New York when a strangely agitated man sidled up to her and, whipping his hand out of his pocket, threw some liquid in her face. The liquid burnt frightfully. As her screams resounded down the street, the culprit was easily caught. Thus it came about that Wells was sentenced to prison for throwing acid on a street-walker. Unable to bear the disgrace and confinement, he cut his radial artery at the wrist and bled himself to death in his cell.

His death added to Morton's troubles. Mrs. Wells petitioned Congress to recognize her husband's claims, and the rumor gained credence that Morton was a fiend who, having stolen the credit for anaesthesia, had persecuted the real discoverer into madness and suicide.

Meanwhile, Jackson had not been idle. The day after the patent was granted, he had sent a sealed letter to a member of the

French Academy of Sciences in which he asserted he was solely
responsible for anaesthesia. He did not, however, give the French-
men permission to break the seal until January 1847, when there
could be no more doubt that the new method was really of great
importance. Although Morton saw him several times a week, he
heard nothing of Jackson's claim until word came back from
Paris.

Jackson's story was as follows: During February 1842, while
delivering a chemical lecture, he accidentally inhaled some
chlorine gas. He resorted to the antidote prescribed in textbooks,
the alternate inhalation of ammonia and ether. Since his throat was
still sore the next morning, he seated himself in a rocking chair
and inhaled some more ether from a towel. Noticing that while
under its influence he was immune to pain, the story continues,
he decided then and there "that I had made a discovery I had so
long a time been in quest of: a means of rendering the nerves
of sensation temporarily insensible to pain." Since the idea had
occurred to him, the discovery was of course accomplished.
Having no medical patients of his own, he did not bother to prove
his theory by actual tests until 1844, when he requested Morton
to undertake experiments as his agent. Morton, he insisted, de-
served no more credit than a nurse deserves for carrying out a
doctor's orders. . . .

"We have proofs," Jackson wrote a few months later, "that
Morton is a swindler, and that he has tried to bribe his workmen
to certify falsehoods. . . . He is accused of swindling with forged
letters of credit on persons in St. Louis, New Orleans, etc." When
the French Academy of Sciences presented Morton with a gold
medal, Jackson insisted that the medal was a forgery made without the academy's knowledge, and, strange to say, this story,
so easily disproved, circulated in American newspapers for
years. . . .

Morton gave way to a persecution complex that culminated in
alarming physical symptoms. "I have become," he wrote a friend,
"a perfect sensitive plant . . . My nervous system seems so
completely shattered that a trifling surprise or sudden noise sends
a shock all over me. I am so restless that I cannot lie or sit long
in any position by day or night. . . ."

In 1849 his friends took up a collection that enabled him to
urge his claims before Congress, where, of course, he had to
compete with the claims of Jackson and Wells. While in Wash-

ington, Morton hid himself away except when he had to go out
on business, and he refused all formal invitations. Bills appro-
priating a hundred thousand dollars for the discoverer of anaesthesia were presented to three sessions of Congress, but they
always got side-tracked in long committee hearings and Congressional debates on the question of who was the discoverer. . . .

The battle among the adherents of Morton, Jackson, and
Wells was wallowing in its usual morass of litigation and Billings-
gate eight years after Morton had patented his discovery, when
a quiet voice was heard speaking from Georgia. During 1854,
Senator Dawson received a letter from one of his constituents,
by name Crawford W. Long, in which Dr. Long asserted that
he had operated with ether as early as 1842, that he had published
an account of his experiments in the *Southern Medical and Surgical Journal* in 1849, and that the Georgia Medical and Surgical
Association had in 1852 unanimously passed a resolution naming
him the discoverer of anaesthesia. He was not seeking any pecuniary reward, Long wrote, but at the urgent insistence of his
friends was putting his claim before Congress so that the credit
for the discovery might not be entirely taken from him. Puzzled
by this new aspect of the ether controversy which had already
raged so long, Senator Dawson showed the letter to Jackson.

In the years that had intervened since his work on anaesthesia,
Long had moved from Jefferson to the metropolis of Athens,
where he became a leading practitioner and the proprietor of the
largest wholesale and retail drug store in northeastern Georgia. . . .

Into the drug store of this genial Southern gentleman there
hurried on March 8, 1854, a spare, angular stranger with dark
hair and eyes, whose swarthy face betrayed signs of agitation. He
demanded the doctor so urgently that the apprentice who was
in charge thought he must be sick and offered to help him. But
the man said his business was not medical and sat down by the
fire to wait. When Long returned, the stranger presented a card
on which were engraved the words, "Dr. Charles T. Jackson."
He explained that, as they both claimed to be the discoverer of
anaesthesia, he thought that perhaps they could compare notes
and come to some understanding.

Long showed Jackson into the office at the back of his store,
but insisted that his apprentice be present. Then, the young man
remembered, he unlocked his desk and with loving care brought
out affidavits concerning his early operations which had been

sworn to by many witnesses. Jackson had his documentary evidence in his pocket; for several hours they examined each other's papers with slow, cautious exactness. It was, in the opinion of the apprentice, "a weary day's work." As the interview went on, Jackson became increasingly glum. Finally he left, saying he would get in touch with Long later.

In a few days he was back in the drug store with the proposal that they lay their claims jointly before Congress, Jackson to claim the theoretical discovery and Long the first practical use. This would have the effect, he pointed out, of completely undermining Morton, but Long indignantly repudiated the scheme, stating that his claim to the discovery of anaesthesia "rests upon the fact of my use of it on March 30, 1842."

Unable to persuade him, Jackson took his leave. To everyone's surprise, he notified Senator Dawson that he withdrew his own claim, since Long was the real discoverer. He could not help asserting, however, that he himself had conceived the idea first, although he had failed to apply it, and that Long had agreed this was the case.

If Jackson's honest acceptance of Long's claim was not an attempt to defeat Morton, motivated by a hate so strong he was willing to defeat himself as well, it argues that he may have been sincere during the entire ether controversy in which he seems to have played so disgraceful a part. Undoubtedly, his mind was unbalanced; he spent the last seven years of his life, 1873-80, in a sanatorium. The consistency with which he claimed discoveries that were not his own suggests a pathological obsession. Not only did he try to get credit for the telegraph and for ether, but he later asserted that Schönbein had stolen the invention of guncotton from him. Since even stable minds tend to paint their rivals in the blackest colors, as every jealous lover knows, Jackson may easily have convinced himself that Morton was the fiend he publicly accused him of being.

Whatever Jackson's motives, his admission of Long's priority ruined Morton's chances of getting any money from Congress. Having long since given up all pretense of practicing dentistry, Morton spent his winters lobbying in Washington and his summers on a farm near Boston, where he tried to forget his troubles by nurturing prize pigs and raising vegetables that carried away the honors at the county fair. However, all this was expensive, and the small sums occasionally granted him by grateful civic societies supplied his only means of support. He was forced to borrow on his dental instruments and finally even on his gold medal. After each new defeat in Washington, his creditors, fearing for their money, descended upon him; naturally Jackson's alliance with Long ruined him completely. All his property went under the hammer. . . .

During reconstruction, Long tried to mitigate the miseries of Athens by serving under the hated federal government as health officer. His fortunes, wounded by the war, gradually mended until he owned two plantations and at his death left an estate of $40,000. His claims to the discovery of anaesthesia, however, had been completely obliterated by the excitement of war and hatred of the South. Disappointment made the subject so painful to him that his children were instructed never to mention ether in his presence. They knew that he kept the proofs of his priority in a green traveling trunk in the attic. When their usually jovial parent came into the house with a preoccupied look on his face and after a curt greeting to his family stamped upstairs to the attic, they knew that the old fever was upon him and that he would spend several hours poring over the affidavits on which his claim to immortality rested. Each new child, when it came to an age where it could understand, was instructed that the most unforgivable sin was to open or even touch the green trunk. "Some day," their mother told them, "it will make your father a great man."

During the war, Morton had administered ether to the wounded after several battles, but peace found him back at the ever more hopeless task of trying to make a fortune from the discovery that had reduced him to poverty. His days and nights were uneasy with pamphlets, litigations, and appeals to medical societies. Again and again friends or scientific bodies had to give him small sums to keep him from starving on the streets.

In July 1868, while a subscription was being got up for Morton's benefit in New York, a magazine article appeared objecting on the grounds that Jackson was the real discoverer. It was a long time since any such claim had been made, and the article agitated Morton, his wife tells us, "to an extent I had never seen before." He rushed to New York, but immediately became so ill with his nervous ailment that his wife was forced to join him. When he felt better, he suggested that they drive to Washington Heights for the night in order to escape the heat of the city. Almost cheerfully he whipped up the hórse, but soon he returned to wondering whether the article would endanger his subscription. He became more and more excited.

"Just as we were leaving the park," Mrs. Morton wrote, "without a word he sprang from the carriage, and for a few moments stood on the ground apparently in great distress. Seeing a crowd gathering about, I took from his pocket his watch, purse, and also his two decorations and the gold medal. Quickly he lost consciousness, and I was obliged to call upon a policeman and a passing druggist, Dr. Swann, who assisted me. We laid my husband on the grass, but he was past recovery."

After an hour wasted in trying to secure a suitable carriage, Morton was finally transported to St. Luke's Hospital. He was dead, killed by apoplexy. "At a glance," his wife continued, "the chief surgeon recognized him, and said to me: 'This is Dr. Morton?'

"I simply replied: 'Yes.'

"After a moment's silence he turned to a group of house pupils and said: 'Young gentlemen, you see lying before you a man who has done more for humanity and the relief of suffering than any man who has ever lived.'

"In the bitterness of the moment, I put my hand in my pocket and, taking out the three medals, laid them beside my husband, saying: 'Yes, and here is all the recompense he has ever received for it.'"

Long outlived his rival by a decade and had the pleasure of seeing his claim reasserted before the world during 1877 by the famous Southern surgeon, Dr. J. Marion Sims. A year later, while delivering a lady in childbirth, he too suffered a stroke. His last words as he expired in his patient's guest-room were inquiries about her condition and directions for her treatment.

The story has been told and the facts lie before us; nothing remains but to judge who was the real discoverer of anæsthesia. Not that it makes much difference any more. The men are all dead, pursued to the end by their tragic destinies, and each in his own way deserves credit. They have all attained immortality.

Yet, since the world pretends to recognize discoveries, since statues are erected and textbooks written, it might be interesting to see where this review of facts has led us. Certainly we can begin by dismissing the claims of Wells and Jackson. Wells did nothing that Long did not do first, and as for Jackson, whatever brilliant ideas he may have carried about in his mind, they hardly went any further than Sir Humphry Davy's speculations had gone more than forty years before.

The controversy between the adherents of Long and the adherents of Morton will probably continue until the history of anæsthesia is no longer written, for the argument hinges on a definition of what constitutes discovery. It is impossible to deny Long's priority in time. Nor is it possible to refute Dr. William H. Welch's statement that we cannot assign Long "any influence upon the historical development of surgical anæsthesia or any share in the introduction to the world at large of the blessings of this matchless discovery. . . ."

The issue, then, is a simple one: do we regard as the discoverer of anæsthesia the man who first used it or the man who first succeeded in giving it to the world? Here is a decision which each individual must make for himself, and amusingly enough it is usually made on geographic lines. Northerners express indignation at the very mention of Long, while doctors south of the Mason and Dixon line regard Morton as a despicable interloper. Perhaps the decision has usually gone to the Boston dentist because the Northern medical profession is more vocal and more powerful.

Let us not forget, however, that the two contenders made the discovery independently and that each according to his opportunities gave it to the world. Might not the warring factions settle the ether controversy amicably at last by agreeing that anæsthesia had two almost simultaneous discoverers, William Thomas Green Morton and Crawford W. Long? Certainly there is enough credit for two to share it.

Indeed, anæsthesia was the first of the four great discoveries made during the nineteenth century that went far to create modern medicine. After Virchow had established the cell doctrine in pathology, after Pasteur and Koch had demonstrated that germs cause contagious diseases, after Lister had developed antiseptic surgery, the foundation was virtually complete for the miraculous structure of healing which is being built higher and higher every year. . . .

1937

The Horse and Buggy Doctor

ARTHUR E. HERTZLER

No OLD doctor would want to record his experiences even if he could. Sick scenes have been all but neglected by the painter, yet no subject in human experience offers a more fruitful opportunity to present intense human emotions. A notable exception is the famous painting "The Doctor" which graces the walls of many homes. This picture is typical in that it shows a fine old doctor sitting beside his little patient, lying with her arm flung out, mute evidence of a terminal stage of the disease. The father and mother are shown in the background paralyzed in their helplessness. The old doctor's face is perfectly calm. What thoughts are racing through his mind? Would he like to join the father and mother in their wail of helplessness? The old doctor too is helpless, but he sticks to his task, rendering his ultimate service to his little patient and to the parents. It was this silent faithfulness of the old doctor in the hour of grief that endeared him to the families that he served. The old country doctor was a man of few words because there were no words.

It is the purpose of this chapter to pull the curtains a little aside to show something of the events in the sick room. The memory of the more tragic scenes will paralyze any pen that attempts to record them, but a few things may be set down as a framework to which those who have experienced such scenes may attach the pictures of their memories.

Viewed from the vantage point of the achievements of medicine of the present day, the accomplishments of the old doctor seem pitiably insignificant. Yet the satisfaction one gets out of life is measured by the efforts one exerts in achieving a worthy end, not in the actual achievement. This philosophy touches the very heart of medical practice as it was then; in a measure it is even true of the experiences of today. The question of what the old doctor did is answered by reference to my old case records now covering more than forty-four years. It is amazing to what degree old scenes are brought back to memory by the reading of a few lines of a case history. It is at once fascinating and depressing, fascinating because it brings to mind the old sturdy pioneers, depressing because, in the light of our present knowledge, the therapeutic measures were so impotent.

From what has already been said it is clear that the country doctor's activities had less to do with the saving of life than with relieving a patient's pain and the mental suffering of the family. Whatever one may conclude in retrospect as to the importance of the doctor's ministrations, neither doctor nor patient then doubted the efficacy of the treatment employed. However, the picture must not be painted unduly drab. The patient's sufferings were relieved and in occasional cases the measures employed were unquestionably life-saving.

Let it be remarked that, exalted as are the achievements of the present day, the younger man may well remember that possibly fifty years hence his achievements may seem as puerile as ours do now. Furthermore, what concerns the individual doctor is not so much what medical science can achieve as how much of this he can deliver to his patients. That is the personal element for which each doctor is responsible.

Regardless of what the old doctor was able to accomplish in a therapeutic way, the sense of security inspired by the doctor's arrival affected the patients favorably. The degree of this influence depended on faith, which again was based on personality and previous experiences. The most striking effect was on the family and it became obvious before one even approached the patient or started to render any service. If this be so how did we differ from the quack and the cultist of today? The answer is simple: We had measures capable of relieving suffering even though we could not curtail the disease. The quack and the cultist has only the influence of his presence which faith in him may bring. Beyond this he stands in his own barren pasture and reaches over the fence that separates him from regular medicine and surreptitiously garners the luscious clover of science. The cultist and the handsome quack may rival us in inspiring confidence in the malingerer or the hysteric. Let it be repeated that this type of treatment is effective only for imaginary ills which disappear on request or whenever the complainer tires of them.

The proof that the cultist recognizes the ineffectiveness of his treatment is found in the fact that when he himself is sick he wants a regular doctor. I want to say for him—that he makes a most agreeable and obedient patient.

Broadly speaking, the influence of personal contact in relieving the patient was in inverse proportion to the intelligence and the past experience of the patient. For instance I once examined an old lady's chest with my stethoscope, an instrument she had never seen and mistook for a means of treatment. After taking a few deep breaths she enthusiastically declared that she already felt greatly relieved. In appraising service rendered by the doctor at the bedside two things must be considered: the immediate relief of suffering by means of known remedies, and the cure of disease, or at least the staving-off of death. The doctor's most immediate function at the bedside was and is to make the patient as comfortable as possible by whatever means are available. Even today a convincingly careful examination with the assurance that the ailment is trivial or nonexistent relieves many patients permanently. The essential factor is that the patient have faith in the ability of the doctor.

The fact stands out with striking prominence as I review my old case histories. In ability to make the patient comfortable the old doctor could show cards and spades to his modern prototype. It was his chief function because in many cases he was unable to determine the nature of the disease. Morphine will relieve pain no matter if the doctor knows the cause of pain or not. These remarks apply to bedside medicine in acute cases. In chronic disease not attended by acute suffering the task at hand is to discover the organic lesion. This remark is, of course, irrelevant to the present discussion because in the old days there were no refinements of diagnosis as we, even we country doctors, know them today. In acute cases the relief of suffering and the diagnosis of the disease should go hand in hand. Young men should realize that the former need not be neglected in order to achieve the latter; that in fact it may be made a valuable ally—that is to say, while the doctor is relieving the suffering he may determine its degree. If an indifferent remedy relieves a "terrible pain," the pain simply was not so very bad.

The ability of the old type doctor was enhanced because he remained at the patient's bedside until his suffering was relieved, even though it required many hours to achieve that end. While so engaged the doctor learned much about the nature of the illness. If he was not impressed with its seriousness, perhaps because of the prompt relief obtained from some minor treatment, he knew there was little likelihood of any serious organic lesion. Yet it must not be assumed that all serious acute diseases are accompanied by pain. This is particularly true in those afflictions associated with vascular accidents. But in the majority of these cases there isn't much the doctor can do. Happily they are most common in the aged in whom serious disease often comes rather as a benediction than as a disaster.

No reproach attaches to the practice of masterly inactivity, for in most cases the disease was self-limited and all that could be done was to make the patient comfortable until the disease ran its course. The modern doctor with his patient in a modern hospital does no more, though he does it more scientifically and in the doing adds the distress incident to examination to that caused by the disease. There may be justification for the legendary patient's complaint that "the disease was not so bad but the treatment was terrible." This obviously is true in all acute infectious diseases. Perhaps we did something to control incipient complications, though of course one cannot be sure. For instance, if the urine examination indicated kidney complications we busily combated it, but whether or not what we did served any useful purpose is questionable. Now we know that keeping the patient in bed for long periods is the essential thing.

I still possess my old case books which record nearly every call I have ever made and nearly all the medicines prescribed. In some cases I knew, even in the beginning, that my efforts would be futile in the matter of rendering service to anyone and fruitless in the matter of revenue for myself. Often I knew before I touched harness that the trips would be useless. These cases were chiefly those in which there had been nothing wrong in the first place, or in which the patient had recovered before the doctor got there. A child might have a fall that caused more apprehension to the mother than injury to the victim. A negative finding accomplished something by relieving the minds of the parents, even though it demanded no professional technic. In some instances a discomfort definite enough while it lasted had disappeared before the doctor arrived; nausea from the first round of tobacco had subsided, a kidney stone had passed or a cramp due to green apples had disappeared. Of course, one left some medicine in case of a recurrence of the trouble; this was largely the bunk, but someone had to pay for the axle grease and just plain advice never was productive of revenue unless fortified by a few pills. It was about as important as the deacon's "Amen" during the preacher's sermon—it did no harm and it was an evidence of good faith. Both just little byplays which fooled nobody and contributed to the amenities of human relationship or something like that.

Speaking in the concrete, I soon learned that as I looked on the illness might subside of its own accord after a remedy was applied. However, when or if a favorable result followed my ministrations I never had any doubt as to the causal connection, a happy faith shared by the patient and the family. I believed then that my services in many cases were responsible for favorable results, whereas I know now they were of little value. Even at this distance it is difficult to estimate the worth of the treatment adopted. One can in most cases find consolation in reflecting that the remedy expedited the spontaneous departure of the pain. Even in pneumonia I believed my treatment saved the patient's life. For instance, one winter I attended a large number of pneumonia patients. Very few died. As I battled the elements to reach my patients, I had the greatest personal satisfaction in my achievements. I did not know then as I do now that the epidemic was a mild one and that my efforts to control the disease were futile. But the experience did me good. I learned to endure hardships for the sake of my patients and I made good my boast that if a message could get through to me I would get through to the patient. Stubbornness grows on what it feeds on and this intensified tenacity of purpose stood me in good stead in later years when I had to combat a serious disease with only a remote chance of accomplishing anything. Perhaps when Pope wrote "For fools rush in where angels fear to tread" he had the young doctor in mind. This raises the question as to whether or not anyone with good sense ever accomplishes anything. Most achievements follow the efforts of those too dumb to quit. Life is that way.

The exanthemas of childhood are always tricky business for the young doctor, as I have had many opportunities to discover. The first symptoms are so insidious that in many cases even experts cannot be certain of the diagnosis. An instance in point occurs to me. I once had a case which stumped me because I was unable to determine whether it was German measles or scarlet fever. I had this consolation, however, that the very first patient I saw the distinguished von Leyden present was an exact prototype of my former patient; after lecturing for an hour and fifty minutes von Leyden had ended by saying: "We will observe this patient. If the skin of the palms of the hands and soles of the feet is cast off during convalescence it is scarlet fever; if not, it is German measles."

Grandmother was always a source of apprehension. She knew that patients just got well, for she had followed the course of many cases when no medical talent was available. She was disposed to scoff at the efforts of the young doctor and tolerated his presence merely "to watch for complications." Grandmother had small respect for the young doctor and she usually had some old doctor in mind who in her opinion should have been called. Whiskers indicated maturity and most young doctors attempted to emulate their elders in the matter of hirsute adornment, with the result that they made themselves ridiculous instead of venerable. But Grandmother was vulnerable; her faith in her own ability and a liberal coat of soft soap generally made her a friend of the young doctor. Her theory probably was that the young doctor must be smart to recognize her ability.

In the management of ordinary diseases Grandmother regarded herself as superior to the doctor, an opinion in which I soon learned to concur in many cases. She piled the incipient measles patient high with blankets in order to induce perspiration. After the eruption had completely developed the patient felt better, which was the case also without blankets. But I learned something from these experiences: to wit, keep busy and you are in line to receive credit for whatever salutary results ensue.

Grandmother had other abilities. Diagnosis of eruptive diseases is not always easy and I remember one patient whose eruption was atypical. I reserved judgment. The grandmother arrived. She gave a sniff or two as she untied her bonnet. "Measles," she remarked tersely. I concurred, though I did not know at the time that measles could be diagnosed by the smell. But Grandmother was not the only one who contributed to my education. There were the old prairie doctors who had never seen a medical school but had learned many things by experience. One of them taught me a lesson I still remember. I was called in consultation to determine the nature of an epidemic in a neighborhood in which many young adults had died. The eruption was like measles, but in the midst of some of the patches of eruptions were papules which looked exactly like smallpox. The old doctor said it was measles and events proved he was right. I had never heard of this complication of measles. My diagnosis was hemorrhagic smallpox.

That came the nearest to anything like it I had ever seen. The lesions were hemorrhagic all right, but what I did not know was that they could occur in measles. However, it made little difference so far as the patient was concerned, for when hemorrhagic either disease will nearly always kill the patient. The important point was that my dignity received a terrible jolt. It has since received a lot of other jolts. In fact, it has been jolted until it has disappeared in the circumambient atmosphere. But it is no loss, for as one increases in experience dignity loses most of its value.

Leaving these abstractions, we proceed to the consideration of concrete cases as one met them in country practice. These included just about every disease the human being is heir to; one had to be prepared to meet anything, not only in the nature of disease but also meddlesome neighbors and friends and the dog when he made a country call. It was legal to shoot the dog.

Usually the call was brought by a horseman who dashed up the street on a foaming steed. The movies never produced anything quite so spectacular. The young doc usually answered the call in the same fashion: that is, at first—for he soon came to see how theatrical it was. During the trip he had plenty of time to reflect on the responsibility which awaited him when he reached the patient's bedside. To a young and untried doctor this anticipation was worse than the reality, for a case seldom turned out to be as serious as represented by the messenger. Almost anything from hysteria to postpartum hemorrhage might confront him. The hired man or a boy of the family usually brought the call before there were telephones. Generally, the messenger knew only that there was need for haste and nothing could be learned in advance as to the nature of the illness, though sometimes the hired man would announce that it was about time for an increase in the family. The vulgar might laugh at such a remark but it merely reflected an observant mind.

This lack of preparative information worked a double hardship. The doctor was neither able to take suitable supplies for the condition he was to meet nor to determine which of several calls received simultaneously was the most serious and should be answered first. I always followed this rule: children first, next women, then old men, and finally the adult males. Known cases of hysterics came last. The reason for giving priority to children was that they become violently ill suddenly and require early attention; hours counted. Then too, as it has sometimes been facetiously remarked, if haste was not exercised the child might recover before the doctor arrived. More seriously, the family might have one of those curious compilations, *What to Do until the Doctor Comes*, and might do it too. One hoped to get there before they did. We know now how important haste is in cases of acute abdominal disease, notably in beginning appendicitis and intestinal perforations. In those days the acute intestinal disease of childhood, more than any other disease, justified haste in applying treatment.

As an aside I may mention that once I was confronted by some ladies who requested that I relate to them instances where I had arrived just in time to save a patient's life or, *per contra*, had gotten there just too late. I replied that at the moment I could not think of such an instance but I could recall a number of instances when I arrived too soon—when, in fact, it would have been better for both doctor and patient if I had never arrived. This was perhaps an overstatement of fact in both directions. My idea was to combat the general notion that the hurry hither and yon of doctors is in most instances byplay. Even today the young doctor if nabbed by the police for speeding has as excuse an urgent call. If he doesn't hurry he may receive unjust criticism. A case in point. Once a hospital was criticized in a column-long, front-page article because an ambulance delayed half an hour in picking up a patient who had fallen. Yes, he had fallen several times and in several ways. In fact, he was just plain drunk. He had chosen his bed—to wit, the gutter—and he had a legal right to occupy it, I reckon. At least the public was misled, or at least that portion which was as dumb as the reporter may have been misled.

The young doctor naturally took things more seriously than the seasoned old doctor, both because of the desire to establish himself in the community and because of the belief that his services always were of great importance. That is to say, his ignorance approached that of the patient. Then, too, the old doctor knew the people, both physically and financially, and if the patient's complaints were negative, he had urgent business elsewhere. One of my first calls will explain why. A boy came galloping to my house, the horse covered with foam, knees shaking and obviously at the point of dropping in his tracks. The boy, eyes bulging, shouted: "Come quick, Doc. Mother's terribly sick." I hastily hitched my horse and made the seven miles in considerably less than one hour—some driving! I rushed into the house only to find an assortment of women solemnly sitting about a stove doing nothing—except talking, of course. I asked, "Who's sick?" The lady of the house calmly answered: "Well, Doc, I reckon it's me. I ain't really sick, but I've been porely since Christmas and so Pa thought I better see a doctor. I didn't feel like ridin' to town so we sent for you because you are the new doctor." The significance of that last remark escaped me at the time, but I soon learned that they never paid any doctor anything and that established doctors turned a deaf ear to them. That is the way with deadheads. They make their call sound urgent in order to break down whatever sales resistance the doctor may have. Another thing this case taught me was that deadheads will call the doctor for minor ailments, whereas in similar circumstances those who expect to pay will go to his office. In this case the patient's family of ten or more children seemed to be the trouble. Any experienced doctor can tell from these remarks what was wrong with her.

This family was interesting in another respect. There were no beds for most of its members. All the boys were sewed into their clothes in the fall when cold weather approached. At bedtime blankets were thrown on the floor and the youngsters lay down on them, clothes and all of course, and were asleep at once. They woke up in the morning all dressed and ready for pancakes and 'lasses. In the spring the clothes were ripped off and the child saw himself, for the first time in a number of months. This was before we learned about the more abundant life. The interesting fact, anthropologically speaking, is that the people did not know they were suffering any hardships. It all depends on the point of view.

Even more trying than the false alarmist were those who invariably called the doctor about eleven at night. Such calls became more numerous after telephones came into use at about the turn of the century. Usually the background was something like this: an ailing child would keep the mother worried all day until Father came home. The hungry father took Mother's report lightly at first. But after a few hours, tiring of the child's lamentations, which interfered with his sleep, the father would send one of the boys after the doctor. One father I knew boasted that he never called a doctor before midnight and thus made him earn his money. Of course, this fellow never paid the doctor, so that phrase "earn his money" was merely a facetious hyperbole. . . . Tiring of this sort of thing one night, I phoned a chronic offender at eleven o'clock that I must see him at once about an important matter that concerned us both, a matter that would not bear discussing over the party phone. He demurred, saying he had been asleep in bed and that he was not feeling well. He had caused me this same feeling many times and I had known he would be in bed when I telephoned. I repeated my message in louder tones and hung up the receiver with a bang. In about an hour I heard a horse clattering, rapidly coming down the road. When he came to my door I feigned sleep but at his second knock I admitted him. Then I told him very calmly that I wanted him to bring me that load of hay he had promised. Being on a party line, one of the neighbors learned the facts and there was much kidding. The result was a greater respect for the doctor's hours of rest throughout that neigborhood. But in a measure he got even, for the hay he brought me was all weeds, wholly unfit for horse feed.

The doctor learned to know his families, and calls from such people as these were usually passed up for a while in the hope that in the meantime a legitimate call might come from the same neighborhood. One could then answer the call without feeling that the expenditure of time and effort was a total loss. Such patients as I have described called the doctor for the most trivial affections, because they never intended to pay him for his trouble. The country doctor cannot bluntly refuse a call just because the patient is a confirmed and joyous deadhead. People of this class do sometimes die, though I cannot at this time recall a case. If such a thing did occur the doctor was censured, even though everybody knew it was good riddance.

I never refused a call, no matter what the condition, or what the chances of remuneration. When I announced that I wished to study medicine my father asked me to promise never to refuse to attend a sick person, whether he could or would pay or not. My father, being a farmer, did not realize how exasperating patients can be or how useless some calls. I have kept the faith: that is, almost. I have always refused to attend a drunk with a headache. I figure that he might as well suffer from the present headache as from the one he will acquire as soon as he is relieved. This may sound complicated to some persons but it will be perfectly clear to others, I am sure.

Thereby hangs a tale. We had in our town a chronic inebriate. One day I saw him zigzagging down the sidewalk. Early that evening the wife called to say that her husband was very ill. I assured her I could substantiate her statement, for I had seen him a few hours before. I advised that she put him to bed, expressing my belief that he would be all right in a few days as had been the case many times before. A few hours later she called again, reporting that her husband was dying. I replied that in that case it was not a doctor she wanted but an undertaker. This gave me an idea. I called the undertaker and informed him that Mr. X was in need of his service. Would he attend? As is the wont with morticians even today, he expressed deep sorrow, but in a tone that indicated grief would not incapacitate him for business.

I thought there might be interesting doings, so I cut down the alley and across lots and hid in the shadows of the house. Soon the undertaker approached in his wagon, with his assistant. There were at that time no mortuaries and a body was "laid out" in the parlor or living room of the late lamented. This undertaker was up-to-date and carried a board and a pair of "horses" on which to place the board. On arrival he found the door slightly ajar, but no one visible. Gently pushing open the door, he entered and quietly arranged the board on the supports ready to receive the relict. Just then the wife came in from the kitchen and, recognizing the undertaker, let out a shriek. This partly aroused the patient and he fixed the undertaker with an uncertain gaze. Spying the board, prepared to receive his remains, he sat bolt upright. He took one good look, and then let out a howl that frightened children four blocks away. The bed stood in front of a screened window. The patient dived through the screen of the very window through which I was peeping, carrying the screen with him. He lit running and after two hours' search his friends found him crouched in the corner of a fence many blocks from home.

He stayed sober for the remainder of his sojourn in our town, some three years. I have always remembered with a devilish chuckle that this man's coworker was cured of his bibulous habit during a revival, but his cure lasted only nine months while my low-comedy one lasted at least three years. I took delight in reminding the local minister of the relative merits of the two treatments, because while the professional soul-saver, whom the local minister had called to his aid, was conducting the revival I treated him for a disease decent people do not get.

But to return to our mutton. What the doctor did when he reached the bedside can best be illustrated by citing actual events recorded in my casebooks. Naturally, the diagnostic problems varied greatly. In some cases the probable diagnosis was at once apparent; in many, careful study was needed, and, *voce dulci*, the patient just got well—or else. This was not so bad as it sounds, for as already related, diagnosis or no diagnosis, about all one could do in many cases was to relieve the symptoms, and to do this no pathologic diagnosis was needed. One of my colleagues diagnosed typhoid as malaria in all cases and he had the leading practice in this community: that is, for a while. Most doctors claimed to be able to break up a case of typhoid fever or "typhoid pneumonia"—"if called soon enough." I was too stubborn to follow this policy and boldly declared that if they had it they kept it until they recovered, that the breaking-up claim was all bunk. This cost me heavily, but only for a time. The fates are in the end kind to the stubborn.

The usual procedure for a doctor when he reached the patient's house was to greet the grandmother and aunts effusively and pat all the kids on the head before approaching the bedside. He greeted the patient with a grave look and a pleasant joke. He felt the pulse and inspected the tongue, and asked where it hurt. This done, he was ready to deliver an opinion and prescribe his pet remedy. More modern men had a thermometer and a stethoscope. The temperature was gravely measured, and the chest listened to—or at.

That ritual was followed by every experienced physician. I had ideas of my own. I passed the aged female relatives up, ignored the children and proceeded with the matter at hand. This was not based on bravery on my part, but ignorance. I had not yet learned that most of the things one needs to know in the practice of the art of healing never get into the books. But there were compensating factors. I at least examined my patients as well as I knew how. My puerile attempts at physical examination impressed my patients and annoyed my competitors, which, of course, I accepted as a two-time strike. Word went out that the young doctor "ain't very civil but he is thorough." Only yesterday one of my old patients recalled that when I came to see her young son I "stripped him all off and examined him all over." Members of that family have been my patients for the intervening forty years, so impressed were they. Incidentally, it may be mentioned that in this case I discovered a pleurisy with effusion which had not been apparent to my tongue-inspecting colleague.

The great majority of the country doctor's calls were for

trivial and obvious conditions, such as sore throat with or without special involvement of the tonsils, recognizable at a glance. Grandmother might have a renewal of her attacks of bronchitis or asthma, or Father might have lumbago or rheumatiz. These conditions could sometimes be diagnosed while one was driving into the yard. Simple remedies sufficed and one came a day or two later to see how the patient was progressing.

If there was an injury involving the skin one sewed it up without ceremony. The patient was supposed to submit to this without a squawk. If the kids received the injury while up to devilment they stood it heroically, but if they received it in line of duty they did not fancy, there were likely to be loud lamentations. But the ordeal was brief. In case of fracture one went out in the barnyard and hunted himself a suitable board, a loose one if he could find it—otherwise he forcibly removed one from its moorings. From these he fashioned a splint, perhaps with the aid of a bed sheet, if there was such a thing in the house. X-rays were unknown but the results obtained by the country doctor of experience were surprisingly good. At least none died as now sometimes happens when fractures are operated on. Legs, it may be mentioned, in those days were regarded as things to be used, not to look at. Therefore, if a useful limb resulted, everybody was satisfied, even though the result was not a thing of beauty.

Though many of the calls involved trivial and ephemeral diseases, there were many serious and arduous problems to meet such as try the souls of even experienced men. At the top of these stood epidemics of typhoid fever. My introduction to this disease was an epidemic of sixteen cases scattered over a wide territory. This number required a great deal of time, since it was supposed that an attentive doctor would see each patient at least once a day—during the most serious period of the disease sometimes several times a day—and stay all night at the terminal stages.

Happily, no other disease, I can now say, demanded so much of the doctor as typhoid fever. This disease is so insidious and protean in its onset as to try the skill of the most learned. Obviously, it was a great scheme to diagnose any sort of obscure disease as typhoid fever, as my competitors did. For if the diagnosis proved wrong the doctor could say he had broken it up; if it proved correct he got credit for great diagnostic acumen. This worked a great hardship on me, but I stuck to my guns. Word finally went around, "That boy is honest."

The history generally gleaned on the first visit was something like this: headache and backache for a few days with complete loss of appetite. Usually there were general abdominal pains most marked in the appendicial region. Abdominal distention soon followed. Fortunately for our peace of mind, appendicitis was not operated on in those days, and the responsibility of a differentiation was not great. So one just waited to see which it would turn out to be. If there were other cases of typhoid fever in the family, or even in the neighborhood, this was sufficient to make the diagnosis of typhoid fever probable, even in the early stages. Examination showed a distended abdomen, some tenderness and gurgling in the region of the appendix. Later, in many cases, rose spots appeared on the abdomen and, to the practiced eye, clinched the diagnosis; but my eye then wasn't very practiced. The temperature varied usually with the duration of the disease, gradually ascending day by day until the maximum of 104° or 105° was reached. In the early days there were no laboratory tests to be made and observation of the course of the disease was the only means of arriving at a diagnosis.

As the fever increased, the tongue and lips became covered with a dirty crust and there was a low muttering delirium. As the end of the third week approached, the possibility of the dreaded hemorrhage and perforation kept both doctor and family in a high state of dread, and every change that might indicate the advent of these disasters was keenly watched for. If any untoward symptom appeared, a messenger was dispatched for the doctor, though there was nothing he could do when he got there. Irritating occurrences were common. Sometimes a new arrival, usually an ancient relative or the minister, observing the patient for the first time, would express the opinion that the patient did not look right and advise that the doctor be called. This, of course, was to impress the relatives with their great interest in the welfare of the patient. Such solicitude was noted particularly if the patient was a rich uncle. Fortunately ministers always visited the patient in midafternoon and one could answer the call before bedtime. I suggested to one young divine that in my opinion his great solicitude for the patient was inspired by the large number of young chickens in the barnyard.

Those weary trips were galling because one was fully convinced before starting that the call was wholly useless and was instigated by some fool interfering with what did not concern him. One cannot blame the doctor for educating the cleric not to butt in. One could not refuse the call because a complication might actually have developed and, if it had, the death of the patient would be attributed to the negligence of the doctor. There being no lawyers, there were no malpractice suits. Malpractice suits, it may be remarked in passing, are dependent on the presence of a lawyer in a state of malnutrition, and have no relation whatever to the acts of the doctor. The doctors of that day were tried at the quilting bees of the community, not in courts of law. This made it necessary for the doctor to make a display of great activity, a show staged for the benefit of the relatives. Those who feed on this sort of bunk now employ irregulars, who surpass regular doctors in the practice of legerdemain, though some of us were quite skilled in that line when occasion required.

Under certain conditions the doctor was able to be of some service. When the stage of high temperature and delirium was reached cold sponging was demanded, or at least that was the consensus of professional opinion at that time. There being no trained nurse, it fell to the doctor's lot to do the job. It usually required one to two hours of sponging to reduce the temperature to 103°. One was rewarded for his efforts by seeing the patient sleep peacefully, free from muttering, for several hours. I want to say to the young doctors of today that two hours spent bathing a delirious patient seems quite a long time. Occasionally a mother or a neighbor would undertake the task.

Typhoid fever, like most infectious diseases, had a way of affecting chiefly the most ignorant, and I might say the most impecunious also, so that all the doctor got for his pains was the satisfaction of doing his duty and the knowledge that perhaps he had saved another moron to join the great group of unemployables. The disease, of course, did not confine itself to this class, and distressingly often attacked those who were stricken while aiding an unfortunate neighbor. I know the graves of several such victims. I may say in passing that I figured up the per hour collections in an epidemic of typhoid extending over three months. It averaged a little less than twenty cents an hour, not counting the expense of the team.

Though a typical case of typhoid fever was usually easily enough diagnosed—that is, if one observed it for a week or two— many diagnostic problems presented themselves. An apparently typical pneumonia might end up as a typical typhoid fever. I made such an error which caused me great distress. Just at that time Osler reported three cases in which he made this same mistake. I felt better then. Sometimes a typhoid patient would begin with a sudden severe pain in the region of the appendix. Since, as noted, appendicitis cases were not operated on, a diagnosis was just a matter of professional pride. After appendicitis became an operable disease, many useless operations were performed. Ignorance sometimes saves the doctor from doing foolish things.

The disease sometimes runs a very peculiar course. One of my patients ran a temperature for nearly twenty weeks. Some ran the usual course, were temperature-free for a few days and then started all over again. Most perplexing were two husky young farmers who began their disease on almost the same day and progressed uniformly in a typical way. On about the tenth day one developed a severe headache and neck retraction. I stayed with him through the whole night. Nothing I could or dared to do relieved him. At daylight he died. Spinal punctures were then unknown. I hastened to visit the other patient and found him peacefully eating his breakfast, fever-free.

At the end of this grueling summer I emulated my patients and took typhoid fever myself.

During the summer season digestive-tract diseases were common, particularly among children, and when I was not sponging typhoid patients I was giving enemas to convulsed babies. Doing this, I have no doubt, saved the lives of many children. There was no ice, no sanitation, and there were few screens. Many children died in their second year, that dreaded "second summer."

When word came that a baby was in convulsions, I would drop everything else and hasten to attend. I would find a child in convulsions, with a temperature of 105°. A hasty dose of castor oil was administered, followed by an enema which was perhaps repeated. If the convulsions did not cease the child was placed in a tepid water-filled washtub. After the convulsions ceased it was given salol and bismuth. One of these children that I bathed for six hours one night is now in a penitentiary. At least he is not listed as unemployed, and that is something. Nearly all my babies recovered, whereas those my colleagues treated with Dover's powders or other opiates died. This experience gave me my real start. The word went out, "That young doc stays with them until they get well or die."

In looking back over forty years I am glad to say no branch

of medicine has made greater advances than that dealing with the feeding of babies. The young specialists in diseases of children, inheriting the modern knowledge from their teachers, know nothing of the trials of long ago. The art of feeding has now reached such a state of perfection that the acute convulsive diseases are now almost unknown.

If I were a great artist given to paint but one picture I should depict a young mother sitting before the crib of a convulsing baby, with the crushed father in the background. In cases of tragedy the mother nearly always stands up better than the father. No one who knows women as well as the family doctor ever calls them the weaker sex. That phrase was spawned in the parlor by some goof who did not realize that the "weakling" was pulling in the line.

Convulsions in adults, as seen in lockjaw, for example, are terrible to witness, but they are infinitely worse in a child with so-called summer complaint. The cherubic little body is contorted into the most impossible shapes: eyes half open, the balls rolled upward; face twitching and pale or bluish-white. After a few minutes of violent muscular contraction there is slight relaxation and one hopes that it is ended; but not for long, because the contractions soon reappear, perhaps even worse than before. With slight variations this may continue for hours, even days. Usually after a time a diarrhea begins and the child rapidly emaciates, becoming quickly only a skeleton, a mere shadow of its former self. The convulsions are generally absent now, but the temperatures rises rapidly, trying the registering capacity of the clinical thermometer. The child lies panting, head buried in the pillow. The limbs grow cold. There is a slight quiver. The emaciated little limbs suddenly straighten, then relax. The child is dead.

I have done many desperate and, I hope, life-saving operations but nothing gives me so much pleasure as the memory of those battles with convulsed babies. To see the contracted limbs relax, the head lift itself from the depths of the pillow; to see the light return to the mother's eyes, and the smile to her lips—that is one of the greatest experiences in life. In that final day when Peter says, "You are one of those bloomin' docs. What did you do?" I shall say, "I did it to even the least of these."

I know of what I speak. I have sat and watched my own little daughter in convulsions for twelve hours, as utterly paralyzed with terror as any layman. After a short sleep she awakened and asked, "Where is my doll?"—the sweetest words ever spoken. I have never attended a sick child since that day. That memory freezes the marrow of my bones after more than thirty years. Of course, all sorts of cases were interpolated. My first stomach patients were a husband and wife with identical symptoms. I could not risk my whole practice on one line of treatment, so I gave one antacids, the other hydrochloric acid. Both promptly recovered. They thought it was wonderful that while they both seemed to be identically affected the young doctor discovered a difference that required a different treatment. I recently met the living member of this excellent couple, in good health and still grateful after more than forty years. Such an experience is what makes hard labor worth while. It also illustrates the value of fast thinking—and, incidentally, of keeping one's thoughts to himself.

Similarly happy was my experience with my first case of prostatic irritation. Strümpel's *Practice* stated either salol or boric acid could be used. Instead of tossing a coin I combined them. He got immediate relief. I still use this combination.

Patients are grateful in proportion to the relief obtained, even though the condition does not threaten life. The hardest fight with snowdrifts I have ever made found at its end an ischiorectal abscess. The patient suffered intensely and a simple opening of the abscess, of course, brought instant relief. He thought I had saved his life. In such situations the diplomatic doctor does not dispute his patient's opinion. He just looks grave and modest and for this he need not apologize, since he is up against the law of averages. He is sometimes praised for doing nothing and often condemned for failures that are inevitable, despite the fact that his measures are both correct and timely. There is one consoling thought: it is generally the ignorant who condemn the doctor. Intelligent people give him credit for doing his best though it be futile, or even unwise or mistaken; having achieved something themselves in their own lives, they know that, contrary to the teaching of the Sunday schools, to do our best is often not enough.

Of different import was a case of empyema. To answer the call eight miles from town I battled mud for three hours. As I entered the sickroom I saw a boy fourteen years of age half sitting up in bed in deep cyanosis, with grayish-blue skin and heaving chest, his mouth open and his eyes bulging. It seemed that each gasp would be his last. I threw down my instrument roll, sat flat on the floor with my legs spread under the bed. Grabbing a scalpel I made an incision in his chest wall with one stab—he was too near death to require an anesthetic. As the knife penetrated his chest a stream of pus the size of a finger spurted out, striking me under the chin and drenching me. After placing a drain in the opening, I wrapped a blanket about my pus-soaked body and spent another three hours reaching home. The patient promptly recovered and is now a useful citizen in his town and recently voted for Landon, but I' have never recovered from the memory of that pus bath. Bah!

Just before I began the practice of medicine many women in this neighborhood died of puerperal fever, chiefly due to one doctor who divided his time between practicing medicine and raising hogs. It was his practice to administer a large dose of ergot in order to hasten labor so he could reach home in time to feed the hogs. He sometimes washed his hands after the completion of labor but never before. After making a digital examination, he used his pants—that is, trousers east of the Alleghenies, as a towel.

I was called to see one of his patients in the very first months of my practice. The following, printed elsewhere, is a better description than I could write now:

A woman in her eighth puerperium had been overcome on the third day after labor by a violent chill and high fever. When I saw her on the fifth day she lay motionless, eyes sunken, wide open, and fixed. Her respiration was labored and rapid and despite this labor her color presented a mixture of waxy pallor and cyanosis, as though some vulgar hand had soiled a marble statue of Distress, or Nature herself was seeking to soften the awful picture to spare the untried sensibilities of the embryo Aesculapian. The distended intestine found little resistance from the lax abdominal muscles and ballooned out to an astonishing degree. My first thought as I saw the patient lying in bed was that a canopy had been formed for her out of barrel hoops to prevent friction from the bed-clothes. My astonishment at finding the whole mass was belly knew no bounds. My eyes at this sight, I am sure, rivaled the patient's in fixity and wideness and my respiration was equally labored. As I sought to feel her pulse the cold clammy skin made me shrink and as I sought the pulse I could find but a quivering string and because of the pounding of my own heart I never knew its rate. As I turned from this scene, standing about the room were the seven older children, the eldest a girl of twelve. These, too, were wild eyed and short of breath. Approaching the cradle I sought to calm myself by viewing the child. Much to my consternation here lay a replica of the mother herself. The infant vainly sought to emulate its mother in girth of abdomen but far exceeded her in rate of respiration. In one particular only was there essential difference. Instead of the waxy gray of the mother it presented a peculiar ochre yellow, the result of cord infection.

Noting my discomfiture, the old doctor with whom I was in consultation said, "Never saw anything like it, did you, boy?" I had not, nor have I since.

I have the greatest pleasure in reporting that no case of puerperal fever has happened to me or any of my assistants. In fact, puerperal infection is rare, really almost unknown, among country doctors. The disease is not so rare, I read, in the hands of specialists in lying-in hospitals. I say this with pride in the country doctor, not in derision of the specialist under ideal surroundings.

There were many trials for the country doctor in attending labor cases. The following stands out. The patient was nearly forty years of age, small, chunky. A glance indicated that a difficult job was ahead. Only the husband was with her. The night was stormy. As soon as I arrived the husband, a half-wit, departed for a destination unknown and I was left alone with the patient. There was a little stove and a basket of corncobs. After a delay of many hours it became evident that instruments would be required. I had no anesthetic. The patient was in great distress. Her intelligence was just one jump ahead of her husband's. It was necessary to get on the bed and hold the patient's legs with my knees while I applied the forceps. I finally got a fine boy who, despite the none too high estate of his parents, grew up to be a fine young man. I felt that he was in a measure my boy, for I had earned him. He died in the war to save democracy, or to end wars, or whatever it was.

In most cases there was some woman about to care for the new arrival. Sometimes there was no one but the husband. A husband in a case of this sort is just one big cipher. In my first cases in such circumstances I attempted to wash the new arrival myself. Trying to wash a new baby is some sleight-of-hand job. Naturally I had no lap, so I would place the object of my efforts on the kitchen table, which was invariably covered with oil cloth. These youngsters are as slick as greased pigs. So, in order to prevent the baby falling to the floor, I was obliged to grasp one leg firmly with one hand, which left only one available for performing the ablutions. After a few such experiences I carried a bottle of sweet oil and just anointed it all over, rolled it in whatever was available and allowed it to await the ministrations of more experienced hands.

Even conducting a labor lone-handed was not the worst that could befall one. Some of the mothers or mothers-in-law were considerably worse than useless. My assistant and I had an experience that illustrates this. It was a case in which instruments would be needed and I worried about how to get rid of that mother. I had no need to worry. That resourceful assistant of mine was seldom at a loss in meeting any situation. He stared at the mother for a moment and asked if she was subject to heart disease. She stammered that she had been, though obviously it was a new thought to her. He stated very solicitously, after he had listened to her heart, that it would be safest for her to go out into the yard, as it might be necessary to give the patient an anesthetic. She not only went into the yard but across the barn-yard into the pasture beyond. After everything was attended to she was recalled.

The most common pests were those who urged that something should be done to hasten labor, declaring that their doctor always gave them something to hasten the process. This type I set to boiling water, stating that it might be necessary to give the patient a Sitz bath. It takes quite a while to boil a tub of water in a teakettle. This kept them busy in the kitchen boiling water and out of the way until labor was terminated. Of course, one never intended to make use of the tub of water. . . .

Whether an incident is funny or tragic often depends on the viewpoint. Here is a case. I received a call from a doctor in a neighboring town. He had a patient, a young lady afflicted with a serious heart disease. Would I come? I would. It was a rainy day and the road was a sea of mud. I drove my horse until he became exhausted. Then I importuned a farmer to take me the rest of the way. His outfit was a farm wagon and a very sophisticated span of mules. When I arrived at the house the family doctor was awaiting me. The patient had been employed in a neighboring town. Previously always in the best of health, she had suddenly been taken seriously ill. The symptoms were very confusing to the doctor. Rapid respiration was all he could see and he concluded the trouble was a weak heart. I saw a fine plump girl with pink cheeks. She had been weeping. Her pulse was slower than mine and as regular. Knowing the disposition of the doctor, I asked him and the family to let me talk to the patient alone. It was a risk but necessary. I sat down on the edge of the bed and talked to her like a child, for she was only a child, though nineteen years old. "Now tell me," I began, "now tell me just what happened to him." She burst out weeping. "I don't know," she sobbed. "He just up and married another girl." I inquired in detail all about him, his appearance, his occupation and all that. No occupation, very handsome, with brown curly hair. I evaluated him in my own way. Handsome men, I volunteered, live off either the earnings of their wives or of their fathers-in-law. The commercial value of curly brown hair, figured in terms of buckwheat cakes, I opined, was not very high.

I talked to her at length on how fortunate she was that fate had intervened for her. Mere child, fine figure of a girl, beautiful face, young, she had no need to grieve. In calling a young girl beautiful one runs no risk of offending. One may take a cue from the newspapers. Every female that gets into devilment, if under seventy years of age, is referred to as "attractive." This, I presume, is following the usual newspaper habit of giving the people what they want: to wit, bunk. I explained to her that fate had much better things in store for her. I administered this sort of talk for a while and finally her face began to relax, just as that of a nine-month-old baby does when she is about to reach out her arms to you. I wrapped a blanket about her and said, "Let's go out and tell Mother you are all right." She tripped lightly out of the bedroom, through the living room and into the kitchen where the family doctor and the family were talking. The mother's look as she beheld her smiling daughter walking for the first time in weeks was something you do not see in books. "She will be all right," I assured the doctor. Then I sought the farmer and his mules and made the trip home; elapsed time, fourteen hours for the round trip. Now, is this tale funny or is it tragic?

In the same community, some years later, I received a call from that same doctor. A girl was in a terrible condition. She worked in a neighboring town and had come home sick, with a high fever and in terrible pain. That sounded suspicious but I could learn nothing further from the doctor. Mud as usual, and the team walked every foot of the way. Time, seven hours. The doctor was awaiting me. He announced that since calling me the patient had become much better and was now quietly sleeping. She had an abscess where no lady ever has an abscess. The abscess had burst of its own accord and the patient was at once relieved. There was nothing to do professionally but I did make some remarks of a general nature. I had read during the trip out; I was too mad to read on the way back. I made uncomplimentary remarks, with special reference to professional incompetency and the general cussedness of humanity, all the way back. Twice seven hours. Of course, having done nothing I was entitled to no pay. But then that family never paid anyone anyway, so there was no occasion to make a concrete application of this remark. Five dollars for the team and fourteen hours on the road was all I was out. Personally I never could detect any humor in this incident.

Another case had a decidedly amusing feature. I was called to see an old Civil War veteran with a chestful of fluid which caused him much difficulty in breathing. That the family doctor had made the correct diagnosis was proved by examination. While I was preparing my apparatus to relieve the old man of his fluid he bawled out, "Say, Doc, you are the homeliest man I seen since I saw Old Abe." "Say, Pa, you better shet up," his wife called from the kitchen. "Old Abe saved your hide onst; maybe this young feller kin now." A death sentence for sleeping on guard when he was a boy in the army had been commuted by the martyred President. Fortunately, the old lady's prediction came true; he promptly recovered. "I oughtn't to have said what I did," he said to his family doctor, who relayed it to me, "I mighta knowed he must be good for something or somebuddy wooda shot him long ago." As an apology without loss of dignity this always has seemed to me a masterpiece. Low comedy such as this between patient and doctor was common in those days. Many of the older men were war veterans first and pioneers afterward—he-men all the while. Fearless and uncomplaining, they fought grasshoppers and drought uncomplainingly, voted their ticket straight and asked no return. We shall not see their like again.

The foregoing may be regarded as in general the business of the practice of medicine followed by all of us, modified by each doctor's idiosyncrasies and by the situations which arose.

The more intimate experiences do not permit telling and the more ridiculous would be out of place. Often, too, they are so intimately blended. The events recounted here are sufficient to give a general idea of the life we old fellows used to lead.

The human side varied much according to the doctor's bringing up and his general view of life. Despite what I have written and what I may write, I have always had close association with many ministers of the gospel and we often compared notes as to our personal point of view. The ministers of the old days were not learned in a book sense, but many were men of great earnestness and high purpose. These men in general had an idea that something notable should take place at the moment of dissolution and seemed to think I should provide pabulum for their discourses. I had to tell them that saints and sinners died alike and that at the time of death, whatever might have been the antecedents, there was no pain. I have seen only one man who looked on death with terror and he was a sanctimonious old sinner, the pillar of his church, at the sight of whom one just instinctively grasped one's pocketbook.

In most cases death is preceded by a dulling of the mental processes as the circulation to the brain lessens due to the failing heart. Those who die just go to sleep. Even in diseases in which consciousness is retained until the last, as in peritonitis, there is no fear. I have sat beside the bed of such cases and talked of things in general, such casual things as the prospect of quail hunting and the like, while the cooling hands denoted the approach of death. Anyone who ever became unconscious during the course of any disease has experienced the sensation of death. Only favorable circumstances brought him back to consciousness again.

In the old day we remained with our patients during their last hours. We saw to it that they did not suffer. The interest in such a situation attached not to the dying but to the living. I can confirm that old saying that in the deepest sorrow there is no weeping. I have sat more than once on the side of a cradle with a mother while a baby died. Our eyes met as the last quiver passed over the little body. She recognized as well as I that life had become extinct. There was no weeping.

The saddest sight I have ever seen was at the deathbed of an old couple who had lived together many years. Both had pneumonia. I watched the passing of the aged wife and then went to see the husband. I made not a sound. "Mother's dead?" he queried. I did not need to answer. He closed his eyes, folded his hands over his chest and in a short time he also was dead. Don't ask me the meaning. The finest scenes I have witnessed have been the serene old age of such couples. As far as I can see, in order to arrive at the same place at the same time it is necessary to travel together. To so travel it seems that the burdens of life must be borne share and share alike. Whatever the more abundant life may be, this, I am sure, is the most abundant death.

Contrary to general belief, husbands are more nearly crushed than wives at the death of the mate. This is confirmed by the number of bereaved husbands who take their own lives on the graves of their departed wives. Such suicides are not unusual among men but are rare among women. I have said again and again, and I say it once more, that whoever it was that first called women the weaker sex certainly was not a country doctor.

Doctors nowadays do not stay with their patients during the last scene. What do they accomplish by remaining? Scientifically nothing; humanly much. I know of what I speak. In the saddest hour of my life, at the deathbed of my daughter, on one side was the magnificent and always faithful Carrie the nurse, on the other side the incomparable Dr. Campbell, calmly applying measures of resuscitation which he and I knew were utterly futile. Yet futile though it was, the battle of these professions inspires an indescribable measure of comfort. I know that my last conscious moments will picture that scene: nurse on one side of the bed, doctor on the other. Though scientifically futile, if my presence in a similar situation ever brought an equal amount of comfort to anyone I am sure it was more worth while than anything else I have ever done. Our mission in life is to lessen human suffering as much as we can.

On the whole those arduous experiences were happy days. When the roads were good and the trip not too long I took my black-eyed little daughter with me. Later on, she had a sister who was anything but black-eyed and another sister halfway between. No one ever achieves more than that, a reasonably assured living and happy children. No music of earth has greater worth than the prattle of a healthy child, it is said. I was established in practice, all school debts paid, eating three meals a day, with a prospect of earning enough to educate my children. Nobody expected anybody to break up typhoid fever or pneumonia and the diagnosis of typhoid fever was often a long and even uncertain procedure. Also there sometimes were diseases that just could not be diagnosed with certainty, and a confession of these facts implied not ignorance but courage and honesty. I had arrived. Beyond this fundamental fact no doctor ever achieves a higher estate.

1938

The Young Practitioner*

OLIVER WENDELL HOLMES

THE occasion which calls us together reminds us not a little of that other ceremony which unites a man and woman for life. The banns have already been pronounced which have wedded our young friends to the profession of their choice. It remains only to address to them some friendly words of cheering counsel, and to bestow upon them the parting benediction.

This is not the time for rhetorical display or ambitious eloquence. We must forget ourselves, and think only of them. To us it is an occasion; to them it is an epoch. The spectators at the wedding look curiously at the bride and bridegroom; at the bridal veil, the orange-flower garland, the giving and receiving of the ring; they listen for the tremulous "I will," and wonder what are the mysterious syllables the clergyman whispers in the ear of the married maiden. But to the newly-wedded pair what meaning in those words, "for better, for worse," "in sickness and in health," "till death us do part!" To the father, to the mother, who know too well how often the deadly nightshade is interwoven with the wreath of orange-blossoms, how empty the pageant, how momentous the reality!

You will not wonder that I address myself chiefly to those who

* A Valedictory Address delivered to the Graduating Class of the Bellevue Hospital College, March 2, 1871.

are just leaving academic life for the sterner struggle and the larger tasks of matured and instructed manhood. The hour belongs to them; if others find patience to listen, they will kindly remember that, after all, they are but as the spectators at the wedding, and that the priest is thinking less of them than of their friends who are kneeling at the altar.

I speak more directly to you, then, gentlemen of the graduating class. The days of your education, as pupils of trained instructors, are over. Your first harvest is all garnered. Henceforth you are to be sowers as well as reapers, and your field is the world. How does your knowledge stand to-day? What have you gained as a permanent possession? What must you expect to forget? What remains for you yet to learn? These are questions which it may interest you to consider.

There is another question which must force itself on the thoughts of many among you: "How am I to obtain patients and to keep their confidence?" You have chosen a laborious calling, and made many sacrifices to fit yourselves for its successful pursuit. You wish to be employed that you may be useful, and that you may receive the reward of your industry. I would take advantage of these most receptive moments to give you some hints which may help you to realize your hopes and expectations. Such is the outline of the familiar talk I shall offer you.

Your acquaintance with some of the accessory branches is probably greater now than it will be in a year from now,—much greater than it will be ten years from now. The progress of knowledge, it may be feared, or hoped, will have outrun the text-books in which you studied these branches. Chemistry, for instance, is very apt to spoil on one's hands. "*Nous avons changé tout celà*" might serve as the standing motto of many of our manuals. Science is a great traveller, and wears her shoes out pretty fast, as might be expected.

You are now fresh from the lecture-room and the laboratory. You can pass an examination in anatomy, physiology, chemistry, materia medica, which the men in large practice all around you would find a more potent sudorific than any in the Pharmacopœia. These masters of the art of healing were once as ready with their answers as you are now, but they have got rid of a great deal of the less immediately practical part of their acquisitions, and you must undergo the same depleting process. Hard work will train it off, as sharp exercise trains off the fat of a prize-fighter.

Yet, pause a moment before you infer that your teachers must have been in fault when they furnished you with mental stores not directly convertible to practical purposes, and likely in a few years to lose their place in your memory. All systematic knowledge involves much that is not practical, yet it is the only kind of knowledge which satisfies the mind, and systematic study proves, in the long-run, the easiest way of acquiring and retaining facts which are practical. There are many things which we can afford to forget, which yet it was well to learn. Your mental condition is not the same as if you had never known what you now try in vain to recall. There is a perpetual metempsychosis of thought, and the knowledge of to-day finds a soil in the forgotten facts of yesterday. You cannot see anything in the new season of the guano you placed last year about the roots of your climbing plants, but it is blushing and breathing fragrance in your trellised roses; it has scaled your porch in the bee-haunted honey-suckle; it has found its way where the ivy is green; it is gone where the woodbine expands its luxuriant foliage. . . .

But your education has, after all, been very largely practical. You have studied medicine and surgery, not chiefly in books, but at the bedside and in the operating amphitheatre. It is the special advantage of large cities that they afford the opportunity of seeing a great deal of disease in a short space of time, and of seeing many cases of the same kind of disease brought together . . . You have not learned all that art has to teach you, but you are safer practitioners to-day than were many of those whose names we hardly mention without a genuflection. I had rather be cared for in a fever by the best-taught among you than by the renowned Fernelius or the illustrious Boerhaave, could they come back to us from that better world where there are no physicians needed, and, if the old adage can be trusted, not many within call. I had rather have one of you exercise his surgical skill upon me than find myself in the hands of a resuscitated Fabricius Hildanus, or even of a wise Ambroise Paré, revisiting earth in the light of the nineteenth century.

You will not accuse me of underrating your accomplishments. You know what to do for a child in a fit, for an alderman in an apoplexy, for a girl that has fainted, for a woman in hysterics, for a leg that is broken, for an arm that is out of joint, for fevers of every color, for the sailor's rheumatism, and the tailor's cachexy. In fact you do really know so much at this very hour, that nothing but the searching test of time can fully teach you the limitations of your knowledge.

Of some of these you will permit me to remind you. You will never have outgrown the possibility of new acquisitions, for Nature is endless in her variety. But even the knowledge which you may be said to possess will be a different thing after long habit has made it a part of your existence. The *tactus eruditus* extends to the mind as well as to the finger-ends. Experience means the knowledge gained by habitual trial, and an expert is one who has been in the habit of trying. This is the kind of knowledge that made Ulysses wise in the ways of men. Many cities had he seen, and known the minds of those who dwelt in them. This knowledge it was that Chaucer's Shipman brought home with him from the sea:

"In many a tempest had his berd be shake."

This is the knowledge we place most confidence in, in the practical affairs of life.

Our training has two stages. The first stage deals with our intelligence, which takes the idea of what is to be done with the most charming ease and readiness. Let it be a game of billiards, for instance, which the marker is going to teach us. We have nothing to do but to make this ball glance from that ball and hit that other ball, and to knock that ball with this ball into a certain cæcal *sacculus* or *diverticulum* which our professional friend calls a pocket. Nothing can be clearer; it is as easy as "playing upon this pipe," for which Hamlet gives Guildenstern such lucid directions. But this intelligent *Me*, who steps forward as the senior partner in our dual personality, turns out to be a terrible bungler. He misses those glancing hits which the hard-featured young professional person calls "carroms," and insists on pocketing his own ball instead of the other one.

It is the *un*intelligent *Me*, stupid as an idiot, that has to try a thing a thousand times before he can do it, and then never knows how he does it, that at last does it well. We have to educate ourselves through the pretentious claims of intellect, into the humble accuracy of instinct, and we end at last by acquiring the dexterity, the perfection, the certainty, which those masters of arts, the bee and the spider, inherit from Nature.

Book-knowledge, lecture-knowledge, examination-knowledge, are all in the brain. But work-knowledge is not only in the brain, it is in the senses, in the muscles, in the ganglia of the sympathetic nerves,—all over the man, as one may say, as instinct seems diffused through every part of those lower animals that have no such distinct organ as a brain. See a skilful Surgeon handle a broken limb, see a wise old physician smile away a case that looks to a novice as if the sexton would soon be sent for; mark what a large experience has done for those who were fitted to profit by it, and you will feel convinced that, much as you know, something is still left for you to learn.

May I venture to contrast youth and experience in medical practice, something in the way the man painted the lion, that is, the lion under?

The young man knows the rules, but the old man knows the exceptions. The young man knows his patient, but the old man knows also his patient's family, dead and alive, up and down for generations. He can tell beforehand what diseases their unborn children will be subject to, what they will die of if they live long enough, and whether they had better live at all, or remain unrealized possibilities, as belonging to a stock not worth being perpetuated. The young man feels uneasy if he is not continually doing something to stir up his patient's internal arrangements. The old man takes things more quietly, and is much more willing to let well enough alone. All these superiorities, if such they are, you must wait for time to bring you. In the meanwhile (if we will let the lion be uppermost for a moment), the young man's senses are quicker than those of his older rival. His education in all the accessory branches is more recent, and therefore nearer the existing condition of knowledge. He finds it easier than his seniors to accept the improvements which every year is bringing forward. New ideas build their nests in young men's brains. "Revolutions are not made by men in spectacles," as I once heard it remarked, and the first whispers of a new truth are not caught by those who begin to feel the need of an ear-trumpet. Granting all these advantages to the young man, he ought, nevertheless, to go on improving, on the whole, as a medical practitioner, with every year, until he has ripened into a well-mellowed maturity. But, to improve, he must be good for something at the start. If you ship a poor cask of wine to India and back, if you keep it a half a century, it only grows thinner and sharper.

You are soon to enter into relations with the public, to expend your skill and knowledge for its benefit, and find your support in the rewards of your labor. What kind of a constituency is this which is to look to you as its authorized champions in the struggle of life against its numerous enemies?

In the first place, the persons who seek the aid of the physician are very honest and sincere in their wish to get rid of their complaints, and, generally speaking, to live as long as they can. However attractively the future is painted to them, they are attached to the planet with which they are already acquainted. They are addicted to the daily use of this empirical and unchemical mixture which we call air, and would hold on to it as a tippler does to his alcoholic drinks. There is nothing men will not do, there is nothing they have not done, to recover their health and save their lives. They have submitted to be half-drowned in water, and half-choked with gases, to be buried up to their chins in earth, to be seared with hot irons like galley-slaves, to be crimped with knives, like cod-fish, to have needles thrust into their flesh, and bonfires kindled on their skin, to swallow all sorts of abominations, and to pay for all this, as if to be singed and scalded were a costly privilege, as if blisters were a blessing, and leeches were a luxury. What more can be asked to prove their honesty and sincerity?

This same community is very intelligent with respect to a great many subjects—commerce, mechanics, manufactures, politics. But with regard to medicine it is hopelessly ignorant and never finds it out. I do not know that it is any worse in this country than in Great Britain, where Mr. Huxley speaks very freely of "the utter ignorance of the simplest laws of their own animal life, which prevails among even the most highly-educated persons." And Cullen said before him: "Neither the acutest genius nor the soundest judgment will avail in judging of a particular science, in regard to which they have not been exercised. I have been obliged to please my patients sometimes with reasons, and I have found that any will pass, even with able divines and acute lawyers; the same will pass with the husbands as with the wives." If the community could only be made aware of its own utter ignorance, and incompetence to form opinions on medical subjects, difficult enough to those who give their lives to the study of them, the practitioner would have an easier task. But it will form opinions of its own, it cannot help it, and we cannot blame it, even though we know how slight and deceptive are their foundations.

This is the way it happens: Every grown-up person has either been ill himself or had a friend suffer from illness, from which he has recovered. Every sick person has done something or other by somebody's advice, or of his own accord, a little before getting better. There is an irresistible tendency to associate the thing done, and the improvement which followed it, as cause and effect. This is the great source of fallacy in medical practice. But the physician has some chance of correcting his hasty inference. He thinks his prescription cured a single case of a particular complaint; he tries it in twenty similar cases without effect, and sets down the first as probably nothing more than a coincidence. The unprofessional experimenter or observer has no large experience to correct his hasty generalization. He wants to believe that the means he employed effected his cure. He feels grateful to the person who advised it, he loves to praise the pill or potion which helped him, and he has a kind of monumental pride in himself as a living testimony to its efficacy. So it is that you will find the community in which you live, be it in town or country, full of brands plucked from the burning, as they believe, by some agency which, with your better training, you feel reasonably confident had nothing to do with it. Their disease went out of itself, and the stream from the medical fire-annihilator had never even touched it.

You cannot and need not expect to disturb the public in the possession of its medical superstitions. A man's ignorance is as much his private property, and as precious in his own eyes, as his family Bible. You have only to open your own Bible at the ninth chapter of St. John's Gospel, and you will find that the logic of a restored patient was very simple then, as it is now, and very hard to deal with. My clerical friends will forgive me for poaching on their sacred territory, in return for an occasional raid upon the medical domain of which they have now and then been accused.

A blind man was said to have been restored to sight by a young person whom the learned doctors of the Jewish law considered a sinner, and, as such, very unlikely to have been endowed with a divine gift of healing. They visited the patient repeatedly, and evidently teased him with their questions about the treatment, and their insinuations about the young man, until he lost his temper. At last he turned sharply upon them: "Whether he be a sinner or no, I know not: one thing I know, that, whereas I was blind, now I see."

This is the answer that always has been and always will be given by most persons when they find themselves getting well after doing anything, no matter what,—recommended by anybody, no matter whom. Lord Bacon, Robert Boyle, Bishop Berkeley, all put their faith in panaceas which we should laugh to scorn. They had seen people get well after using them. Are we any wiser than those great men? Two years ago, in a lecture before the Massachusetts Historical Society, I mentioned this recipe of Sir Kenelm Digby for fever and ague: Pare the patient's nails; put the parings in a little bag, and hang the bag round the neck of a live eel, and place him in a tub of water. The eel will die, and the patient will recover.

Referring to this prescription in the course of the same lecture, I said: "You smiled when I related Sir Kenelm Digby's prescription, with the live eel in it; but if each of you were to empty his or her pockets, would there not roll out, from more than one of them, a horse-chestnut, carried about as a cure for rheumatism?" Nobody saw fit to empty his or her pockets, and my question brought no response. But two months ago I was in a company of educated persons, college graduates every one of them, when a gentleman, well known in our community, a man of superior ability and strong common-sense, on the occasion of some talk arising about rheumatism, took a couple of very shiny horse-chestnuts from his breeches-pocket, and laid them on the table, telling us how, having suffered from the complaint in question, he had, by the advice of a friend, procured these two horse-chestnuts on a certain time a year or more ago, and carried them about him ever since; from which very day he had been entirely free from rheumatism.

This argument, from what looks like cause and effect, whether it be so or not, is what you will have to meet wherever you go, and you need not think you can answer it. In the natural course of things some thousands of persons must be getting well or better of slight attacks of colds, of rheumatic pains, every week, in this city alone. Hundreds of them do something or other in the way of remedy, by medical or other advice, or of their own motion, and the last thing they do gets the credit of the recovery. Think what a crop of remedies this must furnish, if it were all harvested!

Experience has taught, or will teach you, that most of the wonderful stories patients and others tell of sudden and signal cures are like Owen Glendower's story of the portents that announced his birth. The earth shook at your nativity, did it? Very likely, and

"So it would have done,
At the same season, if your mother's cat
Had kittened, though yourself had ne'er been born."

You must listen more meekly than Hotspur did to the babbling Welshman, for ignorance is a solemn and sacred fact, and, like infancy, which it resembles, should be respected. Once in a while you will have a patient of sense, born with the gift of observation, from whom you may learn something. When you find yourself in the presence of one who is fertile of medical opinions, and affluent in stories of marvellous cures,—of a member of Congress whose name figures in certificates to the value of patent medicines, of a voluble dame who discourses on the miracles she has wrought or seen wrought with the little jokers of the sugar-of-milk globule-box, take out your watch and count the pulse; also note the time of day, and charge the price of a visit for every extra fifteen, or, if you are not very busy, every twenty minutes. In this way you will turn what seems a serious dispensation into a double blessing, for this class of patients loves dearly to talk, and it does them a deal of good, and you feel as if you had earned your money by the dose you have taken, quite as honestly as by any dose you may have ordered.

You must take the community just as it is, and make the best of it. You wish to obtain its confidence; there is a short rule for doing this which you will find useful,—*deserve it*. But, to deserve it in full measure, you must unite many excellences, natural and acquired.

As the basis of all the rest, you must have all those traits of character which fit you to enter into the most intimate and confidential relations with the families of which you are the privileged friend and counsellor. Medical Christianity, if I may use such a term, is of very early date. By the oath of Hippocrates, the practitioner of ancient times bound himself to enter his patient's house with the sole purpose of doing him good, and so to conduct himself as to avoid the very appearance of evil. Let the physician of to-day begin by coming up to this standard, and add to it all the more recently discovered virtues and graces.

A certain amount of natural ability is requisite to make you a good physician, but by no means that disproportionate development of some special faculty which goes by the name of genius. A just balance of the mental powers is a great deal more likely to be useful than any single talent, even were it the power of observation, in excess. For a mere observer is liable to be too fond of facts for their own sake, so that, if he told the real truth, he would confess that he takes more pleasure in a post-mortem examination which shows him what was the matter with a patient, than in a case which insists on getting well and leaving him in the dark as to its nature. Far more likely to interfere with the sound practical balance of the mind is that speculative, theoretical tendency which has made so many men noted in their day, whose fame has passed away with their dissolving theories. Read Dr. Bartlett's comparison of the famous Benjamin Rush with his modest fellow-townsman Dr. William Currie, and see the dangers into which a passion for grandiose generalizations betrayed a man of many admirable qualities.

I warn you against all ambitious aspirations outside of your profession. Medicine is the most difficult of sciences and the most laborious of arts. It will task all your powers of body and mind if you are faithful to it. Do not dabble in the muddy sewer of politics, nor linger by the enchanted streams of literature, nor dig in far-off fields for the hidden waters of alien sciences. The great practitioners are generally those who concentrate all their powers on their business. If there are here and there brilliant exceptions, it is only in virtue of extraordinary gifts, and industry to which very few are equal.

To get business a man must really want it; and do you suppose that when you are in the middle of a heated caucus, or half-way through a delicate analysis, or in the spasm of an unfinished ode, your eyes rolling in the fine frenzy of poetical composition, you want to be called to a teething infant, or an ancient person groaning under the griefs of a lumbago? I think I have known more than one young man whose doctor's sign proclaimed his readiness to serve mankind in that capacity, but who hated the sound of a patient's knock, and as he sat with his book or his microscope, felt exactly as the old party expressed himself in my friend Mr. Brownell's poem—

"All I axes is, let me alone."

The community soon finds out whether you are in earnest, and really mean business, or whether you are one of those diplomaed dilettanti who like the amusement of *quasi* medical studies, but have no idea of wasting their precious time in putting their knowledge in practice for the benefit of their suffering fellow-creatures.

The public is a very incompetent judge of your skill and knowledge, but it gives its confidence most readily to those who stand well with their professional brethren, whom they call upon when they themselves or their families are sick, whom they choose to honorable offices, whose writings and teachings they hold in esteem. A man may be much valued by the profession and yet have defects which prevent his becoming a favorite practitioner, but no popularity can be depended upon as permanent which is not sanctioned by the judgment of professional experts, and with these you will always stand on your substantial merits.

What shall I say of the personal habits you must form if you wish for success? Temperance is first upon the list. Intemperance in a physician partakes of the guilt of homicide, for the muddled brain may easily make a fatal blunder in a prescription and the unsteady hand transfix an artery in an operation. Tippling doctors have been too common in the history of medicine. Paracelsus was a sot, Radcliffe was much too fond of his glass, and Dr. James Hurlbut of Wethersfield, Connecticut, a famous man in his time, used to drink a square bottle of rum a day, with a corresponding allowance of opium to help steady his nerves. We commonly speak of a man as being the worse for liquor, but I was asking an Irish laborer one day about his doctor, who, as he said, was somewhat given to drink. "I like him best when he's a little that way," he said; "then I can spake to him." I pitied the poor patient who could not venture to allude to his colic or his pleurisy until his physician was tipsy.

There are personal habits of less gravity than the one I have mentioned which it is well to guard against, or, if they are formed, to relinquish. A man who may be called at a moment's warning into the fragrant boudoir of suffering loveliness should not unsweeten its atmosphere with reminiscences of extinguished meerschaums. He should remember that the sick are sensitive and fastidious, that they love the sweet odors and the pure tints of flowers, and if his presence is not like the breath of the rose, if his hands are not like the leaf of the lily, his visit may be unwelcome, and if he looks behind him he may see a window thrown open after he has left the sick-chamber. I remember too well the old doctor who sometimes came to help me through those inward griefs to which childhood is liable. "Far off his coming"—shall I say "shone," and finish the Miltonic phrase, or leave the verb to the happy conjectures of my audience? Before him came a soul-subduing whiff of ipecacuanha, and after him lingered a shuddering consciousness of rhubarb. He had lived so much among his medicaments that he had at last become himself a drug, and to have him pass through a sick-chamber was a stronger dose than a conscientious disciple of Hahnemann would think it safe to administer.

Need I remind you of the importance of punctuality in your engagements, and of the worry and distress to patients and their friends which the want of it occasions? One of my old teachers always carried two watches, to make quite sure of being exact, and not only kept his appointments with the regularity of a chronometer, but took great pains to be at his patient's house at the time when he had reason to believe he was expected, even if no express appointment was made. It is a good rule; if you call too early, my lady's hair may not be so smooth as could be wished, and, if you keep her waiting too long, her hair may be smooth, but her temper otherwise.

You will remember, of course, always to get the weather-gage of your patient. I mean, to place him so that the light falls on his face and not on yours. It is a kind of ocular duel that is about to take place between you; you are going to look through his features into his pulmonary and hepatic and other internal machinery, and he is going to look into yours quite as sharply to see what you think about his probabilities for time or eternity.

No matter how hard he stares at your countenance, he should never be able to read his fate in it. It should be cheerful as long as there is hope, and serene in its gravity when nothing is left but resignation. The face of a physician, like that of a diplomatist, should be impenetrable. Nature is a benevolent old hypocrite; she cheats the sick and the dying with illusions better than any anodynes. If there are cogent reasons why a patient should be undeceived, do it deliberately and advisedly, but do not betray your apprehensions through your tell-tale features.

We had a physician in our city whose smile was commonly reckoned as being worth five thousand dollars a year to him, in the days, too, of moderate incomes. You cannot put on such a smile as that any more than you can get sunshine without sun;

there was a tranquil and kindly nature under it that irradiated the pleasant face it made one happier to meet on his daily rounds. But you can cultivate the disposition, and it will work its way through to the surface,—nay, more,—you can try to wear a quiet and encouraging look, and it will react on your disposition and make you like what you seem to be, or at least bring you nearer to its own likeness.

Your patient has no more right to all the truth you know than he has to all the medicine in your saddle-bags, if you carry that kind of cartridge-box for the ammunition that slays disease. He should get only just so much as is good for him. I have seen a physician examining a patient's chest stop all at once, as he brought out a particular sound with a tap on the collar-bone, in the attitude of a pointer who has just come on the scent or sight of a woodcock. You remember the Spartan boy, who, with unmoved countenance, hid the fox that was tearing his vitals beneath his mantle. What he could do in his own suffering you must learn to do for others on whose vital organs disease has fastened its devouring teeth. It is a terrible thing to take away hope, even earthly hope, from a fellow-creature. Be very careful what names you let fall before your patient. He knows what it means when you tell him he has tubercles or Bright's disease, and, if he hears the word carcinoma, he will certainly look it out in a medical dictionary, if he does not interpret its dread significance on the instant. Tell him he has asthmatic symptoms, or a tendency to the gouty diathesis, and he will at once think of all the asthmatic and gouty old patriarchs he has ever heard of, and be comforted. You need not be so cautious in speaking of the health of rich and remote relatives, if he is in the line of succession.

Some shrewd old doctors have a few phrases always on hand for patients that will insist on knowing the pathology of their complaints without the slightest capacity of understanding the scientific explanation. I have known the term "spinal irritation" serve well on such occasions, but I think nothing on the whole has covered so much ground, and meant so little, and given such profound satisfaction to all parties, as the magnificent phrase "congestion of the portal system."

Once more, let me recommend you, as far as possible, to keep your doubts to yourself, and give the patient the benefit of your decision. Firmness, gentle firmness, is absolutely necessary in this and certain other relations. Mr. Rarey with Cruiser, Richard with

Lady Ann, Pinel with his crazy people, show what steady nerves can do with the most intractable of animals, the most irresistible of despots, and the most unmanageable of invalids.

If you cannot acquire and keep the confidence of your patient, it is time for you to give place to some other practitioner who can. If you are wise and diligent, you can establish relations with the best of them which they will find it very hard to break. But, if they wish to employ another person, who, as they think, knows more than you do, do not take it as a personal wrong. A patient believes another man can save his life, can restore him to health, which, as he thinks, you have not the skill to do. No matter whether the patient is right or wrong, it is a great impertinence to think you have any property in him. Your estimate of your own ability is not the question, it is what the patient thinks of it. All your wisdom is to him like the lady's virtue in Raleigh's song:—

> "If she seem not chaste to me,
> What care I how chaste she be?"

What I call a good patient is one who, having found a good physician, sticks to him till he dies. But there are many very good people who are not what I call good patients. I was once requested to call on a lady suffering from nervous and other symptoms. It came out in the preliminary conversational skirmish, half medical, half social, that I was the *twenty-sixth* member of the faculty into whose arms, professionally speaking, she had successively thrown herself. Not being a believer in such a rapid rotation of scientific crops, I gently deposited the burden, commending it to the care of number twenty-seven, and, him, whoever he might be, to the care of Heaven.

If there happened to be among my audience any person who wished to know on what principles the patient should choose his physician, I should give him these few precepts to think over:—

Choose a man who is personally agreeable, for a daily visit from an intelligent, amiable, pleasant, sympathetic person will cost you no more than one from a sloven or a boor, and his presence will do more for you than any prescription the other will order.

Let him be a man of recognized good sense in other matters, and the chance is that he will be sensible as a practitioner.

Let him be a man who stands well with his professional brethren, whom they approve as honest, able, courteous.

Let him be one whose patients are willing to die in his hands, not one whom they go to for trifles, and leave as soon as they are in danger, and who can say, therefore, that he never loses a patient.

Do not leave the ranks of what is called the regular profession, unless you wish to go farther and fare worse, for you may be assured that its members recognize no principle which hinders their accepting any remedial agent proved to be useful, no matter from what quarter it comes. The difficulty is that the stragglers, organized under fantastic names in pretentious associations, or lurking in solitary dens behind doors left ajar, make no real contributions to the art of healing. When they bring forward a remedial agent like chloral, like the bromide of potassium, like ether, used as an anæsthetic, they will find no difficulty in procuring its recognition.

Some of you will probably be more or less troubled by the pretensions of that parody of mediæval theology which finds its dogma of hereditary depravity in the doctrine of *psora*, its miracle of transubstantiation in the mystery of its triturations and dilutions, its church in the people who have mistaken their century, and its priests in those who have mistaken their calling. You can do little with persons who are disposed to accept these curious medical superstitions. The saturation-point of individual minds with reference to evidence, and especially medical evidence, differs, and must always continue to differ, very widely. There are those whose minds are satisfied with the decillionth dilution of a scientific proof. No wonder they believe in the efficacy of a similar attenuation of bryony or pulsatilla. You have no fulcrum you can rest upon to lift an error out of such minds as these, often highly endowed with knowledge and talent, sometimes with genius, but commonly richer in the imaginative than the observing and reasoning faculties.

Let me return once more to the young graduate. Your relations to your professional brethren may be a source of lifelong happiness and growth in knowledge and character, or they may make you wretched and end by leaving you isolated from those who should be your friends and counsellors. The life of a physician becomes ignoble when he suffers himself to feed on petty jealousies and sours his temper in perpetual quarrels. You will be liable to meet an uncomfortable man here and there in the profession,—one who is so fond of being in hot water that it is a wonder all the albumen in his body is not coagulated. There are common barrators among doctors as there are among lawyers,— stirrers up of strife under one pretext and another, but in reality because they like it. They are their own worst enemies, and do themselves a mischief each time they assail their neighbors. In my student-days I remember a good deal of this Donnybrook-Fair style of quarrelling, more especially in Paris, where some of the noted surgeons were always at loggerheads, and in one of our lively Western cities. Soon after I had set up an office, I had a trifling experience which may serve to point a moral in this direction. I had placed a lamp behind the glass in the entry to indicate to the passer-by where relief from all curable infirmities was to be sought and found. Its brilliancy attracted the attention of a devious youth, who dashed his fist through the glass and upset my modest luminary. All he got by his vivacious assault was that he left portions of integument from his knuckles upon the glass, had a lame hand, was very easily identified, and had to pay the glazier's bill. The moral is that, if the brilliancy of another's reputation excites your belligerent instincts, it is not worth your while to strike at it, without calculating which of you is likely to suffer most, if you do.

You may be assured that when an ill-conditioned neighbor is always complaining of a bad taste in his mouth and an evil atmosphere about him, there is something wrong about his own secretions. In such cases there is an alterative regimen of remarkable efficacy: it is a starvation-diet of letting alone. The great majority of the profession are peacefully inclined. Their pursuits are eminently humanizing, and they look with disgust on the personalities which intrude themselves into the placid domain of an art whose province it is to heal and not to wound.

The intercourse of teacher and student in a large school is necessarily limited, but it should be, and, so far as my experience goes, it is, eminently cordial and kindly. You will leave with regret, and hold in tender remembrance, those who have taken you by the hand at your entrance on your chosen path, and led you patiently and faithfully, until the great gates at its end have swung upon their hinges, and the world lies open before you. That venerable oath to which I have before referred bound the student to regard his instructor in the light of a parent, to treat his children like brothers, to succor him in his day of need. I trust the spirit of the oath of Hippocrates is not dead in the hearts of the students of to-day. They will remember with gratitude every earnest effort, every encouraging word, which has helped them in their difficult and laborious career of study. The names they read on their diplomas will recall faces that are like family-portraits in their memory, and the echo of voices they have listened to so long will linger in their memories far into the still evening of their lives.

One voice will be heard no more which has been familiar to many among you. It is not for me, a stranger to these scenes, to speak his eulogy. I have no right to sadden this hour by dwelling on the deep regrets of friendship, or to bid the bitter tears of sorrow flow afresh. Yet I cannot help remembering what a void the death of such a practitioner as your late instructor must leave in the wide circle of those who leaned upon his counsel and assistance in their hour of need, in a community where he was so widely known and esteemed, in a school where he bore so important a part. There is no exemption from the common doom for him who holds the shield to protect others. The student is called from his bench, the professor from his chair, the practitioner in his busiest period hears a knock more peremptory than any patient's midnight summons, and goes on that unreturning visit which admits of no excuse, and suffers no delay. The call of such a man away from us is the bereavement of a great family. Nor can we help regretting the loss for him of a bright and cheerful earthly future; for the old age of a physician is one of the happiest periods of his life. He is loved and cherished for what he has been, and even in the decline of his faculties there are occasions when his experience is still appealed to, and his trembling hands are looked to with renewing hope and trust, as being yet able to stay the arm of the destroyer.

But if there is so much left for age, how beautiful, how inspiring is the hope of youth! I see among those whom I count as listeners one by whose side I have sat as a fellow-teacher, and by whose instructions I have felt myself not too old to profit. As we borrowed him from your city, I must take this opportunity of telling you that his zeal, intelligence, and admirable faculty as an instructor were heartily and universally recognized among us. We return him, as we trust, uninjured, to the fellow-citizens who have the privilege of claiming him as their own.

And now, gentlemen of the graduating class, nothing remains but for me to bid you, in the name of those for whom I am commissioned and privileged to speak, farewell as students, and welcome as practitioners. I pronounce the two benedictions in the same breath, as the late king's demise and the new king's accession are proclaimed by the same voice at the same moment. You would hardly excuse me if I stooped to any meaner dialect than the classical and familiar language of your prescriptions, the same in which your title to the name of physician is, if, like our own institution, you follow the ancient usage, engraved upon your diplomas.

Valete, JUVENES, *artis medicos studiosi; valete, discipuli, valete, filii!*

Salvete, VIRI, *artis medicos magistri; salvete, amici; salvete, fratres!*

Edition of 1891

The Surgical Operations on President Cleveland in 1893

W. W. KEEN

ON AUGUST 29, 1893, the Philadelphia Press published a three-column dispatch, or letter, from "Holland"—Mr. E. J. Edwards—its New York correspondent, startling the whole country by giving the first intimation of an alleged serious operation upon President Cleveland, performed by Dr. Joseph D. Bryant, of New York, on board Commodore E. C. Benedict's yacht, the Oneida. He gave the names of the medical men present and many details of the operation. This was said to have been done on July first, immediately after Mr. Cleveland had called the special session of Congress for August seventh.

Holland stated that the operation consisted in the removal of some teeth and of considerable bone, as far as the orbital plate of the upper jaw on one side. This dispatch was substantially correct, even in most of the details, as will be seen later.

The news was immediately spread broadcast and at once gave rise to an animated controversy. At the time of the publication of the dispatch Mr. Cleveland had been in Washington for the special session of Congress on August seventh, and four days later had gone to Gray Gables, his summer home on Buzzard's Bay, for rest and recuperation, as was publicly alleged. He returned to Washington on August thirtieth. On September fifth he opened the First Pan-American Medical Congress, in Washington, when his voice was "even clearer and more resonant" than on March fourth at his inauguration. Two weeks later he spoke at the Centenary of the Founding of the City of Washington. He met many persons officially and socially. No scar or other evidence of an operation existed, his voice did not betray him, and his general health was evidently as good as could be expected of one who had endured a horde of pestiferous officeseekers and the terrible anxieties of the existing financial crisis.

Many newspapers denied that any operation had been performed; others said that, at the most, it consisted in the removal of two teeth and possibly a little rough bone. They cited not only the lack of physical evidence already mentioned, but the statements of Doctor Bryant, of Cabinet officers, of the President's private secretary, and a signed statement by Mr. L. Clarke Davis, editor of the Public Ledger and a close friend of the President, who wrote that Holland's statement "had a real basis of a toothache." Some papers denounced Holland's letter as "infamous," and claimed that the whole story was a "cancer fake," and so on.

Doctor Bryant, who was the only spokesman for all the medical men who had participated in the operation, was naturally unwilling to discuss his patient's case for professional reasons, and the weighty additional reason of the serious influence of any full statement he might make upon the tense and disastrous financial crisis. He rightly minimized the operation as far as possible.

But many papers pointed to the recent denials of the doctors in the case of General Grant, and of other public men, which proved to be inexact. They declared the alleged statement of Colonel Lamont, the Secretary of War, Mr. Cleveland's most intimate friend, who had also been on board the Oneida during the operation, that the President was "a sick man—how sick we cannot tell," was the correct statement of the actual facts.

To comprehend the grave responsibilities resting on Mr. Cleveland's surgeons and the necessity of preserving absolute secrecy as to any serious operation having been performed upon the President, it is essential to understand the financial panic then in progress. This Burton describes as a crisis "which in its severity has rarely been surpassed"; and Charles Francis Adams, in his Autobiography, calls it "the most deep-seated financial storm in the history of the country." It was a crisis that would have been changed into a national disaster had the actual facts become known before Congress assembled on August seventh. As the Nation said on August third—long before the operation was known: "A great deal is staked upon the continuance of a single life."

On the very day when Holland's letter was published the Commercial and Financial Chronicle said editorially: "Mr. Cleveland is about all that stands between this country and absolute disaster, and his death would be a great calamity."

Had the seriousness of the operation on Mr. Cleveland become known earlier than it did, and before his evident good health put to rest the fears of the community and emboldened the sound-money men in Congress, the panic would have become a rout. The reason for these strong statements is that Mr. Stevenson, the Vice President, was a pronounced silver man. Had the very serious nature of the operation become known, the public would at once have jumped to the conclusion that the President was doomed. Cleveland would at once become the setting sun, Stevenson the rising sun, and the Silver Clause of the Sherman Act almost certainly would not have been repealed. What that would have meant to the country can scarcely be imagined.

"To Mr. Cleveland—and we might say to Mr. Cleveland alone—belongs the honor of securing the passage of the Repeal Bill." —(The Nation, October 26, 1893.)

The financial crisis was acute, even world-wide. In 1879, after a long interruption, the United States had resumed specie payments. In 1871 Germany had demonetized silver. In 1877 the three Latin nations had done the same. Switzerland and Greece, and shortly afterward the three Scandinavian nations, followed their example. In 1892 the leading nations of the world were in a wild scramble for gold. Austria-Hungary was seeking one hundred million dollars for a resumption of specie payments, and the Bank of France was adding to its supply. Russia, on January 31, 1893, had accumulated four hundred and fifty million dollars. The Bank of England, in order not to lose its gold, had kept its discount rate at three per cent, though in the general market the rate was only one per cent. . . .

In the United States the situation was deplorable. From 1879 to 1890 our business had been conducted on a gold basis. But the silver heresy had spread far and wide among our people, and the influence especially of the senators from our northwestern silver-producing states was energetically used. . . .

In 1890 we had, in all, a gold reserve of over one hundred and eighty-five million dollars—eighty-five millions in excess of the hundred millions set aside to guarantee the integrity of over three hundred and forty-six million dollars of greenbacks. By January 31, 1893, this reserve had fallen to one hundred and eight million dollars. On Mr. Cleveland's accession—March fourth—it had fallen to less than one hundred and one million dollars. The Treasury was kept solvent only by omitting payments into the sinking fund and by not expending appropriations voted by Congress. The Secretary of the Treasury also begged patriotic banks and bankers to let the Government have their gold. But this gold soon disappeared in redeeming paper money. He also repeatedly sold bonds. Even these bonds, to a degree, defeated their own object; for the purchasers drew some of the gold they paid into the Treasury for the bonds by presenting to the Treasury its own notes, which the secretary was obliged to redeem in gold on penalty of seriously impairing the credit of the United States.

The Sherman Act had been passed in 1890. It was an almost fatal "truce," as Mr. Cleveland called it, between the advocates of free coinage of silver and their opponents. This Act imposed an additional yearly purchase of· fifty-four million ounces of silver, against which Treasury notes were issued, all redeemable in gold. From 1789 to 1878—eighty-nine years—we had coined only eight million silver dollars. From 1878 to 1893—only fifteen years—we had coined over four hundred and nineteen millions. In silver bullion, cart-wheel dollars—which nobody wanted—and subsidiary coinage we had six hundred and thirty-five million dollars of silver on hand! . . .

It seems to us now passing strange that Congress persisted in such self-evident folly, in spite of the public action of Chambers of Commerce and other similar organizations, the opinions of financial experts, and Mr. Cleveland's repeated but vain appeals for relief: but "something had to be done for silver." When an anxious husband was told by the doctor that he was at the end of his resources and that all that could be done for his wife was to "trust in the Lord," "Oh, doctor," was the reply, "it isn't really as bad as that, is it?"

In our similar financial emergency—and most appropriately in Denver, the "silver capital," where six banks failed in two days— the clergymen evidently thought it was "really as bad as that," and urged the President to appoint a day of fasting and prayer.

No wonder that the loss of confidence in the ability of the Government to sustain its credit, and the various sinister influences already described, precipitated a panic!

At his inauguration, on March fourth, Mr. Cleveland declared he would exhaust all his legal powers to prevent any depreciation of the currency. To that end the Secretary of the Treasury boldly trenched upon the hundred-million-dollar gold-reserve fund, but gave ominous warning that the Treasury would pay gold for Treasury notes only so long as it had gold lawfully available for that purpose. Before the crisis finally ended the gold reserve had fallen to only forty million dollars.

Our population in 1893 was just about sixty-six millions. During that year six hundred and forty-two banks suspended. Presumably this would be equal approximately to the suspension of one thousand banks in 1917. The most vivid appreciation of the seriousness of the situation can best be had by reading the "summary of the news" in the Philadelphia Public Ledger, or other newspapers, for 1893, or even for the middle six months of that year. Scarcely a day passed without several and sometimes many suspensions. Bank failures occurred, banks and trust companies closed their doors, receiverships and business embarrassments, even of large concerns, appeared in dismal reiteration. At Golden City, Colorado—a singularly inappropriate place—the silver men once went so far as to burn Mr. Cleveland in effigy. . . .

When Congress met in special session, on August seventh, Mr. Cleveland's message urged the absolute repeal of the Sherman Act, without any substitute and without any compromise. On August eleventh Mr. Cleveland returned to Gray Gables. While there he was rejoiced to learn that the House had passed the repeal on August twenty-eighth by 239 to 101 votes—more than two to one. The repeal then went to the Senate.

The day after the vote in the House Holland's letter disclosing the operation was published.

Though there was believed to be a majority of the Senate in favor of repeal, in spite of the fact that seven silver states, with only one-sixtieth of the population, had about one-sixth of the membership of the Senate, the battle raged long and fiercely. "Senatorial courtesy" prevented "cloture," and the weary debate went on and on until the obstruction became a scandal. Jones, of Nevada, covered one hundred closely printed pages of the Congressional Record with his speech. Allen, of Nebraska, spoke for fourteen hours. An attempt at a continuous session, to wear out one side or the other, failed after thirty-eight hours. Late in October the Senate did not formally adjourn for fourteen days.

Wild schemes, also, were proposed to alter the proportion of gold and silver from one to sixteen to one to seventeen, eighteen, nineteen; and even twenty to one. The last was actually proposed by Senator Vest, of Missouri. Secretary Carlisle gave it its quietus with a bare bodkin thrust by showing that the recoinage of our silver would require several years, during which time there would be two sorts of dollars of different values, and would cost one hundred and twelve million dollars!

Finally, on October thirtieth, the repeal passed the Senate by 48 to 37 votes—including five "pairs."

The country was thus saved from the dire disaster that threatened; but the noxious effects of the silver heresy did not pass away until the election of 1896.

This, then, was the threatening situation, which was at its very worst when Doctor Bryant and I operated. The operation itself was as nothing compared with scores that both of us had performed; but on it hung the life not only of a human being and an illustrious ruler but the destiny of a nation. It was by far the most responsible operation in which I ever took part.

On Sunday, June eighteenth, Dr. R. M. O'Reilly—later Surgeon-General of the United States Army—the official medical attendant on officers of the Government in Washington, examined a rough place on the roof of Mr. Cleveland's mouth. He found an ulcer as large as a quarter of a dollar, extending from the molar teeth to within one-third of an inch of the middle line and encroaching slightly on the soft palate, and some diseased bone. The pathologist at the Army Medical Museum—who was kept in ignorance, of course, of the name of the patient—reported, on a small fragment which Doctor O'Reilly removed, that it was strongly indicative of malignancy.

Doctor O'Reilly, foreseeing the need for an operation, advised Mr. Cleveland to consult Dr. Joseph D. Bryant, long his medical attendant and intimate friend. Doctor Bryant quickly went to Washington and confirmed the diagnosis. The President, after the examination, with no apparent concern, inquired:

"What do you think it is, doctor?"

To which Doctor Bryant replied:

"Were it in my mouth I would have it removed at once."

This answer settled the matter.

During the discussion as to what arrangements could be made, "the President would not under any circumstances consent . . . to a time and place that would not give the best opportunity of avoiding disclosure, and even a suspicion that anything of significance had happened to him. The strong desire to avoid notoriety . . . was dwarfed by the fear he had of the effect on the public of a knowledge of his affliction, and on the financial questions of the time." He decided that July first was the earliest suitable date. Colonel Lamont, the Secretary of War, and a close personal friend, was then informed of the facts, and it was soon arranged that to secure secrecy the operation should be done on Commodore Benedict's yacht, the *Oneida*.

The next question was as to how soon the President could probably safely return to Washington. August seventh was decided on.

Meantime Doctor Bryant had written me, asking for a consultation "in a very important matter." As I was about to go to New England I suggested that I should go to New York at noon and that we meet at three-fifteen on the deserted deck of the Fall River boat, which did not leave till six P.M. There, without any interruption, we laid all necessary plans. The living rooms on the *Oneida* were prepared and disinfected; an operating table and all the necessary instruments, drugs, dressings, and so on, were sent on board. Arrangements were made with Dr. Ferdinand Hasbrouck, a dentist accustomed to giving nitrous oxide, to assist.

On June thirtieth I reached New York City in the evening, went to Pier A, and was taken over to the yacht. Dr. E. G. Janeway, of New York; Doctor O'Reilly; Dr. John F. Erdmann, Doctor Bryant's assistant; and Doctor Hasbrouck had also secretly gone to the yacht. The President, Doctor Bryant and Secretary Lamont, at a later hour on arrival from Washington, openly drove to Pier A, whence they were taken to the yacht.

Just before he left Washington, on June thirtieth, Mr. Cleveland issued a call for a special session of Congress on August seventh, with the object of relieving the financial dangers by the repeal of the Silver Clause of the Sherman Act.

On arriving on the yacht the President lighted a cigar, and we sat on deck smoking and chatting till near midnight. Once he burst out with "Oh, Doctor Keen, those officeseekers! Those officeseekers! They haunt me even in my dreams!" I had never met him before; but during that hour or more of conversation I was deeply impressed by his splendid personality and his lofty patriotism. I do not believe there was a more devoted patriot living.

He passed a good night, sleeping well without any sleeping medicine. Before he dressed, Doctor Janeway made a most careful examination of his chest and found nothing wrong. There was little if any arteriosclerosis. His pulse was ninety. His kidneys were almost entirely normal.

I then examined him myself. He stated that he was sure the rough place was of recent origin; that it was not there on March fourth, when he had been inaugurated, but had been first observed about six or eight weeks before July first. There were no perceptibly enlarged glands. I confirmed the facts as to the ulcer and deemed the growth to be unquestionably malignant. During the morning his mouth was repeatedly cleansed and disinfected.

The anesthetic troubled us. Our anxiety related not so much to the operation itself as to the anesthetic and its possible dangers. These might easily arise in connection with the respiration, the heart, or the function of the kidneys, etc., dangers which are met with not infrequently as a result of administering an anesthetic, especially in a man of Mr. Cleveland's age and physical condition. The patient was 56 years of age, very corpulent, with a short thick neck, just the build and age for a possible apoplexy—an accident which had actually occurred to one of my patients. He was also worn out mentally and physically by four months of exacting labor and the officeseekers' importunities. Twenty-four years ago we had not the refined methods of diagnosis, nor had we the greatly improved methods of anesthesia which we have to-day. After canvassing the whole matter we decided to perform at least the earliest steps of the operation under nitrous oxide, and the later, if necessary, under ether. Doctor Hasbrouck was of opinion that we could not keep the patient well anesthetized with nitrous oxide long enough to complete the operation satisfactorily.

Doctor Bryant and Secretary Lamont had spent the night at their homes, but returned to the yacht the next morning—July first. The yacht then proceeded up the East River at half speed while the operation was performed.

Commodore Benedict and Secretary Lamont remained on deck during the operation. The steward was the only other person present, to fetch and carry. I have always thought that due credit was not given to him, and to the captain and crew, for their never betraying what had taken place. They knew Mr. Cleveland very well, for he had traveled over fifty thousand miles on the yacht and his mere presence was no novelty. Any curiosity as to the evidently unusual occurrences was allayed by the statement that the President had to have two very badly ulcerated teeth removed and that fresh, pure air, and disinfected quarters and skilled doctors, all had to be provided, lest blood poisoning should set in—a very serious matter when the patient was the just-inaugurated President of the United States.

Doctor Hasbrouck first extracted the two left upper bicuspid teeth under nitrous oxide. Doctor Bryant then made the necessary incisions in the roof of the mouth, also under nitrous oxide.

At one-fourteen P.M. ether was given by Doctor O'Reilly. During the entire operation Doctor Janeway kept close watch upon the pulse and general condition. Doctor Bryant performed the operation, assisted by myself and Doctor Erdmann.

The entire left upper jaw was removed from the first bicuspid tooth to just beyond the last molar, and nearly up to the middle line. The floor of the orbit—the cavity containing the eyeball —was not removed, as it had not yet been attacked. A small portion of the soft palate was removed. This extensive operation was decided upon because we found that the antrum—the large hollow cavity in the upper jaw—was partly filled by a gelatinous mass, evidently a sarcoma. This diagnosis was later confirmed by Dr. William H. Welch, of the Johns Hopkins Hospital, who had also examined the former specimens.

The entire operation was done within the mouth, without any external incision, by means of a cheek retractor, the most useful instrument I have ever seen for such an operation, which I had brought back with me from Paris in 1866. The retention of the floor of the orbit prevented any displacement of the eyeball. This normal appearance of the eye, the normal voice, and especially the absence of any external scar, greatly aided in keeping the operation an entire secret.

Only one blood vessel was tied. Pressure, hot water, and at one point the galvanocautery, checked the bleeding. The hemorrhage was not large, probably about six ounces—say, a tumblerful— in all. At the close of the operation, at one-fifty P.M., the pulse was only eighty. The large cavity was packed with gauze to arrest the subsequent moderate oozing of blood. At two-fifty-five P.M. a hypodermic of one-sixth of a grain of morphine was given—the only narcotic administered at any time.

What a sigh of intense relief we surgeons breathed when the patient was once more safe in bed can hardly be imagined!

Mr. Cleveland's temperature after the operation was 100.8 degrees Fahrenheit, and never thereafter rose above 100 degrees. His pulse was usually ninety or a little over. With the packing in the cavity his speech was labored but intelligible; without the packing it was wholly unintelligible, resembling the worst imaginable case of cleft palate. Had this not been so admirably remedied by Doctor Gibson, secrecy later would have been out of the question.

In turn with the others, I sat by Mr. Cleveland's bedside much of the time that evening and the next day, reading to him at times to help pass the time. Doctor Bryant's and my own full notes say nothing about any stimulant. They would have recorded the stimulant if any had been administered. My recollection, also, is clear that none was given. Our notes do not record the exact day when Mr. Cleveland was able to get out of bed, but my recollection is that it was late on July second. That he was up and about on July third is certain, for I saw in Commodore Benedict's guest register on the *Oneida* the signatures of the President, Secretary Lamont and Doctor Bryant on July third, the second day after the operation.

Doctor Hasbrouck had been landed at New London on July second. I left the yacht at Sag Harbor early on July fourth and came directly home. On July fifth, in the evening, the yacht reached Gray Gables, and "the President walked from the launch to his residence with but little apparent effort."

During such an operation, especially in operations on bone, with the parts bathed with blood, it is often impossible to judge accurately whether all the diseased tissue has certainly been removed. When, later, he could see clearly the condition of the

parts, Doctor Bryant was not quite satisfied with the appearance
at one point. At his request, Doctors Janeway, Erdmann and I
again boarded the *Oneida* at New York, with precautions for
secrecy similar to those on the former occasion. We picked up
Mr. Cleveland at Gray Gables; and on July seventeenth Doctor
Bryant, with our assistance, removed all the suspicious tissue and
cauterized the entire surface with the galvanocautery. This operation was brief and the President recovered quickly. On July
nineteenth, again the second day after the operation, the same
three signatures appear in Commodore Benedict's register. This
second operation was never discovered by anyone.

On the evening of the eighteenth I was put ashore at Newport
just before the Fall River boat was due, on her way to New
York. Then an amusing encounter almost betrayed me. My intention was to get a stateroom and seclude myself there at once.
At the head of the stairs on my way to the stateroom, whom
should I meet but my brother-in-law, Mr. Spencer Borden, of
Fall River!

"Hello! What are you doing here?" was his greeting.

I said very nonchalantly that I had had a consultation near by,
and had had no time to visit the family in Fall River, as I had
reached Newport only a few minutes before. Knowing my reticence in such matters and respecting my sense of duty, he did
not press the question as to where the consultation had been held.
When Holland's account was published, six weeks later, with
swift intuition Mr. Borden exclaimed that that surely was my
consultation when he met me on the boat!

Mr. Cleveland left Gray Gables for the special session of Congress on August fifth. He returned to Gray Gables for rest and
recuperation on August eleventh. Finally he went to Washington
for the winter on August thirtieth and reached the White House
on September first; on which date Doctor Bryant's notes say: "All
healed."

After the first operation, while the President was at Gray
Gables, Dr. Kasson C. Gibson, of New York, fitted Mr. Cleveland
with an artificial jaw of vulcanized rubber. With this in place,
his speech was excellent, even its quality not being altered. On
October fourteenth Mr. Cleveland, in a letter to Doctor Gibson,
expressed his lively satisfaction after trying a new and even better
and more comfortable plate made by Doctor Gibson.

I went to Washington at intervals several times afterward to examine Mr. Cleveland's mouth and never found anything wrong. These brief visits were always a great pleasure, at the time as well as in retrospect, since I made the more intimate acquaintance of both the President and Mrs. Cleveland and their lovely family.

Now, after the lapse of nearly a quarter of a century, it is even more evident than it was at the time that the instant decision of Mr. Cleveland himself, concurred in by his professional advisers and such friends as Secretary Lamont and Commodore Benedict, to keep the operation a profound secret was wise, and one may say imperative. What the consequences would have been had it become known at once we can only surmise, and shudder!

Mr. Cleveland died June 24, 1908, fifteen years after our operations. I was then in Europe. That he should have survived after the removal of a sarcoma of the jaw without local recurrence for so unusually long a period was a great satisfaction to Doctor Bryant and his colleagues.

Long before his death Mr. Cleveland had "come into his own." He passed away as the "foremost American citizen," respected and honored by all parties and in all ranks of life. To me it is a rare satisfaction to have been associated with him so closely and to have been able to assist my trusted friend Bryant in doing a most important service to our beloved country.

1917

Peruna and the Bracers

SAMUEL HOPKINS ADAMS

A DISTINGUISHED public health official and medical writer once made this jocular suggestion to me:

"Let us buy in large quantities the cheapest Italian vermouth, poor gin and bitters. We will mix them in the proportion of three of vermouth to two of gin, with a dash of bitters, dilute and bottle them by the short quart, label them '*Smith's Reviver and Blood Purifier; dose, one wineglassful before each meal*'; advertise them to cure erysipelas, bunions, dyspepsia, heat rash, fever and ague, and consumption; and to prevent loss of hair, smallpox, old age, sunstroke and near-sightedness, and make our everlasting fortunes selling them to the temperance trade."

"That sounds to me very much like a cocktail," said I.

"So it is," he replied. "But it's just as much a medicine as Peruna and not as bad a drink."

Peruna, or, as its owner, Dr. S. B. Hartman, of Columbus, Ohio (once a physician in good standing), prefers to write it, Pe-ru-na, is at present the most prominent proprietary nostrum in the country. It has taken the place once held by Greene's Nervura and by Paine's Celery Compound, and for the same reason which made them popular. The name of that reason is alcohol.* Peruna is a stimulant pure and simple, and it is the more dangerous in that it sails under the false colors of a benign purpose.

According to an authoritative statement given out in private circulation a few years ago by its proprietors, Peruna is a compound of seven drugs with cologne spirits. The formula, they assure me, has not been materially changed. None of the seven drugs is of any great potency. Their total is less than one-half of 1 per cent. of the product. Medicinally they are too inconsiderable, in this proportion, to produce any effect. There remains to Peruna only water and cologne spirits, roughly in the proportion of three to one. Cologne spirits is the commercial term of alcohol.

WHAT PERUNA IS MADE OF

Any one wishing to make Peruna for home consumption may do so by mixing half a pint of cologne spirits, 190 proof, with a pint and a half of water, adding thereto a little cubebs for flavor and a little burned sugar for color. Manufactured in bulk, so a former Peruna agent estimates, its cost, including bottle and wrapper, is between fifteen and eighteen cents a bottle. Its price is $1.00. Because of this handsome margin of profit, and by way of making hay in the stolen sunshine of Peruna advertising, many imitations have sprung up to harass the proprietors of the alcohol-and-water product. Pe-ru-vi-na, P-ru-na, Purina, Anurep (an obvious inversion); these, bottled and labeled to resemble Peruna, are self-confessed imitations. From what the Peruna people tell me, I gather that they are dangerous and damnable frauds, and that they cure nothing.

What does Peruna cure? Catarrh. That is the modest claim for it; nothing but catarrh. To be sure, a careful study of its literature

* Dr. Ashbel P. Grinnell of New York City, who has made a statistical study of patent medicines, asserts as a provable fact that more alcohol is consumed in this country in patent medicines than is dispensed in a legal way by licensed liquor venders, barring the sale of ales and beer.

will suggest its value as a tonic and a preventive of lassitude. But
its reputation rests on catarrh. What is catarrh? Whatever ails
you. No matter what you've got, you will be not only enabled,
but compelled, after reading Dr. Hartman's Peruna book, "The
Ills of Life," to diagnose your illness as catarrh and to realize
that Peruna alone will save you. Pneumonia is catarrh of the lungs;
so is consumption. Dyspepsia is catarrh of the stomach. Enteritis
is catarrh of the intestines. Appendicitis—surgeons, please note
before operating—is catarrh of the appendix. Bright's disease is
catarrh of the kidneys. Heart disease is catarrh of the heart.
Canker sores are catarrh of the mouth. Measles is, perhaps, catarrh
of the skin, since "a teaspoonful of Peruna thrice daily or oftener
is an effectual cure" ("The Ills of Life"). Similarly, malaria, one
may guess, is catarrh of the mosquito that bit you. Other diseases
not specifically placed in the catarrhal class, but yielding to
Peruna (in the book), are colic, mumps, convulsions, neuralgia,
women's complaints and rheumatism. Yet "Peruna is not a cure-
all," virtuously disclaims Dr. Hartman, and grasps at a golden
opportunity by advertising his nostrum as a preventive against
yellow fever! That alcohol and water, with a little coloring matter
and one-half of 1 per cent. of mild drugs, will cure all or any
of the ills listed above is too ridiculous to need refutation. Nor
does Dr. Hartman himself personally make that claim for his
product. He stated to me specifically and repeatedly that no drug
or combination of drugs, with the possible exception of quinine
for malaria, will cure disease. His claim is that the belief of the
patient in Peruna, fostered as it is by the printed testimony, and
aided by the "gentle stimulation," produces good results. It is well
established that in certain classes of disease the opposite is true.
A considerable proportion of tuberculosis cases show a history
of the Peruna type of medicine taken in the early stages, with the
result of diminishing the patient's resistant power, and much of
the typhoid in the middle west is complicated by the victim's
"keeping up" on this stimulus long after he should have been
under a doctor's care. But it is not as a fraud on the sick alone
that Peruna is baneful, but as the maker of drunkards also.

"It can be used any length of time without acquiring a drug
habit," declares the Peruna book, and therein, I regret to say,
lies specifically and directly. The lie is ingeniously backed up by
Dr. Hartman's argument that "nobody could get drunk on the
prescribed doses of Peruna."

Perhaps this is true, though I note three wineglassfuls in forty-five minutes as a prescription, which might temporarily alter a prohibitionist's outlook on life. But what makes Peruna profitable to the maker and a curse to the community at large is the fact that the minimum dose first ceases to satisfy, then the moderate dose, and finally the maximum dose; and the unsuspecting patron, who began with it as a medicine, goes on to use it as a beverage, and finally to be enslaved by it as a habit. A well-known authority on drug addictions writes me:

"A number of physicians have called my attention to the use of Peruna, both preceding and following alcohol and drug addictions. Lydia Pinkham's Compound is another dangerous drug used largely by drinkers; Paine's Celery Compound also. I have in the last two years met four cases of persons who drank Peruna in large quantities to intoxication. This was given to them originally as a tonic. They were treated under my care as simple alcoholics."

THE GOVERNMENT FORBIDS THE SALE OF PERUNA TO INDIANS

Expert opinion on the non-medical side is represented in the government order to the Indian Department, the kernel of which is this:

"In connection with this investigation, please give particular attention to the proprietary medicines and other compounds which the traders keep in stock, with special reference to the liability of their misuse by Indians on account of the alcohol which they contain. The sale of Peruna, which is on the lists of several traders, is hereby absolutely prohibited. As a medicine, something else can be substituted; as an intoxicant, it has been found too tempting and effective. Anything of the sort, under another name, which is found to lead to intoxication, you will please report to this office.

"[Signed] F. C. LARRABEE, Acting Commissioner."

Specific evidence of what Peruna can do will be found in the following report, verified by special investigation:

PINEDALE, WYO., Oct. 4.—(Special.)—"Two men suffering from delirium tremens and one dead is the result of a Peruna intoxication which took place here a few days ago. C. E. Armstrong, of this place, and a party of three others started out on a camping trip to the Yellowstone country, taking with them several bottles of whisky and ten bottles of Peruna, which one of the members of the party was taking as a tonic. The trip lasted over a week. The whisky was exhausted and for two days the party was without liquor. At last some one suggested that they use Peruna, of which nine bottles remained. Before they stopped the whole remaining supply had been consumed and the four men were in a state of intoxication, the like of which they had never known before. Finally, one awoke with terrible cramps in his stomach and found his companions seemingly in an almost lifeless condition. Suffering terrible agony, he crawled on his hands and knees to a ranch over a mile distant, the process taking him half a day. Aid was sent to his three companions. Armstrong was dead when the rescue party arrived. The other two men, still unconscious, were brought to town in a wagon and are still in a weak and emaciated condition. Armstrong's body was almost tied in a knot and could not be straightened for burial."

Here is the testimony from a druggist in a "no license" town:

"Peruna is bought by all the druggists in this section by the gross. I have seen persons thoroughly intoxicated from taking Peruna. The common remark in this place when a drunken party is particularly obstreperous is that he is on a 'Peruna drunk.' It is a notorious fact that a great many do use Peruna to get the alcoholic effect, and they certainly do get it good and strong. Now, there are other so-called remedies used for the same purpose, namely, Gensenica, Kidney Specific, Jamaica Ginger, Hostetter's Bitters, etc."

So well recognized is this use of the nostrum that a number of the Southern newspapers advertise a cure for the "Peruna habit," which is probably worse than the habit, as is usually the case with these "cures." In southern Ohio and in the mountain districts of West Virginia the "Peruna jag" is a standard form of intoxication.

TWO TESTIMONIALS

A testimonial-hunter in the employ of the Peruna company was referred by a Minnesota druggist to a prosperous farmer in the neighborhood. The farmer gave Peruna a most enthusiastic "send-off"; he had been using it for several months and could say, etc. Then he took the agent to his barn and showed him a heap of empty Peruna bottles. The agent counted them. There were seventy-four. The druggist added his testimonial. "That old boy has a 'still' on all the time since he discovered Peruna," said he. "He's my star customer." The druggist's testimonial was not printed.

At the time when certain Chicago drug stores were fighting some of the leading patent medicines, and carrying only a small stock of them, a boy called one evening at one of the downtown shops for thirty-nine bottles of Peruna. "There's the money," he said. "The old man wants to get his before it's all gone." Investigation showed that the purchaser was the night engineer of a big downtown building and that the entire working staff had "chipped in" to get a supply of their favorite stimulant.

"But why should any one want to get drunk on Peruna when he can get whisky?" argues the nostrum-maker.

There are two reasons, one of which is that in many places the "medicine" can be obtained and the liquor can not. Maine, for instance, being a prohibition state, does a big business in patent medicines. So does Kansas. So do most of the no-license counties in the South, though a few have recently thrown out the disguised "boozes." Indian Territory and Oklahoma, as we have seen, have done so because of Poor Lo's predilection toward curing himself of depression with these remedies, and for a time, at least, Peruna was shipped in in unlabeled boxes.

United States District Attorney Mellette, of the western district of Indian Territory, writes: "Vast quantities of Peruna are shipped into this country, and I have caused a number of persons to be indicted for selling the same, and a few of them have been convicted or have entered pleas of guilty. I could give you hundreds of specific cases of 'Peruna drunk' among the Indians. It is a common beverage among them, used for the purposes of intoxication."

The other reason why Peruna or some other of its class is often the agency of drunkenness instead of whisky is that the drinker of Peruna doesn't want to get drunk, at least she doesn't know that she wants to get drunk. I use the feminine pronoun advisedly, because the remedies of this class are largely supported by women. Lydia Pinkham's variety of drink depends for its popularity chiefly on its alcohol. Paine's Celery Compound relieves depression and lack of vitality on the same principle that a cocktail does, and with the same necessity for repetition. I knew an estimable lady from the middle West who visited her dissipated

brother in New York—dissipated from her point of view, because she was a pillar of the W. C. T. U., and he frequently took
a cocktail before dinner and came back with it on his breath,
whereon she would weep over him as one lost to hope. One day,
in a mood of brutal exasperation, when he hadn't had his drink
and was able to discern the flavor of her grief, he turned on her:
"I'll tell you what's the matter with you," he said. "You're
drunk—maudlin drunk!"

She promptly and properly went into hysterics. The physician
who attended diagnosed the case more politely, but to the same
effect, and ascertained that she had consumed something like a
half a bottle of Kilmer's Swamp-Root that afternoon. Now,
Swamp-Root is a very creditable "booze," but much weaker in
alcohol than most of its class. The brother was greatly amused
until he discovered, to his alarm, that his drink-abhorring sister
couldn't get along without her patent medicine bottle! She was
in a fair way, quite innocently, of becoming a drunkard.

Another example of this "unconscious drunkenness" is recorded
by the *Journal of the American Medical Association:* "A respected
clergyman fell ill and the family physician was called. After examining the patient carefully the doctor asked for a private interview with the patient's adult son.

" 'I am sorry to tell you that your father undoubtedly is suffering from chronic alcoholism,' said the physician.

" 'Chronic alcoholism! Why, that's ridiculous! Father never
drank a drop of liquor in his life, and we know all there is to
know about his habits.'

" 'Well, my boy, it's chronic alcoholism, nevertheless, and at
this present moment your father is drunk. How has his health
been recently? Has he been taking any medicine?'

" 'Why, for some time, six months, I should say, father has
often complained of feeling unusually tired. A few months ago
a friend of his recommended Peruna to him, assuring him that
it would build him up. Since then he has taken many bottles of
it, and I am quite sure that he has taken nothing else.' "

From its very name one would naturally absolve Duffy's Malt
Whiskey from fraudulent pretense. But Duffy's Malt Whiskey is
a fraud, for it pretends to be a medicine and to cure all kinds
of lung and throat diseases. It is especially favored by temperance
folk. "A dessertspoonful four to six times a day in water and a
tablespoonful on going to bed" (personal prescription for con-
sumptive), makes a fair grog allowance for an abstainer.

MEDICINE OR LIQUOR?

"You must not forget," writes the doctor in charge, by way of allaying the supposed scruples of the patient, "that taking Duffy's Malt Whiskey in small or medicinal doses is not like taking liquor in large quantities, or as it is usually taken. Taking it a considerable time in medicinal doses, as we direct, leads to health and happiness, while taken the other way it often leads to ruin and decay. If you follow our advice about taking it you will always be in the temperance fold, without qualm of conscience."

It has testimonials ranging from consumption to malaria, and indorsements of the clergy. The whiskey has its recognized place behind the bar, being sold by the manufacturers to the wholesale liquor trade and by them to the saloons, where it may be purchased over the counter for 85 cents a quart. This is cheap, but Duffy's Pure Malt Whiskey is not regarded as a high-class article.

When this series of articles was first projected *Collier's* received a warning from "Warner's Safe Cure," advising that a thorough investigation would be wise before "making any attack" on that preparation. I have no intention of "attacking" this company or any one else, and they would have escaped notice altogether, because of their present unimportance, but for their letter. The suggested investigation was not so thorough as to go deeply into the nature of the remedy, which is an alcoholic liquid, but it developed this interesting fact: Warner's Safe Cure, together with all the Warner remedies, is leased, managed and controlled by the New York and Kentucky Distilling Company, manufacturers of standard whiskies, which do not pretend to remedy anything but thirst. Duffy's Malt Whiskey is another subsidiary company of the New York and Kentucky concern. This statement is respectfully submitted to temperance users of the Malt Whiskey and the Warner remedies.

SOME ALCOHOL PERCENTAGES

Hostetter's Bitters contain, according to an official state analysis, 44 per cent. of alcohol; Lydia Pinkham appeals to suffering womanhood with 20 per cent. of alcohol; Hood's Sarsaparilla cures "that tired feeling" with 18 per cent.; Burdock's Blood Bitters, with 25 per cent.; Ayer's Sarsaparilla, with 26 per cent., and Paine's Celery Compound, with 21 per cent. The fact is that any of these remedies could be interchanged with Peruna or with

each other, so far as general effect goes, though the iodid of
potassium in the sarsaparilla class might have some effect (as likely
to be harmful as helpful) which would be lacking in the simpler
mixtures.

If this class of nostrum is so harmful, asks the attentive reader
of newspaper advertising columns, how explain the indorsements
of so many people of prominence and reputation? "Men of prominence and reputation" in this connection means Peruna, for
Peruna has made a specialty of high government officials and
people in the public eye. In a self-gratulatory dissertation the
Peruna Company observes in substance that, while the leading
minds of the nation have hitherto shrunk from the publicity
attendant on commending any patent medicine, the transcendent
virtues of Peruna have overcome this amiable modesty, and one
and all, they stand forth its avowed champions. This is followed
by an ingenious document headed, "Fifty Members of Congress
Send Letters of Indorsement to the Inventor of the Great Catarrh
Remedy, Pe-ru-na," and quoting thirty-six of the letters. Analysis
of these letters brings out the singular circumstance that in
twenty-one of the thirty-six there is no indication that the writer
has ever tasted the remedy which he so warmly praises. As a
sample, and for the benefit of lovers of ingenious literature, I
reprint the following from a humorous member of Congress:

"My secretary had as bad a case of catarrh as I ever saw, and
since he has taken one bottle of Peruna he seems like a different
man.
"Taylorville, N. C.   ROMULUS Z. LINNEY."

The famous letter of Admiral Schley is a case in point. He
wrote to the Peruna Company:

"I can cheerfully say that Mrs. Schley has used Peruna, and I
believe with good effect. [Signed]   W. S. SCHLEY."

This indorsement went the rounds of the country in half-page
blazonry, to the consternation of the family's friends. Admiral
Schley seems to have appreciated that this use of his name was
detrimental to his standing. He wrote to a Columbus religious
journal the following letter:

"1826 I STREET, WASHINGTON, D. C., Nov. 10, 1904.
"*Editor Catholic Columbian*:—The advertisement of the Peruna Company, inclosed, is made without any authority or
approval from me. When it was brought to my attention first I

wrote the company a letter, stating that the advertisement was offensive and must be discontinued. Their representative here called on me and stated he had been directed to assure me no further publication would be allowed, as it was without my sanction.

"I would say that the advertisement has been made without my knowledge or consent and is an infringement of my rights as a citizen.

"If you will kindly inform me what the name and date of the paper was in which the inclosed advertisement appeared I shall feel obliged.

"Very truly yours, W. S. SCHLEY."

Careful study of this document will show that this is no explicit denial of the testimonial. But who gives careful study to such a letter? On the face of it, it puts the Peruna people in the position of having forged their advertisement. Ninety-nine people out of a hundred would get that impression. Yet I have seen the testimonial, signed with Admiral Schley's name and interlined in the same handwriting as the signature, and I have seen another letter, similarly signed, stating that Admiral Schley had not understood that the letter was to be used for such advertising as the recipient based on it. If these letters are forgeries the victim has his recourse in the law. They are on file at Columbus, Ohio, and the Peruna Company would doubtless produce them in defense of a suit.

WHAT THE GOVERNMENT CAN DO

One thing that the public has a right to demand in its attitude toward the proprietary medicines containing alcohol: that the government carry out rigidly its promised policy no longer to permit liquors to disguise themselves as patent medicines, and thereby escape the tax which is put on other (and probably better) brands of intoxicants. One other demand it should make on the purveyors of the concoctions: that they label every bottle with the percentage of alcohol it contains; then the innocent clergyman who writes testimonials to Duffy, and the W. C. T. U. member who indorses Peruna, Lydia Pinkham, Warner, and their compeers, will know when they imbibe their "tonics," "invigorators," "swamp roots," "bitters," "nerve-builders," or "spring medicines," that they are sipping by the tablespoon or wineglassful what the town tippler takes across the license-paying bar.

1905

The Turn of the Century— and Beyond

Part 5

The Turn of the Century— and Beyond

SYNOPSIS

WHAT *makes a man decide to become a doctor? Why is the profession still basically an Art, as well as a Science? Light is thrown on these questions in the first three brief selections included in Part V: "The Doctor," by Robert Louis Stevenson, whose malady made him well-acquainted with the breed; "On Becoming a Doctor," by Holmes, Sims, Freud, Grenfell, Cannon and Ellis; and "The Art of Medicine," by the world-famous Hopkins and Harvard surgeon, Harvey Cushing.*

Cushing's theme is on medicine as practice; but as Professor Cannon points out in "The Career of the Investigator," practice is only one of a number of avenues open to the young student of medicine. The emphasis in his paper is on research—the study not of what is known but of what is still to be learned. In this and in the following paper, "Gains From Serendipity," the man who followed in the footsteps of Bernard to become one of the foremost physiologists offers some of the wisest and most enlightening things that have been written on the subject. There is no question that laboratory research is responsible for the vast majority of all advances made in the field of modern medicine. Professor Zinsser writes briefly about the adventurous charms of "Laboratories"; while some of the tools available for the laboratory technician as well as the practitioner are discussed in "Chemistry in the Service of Medicine," by Edwin W. Slosson and "The Doctor and the Physicist," by George Russell Harrison.

493

We now come to some of the great discoveries of the period. Toward the end of the last century it was said by an eminent physicist that the science had reached an impasse, that it had explained everything that required explanation. Even as he made the statement, the new physics, which has influenced our lives so profoundly, was being born in the work of Becquerel, Madame Curie and Roentgen. The discovery which had the most immediate effect on medicine is described in Roentgen's classic paper, reprinted here, "On a New Kind of Rays." Working in his laboratory in Würzburg, Roentgen noticed that a Crookes tube which had been completely covered could cause paper which had been coated with certain metallic salts to glow. Further, when he held his hand in front of the paper, the invisible rays from the tube cast the shadow of his bones. The discovery resulted in amusing popular misconceptions: X-ray proof clothing was advertised for modest ladies and in New Jersey a legislative bill was introduced to prohibit the use of X-rays in opera glasses. The discovery has had repercussions in every field of science. In medicine it has proved to be one of the most powerful diagnostic tools available to doctors.

When the X-ray was first discovered, one professor remarked that he hoped it would help him penetrate the skulls of his less intelligent students. It is not too far fetched to say that for such a purpose the discoveries in psychoanalysis of Sigmund Freud can be compared with that of Roentgen. Here indeed was the discovery of a whole new world—the world of the subconscious —and a new method of understanding what happens in the minds of both normal and abnormal individuals. Dr. Brill, who writes "The Psychology of Sigmund Freud," is one of the leading practitioners of psychoanalysis in the United States.

The next three selections deal with dramatic episodes in one of the most important branches of modern medicine, the study of tropical diseases. Of all these diseases, the most widespread and important is malaria. In fact, it has been stated that the toll which malaria has taken in the form of incapacitation and death has been greater than that of any other disease of any sort. The first step to a discovery of its true nature was made by Alphonse Laveran, an army surgeon in Algeria, in 1880. In that year, he discovered a microscopic animal parasite in the blood of victims of the disease. In 1897, Ronald Ross discovered this same parasite in the stomach of anopheles mosquitoes which had sucked the blood of malarial patients. The next year, he showed that the parasite was trans-

mitted to victims on whom the mosquito subsequently fed. The method of transmittal was entirely different from that of most other diseases—an insect was the villain of the piece. Ross was an extraordinarily gifted human being—a poet, novelist, musician and painter, as well as a scientist. He describes the moment of discovery in "Malaria," an excerpt from his autobiography.

In his Dedication to Ross in "The Story of Medicine," Professor Victor Robinson writes as follows: "Sanitarians have realized that the malaria-fighter 'must learn to think like a mosquito and act like a larva.' The most effective of all mosquito hunters, the man who emerged from the swamps with the truth beneath the cracked eye-piece of his microscope, is Ronald Ross. Obstructed by officials, sick from heat and work and worry, his painful eyes finally looked at the cause of malaria. Mosquito Day—August 20, 1897—must be regarded as the birthday of a new era in public health. The spirit of Ross sent Walter Reed on his Cuban adventure, from which he returned with proof that in the bite of the mosquito lies the mystery of yellow fever. The work of Ross was the inspiration of Gorgas in the uncertain years on the fatal Isthmus. After ships began to sail through the interoceanic waterway, Gorgas never hesitated to state that the preventive discovery of Ross enabled the building of the Panama canal."

The above paragraph introduces a subject which was the basis for a play by Sidney Howard, as well as for innumerable books and articles. The scenes of misery and degradation which occurred when yellow fever struck at a community are described in "The Ravages of Yellow Fever," four eye-witness accounts, including one by the pioneer Philadelphia physician, Dr. Benjamin Rush. (All of these accounts, incidentally, appeared in the biography, "Walter Reed and Yellow Fever," a notable work by Howard A. Kelly, one of the "big four" of Johns Hopkins.) The first move in the direction of the abolition of the disease, the famous experimental work in Cuba during the Spanish-American work, is here described by one of the members of the Yellow Fever Commission, Dr. Aristides Agramonte, in "The Inside Story of a Great Medical Discovery." With the knowledge which this discovery had placed in his hands, the chief sanitary officer of Havana, Dr. William C. Gorgas, proceeded by the systematic destruction of mosquitoes to free the city from the disease for the first time in 150 years. In 1896, deaths in Havana from Yellow Fever numbered 1282. In 1900 there were 310. In 1902, 1903 and 1904 not a single death occurred.

But the work was still not finished. What was the parasite which caused the disease? Actually, it has turned out to be a virus, but before that fact was to become known, famous scientists like Noguchi of the Rockefeller Institute, were to die of the disease while investigating it. And as this is written, in October of 1951, comes the announcement of the award of the Nobel Prize to Dr. Max Theiler, of the Rockefeller Foundation, for his development of 17-D, the yellow fever vaccine with which over 8,000,000 members of the armed forces alone were protected during World War II.

Another disease, seemingly similar yet actually utterly different, which owes its eradication to American science, is the subject of the next selection, "Goldberger and Pellagra," by Robert P. Parsons. Like scurvy, pellagra is one of the great deficiency diseases, caused directly by poverty and resultant undernourishment. Contagion has nothing whatever to do with its appearance but reactionary public health officials of the American South, where it was especially prevalent, were unwilling to admit the fact. Dr. Parsons of the United States Navy here tells in dramatic fashion how Joseph Goldberger of the U. S. Public Health Service proved the facts about pellagra and forced their acceptance.

The initial clue to another deficiency disease, pernicious anemia, came from Dr. George Richard Minot and Dr. William P. Murphy. The former writes about it in the short article entitled "Anemia." In 1926, they showed that there was an active ingredient in liver which benefited victims of the disease. Patients were at first required to eat enormous quantities of liver every day. Gradually extracts were developed, and it is now known that the active ingredient is Vitamin B-12, isolated in 1948, and containing cobalt. In contrast to the pounds of liver formerly required, it is effective in quantities which are measured in millionths of an ounce.

From the earliest times the importance of the "ductless" glands, now referred to as the glands of internal secretion, has been appreciated. Ten centuries before the Christian era, the Hindus referred to glandular secretions. Glandular medicine, especially the administering of sex glands, goes back to remote antiquity. And in the contemporary work on ACTH, discussed later, we see that developments in the field are still far from completion. As a bridge between the old and the new, we offer a general roundup, "The Story of the Glands of Internal Secretion," by

Walter Timme, Professor of Clinical Neurology at the College of Physicians and Surgeons at Columbia.

What decides a young man's choice of a medical school? Today there are many fine medical schools in every section of the country, and with present crowded conditions, it is often a question of where he will be admitted. At the beginning of the century, the situation was entirely different. The leading hospital, as well as the leading medical school, was Johns Hopkins in Baltimore. In 1873, Johns Hopkins, a wealthy merchant and banker, bequeathed thirteen acres of land to the Trustees of the Johns Hopkins Fund for the erection of a hospital. He insisted that the medical and surgical staff should be of the highest character, that a training school for nurses be established and that the hospital should ultimately form part of the Medical School of the University.

A man of great vision, John Shaw Billings, was appointed Medical Advisor to the Trustees. In his report, "The Johns Hopkins Hospital," reprinted here in part, he insisted on the revolutionary idea of the importance of original investigation; and on the equally important need of obtaining good men to do the work. He set out to find the best men obtainable. The first of these was the noted pathologist William H. Welch; the second, appointed physician-in-chief, was the Canadian, William Osler. Later, other distinguished physicians, among them William S. Halsted and Howard A. Kelley, were to join them to make up a faculty of dazzling brilliance. "The big four" were to have a profound effect on the development of medicine in America. Their students entered into every facet of our medical life. Among them were Reed, Carroll and Lazear, of the Yellow Fever Commission; the Mayo brothers; Cushing, the great brain surgeon; Simon Flexner, first director of the Rockefeller Institute for Medical Research. They are the subjects of the account entitled, "My Medical Colleagues," by J. M. T. Finney. Here they are, not only in their greatness, but in the very human traits which influenced their lives and work.

Of them all, Osler was perhaps the most charming person as well as the most influential writer. His text book of medicine was standard in medical schools for many years. His non-technical writings, such as "Æquanimitas," were read avidly by teachers, practitioners and students. From these "Writings," we have taken three brief but typical quotations.

Our final selections are descriptions in their own words of the medical experiences of three widely different kinds of physician, each of eminent stature in his field. Hans Zinsser, the noted bacteriologist, author of "Rats, Lice and History" from which we have already quoted, spent some time as a practitioner before he turned to the laboratory work which was to be his true career. From his fascinating "As I Remember Him," we take his account of "Medical Practice," a selection which is typical of the amusing and occasionally heartbreaking experiences of the young doctor starting out.

The second of these personal experiences, "Leprosy in the Philippines," comes from the famous book by Victor Heiser, "An American Doctor's Odyssey." Heiser was a member of the International Health Division of the Rockefeller Foundation, which has had a profound effect on public health work throughout the world, and which has done so much to stamp out disease. Heiser was Health Director of the Philippines at the time of the leprosy episode. The reader can console himself with the fact that the painful scenes described here need no longer be enacted. The policy of strict segregation is no longer standard practice. Even more important, the administration of the loathsome-tasting chaulmoogra oil is being abandoned in favor of the modern drugs, the sulfones. These are proving beneficial in the treatment of many cases, and some specialists even hold out the hope that sanatoria for lepers (or as they are now known, sufferers from Hansen's disease) can be closed within a matter of decades.

Finally, in "On the Edge of the Primeval Forest," are related the experiences of a medical missionary who is also a great philosopher and musician, Albert Schweitzer. A world authority on Bach, Schweitzer felt impelled to give up his life to service of his fellow men. Here he explains what impelled him to make the move and describes his early experiences in French Equatorial Africa among natives who still felt the "supernatural power for evil which one man can exert over another" and who continued to practice fetishism and other forms of magic. Schweitzer's influence has not been restricted to Africa. It is so large that he has been called the greatest man living today. His remarkable "Philosophy of Civilization" and his other philosophical works reveal a profound belief in his fellow man and a "reverence for life" which his own actions have completely exemplified.

The Doctor

ROBERT LOUIS STEVENSON

HE IS the flower (such as it is) of our civilization; and when the stage of man is done with, and only remembered to be marveled at in history, he will be thought to have shared as little as any in the defects of the period, and most notably exhibited the virtues of the race. Generosity he has, such as is possible to those who practise an art, never to those who drive a trade; discretion, tested by a hundred secrets; tact, tried in a thousand embarrassments; and what are more important, Heraclean cheerfulness and courage. So it is that he brings air and cheer into the sickroom, and often enough, though not so often as he wishes, brings healing.

On Becoming a Doctor

I

OLIVER WENDELL HOLMES

I MUST announce to you the startling position that I have been a medical student for more than six months, and am sitting with Wistar's Anatomy beneath my quiescent arm, with a stethoscope on my desk, and the blood-stained implements of my ungracious profession around me. I do not know what you will say,—but I cannot help it . . . I know I might have made an indifferent lawyer,—and I think I may make a tolerable physician,—I did

not like the one, and I do like the other. And so you must know
that for the last several months I have been quietly occupying a
room in Boston, attending medical lectures, going to the Massachusetts Hospital, and slicing and slivering the carcasses of better
men and women than I ever was myself or am like to be. It is a
sin for a puny little fellow like me to mutilate one of your six-
foot men as if he was a sheep,—but *vive la science*!

I must write a piece and call it records of the dissecting room,
so let me save all my pretty things, as plums for my pudding. If
you would die fagged to death like a crow with the king birds
after him,—be a schoolmaster; if you would wax thin and savage,
like a half-fed spider,—be a lawyer; if you would go off like an
opium-eater in love with your starving delusions,—be a doctor.

1831

II

J. MARION SIMS

I HAVE been asked many times why I studied medicine. There
was no premonition of the traits of a doctor in my career as a
youngster; but it was simply in this way:

At that day and time, the only avenues open to a young man
of university education were those of the learned professions. A
graduate of a college had either to become a lawyer, go into the
church, or to be a doctor. I would not be a lawyer; I could not
be a minister; and there was nothing left for me to do but to be a
doctor—to study medicine or to disgrace my family; for it was
generally thought that a man who had gone through college,
and came back and settled down as a merchant's clerk, couldn't
have had much in him if he didn't take to a profession. So there
was nothing else left for me but to study medicine. One day my
father said, "I guess you had better go down and see Mr. Howard
about your beginning your studies with him."

I said: "Father, I know that I have been a great disappointment
to you. I knew from the outset that you wanted me to become
a lawyer. It is impossible for me to be a lawyer; I have neither the
talent nor the gifts necessary for the profession. I cannot enter
Mr. Howard's office." He said: "What in the world are you going
to do, then?"

I said: "If I hadn't gone to college I know what I should have done. I would have accepted Mr. Stringfellow's offer of three hundred dollars a year, and gone into his store two years ago, and by this time I should be getting five hundred dollars a year. But as it is, I suppose I must study a profession, so long as I have had a university education, and there is nothing else left for me but the study of medicine, if I *must* take a profession."

He said to me: "My son, I confess that I am disappointed in you, and if I had known this I certainly should not have sent you to college."

I replied: "I did not want to go; I knew that you were not able to send me there, and I knew that you would be disappointed, and that I should make you unhappy. I am sure that you are no more unhappy about it than I am now. But if I must study a profession, there is nothing left for me to do but to study medicine."

He replied: "Well, I suppose that I can not control you; but it is a profession for which I have the utmost contempt. There is no science in it. There is no honor to be achieved in it; no reputation to be made, and to think that *my* son should be going around from house to house through this country, with a box of pills in one hand and a squirt in the other, to ameliorate human suffering, is a thought I never supposed I should have to contemplate."

However, he told me to go and see Dr. Churchill Jones, and make arrangements to study medicine. The next morning, I felt happily relieved at having been enabled to pass through that terrible ordeal with my poor disappointed father. I began immediately to read medicine with Dr. Jones. Dr. Churchill Jones was a man of very great ability. The people in the country around had very great respect for and confidence in him as a physician. But, unfortunately, he drank. That, for a time, seemed to unfit him for the duties of his profession. Besides, he had no facilities for medical instruction, for he had few or no books; and I read anatomy, read the practice, and all the medical books I could get hold of, without any teacher, or reading to any profit whatever. I was very glad when I was able to leave his office, and go to attend medical lectures. But he was a very great surgeon, and from him I imbibed a desire to distinguish myself in surgery, if I ever should become a doctor.

1888

III

SIGMUND FREUD

I WAS born on May 6th, 1856, at Freiberg in Moravia, a small town in what is now Czecho-Slovakia. . . .

Although we lived in very limited circumstances, my father insisted that, in my choice of a profession, I should follow my own inclinations. Neither at that time, nor indeed in my later life, did I feel any particular predilection for the career of a physician. I was moved, rather, by a sort of curiosity, which was, however, directed more towards human concerns than towards natural objects; nor had I recognized the importance of observation as one of the best means of gratifying it. At the same time, the theories of Darwin, which were then of topical interest, strongly attracted me, for they held out hopes of an extraordinary advance in our understanding of the world; and it was hearing Goethe's beautiful essay on Nature read aloud at a popular lecture just before I left school that decided me to become a medical student.

Edition of 1935

IV

WILFRED T. GRENFELL

NONE of our family on either side, so far as I can find out, had ever practised medicine. My own experience of doctors had been rather a chequered one, but at my father's suggestion I gladly went up and discussed the matter with our country family doctor. He was a fine man, and we boys were very fond of him and his family, his daughter being our best girl friend near by. He had an enormous practice, in which he was eminently successful. The number of horses he kept, and the miles he covered with them, were phenomenal in my mind. He had always a kind word for every one, and never gave us boys away, though he must have known many of our pranks played in our parents' absence. The only remaining memory of that visit was that the old doctor brought down from one of his shelves a large jar, out of which he produced a pickled human brain. I was thrilled with entirely new emotions. I had never thought of man's body as a machine. That this weird, white-puckered-up mass could be the producer or transmitter of all that made man, that it controlled our physical strength and growth, and our responses to life, that it made one into "Mad G." and another into me—why, it was absolutely marvelous. It attracted me as did the gramophone, the camera, the automobile.

My father saw at once on my return that I had found my real interest, and put before me two alternative plans, one to go to Oxford, where my brother had just entered, or to join him in London and take up work in the London Hospital and University, preparatory to going in for medicine. I chose the latter at once— a decision I have never regretted.

1919

V

WALTER B. CANNON

WHEN I was a boy my father had expressed a wish that I might become a doctor. Somewhat vaguely I had that intent when I entered Harvard College. It was not until I had passed about halfway through the college period and had studied chemistry and biology to a considerable degree that the resolution became definitely formulated. At that time I was attracted by the possibility of devoting my life to neurology and psychiatry. With this aim I undertook work on the structure of the brain and in psychology. While in the Medical School I paid special attention to courses concerned with diseases of the nervous system. It is probable that if, while a first-year student of medicine, I had not undertaken research on the physiology of the digestive tract by use of the then newly discovered X-rays, I would have become a neurologist.

My father's wish that I might become a physician was there-fore never realized. Instead of engaging in practice I engaged in teaching medical students. This was what my predecessor, Dr. Bowditch, had done. He told the tale of a conversation between one of his children and a little companion. The companion asked, "Has your father many patients?" and the answer was, "He has no patients." "What! A doctor and no patients?" Thereupon the apologetic answer, "Oh, no, he is one of those doctors who don't know anything!" Possibly the children of other physiologists suffer from the same sense of inferiority. One of my daughters, on being informed proudly by a little friend that *her* father was a doctor, remarked somewhat sadly, "*My* father is only a father!"

1945

VI

HAVELOCK ELLIS

EVER since I had left school—and even before—I had never had the slightest idea how to gain my living. I never felt the faintest real vocation for any course of life. If asked what I would like to be, I could only have answered as Diderot answered in youth, 'Mais rien, mais rien du tout.' With me, as with Diderot, a creature of superabundant energy, this was far from meaning laziness or indifference. It was merely the mark of one whose temperament is too obstinately aboriginal to be fitted into one of the existing frameworks of life. I was most anxious and worried over the matter. My mother had once suggested that being fond of books, I might be a bookseller, but that idea had not the slightest attraction for me; indeed, none of the families I proceeded from, except the Olivers, had ever been drawn to business, or made any success in business, and in books as books, moreover, I never took an interest. It might possibly be said that it was by an unconscious atavistic impulse—I knew nothing then of my remote ecclesiastical ancestry—that the first profession I ever thought of entering, when about the age of fifteen, was the Church. The idea was, in fact, most likely the natural outcome of my own religious attitude and environment, and the fact that my friend Mackay was at that time preparing to become a clergyman. But it was a career for which I was in every respect singularly unsuited, and the idea, which never took deep root, was soon effaced when shortly afterwards I lost my early faith in Christianity. The occupation of teaching which I had fallen into on reaching Australia was as unsuitable for me as the Church, and from the first I merely adopted it as a temporary resource. I never had any wish to devote myself to teaching and I have always been rather sceptical about what is falsely called "education." At some time in Australia I believe that the idea of a legal career floated passingly across my mind, but for me it was as absurd as any of the others. My future career in life remained a puzzling and painful problem to which I could never see any solution.

The question was still in that position, when, a few weeks after the experience I have just told, I began to read the *Life and Letters of James Hinton* by Ellice Hopkins, and by a strange chance Hinton was fated to have as decisive an influence on my practical work in life as. already on my spiritual welfare. I was still in the first chapter of the book, reading as I lay—it was sometimes my position when tired after the day's work—full length on the hard bench in my schoolroom, on which I usually sat in the absence of a chair; a position more or less horizontal is always with me the most favorable to mental activity. As I read, in completely calm and disinterested manner, I came to that point in the narrative where it is stated that on the advice of the family doctor it was decided that young James should enter the medical profession, as giving the necessary scope to his mental activity, and was accordingly placed at Saint Bartholomew's Hospital Medical School, having just reached his twentieth year, the age I had myself then almost reached. Suddenly I leapt to my feet as though I had been shot. "I will become a doctor!" a voice within me seemed to say. Therewith, in that instant, the question that had worried me for so many years was once and for all decided. On the conscious plane, difficult problems, especially if of a practical nature, are only settled in my mind with the greatest hesitation and much swaying back and forth between the arguments on this side and on that, and even to the end I remain uncertain, although, when once the decision is made, I doubt no more and never turn back. But now, in settling the greatest practical question of life, I settled it in an instant, without even any deliberation at all—for the idea of becoming a doctor had never before so much as entered my head—and settled it so finally that I never once called my decision in question.

. . . I quickly realized that the career of an ordinary medical practitioner had no attractions for me. As soon as I began to reflect on the meaning of that sudden conviction, I saw that the main reason why I wanted to be a doctor was not because I wanted a doctor's life, but because I needed a doctor's education. A doctor's career was not my career, but a doctor's training was the necessary portal to my career. Therein I was entirely right. I might have been tempted to say, like some clever and brilliant people I can think of, that of the things I wanted to know medicine had little to teach and that I could best work in complete independence of traditional investigation. I was fortunately saved from that fate by a primitive trait of my mental constitution. My most revolutionary impulses are combined with an equally strong impulse to reverence tradition and seek out its bases. Just as I could not undertake to study the revolutionary Rabelais without investigating the whole history of the fifteenth century, so I could not reach my own new conception of sex without studying the established conventions of medical science. It has been fortunate for me that it is so. If I had not studied medicine from the beginning, if I had not been a duly accredited practitioner in medicine, surgery, and midwifery, I could never have gained a confident grasp of the problem of sex, I could never have set forth my own personal investigations and results in the volumes of my *Studies*, and I could never have found a decent firm to publish them. I should have spent my days in an almost helpless struggle, and my life-blood would have been drunk by the thirsty sands of time. I should have dropped and left no mark. By adopting the medical profession I acquired the only foundation on which I could build my own work.

1939

The Art of Medicine

HARVEY CUSHING

THE ideals and standards of the profession having been the same these past two thousand years and more, the difficulties of living up to them are, it may be assumed, no greater now than they ever have been. And, so far as concerns the intrinsic diffi- culties of actual practice of the Art, it may well enough be argued that they grow increasingly less now that the instruments of precision come to replace the cruder, old-time methods of obser- vation of the patient's symptoms, many of which can now be estimated and recorded with some approach to mathematical accuracy.

Medicine, in short, becomes constantly more exact and scientific in its procedures. It is prompt to adopt for its own uses new knowledge of most varied kinds that comes from the chemist, the physicist, and the biologist, whose primary motive is the extension of knowledge and who admit little if any interest in the application of their discoveries by the medical profession. Roentgen could hardly have dreamed that his discovery would revolutionize our methods of diagnosis; the Curies that radium would prove to be an effective agent in combating certain kinds of malignant tumors; or Faraday that his alternating current would some day be utilized in place of the scalpel to make dissection a relatively bloodless procedure.

You will see, then, that a distinction is drawn between the Art and the Science of Medicine. The Art in its Hippocratic sense has reference among other things to the practising doctor's ability to inspire confidence in his patients and their relatives. This requires on his part an understanding of human nature, abounding unselfishness, unflagging sympathy, and observance of the Golden Rule. It calls for the exercise of that sort of benevolent common sense in the handling of many domestic problems, not always actually relating to ill health, which so often makes the general practitioner an indispensable "familiar" in those households that have learned to accept him as trusted confidant and adviser. . . .

The general practitioner may hold this sort of intimate and responsible relationship with a few families in a town or city, or his influence may spread over a large country district or be still more widely felt even than that. Wilfred Grenfell as the doctor of the Labrador may be mentioned as one in whom the Art is exemplified at its best; and the same qualities that have enabled him to salvage the souls and bodies of the stray dwellers on that dour coast, by teaching them how spiritually and economically and physically their condition could be improved, exist in countless other Grenfells in smaller and less picturesque fields of work, unnoticed, though perhaps at your very door, who no less perfectly understand and practise the Art of Medicine.

1940

The Career of the Investigator[1]

WALTER B. CANNON

SCARCELY more than a generation ago the graduate in medicine had his professional career marked out for him with a fair degree of definiteness. Private practise, as exemplified in the functions of the family physician, offered, apart from surgery, almost the only opportunity for the use of a medical training. During the past thirty years how extensively have medical activities become diversified. The paths of service that now invite the young physician are so varied that every graduate should be able to select a way for employing his peculiar powers to the best advantage. Quite apart from the conventional career of the physician, the surgeon, or the different specialists, are the opportunities for usefulness in the widespread movements which are socializing medicine. In professional service at hospitals and sanatoriums important work can be done; in boards of health, municipal, state and national; in public propaganda for temperance, for the prevention of infant mortality, for industrial hygiene, for the care of school children; in the campaigns against tuberculosis and venereal disease—in all these activities the possibilities of applying a medical education usefully to social needs are numerous and are yearly increasing.

Still another new career open to the young graduate is that of research in the medical sciences. . . .

As children we all have an instinctive curiosity concerning the world about us, a curiosity which most of us gradually lose as we fit ourselves into the social conventions. The investigator is one, however, in whom this natural curiosity still persists. He has never got past the annoying stage of asking "Why?" The events occurring on every side which are matters of course to most men, startle him into wonderment. Why does the spinning top not fall? Why do animals breathe faster when they run? Why does disturbed water take the form of waves? Why do roots grow downward? Why does the mouth become dry when one speaks in public? Such are the questions that arise. The answers to them may be incalculably valuable to mankind. The microscope re-

[1] Address to the graduating class of the Yale Medical School, June, 1911.

vealed to Pasteur strange organisms in bad-tasting wines. Why may not the disease of the wine, he asked himself, be due to the growth of these unusual germs within it? And later when he found germs also in silk worms, the further question was suggested, Why may not animals likewise become diseased in exactly the same manner? Whether the surmises of the investigator are true, the testimony of other men usually does not tell. He must turn to nature herself and put the idea to the test of observation and experiment.

This process of scientific inquiry involves peculiar qualifications which can not be disregarded by any one who thinks of trying it. Research implies in the first place *seeking again* over a region which has been previously traversed in order to learn what other men have done and the point where their labors ended. To make progress sure, therefore, previous records must be carefully studied. The failure to pay this just tribute to those who have labored before has not seldom led to fruitless effort or to vain repetition of work already well done. Marking the boundaries demands, then, a scholarly acquaintance with earlier discoveries; and the painstaking methods of the scholar must be used.

An ingenious and inventive imagination is a second requirement. It serves to indicate where the problems lie and also to suggest possible methods for solving them. The mind must be hospitable to all ideas thus presented, and yet it must receive them with skeptical scrutiny. By critically considering a plan for solving a problem it is often possible to select central tests, which are strategically related to the logic of the entire research. The physiologist Goltz is said to have done his most important work while fishing, for he employed that time in devising the crucially significant experiments.

Not all inquiries, however, can be ended by a relatively small number of crucial tests. Some investigations, like the important breeding experiments of de Vries, require years before they can be brought to a conclusion. Patience and an enthusiasm which is intelligently persistent are therefore essential qualities for the man in quest of new truths. The hopeful spirit is especially needed when, at the end of a long search, the investigator finds that he has only his labor for his pains—when his leading idea has proved to be false. That disheartening event is what Huxley called the tragedy of science—"the slaying of a beautiful hypothesis by an ugly fact."

The very soul of research, finally, is the highest degree of honesty. The investigator should see clearly and accurately with an eye single to the truth. He has to consider not only the observations which fit his theory, but any others as well. The erratic cases invariably make trouble, but they are often disguised blessings. They may indeed be of far greater moment than those which have been anticipated, for they may point the way to entirely unsuspected facts. In my early studies on digestion I well remember how much I was annoyed by the repeated failure of some animals to show any signs of digestive activity during the period of observation. You can imagine how suddenly my vexation changed to deep interest when the troublesome inhibition was found to be an accompaniment of fright or anxiety which these animals showed while being looked through with the X-rays.

After the investigator has completed his examination of a group of questions which have interested him, his leading idea, his tests and his results must be described with scrupulous exactness. In thus reporting his work he should strive to be like clearest crystal, receiving the light and transmitting it untinged by any trace of color.

Scientific activity implies, of course, thorough disinterestedness. The investigator asks no favors and renders none. Any intimation that he act as a retainer or special pleader, any hint or suggestion that he restrict his explorations within certain limits lest he injure cherished traditions, is a step towards the confinement of the free spirit of intellectual inquiry. Rather than surrender that freedom of inquiry or the right of untrammelled announcement of fresh discoveries, men of science have in the past submitted to tortures and painful death, and you may be sure that, if need be, they will be ready to sacrifice themselves again. So exalted is the regard in which the man of science holds the ideal to which his life is devoted that he would find in these words of Fichte his solemn pledge:

> To this I am called, to bear witness to the Truth. My life, my fortunes, are of little moment; the results of my life are of infinite moment. I am a Priest of Truth; I am in her pay; I have bound myself to do all things, to venture all things, to suffer all things for her. If I should be persecuted and hated for her sake, if I should even meet death in her service, what wonderful thing is it I shall have done—what but that which I clearly ought to do?

The satisfactions of a life devoted to investigation, like the satisfactions of other careers, arise from the profitable use of one's powers. The peculiar powers which are needed for research I have just described. The employment of these powers in perfect freedom, and the immeasurably important results that flow therefrom, render the satisfactions of productive scholarship especially keen. These satisfactions we may now consider in relation to the special qualifications of the investigator.

The requirement that the investigator learn what other men have done before him in the field he seeks to enlarge gives him an unusual realization of the part he may be playing in the promotion of natural knowledge. Knowledge grows like the picture in the dissected puzzle. Every addition must fit the parts already arranged in order to possess significance, and also every addition makes possible the fitting of new parts whose positions in the enlarging picture become thereby suddenly revealed. One of the delights of research, therefore, is the sense that every bit of new knowledge finds its place in the structure of truth, and that sooner or later it will be required for the further building of that structure. The relation which the fresh contribution bears to that already established, the discoverer clearly sees; what relation it will certainly bear to further contributions he may never know. How little did the men who studied the minute differences among mosquitoes, and who recorded the breeding habits of those insects realize their important rôle in abolishing the pestilence of yellow fever, and in bringing about the immense social and political changes which will result from that conquest.

Because every discovery becomes the basis for further discovery the imagination of the investigator is constantly stimulated. New facts suggest in turn other facts and point to unsuspected relations between things that have long been known. Bayliss and Starling's discovery of a natural chemical stimulant which induces secretion of the pancreas led directly to the explanation of continued gastric secretion, and also to finding the marvelous mechanism by which the mammary glands are prepared for the giving of milk. Thus, though the interests of the man of science seem at the moment narrow and restricted, they may nevertheless lead his thought out into many diverse realms of knowledge. These excursions of the imagination offer repeated suggestions for fresh adventure. The look therefore is always forward to what may be seen when the next step is taken. Seeking new things becomes in time a fixed habit. Past achievements neither satisfy interest nor hold attention—they become fused with the established routine from which it is a happiness to escape. The chance of beholding unsuspected wonders, or the possibility of finding that something imagined is really true is a constant incitement to further search and furnishes the zest and interest which are among the best rewards of the investigator.

Much happiness is found also in that single-mindedness, which, as we have seen, is one of the prime conditions in the pursuit of knowledge. It implies freedom from bigotry and prejudice, freedom from many of the influences and motives that to their regret men feel compelled to respect for purposes of prudence or policy. The intrusion of any other motive, save that of discovering and telling the truth, only tends to distract the mind of the investigator from his absorbing work. Faraday, whose life as a man of science was near perfection, wrote:

> Do not many fail because they look rather to the renown to be acquired than to the pure acquisition of knowledge. and the delight which the contented mind has in acquiring it for its own sake? I am sure I have seen many who would have been good and successful pursuers of science and have gained themselves a high name, but that it was the name and the reward they were always looking forward to—the reward of the world's praise. In such there is always a shade of envy or regret over their minds, and I can not imagine a man making discoveries in science under these feelings.

Single-mindedness involves also a relative indifference to those motives of money-getting which prevail in commercial life. Success in research is fortunately not measured by money standards. And yet research flourishes best where there is free time to spend in thought and experiment. This time element is essential. The investigator may be made to dwell in a garret, he may be forced to live on crusts and wear dilapidated clothes, he may be deprived of social recognition, but if he has time, he can steadfastly devote himself to research. Take away his free time, and he is utterly destroyed as a contributor to knowledge. Free time and absence of the money motive, however, are found together only among the indolent poor and the indolent rich; and the observation has been made that neither of these classes is likely to contribute men of science. The industry of the investigator which results in new knowledge—knowledge in its unprofitable infancy—does not possess commercial value. Until recently indeed any money value of research had not been recognized. In the unappreciative past deplorable instances were known of struggles with poverty and want, going hand in hand with persistent loyalty to truth-seeking. Now, however, accumulated wealth is giving leisure for men to carry on their investigations free from the worries of uncertain livelihood. What they receive may not be much, but it is sufficient to permit them to look upon the scramble for wealth without envy or regret.

Fortunately, the provisions which enable men to pursue careers in science are found mainly in great universities, through which a stream of youth is constantly passing. There men who are moved by the instinct of investigation usually find their most congenial surroundings. Freedom of inquiry is the ancient tradition of the university spirit, leisure is recognized as a requisite for meditative observation, and the youth who resort to these centers of learning can be awakened to wonder at nature's hidden secrets, and can be stimulated to undertake with ardor the struggle to possess them. The peculiar richness of university life flows from memories of the transforming powers of the progressive and original minds who have by their eagerness for the truth and their freedom from worldliness inspired their students with their own ideals.

The greatest compensation, after all, for the truth seeker is the discovery of the truth. The value of labor that brings a revelation of new knowledge does not cease with the day; it remains as a permanent acquisition for the race. There is really great satisfaction to the investigator in this thought of the "durable results of the perishable years." But not only because of the permanence of truth is there pleasure in discovery—it is the marvel of beholding for the first time an unknown aspect of nature that fascinates men of science, and through difficulties and repeated disappointments holds them to the search. Only he who has had the experience knows the thrill that comes when that which was imagined proves to be true. One who was in Faraday's laboratory when the influence of the earth's magnetism on a wire conducting an electric current was first tested, has written: "All at once Faraday exclaimed, 'Do you see, do you see, do you see!' as the wire began to revolve, and I shall never forget the enthusiasm expressed in his face and the sparkling in his eyes." Kepler knew the joy which rewards the scientific discoverer when he completed the evidence that established his third law of planetary motion. Even one whose pulses have not quickened with the excitement of discovery can understand perhaps how he must have felt as he burst into triumphant exultation:

> What I prophesied two-and-twenty years ago, . . . what sixteen years ago I urged as a thing to be sought, . . . that for which I devoted the best part of my life to astronomical contemplations, at length I have brought to light and recognized its truth beyond my most sanguine expectations. It is not eighteen months since I got the first glimpse of light, three months since the dawn, very few days since the unveiled sun burst upon me. Nothing holds me; I will indulge my sacred fury. If you forgive me, I rejoice; if you are angry, I can bear it. The die is cast, the book is written, to be read either now or by posterity, I care not which. It may well wait a century for a reader, as God has waited six thousand years for an observer.

The scientific investigator may not seek particularly for knowledge which can meet at once some material need. Like the artist, he is more prone to direct his efforts towards that which will for the moment properly gratify an absorbing interest of his mind. If the new knowledge has, when discovered, an immediate practical value, so much the better; but the direct search for understanding has certainly always proved the most effective motive in scientific labors. Because of this attitude the investigator should not be regarded as self-centered, or neglectful of duties to the general good. He is serving best his own generation in so far as he makes his standard of work thorough and honest. In so far as he does that, he is serving best future generations as well, for only thus can the results of his work be used later as a basis for further advancement. And since the interrelations of phenomena are so manifold the conviction is justified that every bit of honest work can finally be utilized in forming the body of truth. Although the investigator may labor, therefore, primarily to satisfy his own curiosity, and to secure for his craftsmanship that inner approval sought by every conscientious worker, nevertheless he is making permanent additions to the world's values. There is about his life, as Professor Royce has noted, an element of noble play . . . One plays with silk and glass and amber, with kites that one flies beneath thunder clouds, with frog legs and with acid. The play is a mere expression of a curiosity which former centuries might have called idle. But the result of this play re-creates an industrial world. And so it is everywhere with our deeper curiosity. There is a sense in which it is all superfluous. Its immediate results seem but vanity. One could surely live without them, yet for the future and for the spiritual life of mankind, these results are destined to become of vast import.

Sometimes the worker in science lives to see his services used for the relief of human need. When Davy's studies of combustion enabled him to invent the safety lamp, he gave the invention freely to the world. He knew then that thenceforth for all time toilers in the mines could protect themselves against the dangers of destruction. There is no realm, however, in which the deep satisfaction of seeing discovery applied to human service is more likely to be experienced than in the realm of medical research. Consider how great must have been the joy of Pasteur and of Lister when they realized that the consequences of their investigations must lessen forever plague and pestilence and pain in men, and in the lower animals as well, and must permanently remove much of the blind struggle against mysterious agencies of disease and death. The letter which Walter Reed wrote to his wife on New Year's eve, 1900, at the end of his experiments on the transmission of yellow fever, tells something of the joy of such service —"The prayer that has been mine for twenty years," he concludes, "that I might be permitted in some way or at some time to do something to alleviate human suffering, has been granted! A thousand Happy New Years." And a thousand happy new years there will be for thousands of men and women and children, because of that one research in Cuba.

Through the employment of methods of scientific inquiry to medical problems more progress has been made during the past sixty years towards an understanding of the nature of diseases and their control than had been made in the previous twenty-three centuries. Think for a moment of what has been learned about diphtheria and tetanus, about meningitis and rabies, about tuberculosis and syphilis, about dysentery and cholera and typhoid fever. How fundamentally our attitude toward these diseases has altered as the discoveries of medical investigators have given us insight and powers to control. What great progress we have already made in this relatively short period towards the relief of man's estate. Still we must not forget that there are immense labors yet to be accomplished. We are yet surrounded by innumerable mysteries, which can only be solved by persistent research. Not all men are fitted by temperament or training to engage in this great work, but more are thus fitted, I am sure, than are awakened to its opportunities. For those of you who are ready, here is a challenge to the supreme use of all your powers— to your imagination, your ingenuity, your patience and enthusiasm, and to your spirit of disinterested service.

1911

Gains from Serendipity

WALTER B. CANNON

In 1754 Horace Walpole, in a chatty letter to his friend Horace Mann, proposed adding a new word to our vocabulary, "serendipity." The word looks as if it might be of Latin origin. It is rarely used. It is not found in the abridged dictionaries. When I mentioned serendipity to one of my acquaintances and asked him if he could guess the meaning, he suggested that it probably designated a mental state combining serenity and stupidity—an ingenious guess, but erroneous.

Walpole's proposal was based upon his reading of a fairy tale entitled *The Three Princes of Serendip*. Serendip, I may interject, was the ancient name of Ceylon. "As their highnesses traveled," so Walpole wrote, "they were always making discoveries, by *accident* or *sagacity*, of things which they were not in quest of." When the word is mentioned in dictionaries, therefore, it is said to designate the happy faculty, or luck, of finding unforeseen evidence of one's ideas or, with surprise, coming upon new objects or relations which were not being sought.

Readers who remember Bible stories will recall that Saul, the son of Kish, was sent forth to find his father's asses, which were lost. In the discouragement of his failures to find them he consulted one, Samuel, a seer. And Samuel told him not .to set his mind on them for they had been found, but to know that he was chosen to rule over all the tribes of Israel. So it was announced, and the people shouted their approval. Thus modest Saul, who went out to seek lost asses, was rewarded by a kingdom. That is the earliest record of serendipity I am aware of.

Probably the most astounding instance of accidental discovery in either ancient or modern history was the finding of the western hemisphere by Columbus. He sailed away from Spain firm in the faith that by going west he would learn a shorter route to the East Indies; quite unexpectedly he encountered a whole new world. It is noteworthy that he was not aware of the significance of what he had found. Indeed, it has been said that he did not know where, in fact, he was going nor where he was when he arrived nor where he had been after his return, but nevertheless he had had the most unique adventure of all time. He realized that he had had a remarkable experience and, by extending the knowledge of what he had done, he laid a course which others might follow. Such consequences have been common when accident has been favorable to one engaged in a search and the enterprise has proved fruitful.

In the records of scientific investigation this sort of happy use of good fortune has been conspicuous. A good example is afforded by the origin and development of our acquaintance with electrical phenomena. It is reported that some frogs' legs were hanging by a copper wire from an iron balustrade in the Galvani home in Bologna; they were seen to twitch when they were swung by the wind and happened to touch the iron. Whether the twitching was first noted by Luigi Galvani, the anatomist and physiologist, or by Lucia Galvani, his talented wife, is not clear. Certainly that fortuitous occurrence late in the eighteenth century was not neglected, for it started many researches which have preserved the Galvani name in the terms "galvanize" and "galvanism." . . . We now use it, for example, to indicate the disordered state of the heart, because every cardiac contraction sends forth through our bodies an electrical wave, a wave that has a different shape according to the damage in the heart muscle. Only recently have we begun to employ animal electricity to give us information about conditions in the brain. That marvelous organ composed of many billions of nerve cells can display rhythmic electrical pulsations and, when extremely delicate instruments are applied to the scalp, they can reveal the different types of pulsations in rest and activity and the modification in some states of disease. . . .

In the biological sciences serendipity has been quite as consequential as in the physical sciences. Claude Bernard, for example, had the idea that the impulses which pass along nerve fibers set up chemical changes producing heat. In an experiment performed about the middle of the last century he measured the temperature of a rabbit's ear and then severed a nerve which delivers impulses to that structure expecting, in accordance with his theory, that the ear deprived of nerve impulses would be cooler than its mate on the other side. To his great surprise it was considerably warmer! Without at first knowing the import of what he had done, he had disconnected the blood vessels of the ear from the nervous influences that normally hold them moderately contracted; thereupon the warm blood from internal organs was flushed through the expanded vessels in a faster flow and the ear temperature rose. Thus by accident appeared the first intimation that the passage of blood into different parts of the body is under the government of nerves—one of the most significant advances in our knowledge of the circulation since Harvey's proof, early in the seventeenth century, that the blood does indeed circulate in the vessels.

Another striking instance of accidental discovery has been described by the French physiologist, Charles Richet, a Nobel laureate. It was concerned with a peculiar sensitiveness toward certain substances—such as white of egg, strawberries, ragweed pollen and numerous others—that we now speak of as *anaphylaxis* or *allergy*. This may result from an initial exposure to the substance which later becomes poisonous to the victim. The phenomenon had been noticed incidentally before Richet's studies, but because it did not receive attention its characteristics were virtually unknown. In his charming little book *Le Savant*, he has told the story of how quite unexpectedly he happened upon the curious fact. He was testing an extract of the tentacles of a sea anemone on laboratory animals in order to learn the toxic dose. When animals which had readily survived that dose were given after a lapse of some time a much smaller dose (as little as one-tenth), he was astounded to find that it was promptly fatal. Richet declares that at first he had great difficulty in believing the result could be due to anything *he* had done. Indeed, he testified that it was in spite of himself that he discovered induced sensitization. He would never have dreamt that it was possible.

Pasteur was led by chance to his method of immunization. One day an old and forgotten bacterial culture was being used for inoculating fowls. The fowls became ill but did not die. This happening was illuminative. Possibly by first using cultures that had little virulence and then repeating the injections with cultures of greater virulence, the animals could be made to develop resistance to infection gradually. His surmise proved correct. By this procedure, as readers of his dramatic biography will remember, he was able to immunize sheep against anthrax and human beings against rabies.

It was an accidental observation which ultimately resulted in the discovery of insulin and the restoration of effective living to tens of thousands of sufferers from diabetes. In the late eighties of the last century, von Mering and Minkowski were studying the functions of the pancreas in digestion. While attempting to secure more evidence they removed that organ from a number of dogs. By good luck a laboratory assistant noticed that swarms of flies gathered round the urine of these animals, a fact which he mentioned to the investigators. When the urine was analyzed, it was found to be loaded with sugar. Thus for the first time experimental diabetes was produced, and the earliest glimpse was given into a possible cause of that disease. We now know that small islands of cells in the pancreas produce an internal secretion which exerts control over the use of sugar in the organism. And we know that when these islands are removed or damaged, sugar metabolism is deranged. An extract from the island cells provides the diabetic sufferer with the insulin he needs.

An unforeseen contingency may occasion scientific advances because of the serious problem it presents. A striking instance is afforded in the use of polished rice. There was no reason to anticipate that the polishing of rice would be harmful to those who depended upon it as a food. Yet removal of the covering from the kernels produced in myriads of victims the disease, beriberi, resulting in immeasurable sorrow and distress. As has been pointed out, however, the study of beriberi, thus unwittingly induced, disclosed not only the cause of that disorder but also started explorations in the whole realm of deficiency diseases and thus led to the discovery of some of the most intimate secrets of cellular processes.

A recent instance of serendipity was the finding of vitamin K, lack of which deprives the blood of an essential element for its coagulation. The Danish investigator, Dam, and his collaborators were working on chemical changes in a certain fatty substance in chicks. They noted that the animals on a special restricted diet often suffered from extensive internal hemorrhages. When the diet was changed to seeds and salts, the bleeding failed to occur. By critical tests the abnormal condition was proved to be due not to lack of any previously known vitamin but to lack of a specific agent contained in the liver fat of swine as well as in certain vegetables and in many cereals. This agent, vitamin K, has proved to be important in surgery. For example, patients afflicted with jaundice, owing to an obstruction in the bile duct, can be relieved by operation; unfortunately in jaundice, however, blood clots very slowly; an operation, therefore, may be attended by disastrous bleeding. This danger can now be readily obviated by feeding vitamin K (with bile salts), for it restores to an effective concentration the deficient element of the clotting process, a benefaction which has come to human beings from a chance observation on chicks.

In the life of an investigator whose researches range extensively, advantages from happy chance are almost certain to be encountered. During nearly five decades of scientific experimenting instances of serendipity have several times been my good fortune. Two experiences I mention elsewhere, but not in relation to serendipity. One was stoppage of the movements of the stomach and intestines in times of anxiety. The other was the strange faster beating of the heart, after all its governing nerves were severed, if the animal became excited or if sympathetic fibers were stimulated in some remote region of the body. This effect, due to an agent carried to the heart by the circulating blood, led to the discovery of *sympathin*. Both phenomena were quite unexpected. Proof that the stoppage of digestive movements was due to emotion was the beginning of many years of research on the influence of fear and rage on bodily functions. And the unraveling of the mystery of sympathin led ultimately to prolonged studies on the chemical mediator that serves to transmit influences from nerve endings to the organs they control.

There are many other examples of serendipity which I might detail; among them Nobel's invention of dynamite, Perkin's stumbling upon the coal-tar dyes, and Pasteur's finding that a vegetable mold causes the watery solution in which it is nurtured to change the direction of the light rays as they pass through. Dynamite placed gigantic powers in the hands of man; the coal-tar dyes have fundamentally affected such varied activities as warfare, textile industries, and medical diagnosis; and Pasteur's casual observation has developed into an immense range of chemical theory and research.

Three legends of accidental leads to fresh insight serve to introduce the next point, which is quite as important as serendipity itself. I refer to the presence of a prepared mind. It is said that the idea of specific gravity came to Archimedes as he noted by chance the buoyancy of his body in water. We have all heard the tale, illustrative even if not authentic, that the concept of a universal law of gravitational force occurred to Isaac Newton when he saw an apple fall from a tree while he lay musing on the grass in an orchard. Of similar import is the story that the possibility of the steam engine suddenly occurred to James Watt when he beheld the periodic lifting of the lid of a tea kettle by the steam pressure within it. Many a man floated in water before Archimedes; apples fell from trees as long ago as the Garden of Eden (exact date uncertain!); and the outrush of steam against resistance could have been noted at any time since the discovery of fire and its use under a covered pot of water. In all three cases it was eons before the significance of these events was perceived. Obviously a chance discovery involves both the phenomenon to be observed and the appreciative, intelligent observer.

I may now add to these legends and their illustrative significance the history of that marvelously powerful enemy of infection, penicillin. In 1929 the English bacteriologist, Alexander Fleming, reported noticing that a culture of pus-producing bacteria underwent dissolution in the neighborhood of a mold which accidentally contaminated it. This was the pregnant hint. A careless worker might have thrown the culture away because of the contamination. Instead, Fleming let the mold grow in broth and thus learned that there passed into the broth from the mold a substance which was highly efficacious in stopping the growth of a wide range of disease-producing germs and destroying them. Furthermore he learned that, when injected, this substance was not itself harmful to animals. The mold, a variety of Penicillium, suggested the name "penicillin." The long struggle of Howard Florey and his associates at Oxford in purifying and standardizing this highly potent agent and in proving its value in human cases cannot be recounted here. The record, however, reports one of the most striking instances of immense value that can result from a combination of chance and an alert intelligence; and shows how a brilliant discovery is made practical by hard labor.

Long ago Pasteur recognized that when accident favors an investigator it must be met by sharp insight, for he uttered the wise and discerning dictum, *"Dans les champs de l'observation, le hasard ne favorise que les esprits preparés."* Even before Pasteur, Joseph Henry, the American physicist, enunciated the same truth when he said, "The seeds of great discoveries are constantly floating around us, but they only take root in minds well prepared to receive them."

1945

Laboratories

HANS ZINSSER

WHILE war service and epidemiological work have their adventurous charms, there comes sooner or later to the investigator trained in laboratories a hunger for his accustomed environment—a sort of nostalgia for the familiar smells of ether, phenol, formalin, xylol, monkeys, and guinea pigs, which are sweeter to the laboratory nose than attar of roses. Moreover, ideas have accumulated, new techniques have been devised, and the heart longs to get back to an occupation which, once in the bones, is harder to shake off than a beloved vice.

There is in this profession, especially as it concerns itself with infectious diseases, a fascination which holds the spirit with feelings that are not exaggerated by the word "passion"; indeed, like the happiest personal passions, it feeds on the intimate daily association of long years and grows, like love, with an increasing familiarity that never becomes complete knowledge. For what can be more happily exciting than to study a disease in all its natural manifestations, isolate its cause, and subject this to precise scrutiny and analysis; to grow it apart from its host, study its manner of multiplication, its habits under artificial conditions, its changes, its possible toxic products; then to carry it back to the animal body and follow the processes by which it injures and kills; explore the details of animal defenses, and pursue it again into the epidemic; examine its manner of conveyance from case to case, its relationship to water and food, animal carriers, insect vectors, its geographical, climatic, and seasonal distribution, the laws of its epidemic waves; and then, with all the weapons of the knowledge gained, to assist in its arrest and circumvention, even contribute to protection and possibly individual cure. For few diseases has all this been entirely done, and in those few in which all necessary knowledge is available—as, for instance, in diphtheria and smallpox—the conquered territory must be occupied by garrisons which one helps in training and disciplining. For it is a war without armistice, and continuous mobilization is the only guarantee of safety. Once one is thoroughly involved in this work, it gets into the blood and few either want to or can escape from its fascinations.

1940

Chemistry in the Service

of Medicine

EDWIN E. SLOSSON

IT USED to be said of the doctor that he put medicines of which he knew little into a body of which he knew nothing. The sting of this jibe is being extracted by the chemist.

From the days of the prehistoric medicine man down to the practitioner of the last century, *materia medica* consisted mostly of certain minerals and uncertain mixtures of plant products, such as had been found, by long and painful experience on the part of the patients, to produce noticeable effects on the body, nobody knew why.

But the physician is no longer dependent upon the chance bounty of nature. Modern medicines are made to order. The synthetic chemist draws a picture of his structural formula in advance as an architect plans his building.

He exchanges methyl and ethyl groups as he pleases; he attaches an arsenic or bromine atom here and there, until he gets a compound that will do the greatest possible harm to the invading microbe and the least possible harm to their involuntary host. In former times the dose that was aimed at a disease germ was as likely as not to kill a phagocyte. But the modern physician uses a rifle instead of a shotgun and is making medicines that hit the mark.

More than that, he is learning something about the chemical compounds that are normally secreted in the body and control the operation of its organs. Some of these hormones have already been isolated and identified; several have been made in the laboratory. The chemist now has his fingers upon the spring that regulates our vital mechanism.

This opens the way to a new epoch in medicine in which the treatment will be nearer to nature's ways. For when the physician gave a dose of quinine, strychnine or salts he was introducing a foreign substance for the purpose of artificially producing the desired reaction. But when he injects directly into the blood a hormone, such as insulin, adrenalin or pituitrin, he is merely restoring a natural substance unnaturally deficient. It is more like feeding than drugging.

Another discovery leads in the same direction. It has been found that our food contains certain substances, called vitamins, which, like the hormones, have a potency amazingly disproportionate to their minute amount in their effect on our health, growth, immunity and emotions. . . . This also puts into the hands of the physician a powerful method for the control of bodily processes in health and disease by natural means. The barrier between biology and chemistry is being broken down by investigators on both sides. . . .

1920's

The Doctor and the Physicist

GEORGE RUSSELL HARRISON

THE wonders which medical workers have already brought about in the diagnosis and treatment of disease suggest that a time may come when the physician will be able to analyze most illnesses as soon as they start, and cure them before damage results. How soon this "golden age of healing" arrives will depend greatly on how close is the collaboration between research workers in medicine and those who work in the sciences on which medicine depends. The physician has long relied on the chemist for curative drugs, and on the physicist for diagnostic instruments and healing rays. In the one field new materials and in the other new devices are being produced in increasing numbers, helping to make imminent new miracles of medicine.

The X-ray and the microscope have extended the vision of the medical observer until he can see through ten inches of living flesh or into a single tissue cell, yet similar but much more powerful tools still await development. Modern electrical devices enable him to listen to faint murmurings of the life processes, or to measure feeble currents arising from heart and brain and nerve; yet electrical body measurements are but little understood. Now newly discovered atomic rays are being brought to help him destroy malignant invaders of the human system, and there is every reason to believe that even more curative rays await discovery. . . .

Medicine is growing in effectiveness as it progresses from the status of an art to that of a science. Progress in a science depends to a great degree on the tools which can be forged to aid it in uncovering truth. For many years the principal tools of the physician were his own five senses, but human eyes have bounded vision as human hands have limited strength. With eyes and ears that see where before were only darkness and silence, the modern healer finds in no mere poetic sense that his strength is as the strength of ten. These more-than-human eyes and ears, this beneficent sharpening of the senses, it is the province of physics and the purpose of physicists to continue to supply.

1941

On a New Kind of Rays

WILHELM CONRAD ROENTGEN

IF THE discharge of a fairly large induction coil be made to pass through a Hittorf vacuum tube, or through a Lenard tube, a Crookes' tube, or other similar apparatus, which has been sufficiently exhausted, the tube being covered with thin, black cardboard which fits it with tolerable closeness, and if the whole apparatus be placed in a completely darkened room, there is observed at each discharge a bright illumination of a paper screen covered with barium platinocyanide, placed in the vicinity of the induction coil, the fluorescence thus produced being entirely independent of the fact whether the coated or the plain surface is turned toward the discharge tube. This fluorescence is visible even when the paper screen is at a distance of two meters from the apparatus.

It is easy to prove that the cause of the fluorescence proceeds from the discharge apparatus, and not from any other point in the conducting circuit.

The most striking feature of this phenomenon is the fact that an active agent here passes through a black cardboard envelope, which is opaque to the visible and the ultraviolet rays of the sun or of the electric arc; an agent, too, which has the power of producing active fluorescence. Hence we may first investigate the question whether other bodies also possess this property.

We soon discover that all bodies are transparent to this agent, though in very different degrees. I proceed to give a few examples: Paper is very transparent;[1] behind a bound book of about one thousand pages I saw the fluorescent screen light up brightly, the printer's ink offering scarcely a noticeable hindrance. In the same way the fluorescence appeared behind a double pack of cards; a single card held between the apparatus and the screen being almost unnoticeable to the eye. A single sheet of tinfoil is also scarcely perceptible; it is only after several layers have been placed over one another that their shadow is distinctly seen on the screen. Thick blocks of wood are also transparent, pine boards 2 or 3 cm. thick absorbing only slightly. A plate of aluminum about 15 mm. thick, though it enfeebled the action seriously, did not cause the fluorescence to disappear entirely. Sheets of hard rubber several centimeters thick still permit the rays to pass through them.[2] Glass plates of equal thickness behave quite differently, according as they contain lead (flint glass) or not; the former are much less transparent than the latter. If the hand be held between the discharge tube and the screen, the

---

[1] By "transparency" of a body I denote the relative brightness of a fluorescent screen placed close behind the body, referred to the brightness which the screen shows under the same circumstances though without the interposition of the body.

[2] For brevity's sake I shall use the expression "rays," and to distinguish them from others of this name, I shall call them "X rays."

darker shadow of the bones is seen within the slightly dark shadow image of the hand itself. Water, carbon disulphide, and various other liquids, when they are examined in mica vessels, seem also to be transparent. That hydrogen is to any considerable degree more transparent than air I have not been able to discover. Behind plates of copper, silver, lead, gold, and platinum, the fluorescence may still be recognized, though only if the thickness of the plates is not too great. Platinum of a thickness of 0.2 mm. is still transparent; the silver and copper plates may even be thicker. Lead of a thickness of 1.5 mm. is practically opaque, and on account of this property this metal is frequently most useful. A rod of wood with a square cross-section (20 by 20 mm.), one of whose sides is painted white with lead paint, behaves differently according as to how it is held between the apparatus and the screen. It is almost entirely without action when the X rays pass through it parallel to the painted side; whereas the stick throws a dark shadow when the rays are made to traverse it perpendicular to the painted side. In a series similar to that of the metals themselves their salts can be arranged with reference to their transparency, either in the solid form or in solution. . . .

All substances with increase in thickness become less transparent. . . .

. . . different metals possess transparencies which are by no means equal, even when the product of thickness and density are the same. . . .

Of special significance in many respects is the fact that photographic dry plates are sensitive to the X rays. We are, therefore, in a condition to determine more definitely many phenomena, and so the more easily to avoid deception; wherever it has been possible, therefore, I have controlled, by means of photography, every important observation which I have made with the eye by means of the fluorescent screen.

In these experiments the property of the rays to pass almost unhindered through thin sheets of wood, paper, and tinfoil is most important. The photographic impressions can be obtained in a nondarkened room with the photographic plates either in the holders or wrapped up in paper. On the other hand, from this property it results as a consequence that undeveloped plates cannot be left for a long time in the neighborhood of the discharge tube, if they are protected merely by the usual covering of pasteboard and paper.

It appears questionable, however, whether the chemical action on the silver salts of the photographic plates is directly caused by the X rays. It is possible that this action proceeds from the fluorescent light which, as noted above, is produced in the glass plate itself or perhaps in the layer of gelatin. "Films" can be used just as well as glass plates.

I have not yet been able to prove experimentally that the X rays are able also to produce a heating action; yet we may well assume that this effect is present, since the capability of the X rays to be transformed is proved by means of the observed fluorescence phenomena. It is certain, therefore, that all the X rays which fall upon a substance do not leave it again as such.

The retina of the eye is not sensitive to these rays. Even if the eye is brought close to the discharge tube, it observes nothing, although, as experiment has proved, the media contained in the eye must be sufficiently transparent to transmit the rays. . . .

The justification for calling by the name "rays" the agent which proceeds from the wall of the discharge apparatus, I derive in part from the entirely regular formation of shadows, which are seen when more or less transparent bodies are brought between the apparatus and the fluorescent screen (or the photographic plate).

I have observed, and in part photographed, many shadow pictures of this kind, the production of which has a particular charm. I possess, for instance, photographs of the shadow of the profile of a door which separates the rooms in which, on one side, the discharge apparatus was placed, on the other the photographic plate; the shadow of the bones of the hand; the shadow of a covered wire wrapped on a wooden spool; of a set of weights enclosed in a box; of a compass in which the magnetic needle is entirely enclosed by metal; of a piece of metal whose lack of homogeneity becomes noticeable by means of the X rays, et cetera. . . .

There seems to exist some kind of relationship between the new rays and light rays; at least this is indicated by the formation of shadows, the fluorescence and the chemical action produced by them both. Now, we have known for a long time that there can be in the ether longitudinal vibrations besides the transverse light vibrations, and, according to the views of different physicists, these vibrations must exist. Their existence, it is true, has not been proved up to the present, and consequently their properties have not been investigated by experiment.

Ought not, therefore, the new rays to be ascribed to longitudinal vibrations in the ether?

I must confess that in the course of the investigation I have become more and more confident of the correctness of this idea, and so, therefore, permit myself to announce this conjecture, although I am perfectly aware that the explanation given still needs further confirmation.

$$Translated\ in\ \frac{1895}{1933}$$

The Psychology
of Sigmund Freud

A. A. BRILL

PSYCHOANALYSIS was unknown in this country until I introduced it in 1908. Ever since then, I have been translating, lecturing and writing on the subject both for physicians and laymen; and I am happy to say that today psychoanalysis, which has encountered so much opposition here, as it did abroad, is firmly established not only in medicine, but also in psychology, sociology, pedagogy and anthropology. . . .

Sigmund Freud was born in 1856 in Freiberg, Moravia, formerly Austria, now Czechoslovakia. He was brought up in Vienna, having lived there since the age of four. In his autobiography, he states: "My parents were Jews and I remained a Jew."

One of the arguments that has been hurled at psychoanalysis on a few occasions is that its originator was a Jew, implying thereby that the theories expressed by Freud do not apply to the rest of mankind. Such an argument, which, if accepted, would also invalidate Christianity, is too stupid to require refutation. Freud's works had the honor of forming part of the sacred pyre on Hitler's accession to power. The fact that the bulk of this pyre was composed of works of non-Jewish thinkers plainly shows that truth knows no creed or race. I feel, however, that Freud's Jewish descent—constitution—as well as the environment to which he was subjected because of it—fate—exerted considerable influence on his personality. One might say that only a Jewish genius, forged in the crucible of centuries of persecution, could have offered himself so willingly on the altar of public opprobrium for the sake of demonstrating the truths of psychoanalysis.

Freud tells us that in college he always stood first, and was hardly ever examined. Despite the very straitened financial condition of his family, his father wanted him to follow his own inclination in the selection of a vocation. He had no special love for medicine at that age, nor did he acquire it later, but rather he was stimulated by a sort of inquisitiveness directed to human relations and objects of nature. He was very much attracted to Darwin's theories because they offered the prospect of an extraordinary advance of human knowledge, and he finally decided to enter the medical school after he had read Goethe's beautiful essay, *Die Natur*. . . .

While still in the university, he worked for a number of years in the physiological laboratory of the famous Ernst Brücke, who was his teacher and gave him as his first task the histology of the nervous system. With only a short interruption Freud worked in the Institute from 1876 until 1882. Then, he discovered that with the exception of psychiatry, the other medical specialties did not attract him. He graduated from the medical school in 1881, and in 1882 he entered Vienna's well known *Allgemeine Krankenhaus* (general hospital). There, he went through the usual routine services, but continued his studies on the anatomy of the brain, in which he became very proficient. It is not generally known that in his early days Freud wrote a number of works on diseases of the nervous system, which were very highly regarded by his contemporaries.

In 1885 he was attracted by the fame of Charcot, who was applying hypnotism to the study and treatment of hysteria and other functional nervous diseases. He remained for a year in Paris as a pupil and translator of this master's works. In 1886 he returned to his native Vienna and "married the girl who waited for me in a far-off city longer than four years." He then entered private practice, but continued as an instructor in the university.

What Freud saw in Charcot's Clinic made a very deep impression on him. While still a student, he also witnessed a performance of the "magnetiser," Hansen, in which a test person became deadly pale when she merged into a cataleptic rigidity, and remained so during the whole duration of the catalepsy. This convinced Freud of the genuineness of hypnotic phenomena, a conviction which remained in him despite the fact that the contemporary professors of psychiatry considered hypnosis fraudulent and dangerous. From Charcot he learned that hypnosis could produce hysterical symptoms as well as remove them, and that hysteria could also occur in men; and from Liébault and Bernheim of the Nancy School he learned that suggestion alone, without hypnotism, was as efficacious as suggestion employed in hypnosis.

When Freud returned to Vienna and demonstrated what he had learned from Charcot, he met with considerable opposition. It was the age of physical therapy, when physicians knew nothing about the psychic factors in disease, when everything was judged by the formula, *Mens sana in corpore sano* (a healthy mind in a healthy body). Every symptom was explained on the basis of some organic lesion, and if nothing physical was discovered, it was assumed that there must be something in the brain to account for the disturbance. The treatment was based on this same deficient understanding; drugs, hydrotherapy, and electrotherapy were the only agents that physicians could use. When the patient was excited, he received some sedative; if he was depressed and felt fatigue, he was given a tonic; and when drugs failed, electricity or cold baths were recommended. All these remedies gave only temporary alleviation, mainly through suggestion. Most of the thoughtful physicians were fully cognizant of this helpless state, but there was nothing else to be done.

During the first few years of his private practice Freud relied mostly on hypnotism and electrotherapy, but he soon realized that the latter failed to benefit the patient, and that the whole idea of electric treatment for functional nervous diseases was fantastic. He had some good results, however, from hypnotic therapy; but he soon found that not every patient could be hypnotized, and that even those who could be, did not remain permanently cured. Attributing such failures to a deficiency in his technique, to an inability on his part to put every patient into a state of somnambulism with its consequent amnesia, he spent some weeks in Nancy with Liébault and Bernheim, to whom he took a recalcitrant patient for treatment. Bernheim made a number of efforts to produce a deep hypnotic state in the patient, but finally had to admit failure. Freud, though disappointed with the technique of hypnotism, learned a great deal from the experiments witnessed there concerning the forceful psychic forces which were still to be investigated. Very soon thereafter, he gradually gave up hypnotism and developed what he called "psychoanalysis." In this connection he makes the following interesting statement: "The importance of hypnotism for the history of the development of psychoanalysis must not be too lightly estimated. Both in theoretic as well as in therapeutic aspects, psychoanalysis is the administrator of the estate left by hypnotism."

In order to give a full account of the development of psychoanalysis, it will be necessary to go back a few years. While Freud still worked in Brücke's laboratory, he made the acquaintance of Dr. Josef Breuer, a prominent general practitioner of high scientific standing. Although Breuer was 14 years older than Freud, they soon became friends and frequently discussed their scientific views and experiences. Knowing Freud's interest in neurology and psychiatry, Breuer gave him an account of a very interesting case of hysteria which he had studied and cured by hypnosis from 1880 to 1882. As this unique case was of the greatest importance to the development of psychoanalysis, it will be worth while to give a few details.

The patient concerned was a young girl of unusual education and talent, who had become ill while nursing her father to whom she was very much attached. Dr. Breuer states that when he took her as a patient she presented a variegated picture of paralyses with contractures, inhibitions and states of psychic confusion. Through an accidental observation Breuer discovered that the patient could be freed from such disturbances of consciousness if she could be enabled to give verbal expression to the effective phantasies which dominated her. Breuer elaborated this experience into a method of treatment. He hypnotized her and urged her to tell him what oppressed her at the time, and by this simple method he freed her from all her symptoms. The significance of the case lay in this fact, that in her waking state the patient knew nothing about the origin of her symptoms, but once hypnotized, she immediately knew the connection between her symptoms and some of her past experiences. All her symptoms were traceable to experiences during the time when she had nursed her sick father. Moreover, the symptoms were not arbitrary and senseless, but could be traced to definite experiences and forgotten reminiscences of that emotional situation.

A common feature of all the symptoms consisted in the fact that they had come into existence in situations in which an impulse to do something had to be foregone because other motives suppressed it. The symptom appeared as a substitute for the unperformed act. As a rule, the symptom was not the result of one single "traumatic" scene, but of a sum of many similar situations. If the patient in a state of hypnosis recalled hallucinatorily the act which she had suppressed in the past, and if she now brought it to conclusion under the stress of a freely generated affect, the symptom was wiped away never to return again. It was remarked that the causes which had given origin to the symptom resembled the traumatic factors described by Charcot in his experimental cases. What was still more remarkable was that these traumatic causes with their concomitant psychic feelings had been entirely lost to the patient's memory, as if they had never happened, while their results—that is, the symptoms, had continued unchanged, as if unaffected by the wear and tear of time, until attacked by Breuer through hypnosis.

Although Breuer, as was mentioned above, told Freud about this wonderful discovery, he did not publish his findings. Freud could not understand why. The discovery seemed to him of inestimable value. But following his return from Nancy in 1889 with the cognition of hypnotic suggestive therapy, Freud decided to test Breuer's method in his own cases, and found ample corroboration of its efficacy during a period of many years. He then urged Breuer to report with him the results of his method, and in 1893 they jointly issued a preliminary communication, *On the Psychic Mechanisms of Hysterical Phenomena.*

As can be seen, Breuer was the spiritual creator of this method of treatment and Freud always gave him full credit for it, although they differed from the very beginning in their basic interpretation of the symptoms. They called their treatment the "cathartic method" because they concluded that the efficacy of it rested on the mental and emotional purging, catharsis, which the patient went through during the treatment. The other conclusion drawn by the authors was that hysteria was a disease of the past, and that, as Freud put it later, the symptom was, as it were, a monument to *some* disagreeable and forgotten (repressed) episode from the patient's life. The patient, however, did not know the meaning of the monument any more than the average German would know the meaning of the Bunker Hill monument. This concept for the first time showed the importance of distinguishing between conscious and unconscious states, which was later amplified and developed by Freud as the psychology of the unconscious. New meaning was given to the affective or emotional factors of life, their fluctuations and dynamism. The symptom was the result of a dammed-up or strangulated affect. The patient could not give vent to the affect because the situation in question made this impossible, so that the idea was intentionally *repressed* from consciousness and excluded from associative elaboration. As a result of this repression, the sum of energy which could not be discharged took a wrong path to bodily innervation, and thus produced the symptom. In other words, the symptom was the result of a conversion of psychic energy into a physical manifestation, such as pain or paralysis. Thus, a pain in the face, diagnosed as neuralgia, might be due to an insult which would ordinarily evoke the thought, "I feel as if he had slapped me in the face." As this insult could not be retaliated against, the strangulated energy remained in a state of repression and gave rise to "neuralgia." The cure or the discharge was effected through what the authors called the process of *abreaction.* The hypnotized patient was led back to the repressed episodes and allowed to give free vent in speech and action to the feelings which were originally kept out of consciousness. . . .

Very soon after the appearance of the *Studies in Hysteria,* Breuer withdrew from the field. He was, after all, unprepared for this specialty, and inasmuch as he enjoyed a stable and lucrative practice and a high reputation as a family physician, the storm which began to gather as his collaborator advanced deeper into the etiology of the neuroses more or less frightened him. Freud, therefore, continued alone to elaborate and perfect the instrument left by his erstwhile friend and collaborator; and as a result, the cathartic method underwent numerous modifications, the most important of which was the giving-up of hypnotism in favor of *free association.* As pointed out above, not everybody could be hypnotized, and since hypnotism was absolutely indispensable to the cathartic treatment at that time, many a worthy patient had had to be given up just because he or she could not be hypnotized. Freud was also dissatisfied with the therapeutic results of catharsis based on hypnotism. Although cures were often very striking, they were often of very short duration and depended mainly on the personal relation between the patient and physician. Moreover, Freud always entertained a feeling of antipathy to the application of hypnotism and suggestion to patients. Speaking of his visit to Bernheim in 1889, he states: "But I can remember even then a feeling of gloomy antagonism against this tyranny of suggestion. When a patient who did not prove to be yielding was shouted at: 'What are you doing? *Vous vous contresuggestionnez!*', I said to myself that this was an evident injustice and violence."

Yet his visit to Bernheim later helped him out of the dilemma of not being able to hypnotize some patients. He recalled the following experiment which he had witnessed there, the object of which was to overcome the post-hypnotic amnesia: On being awakened, the patient could not remember anything that had transpired during hypnosis, but when he was urged to make an effort to recall what had been said to him, he eventually remembered everything. Freud applied the same method to those patients whom he could not hypnotize. He urged them to tell him everything that came to their minds, to leave out nothing, regardless of whether they considered it relevant or not. He persuaded them to give up all conscious reflection, abandon themselves to ·calm concentration, follow their spontaneous mental occurrences, and impart everything to him. In this way he finally obtained those *free associations* which lead to the origin of the symptoms. As he developed this method, he found that it was not as simple as he had thought, that these so-called free associations were really not *free*, but were determined by unconscious material which had to be analyzed and interpreted. He therefore designated this new technique *psychoanalysis*. The cathartic method, however, was ever preserved as a sort of nucleus of psychoanalysis despite the expansions and modifications which Freud gradually made as he proceeded with the new technique.

In the course of working with free associations, Freud gained a tremendous amount of insight into the play of forces of the human mind which he could not have obtained through the former therapeutic procedure. The question as to how the patient could have forgotten so many outer and inner experiences, which could be recalled only in a state of hypnosis and which were difficult to bring to consciousness by means of free association, soon became revealed to him. The forgotten material represented

something painful, something disagreeable, or something frightful, obnoxious to the ego of the patient, which he did not like to
think of consciously. In order to make it conscious, the physician
had to exert himself mightily to overcome the patient's *resistance*,
which kept these experiences in a state of repression and away
from consciousness. The neurosis proved to be the result of a
psychic conflict between two dynamic forces, impulse and resistance, in the course of which struggle the ego withdrew from the
disagreeable impulse. As a result of this withdrawal, the obnoxious
impulse was kept from access to consciousness as well as from
direct motor discharge, but it retained its impulsive energy.

This unconscious process actually is a primary defense mechanism, comparable to an effort to fly away from something. But
in order to keep the disagreeable idea from consciousness, the ego
has to contend against the constant thrust of the repressed impulse
which is ever searching for expression. But despite constant exertion by the ego, the repressed, obnoxious impulse often finds
an outlet through some by-path, and thus invalidates the intention
of the repression. The repressed impulsive energy then settles
by this indirect course on some organ or part of the body, and
this innervation constitutes the symptom. Once this is established,
the patient struggles against the symptom in the same way as he
did against the originally repressed impulses.

To illustrate these mechanisms let us consider the case of an
hysterical young woman. For some months she was courted by a
young man proclaiming his ardent love for her. Suddenly one day
he made an unsuccessful sexual assault upon her, and then disappeared, leaving her in a state of deep depression. She could not
confide in her mother, because from the very beginning of the
affair the mother had forbidden her to see the young man. Three
years later I found her suffering from numerous hysterical conversion symptoms, and attacks of an epileptic character which
had existed for some two and a half years. Analysis showed that
the attacks represented symbolically what had taken place at
the time of the abortive sexual assault. Every detail of the so-
called epileptiform attack—every gesture, every movement—was
a stereotyped repetition of the sexual attack which the patient
was reproducing unconsciously. The other symptoms, too,
were directly traceable to the love affair.

The whole process of this disease can readily be understood
if we bear in mind the various steps of this love situation. The

young woman was healthy and, biotically speaking, ready for mating; her primitive instinct of sex was striving for fulfillment. Consciously, she could think of love only in the modern sense of the term, in which the physical elements are deliberately kept out of sight, Her middle-class, religious environment precluded any illicit sexual activity as far as she was consciously concerned. But, behind it all, the sexual impulses were actively reaching out for maternity. She was sincerely in love with the man, but naturally thought of love as marriage, with everything that goes with it. The sudden shock of coming face to face with the physical elements of sex left a terrific impression on her mind: on the one hand, consciously, she rejected vehemently the lover's physical approaches, and on the other hand, unconsciously, she really craved them. For weeks afterwards she vividly lived over in her mind everything that had happened to her, and, now and then, even fancied herself as having yielded—a thought which was immediately rejected and replaced by feelings of reproach and disgust. Last, but not least, she actually missed the love-making, which she had enjoyed for months prior to the attempted assault. As she could not unburden herself to anyone, she tried very hard to forget everything, and finally seemingly succeeded. But a few weeks later she began to show the symptoms which finally developed into the pathogenic picture which was diagnosed as epilepsy or hystero-epilepsy. These symptoms were the symbolization, or, if you will, a dramatization of the conflict between her primitive self and her ethical self, between what Freud now calls the *Id* and the *Ego*.

To make ourselves more explicit, it will be necessary to say something about the elements of the psychic apparatus. According to Freud's formulation the child brings into the world an unorganized chaotic mentality called the *Id*, the sole aim of which is the gratification of all needs, the alleviation of hunger, self-preservation, and love, the preservation of the species. However, as the child grows older, the part of the id which comes in contact with the environment through the senses learns to know the inexorable reality of the outer world and becomes modified into what Freud calls the ego. This ego, possessing awareness of the environment, henceforth strives to curb the lawless id tendencies whenever they attempt to assert themselves incompatibly. The neurosis, as we see it here, was, therefore, *a conflict between the ego and the id*. The ego, aware of the forces of civilization,

religion and ethics, refused to allow motor discharge to the powerful sexual impulses emanating from the lawless id, and thus
blocked them from attainment of the object towards which they
aimed. The ego then defended itself against these impulses by
repressing them. The young lady in question seemingly forgot
this whole episode. Had the repression continued unabated, she
would have remained healthy. But the repressed material struggled
against this fate, finally broke through as a substitutive formation
on paths over which the ego had no control, and obtruded itself
on the ego as symptoms. As a result of this process, the ego
found itself more or less impoverished, its integrity was threatened
and hurt, and hence it continued to combat the symptom in the
same way as it had defended itself against the original id impulses.

This whole process constitutes the picture of the neuroses, or
rather of the transference neuroses, which comprise hysteria,
anxiety hysteria, and the compulsion neuroses, in contradistinc-
tion to the so-called narcistic neuroses, melancholic depressions,
and to the psychoses, schizophrenia, paranoid conditions and
paranoia proper, in which the underlying mechanisms are somewhat different. In a psychosis, as will be shown later, the illness
results from *a conflict between the ego and the outer world,* and
in the narcistic neurosis from *a conflict between the ego and the
super-ego.* For just as the ego is a modified portion of the id as a
result of contact with the outer world, the super-ego represents
a modified part of the ego, formed through experiences absorbed
from the parents, especially from the father. The super-ego is the
highest mental evolution attainable by man, and consists of a
precipitate of all prohibitions and inhibitions, all the rules of conduct which are impressed on the child by his parents and by
parental substitutes. The feeling of *conscience* depends altogether
on the development of the super-ego.

From the description given here of the mechanism of the
neurosis, scant as it is, one can already see the great rôle attributed
by Freud to the unconscious factor of the mind. Psychoanalysis
has been justly called the "psychology of depths" because it has
emphasized the rôle of the unconscious mental processes. Unlike
those psychologists and philosophers who use such terms as
conscious, co-conscious, and sub-conscious in a very loose and
confused manner, Freud conceives *consciousness* simply as an
organ of perception. One is conscious or aware of those mental
processes which occupy one at any given time. In contrast to this,

the *unconscious* is utterly unknown and cannot be voluntarily recalled. No person can bring to light anything from his unconscious unless he is made to recall it by hypnosis, or unless it is interpreted for him by psychoanalysis. Midway between conscious and unconscious there is a fore-conscious or pre-conscious, which contains memories of which one is unaware, but which one can eventually recall with some effort.

This structure of a conscious fore-conscious, and an actual unconscious, is based on the attempt which Freud made to conceive the psychic apparatus as a composition of a number of forces or systems. It is a theoretical classification, which seems, however, to work well in practice. Bearing in mind these spatial divisions, we can state that whereas *the dream is the royal road to the unconscious*, most of the mechanisms discussed in the *Psychopathology of Everyday Life* belong to the fore-conscious system. This work was written after Freud became convinced that there is nothing arbitrary or accidental in psychic life, be it normal or abnormal. For the very unconscious forces which he found in the neuroses he also found in the common faulty actions of everyday life, like ordinary forgetting of familiar names, slips of the tongue, mistakes in reading or writing, which had hitherto been considered accidental and unworthy of explanation. Freud shows in the *Psychopathology of Everyday Life* that a rapid reflection or a short analysis always demonstrates the disturbing influence behind such slips, and conclusively proves that the same disturbances, differing only in degree, are found in every person, and that the gap between the neurotic and the so-called normal is, therefore, very narrow.

The dream, according to Freud, represents the hidden fulfillment of an unconscious wish. But the wishes which it represents as fulfilled are the very same unconscious wishes which are repressed in neurosis. Dreaming is a normal function of the mind; it is the guardian of sleep in so far as it strives to release tensions generated by unattainable wishes—tensions which, if not removed, might keep the person from sleeping. The dream is not always successful in its efforts; sometimes it oversteps the limits of propriety; it goes too far; and then the dreamer is awakened by the super-ego.

Without going further into the psychology of the dream, enough has been said to show that these twin discoveries—that non-conscious psychic processes are active in every normal person, expressing themselves in inhibitions and other modifications of intentional acts, and that the dreams of mentally healthy persons are not differently constructed from neurotic or psychotic symptoms—gave rise not only to a New Psychology, but to fruitful investigations in many other fields of human knowledge. The ability to interpret the dreams of today made it possible also to interpret the dreams of yesterday. Freudian literature, therefore, abounds in studies throwing new light on mythology, folklore, fairy tales, and ethnology; and psychoanalysis has become as important to the non-medical sciences as to the therapy of the neuroses. . . .

I have always found it hard to understand why Freud's views on sex roused so much opposition. Freud did not enter that realm voluntarily, but was forced by a natural course of events into taking account of the sexual factor in neuroses. Following the discovery of the psychogenesis of hysterical symptoms, first through Breuer's cathartic method and later through the technique of "free association," Freud was led, step by step, to discover and explore the realm of *infantile sexuality*. This discovery was based entirely on empiric material. In probing for the origin of hysterical symptoms, in tracing them back as far as possible, even into childhood, Freud found physical and psychical activities of a definitely sexual nature in the earliest ages of childhood. The necessary conclusion was that the traumas underlying the symptoms were *invariably* of a sexual nature, since all his cases produced similar findings. Finally, therefore, he concluded that sexual activities in childhood could not be considered abnormal, but were on the contrary normal phenomena of the sexual instinct.

In following up these discoveries it was natural that he should also investigate the rôle of sexuality in the extensive syndrome of neurasthenia. To his surprise Freud found that *all* his so-called neurasthenics exhibited some sexual abuses. . . . In the course of these investigations he was able to bring order into the field of neurasthenia—that "garbage can of medicine," as Forel aptly called it—by separating from others those cases which were mainly characterized by anxiety. The results he embodied in his classic paper, *On the Right to Separate from Neurasthenia a Definite Symptom-Complex as "Anxiety Neurosis,"* in which he called attention for the first time to the relation between anxiety and sex. The pursuit of studies in this direction brought him at length to the conviction that all neuroses represent a general

disturbance of the sexual functions; that the *actual neuroses*
(neurasthenia and anxiety neuroses) result from a direct chemical
or toxic disturbance, while the *psychoneuroses* (hysteria and compulsion neuroses) represent the psychic expression of these disturbances. This conclusion, based at first on explorations in the
sexual life of adults, but reënforced and confirmed since 1908
through analyses of children, was finally compressed into the
famous dictum that *"In a normal sex life no neurosis is possible."*
Freud was not the first to discover sexual difficulties in man.
One need only think of literature throughout the ages to realize
that there was abundant material on the subject long before the
appearance of *Three Contributions to the Theory of Sex.* Freud's
special merit lies in the fact that before him sex had been treated
as an isolated phenomenon, or as (more or less) an abnormality,
whereas he paid it the respect of considering it as a component
of the normal personality. In the words of Dr. James J. Putnam,
former professor of neurology at Harvard University, "Freud has
made considerable addition to this stock of knowledge, but he has
done also something of greater consequence than this. He has
worked out with incredible penetration, the part which the instinct plays in every phase of human life and in the development
of human character, and has been able to establish on a firm
footing the remarkable thesis that psychoneurotic illnesses never
occur with a perfectly normal sexual life." Dr. Putnam wrote
those words in his introduction to my first translation (1910) of
Freud's three essays on sex, and I can think of no finer estimate
of Freud's contribution to sexology.

In his study of sex, Freud kept steadily in mind the total human
personality. His formulation of infantile sexuality has opened new
fields of interest in the realm of child study and education which
already are yielding good results. Another concept which has
been enormously helpful to physicians and educators is Freud's
libido theory. In psychoanalysis libido signifies that quantitatively
changeable and not at present measurable energy of the sexual
instinct which is usually directed to an outside object. It comprises
all those impulses which deal with love in the broad sense. Its
main component is sexual love; and sexual union is its aim; but it
also includes self-love, love for parents and children, friendship,
attachments to concrete objects, and even devotion to abstract
ideas.

For those who are unacquainted with Freud's theories of the

neuroses, it will not be amiss to add a few remarks on the paths taken by the libido in neurotic states. The homestead of the libido is the ego; in the child the whole libido is centered in the ego, and we designate it as *ego libido*. The child may be said to be purely egoistic at first; but as he grows older and reaches the narcistic stage of development, we speak of *narcistic libido*, because the former ego libido has now become erotically tinged. Still later, when the child has successfully passed through the early phases of development and can transfer his libido to objects outside himself, that is, when he is genitally pubescent, we speak of *object libido*. Libido thus can be directed 'to outside objects or can be withdrawn back to the ego. A great many normal and pathological states depend on the resulting interchanges between these two forces. The transference neuroses, hysteria and compulsion neuroses, are determined by some disturbance in the give-and-take of object libido, and hence are curable by psychoanalytic therapy, whereas the narcistic neuroses, or the psychoses which are mainly controlled by narcistic libido, can be studied and helped, but cannot as yet be cured by analysis. The psychotic is, as a rule, inaccessible to this treatment because he is unable to transfer sufficient libido to the analyst. The psychotic is either too suspicious or too interested in his own inner world to pay any attention to the physician.

But leaving this problem to the psychoanalytic therapist, one must agree with Freud that by broadening the term sex into love or libido, much is gained for the understanding of the sexual activity of the normal person, of the child, and of the pervert. As will be shown later, the activities of all three spring from the same source, but the manifestations of each depend on the accidental factors to which they have been subjected by their early environments. Moreover, the libido concept loosens sexuality from its close connection with the genitals and establishes it as a more comprehensive physical function, which strives for pleasure in general, and only secondarily enters into the service of propagation. It also adds to the sexual sphere those affectionate and friendly feelings to which we ordinarily apply the term love. To illustrate the application of the libido concept clinically, let us take the case of a nervous child, keeping in mind Freud's dictum that no neurosis is possible in a wholly normal sexual life—a teaching which has aroused more resistance against psychoanalysis than any other utterance of Freud.

An apparently normal girl of about four became very nervous, refused most of her food, had frequent crying spells and tantrums, with consequent loss of weight, malaise, and insomnia, so that her condition became quite alarming. After the ordinary medical measures had been found of no avail, I was consulted. The case was so simple that I could not understand why no one had thought of the cure before I came on the scene. The child had begun to show the symptoms enumerated above, about two months after her mother was separated from her, and she was cured soon after her mother returned to her. I cannot go into the many details of this interesting case, but one can readily see that it differed materially from the case of the young woman mentioned earlier. There we dealt with a disturbance of adult sexuality, here with an emotional disturbance based on a deprivation of mother love in a very sensitive or neurotic child. Nevertheless, it was a disturbance in the child's love life. . . .

. . . *Sublimation*, another term coined by Freud, is a process of deflecting libido or sexual-motive activity from human objects to new objects of a non-sexual, socially valuable nature.

Sublimation gives justification for broadening the concept of sex. Most of our so-called feelings of tenderness and affection, which color so many of our activities and relations in life, originally form part of pure sexuality, and are later inhibited and deflected to higher aims. Thus, I have in mind a number of benevolent people who contributed much of their time and money to the protection and conservation of animals, who were extremely aggressive in childhood and ruthless Nimrods as adults. Their accentuated aggression originally formed a part of their childhood sexuality; then, as a result of training, it was first inhibited and directed to animals, and later altogether repressed and changed into sympathy. Now and then, we encounter cases in which repression and sublimation do not follow each other in regular succession, owing to some weakness or *fixation* which obstructs the process of development. This may lead to paradoxical situations. For example, a man, who was notorious as a great lover of animals, suffered while riding his favorite pony from sudden attacks during which he beat the animal mercilessly until he was exhausted, and then felt extreme remorse and pity for the beast. He would then dismount, pat the horse, appeasing him with lumps of sugar, and walk him home—sometimes a distance of three or four miles. We cannot here go into any analysis of this interesting case; all we can say is that the horse represented a mother symbol, and that the attacks, in which cruelty alternated with compassion, represented the ambivalent feeling of love and hatred which the patient unconsciously felt for his mother.

This patient was entirely changed by analysis, and although he has not given up his interest in animals and still contributes much to their comfort, he is no longer known to the neighborhood boys as "the man who pays a dollar for a sick cat or sick dog." Psychoanalytic literature is rich in clinical material which demonstrates the great benefits accrued from Freud's amplification of the sex concept. It not only gives us an understanding of the broad ramifications of sexual energy hitherto undreamed of, but it has also furnished us with an instrument for treatment and adjustment of many unfortunates who are no more responsible for their perversions than is the victim of infantile paralysis for his malady.

In his effort to understand the mechanism of the expressions observable in those erroneous actions illustrated in the *Psychopathology of Everyday Life*, as well as the distortions in dreams, Freud discerned a remarkable resemblance between these distortions and those found in wit. The following slip of the tongue shows that a slight substitution of one letter not only uncovers the real truth, but also provokes mirth. It was related to me many years ago by one of my patients. She was present at an evening dance of a wealthy, but not too generous, host, which continued until about midnight, when everybody expected a more or less substantial supper. Instead, just sandwiches and lemonade were served. Theodore Roosevelt was then running for President for the second time, under the slogan, "He gave us a square deal." While they were disappointedly consuming this modest repast, the guests were discussing the coming election with the host, and one of them remarked, "There is one fine thing about Teddy; he always give you *a square meal.*"

This *lapsus linguae* not only disclosed unwittingly what the speaker thought of the supper, discharging his hidden disappointment, but it also provoked an outburst of laughter among the guests, for they, through identification with the speaker, found outlet for their own disappointment. But unlike the speaker and the host, who were embarrassed by the mistake, the others experienced a sudden relaxation of the tension generated by disappointment and resentment, which expressed itself in laughter. This slight distortion changed the whole atmosphere of the party. Instead of resentful tension, the majority of the guests now felt relaxed and pleased. There is no doubt that there is a definite connection between faulty actions, dreams and wit. In all of them, the unconscious underlying thoughts are brought to consciousness in some sort of disguise, as if to say, "The truth cannot always be told openly, but somehow it does come out."

. . . Freud's interest in wit was a logical consequence of his free association technique. Once he became convinced that nothing must be ignored—that whatever the patient expressed, be it in mimicry or in sounds, formed part of an effort to release something indirectly because circumstances prevented direct expression—once this fact dawned upon him, it was simply a question of classifying the various forms of distortion and showing in what function of the psychic apparatus they were manifested. The mechanisms of *condensation, displacement, substitution, illogical thinking, absurdity, indirect expressions, elisions,* and *representation through the opposite,* are all present in everyday conversation, but such conventional inaccuracies glide by without any evident impediments. When the thought in question meets with inner resistances, however, a lapse of some kind occurs, which the speaker recognizes and at once excuses by some such expression as "I mean . . ." or "Oh, I made a mistake." The average person readily accepts such excuses, not realizing that by the slip of the tongue the speaker has unconsciously betrayed his resistance to something in the present situation. The disguises seen in the simple lapses of everyday life are even more evident in dreams because *censorship* is more or less abolished during sleep; but fundamentally they are the same. In wit these mental disguises are especially evident, but here they are utilized to produce pleasure. They, too, are products of the unconscious, and show that no matter how much restriction civilization imposes on the individual, he nevertheless finds some way to circumvent it. Wit is the best safety valve modern man has evolved; the more civilization, the more repression, the more need there is for wit. Only relatively civilized people have a sense of humor. The child and the true primitive show no such mechanisms. The child like the savage is still natural and frank. When the child begins to dream, which shows that repressive forces are already at work, he also shows the beginnings of a sense of humor.

The most pronounced psychopathological expressions which point to a deep-seated disturbance are *hallucinations* and *delusions,* which occur in adult psychotics and show a somewhat different kind of disguise. The hallucination as a verbal expression is neither witty nor in any other way distorted. The only thing peculiar about it is that the patient hears, sees, or feels something which is not perceived by anyone else. To be sure, the patient's statements do not concur with the objective facts; yet he is not lying; subjectively speaking, he actually perceives everything he says he does. But we know from Freud that hallucinations represent outward projections of inner feelings. Thus, a woman who has seemingly been living quite contentedly with her husband for five years, hears people say that she is a "bad woman," that her husband is divorcing her, and that she has had illicit relations with a well known movie star. At the same time she complains of peculiar feelings like pin-pricks and electricity in certain parts of her body. These statements could be true, but they are not. We, therefore, call them hallucinatory.

And indeed, the whole picture of the disease in this case showed that the woman suffered from hallucinations of hearing, sight, and sensation. Their meaning became plain when her mother informed me that her son-in-law had been impotent all these years, but that her daughter nevertheless loved him and would not consider leaving him. The hallucinations depicted the wish to be divorced and be married to a real man as a recompense for her drab existence. The annoyance and displeasure caused by "all that talk" and by the peculiar prickling sensations, represented the pangs of conscience, or the feeling of guilt which accompanied her erotic phantasies. The distortion in this whole picture consisted of a fusion of feelings and ideas which had played a part in the conflict in the mind of this sensitive patient. She could not decide one way or the other, so she tore herself entirely away from reality and behaved, as we say, *dereistically*. She abandoned all logic and objectified her phantasies in disguised fashion. . . .

It is quite clear that the distortions manifested in the psychoses are shown by the whole behavior of the person rather than through verbal expressions. Verbal distortions as seen in lapses, errors, blunders in speech and action, are immediate responses to a struggle between the ego and the id. No matter how anxious we are to hide our true nature in adjusting ourselves to the repressive forces of civilization, repression sometimes fails and our real desires come to the surface. The dream is a hidden fulfillment of a repressed wish, or a direct attempt to obtain in phantasy what is denied us in reality. Wit is a direct effort to make use of distortions in order to obtain pleasure from otherwise forbidden sources. Both lapses and dreams are momentary illusions which render a very quick and very brief service to the organism. Wit, on the other hand, is a conscious mechanism for the production of pleasure, the highest or latest development of civilization in this direction. We like to tell jokes and listen to them because for the moment we not only forget inexorable reality, but also obtain pleasure at the expense of our hardships.

But in all these phenomena we remain in touch with reality; the mistake, the dream and the joke amply demonstrate this. The psychosis exhibits alone no compromise with reality, turns its back on reality, as it were. Yet, even in a psychosis, symptoms show that there is a constant struggle between fancy and reality. A chronic schizophrenic may remain in a hospital for years in a state of indifference, but now and then he may suddenly act like a rational being. Sometimes a severe shock, such as an accident or illness which threatens his self-preservative instinct, brings the schizophrenic back to reality for a time. The latest form of therapy for schizophrenics is based on this very idea. I am referring to the insulin or, as it is called, the shock therapy, because the patient receives such a shock through the hypoglycemia that for a time at least he gives up his phantasy world. But it matters little whether hypoglycemia cures or only produces a transient change; the fact that schizophrenics occasionally return to normality spontaneously and then relapse, and the fact that an accidental or experimental shock can drive them back to reality at least for a time, clearly shows that the psychotic, too, is not altogether detached from reality. . . .

That the world which at first turned its back on him [Freud] has now recognized his great services to science and culture is shown by the many honors that have been showered upon him within the last few years. To mention only one of many: His eightieth birthday was an international event. It was celebrated in Vienna at the *Wiener Konzerthaus* and was attended by distinguished scientists from Vienna and abroad. The birthday oration, which was delivered by Thomas Mann, is a masterpiece which has been translated into many languages.

1938

Malaria

RONALD ROSS

THE 20 August 1897—the anniversary of which I always call Mosquito Day—was, I think, a cloudy, dull hot day. I went to hospital at 7 A.M., examined my patients, and attended to official correspondence; but was much annoyed because my men had failed to bring any more larvae of the dappled-winged mosquitoes, and still more because one of my three remaining Anopheles had died during the night and had swelled up with decay. After a hurried breakfast at the Mess, I returned to dissect the cadaver (Mosquito 36), but found nothing new in it. I then examined a small *Stegomyia*, which happened to have been fed on Husein Khan, on the same day (the 16th)—Mosquito 37—which was also negative, of course. At about 1 P.M. I determined to sacrifice the seventh *Anopheles* (A. stephensi) of the batch fed on the 16th, Mosquito 38, although my eyesight was already fatigued. Only one more of the batch remained.

The dissection was excellent, and I went carefully through the tissues, now so familiar to me, searching every micron with the same passion and care as one would search some vast ruined palace for a little hidden treasure. Nothing. No, these new mosquitoes also were going to be a failure; there was something wrong with the theory. But the stomach tissues still remained to be examined—lying there, empty and flaccid, before me on the glass slide, a great white expanse of cells like a large courtyard of flagstones, each one of which must be scrutinised—half an hour's labour at least. I was tired, and what was the use? I must have examined the stomachs of a thousand mosquitoes by this time. But the Angel of Fate fortunately laid his hand on my head; and I had scarcely commenced the search again when I saw a clear and almost perfectly circular outline before me of about 12 microns in diameter. The outline was much too sharp, the cell too small to be an ordinary stomach-cell of a mosquito. I looked a little further. Here was another, and another exactly similar cell.

The afternoon was very hot and overcast; and I remember opening the diaphragm of the sub-stage condenser of the microscope to admit more light and then changing the focus. *In each of these cells there was a cluster of small granules, black as jet* and exactly like .the black pigmént granules of the *Plasmodium* crescents. As with that pigment, the granules numbered about twelve to sixteen in each cell and became blacker and more visible when more light was admitted through the diaphragm. I laughed, and shouted for the Hospital Assistant—he was away having his siesta. "No, no," I said; "Dame Nature, you are a sorceress, but you don't trick me so easily. The malarial pigment cannot get into the walls of the mosquito's stomach; the flagella have no pigment; you are playing another trick upon me!" I counted twelve of the cells, all of the same size and appearance and all containing exactly the same granules. Then I made rough drawings of nine of the cells on page 107 of my notebook, scribbled my notes, sealed my specimen, went home to tea—about 3 P.M., and slept solidly for an hour. . . .

When I awoke with mind refreshed my first thought was; Eureka! the problem is solved! I seemed to have found in my sleep an explanation of the pigment. The flagellated spores grow in the gastric cells of the Dappled-winged Mosquitoes just as the young *Plasmodia* grow in the human blood-cells, and as they grow they absorb haemoglobin from the blood in the mosquito's stomach just as the young *Plasmodia* absorb it from the blood-cell (the "pigment," is of course nothing but altered haemoglobin). I was wrong; my cells were in fact the *female crescents themselves* . . . which had been fertilized by the sperms of the male crescents (which we had called flagellated spores) and were now beginning to grow . . . *still containing their original pigment*, in the gastric cells of the *Anopheles*. Scientifically they are called Zygotes. But any explanation was enough at the time, and I wrote that evening to my wife: "I have seen something very suspicious in my mosquitoes today and hope it may lead to something." Then I added: "Lately I have been putting together those rhymes I used to make on 'Exile'—you remember. I think I will write them out fair. . . ." But another consideration struck me. If these cells were the parasites they should *grow in size* in the last remaining mosquito during the night; and I spent that night in an agony lest my sole surviving friend should perish and go bad before morning!

Next day I went to hospital intensely excited. The last survivor of the batch fed on the 16th, Mosquito 39, was alive. After looking through yesterday's specimen I slew and dissected it with a shaking hand. *There were the cells again,* twenty-one of them, just as before, *only now much larger!* Mosquito 38, the seventh of the batch fed on the 16th, was killed on the fourth day afterwards, that is, on the 20th. This one was killed on the 21st, the fifth day after feeding, and the cells had grown during the extra day. The cells were therefore parasites, and, as they contained the characteristic malarial pigment, were almost certainly the malaria parasites growing in the mosquito's tissues.

The thing was really done. As I said . . . we had to discover two unknown quantities simultaneously—the kind of mosquito which carries the parasite, and the form and position of the parasite within it. We could not find the first without knowing the second, nor the second without knowing the first. By an extremely lucky observation I had now discovered both the unknown quantities at the same moment. The mosquito was the *Anopheles,* and the parasite lives in or on its gastric wall and can be recognized at once by the characteristic pigment. All the work on the subject which has been done since then by me and others during the last twenty-five years has been mere child's play which anyone could do after the clue was once obtained.

That evening I wrote to my wife: "I have seen something very promising indeed in my new mosquitoes," and I scribbled the following unfinished verses in one of my *In Exile* notebooks in pencil:

> This day designing God
> Hath put into my hand
> A wondrous thing. At His command
> I have found thy secret deeds
> Oh million-murdering Death.
>
> I know that this little thing
> A million men will save—
> Oh death where is thy sting?
> Thy victory oh grave?

1923

The Ravages of Yellow Fever[1]

I

A SHORT ACCOUNT OF THE MALIGNANT YELLOW FEVER LATELY PREVALENT IN PHILADELPHIA

MATTHEW CAREY

THE consternation of the people of Philadelphia at this period was carried beyond all bounds. Dismay and affright were visible in the countenance of almost every person. Of those who remained many shut themselves in their houses and were afraid to walk the streets. . . .

The corpses of the most respectable citizens, even those who did not die of the epidemic, were carried to the grave on the shafts of a chair (chaise), the horse driven by a negro, unattended by a friend or relative, and without any sort of ceremony. People hastily shifted their course at the sight of a hearse coming towards them. Many never walked on the footpath, but went into the middle of the streets, to avoid being infected in passing by houses wherein people had died. Acquaintances and friends avoided each other in the streets and only signified their regard by a cold nod. The old custom of shaking hands fell into such disuse that many shrunk back with affright at even the offer of the hand. A person with a crape, or any appearance of mourning, was shunned like a viper. And many valued themselves highly on the skill and address with which they got to the windward of every person they met. Indeed, it is not probable that London, at the last stage of the plague, exhibited stronger marks of terror than were to be seen in Philadelphia from the 24th or 25th of August till pretty late in September.

While affairs were in this deplorable state, and the people at the lowest ebb of despair, we cannot be astonished at the frightful scenes that were enacted, which seemed to indicate a total dissolution of the bonds of society in the nearest and dearest connections. Who, without horror, can reflect on a husband desert-

[1] Selections in "The Ravages of Yellow Fever" were taken from "Walter Reed and Yellow Fever," by Howard A. Kelly, 1906.

ing his wife, united to him, perhaps, for twenty years, in the last
agony—a wife unfeelingly abandoning her husband on his death-
bed—parents forsaking their own children without remorse—
children ungratefully flying from their parents and resigning them
to chance, without an inquiry after their health or safety—masters hurrying off their faithful servants to Bush-Hill, even on
suspicion of the disease, and that at a time when, like Tartarus, it
was open to every visitant, but never returned any—servants
abandoning tender and humane masters, who only wanted a little
care to restore them to health and usefulness—who, I say, can
even now think of these things without horror? . . .

A woman, whose husband and two children lay dead in the
room with her, was seized with the pains of labour, without a
mid-wife, or any other person to assist her. Her cries from the
window brought up one of the carters employed by the committee for the relief of the sick. With his assistance she was delivered
of a child, which died in a few minutes, as did the mother, who
was utterly exhausted by her labour, by the disorder, and by the
dreadful spectacle before her. And thus lay in one room no less
than five dead bodies, an entire family, carried off in an hour or
two. . . .

A profligate, abandoned set of nurses and attendants (hardly
any of good character could at that time be procured) rioted on
the provisions and comforts provided for the sick, who (unless
at the hours when the doctors attended) were left almost entirely
destitute of every assistance. The sick, the dying, and the dead
were indiscriminately mingled together. Not the smallest appearance of order or regularity existed. It was, in fact, a great
human slaughter house, where numerous victims were immolated
at the altar of riot and intemperance. No wonder, then, that a
general dread of the place prevailed through the city, and that a
removal to it was considered as the seal of death. In consequence
there were various instances of sick persons locking their rooms
and resisting every effort to carry them away. At length the poor
were so much afraid of being sent to Bush-Hill that they would
not acknowledge their illness until it was no longer possible to
conceal it. For it is to be observed that the fear of contagion was
so prevalent that as soon as anyone was taken sick an alarm was
spread among the neighbours and every effort was used to have
the sick person hurried off to Bush-Hill, to avoid spreading the

disorder. The cases of poor people forced in this way to the hospital, though labouring only under common colds and common fall fevers, are numerous and afflicting. . . .

1793

II

A NARRATIVE OF THE STATE OF THE BODY AND MIND OF THE AUTHOR DURING THE PREVALENCE OF THE FEVER

BENJAMIN RUSH

BETWEEN the 8th and 15th of September I visited and prescribed for between a hundred and a hundred and twenty patients a day. Several of my pupils visited a fourth or fifth of that number. For a while we refused no calls. In the short intervals of business, which I spent at my meals, my house was filled with patients, chiefly the poor, waiting for advice. For many weeks I seldom ate without prescribing for numbers as I sat at my table. . . . From my constant exposure to the sources of the disease my body became highly impregnated with miasmata. My eyes were yellow and sometimes a yellow tinge was perceptible in my face. My pulse was preternaturally quick and my nights were rendered disagreeable, not only by sweats, but by the want of my usual sleep, produced in part by the frequent knocking at my door and in part by anxiety of mind and the stimulus of the miasmata upon my system. I went to bed in conformity to habit only, for it ceased to afford me rest or refreshment. When it was evening I wished for morning, and when it was morning the prospect of the labours of the day, at which I often shuddered, caused me to wish for the return of evening. The degree of my anxiety may be easily conceived when I say that I had at one time upwards of thirty heads of families under my care; among these were Mr. Josiah Coates, the father of eight, and Mr. Benjamin Scull and Mr. John Morell, both fathers of ten children. They were all in imminent danger, but it pleased God to make me the instrument of saving each of their lives. . . . Every moment in the intervals of my visits to the sick was employed in prescribing in my own house for the poor, or in sending answers to messages from my patients. Time was now too precious (October) to be spent in counting the number of persons who called upon me for advice.

From circumstances I believe it was frequently 150, and seldom less than 50 a day for five or six weeks. The evening did not bring with it the least relaxation from my labours. I received letters every day from the country and from distant parts of the Union containing inquiries into the mode of treating the disease, and after the health and lives of persons who had remained in the city. The business of every evening was to answer these letters and also to write to my family. To these constant labours of body and mind were added distress from a variety of causes. Having found myself unable to comply with the numerous applications that were made to me, I was obliged to refuse many every day. My sister counted forty-seven in one forenoon before eleven o'clock. Many of them left my door with tears, but they did not feel more distress than I did from refusing to follow them. . . . In riding through the streets I was often forced to resist the entreaties of parents imploring a visit to their children, or of children to their parents. I recollect, and even *yet* with pain, that I tore myself away at one time from five persons in Moravian Alley who attempted to stop me, by suddenly whipping my horse and driving my chair as speedily as possible beyond the reach of their cries.

But I had other afflictions besides the distress which arose from the abortive sympathy which I have just described. On the 11th of September my ingenuous pupil, Mr. Washington, fell a victim to his humanity. . . . Scarce had I recovered from the shock of the death of this amiable youth when I was called to weep for another pupil, Mr. Alston, who died in my neighbourhood the next day. . . . At this time a third pupil, Mr. Fisher, was ill in my house. On the 26th of the month Mr. Coxe, my only assistant, was seized with the fever and went to his grandfather's. I followed him with a look which I feared would be the last in my house. At two o'clock my sister, who had complained for several days, yielded to the disease and retired to her bed. My mother followed her, much indisposed, early in the evening. My black servant man had been confined with the fever for several days, and had, on that day, for the first time quitted his bed. My little mulatto boy, of eleven years old, was the only person in my family who was able to afford me the least assistance. . . .

On the 1st of October, at two o'clock, my sister died. I got into my carriage within an hour after she expired and spent the afternoon in visiting patients. According as a sense of duty or of grief has predominated in my mind I have approved of this act or not, ever since. She had borne a share in my labours. She had been my nurse in sickness, and my casuist in my choice of duties. My whole heart reposed itself in her friendship. . . . From this time I declined in health and strength. All motion was painful to me. My appetite began to fail. My night sweats continued. My short and imperfect sleep was disturbed with distressing or frightful dreams. The scenes of them were derived altogether from sick rooms and graveyards. . . . For the first two weeks after I visited patients in the yellow fever I carried a rag wetted with vinegar and smelled it occasionally in sick rooms, but as I saw and felt the signs of the universal presence of miasmata in my system I laid aside this and all other precautions. I rested myself on the bedsides of my patients, and I drank milk or ate fruit in their rooms. Besides being saturated with miasmata I had another security against being infected in sick rooms, and that was, I went into scarcely a house which was more infected than my own. Many of the poor people who called upon me for treatment were bled by my pupils in my shop and in the yard, which is between it and the street. From the want of a sufficient number of bowls to receive the blood it was sometimes suffered to flow and putrefy upon the ground. From this source streams of miasmata were constantly poured into my house and conveyed to my body by the air during every hour of the day and night. . . . My perception of the lapse of time was new to me. It was uncommonly slow. The ordinary business and pursuits of men appeared to me in a light that was equally new. The hearse and the grave mingled themselves with every view I took of human affairs. Under these impressions I recollect being as much struck with observing a number of men employed in digging the cellar of a large house as I should have been at any other time in seeing preparations for building a palace upon a cake of ice. I recollect, further, being struck with surprise, about the first of October, in seeing a man busily employed in laying in wood for the approaching winter. I should as soon have thought of making provision for a dinner on the first day of the year 1800.

After the loss of my health I received letters from friends in the country, pressing me in the strongest terms to leave the city. Such a step had become impracticable. My aged mother was too infirm to be removed, and I could not leave her. I was, moreover, part of a little circle of physicians who had associated themselves in support of the new remedies. This circle would have been broken up by my quitting the city. The weather varied the disease, and in the weakest state of the body I expected to be able, from the reports of my pupils, to assist my associates in detecting its changes and in accommodating our remedies to them. Under these circumstances it pleased God to enable me to reply to one of the letters that urged my retreat from the city that I had resolved to stick to my principles, my practice, and my patients to the last extremity.

Edition of 1809

III

HISTORY OF THE YELLOW FEVER EPIDEMIC OF 1878 IN MEMPHIS, TENN.

J. M. KEATING

Men, women, and children, poured out of the city by every possible avenue of escape. . . . Out by the country roads to the little hamlets and plantations, where many of them were welcome guests in happier days; out by every possible conveyance—by hacks, by carriages, buggies, waggons, furniture vans, and streetdrays; away by bateaux, by anything that could float on the river; and by the railroads, the trains on which, especially on the Louisville road, were so packed as to make the trip to that city, or to Cincinnati, a positive torture to many delicate women every mile of the way. The aisles of the cars were filled and the platforms packed. In vain the railroad officials plead, in vain they increased the accommodations. The stream of passengers seemed to be endless and they were as mad as they were many. The ordinary courtesies of life were ignored, politeness gave way to selfishness, and the desire for personal safety broke through all social amenities. . . . To the cities of the far North and the far West they fled, too many of them to die on the way like dogs, neglected and shunned, as if cursed of God; or, to reach the wished-for goal, only to die, a plague to all about, carrying dismay to those who even then were busying themselves for the relief of the stricken cities of the South. In less than ten days, by the 24th of August, twenty-five thousand people had left the city, and in two weeks after five thousand others were in camp, leaving a little less than twenty thousand to face consequences they could not escape. . . .

By the last week in August the panic was over in the city. All had fled who could, and all were in camp who would go. There were then, it was estimated, about three thousand cases of fever . . . an appalling gloom hung over the doomed city. At night it was silent as the grave, by day it seemed desolate as the desert. There were hours, especially at night, when the solemn oppression of universal death bore upon the human mind, as if the day of judgment was about to dawn. Not a sound was to be heard; the silence was painfully profound. Death prevailed everywhere. Trade and traffic were suspended. The energies of all who remained were engaged in the struggle with death. The poor were reduced to beggary, and even the rich gladly accepted alms. . . . Even the animals felt the oppression and fled from the city. Rats, cats, or dogs were not to be seen. Death was everywhere triumphant. White women were seldom to be met with, children never. The voice of prayer was lifted up only at the bed of pain or death, or in some home circle where anguish was supreme and death threatened, as in a few cases he accomplished, total annihilation. Tears for one loved one were choked by the feeling of uncertainty provoked by the sad condition of another. In one case a family of four was found dead in one room, the bodies partially decomposed. There were no public evidences of sorrow. The wife was borne to the tomb while the husband was unconscious of his loss, and whole families were swept away in such quick succession that not one had knowledge of the other's departure. Death dealt kindly by these. . . . Neither cleanliness nor right living were a shield to stay the hand of the destroyer. He invaded the homes of the most chaste and the den of the vilest. He took innocence and infamy at the same moment and spread terror everywhere. Where sorrow was so general there could be no parade of it. There were no funerals and but little demand for funeral services. The luxuries of woe were dispensed with. In most cases the driver of the hearse and an assistant composed the funeral party. Not infrequently many bodies were left in the cemetery unburied for a night, so hard pressed were the managers for labour, and so numerous were the demands upon what they had. . . . The churches were closed. The congregations dispersed. The members were far apart. Some were safe, many were dead. Only a few survived, and these were manifesting their faith by works. The police were cut down from forty-one to seven. Their ranks were recruited and again were thinned. They were a second and a third time filled up, and yet death was relentless. He was jealous of all sway but his own.

Petty thieving prevailed as an epidemic. This was principally confined to food and clothing, and wood or coal, or both. A few who came to nurse died, leaving full trunks of silverware, bijouterie, bric-a-brac, and clothes, to prove how industriously they could ply two trades and make one cover up and supply the deficiencies of the other. A few of them also made themselves notorious for lewdness and drunkenness. To these vices many deaths were due. They shocked decency and outraged humanity, they were no better than the beasts of the field. Male and female they herded together in vileness. They made of the epidemic a carnival. . . . One of these, a woman who would not or could not control her appetite for strong drink, while stupefied from wine and brandy allowed a poor woman to leave her bed, naked as when born, and wander out into the country one inclement night, calling as she went for the husband who had preceded her to the grave by a few days. . . . In the house of an ex-judge, whence a whole family had been borne to the grave, the victims of neglect, four such nurses died, and in the trunks of one, the worst of them, a woman of seeming refinement, there was found the family plate and wearing apparel of the judge's wife, then absent in Ohio. This woman and her paramours fell victims to the fever which they invited by their debauchery and hastened by their excesses. In the whole range of human depravity there are few parallels to these cases. They illustrate the extremes of degradation; they sounded the lowest depths of vice and shamed even the standards of savage life.

IV

EXPERIENCES WITH YELLOW FEVER

MRS. LENA WARREN

My first great sorrow came to me through this terrible scourge, in 1878, in the town of Grenada, Mississippi, a place of 3000 inhabitants. History records this epidemic as the most terrible death-rate known. In my own family eight members were stricken, and myself and a child of nine years were the only ones to recover. I can recall very distinctly the terrible ordeal we had to undergo, while many noble men and women sacrificed their

THE TURN OF THE CENTURY—AND BEYOND

lives to relieve the helplessness of these unfortunate people. They came from all sections of the country, and as every occasion of this kind is burdened with human beasts of prey, robbing and pilfering the living, dying, and dead, so was this plague-stricken city. Men sent there who represented themselves as nurses from the Howard Benevolent Association were among the worst. My own father, while ill with the fever, was choked, robbed, and left alone to die; I was too ill even to cry out for help, but witnessed the entire affair. It was twenty hours before we were found in this condition. Burning tar, bonfires, and disinfectants of various kinds were placed on the corners of the streets, and yet that peculiar odour from yellow fever could be detected from every direction. The only signs of traffic were waggons hauling the dead; few caskets were seen, but in their stead plain boxes and sometimes dry goods boxes were utilised; they were piled one on top of the other and fastened with ropes to the bed of the waggons. Negroes were procured for this work; they were known to rob the dead and the vacant residences. The following winter several visits were made to the cabins, where clothing, silver, and other valuables were found. On one occasion of this kind I was called by the town marshal to identify some things supposed to have been taken from our house; while looking down on a crowd of negroes I called the marshal's attention to a negro man wearing my father's hat. He proved to be a minister, and we found a waggon-load of various articles at his house. The negroes' work as grave-diggers proved to be very poor, as sixteen inches was afterwards found to be the depth of any grave made during that time. . . .

From the date of a lecture I heard on yellow fever delivered by Dr. R. B. Maury and Dr. R. W. Mitchell, I was possessed of a great desire to come in contact with the disease. When our Government called for volunteer nurses to go to Cuba I availed myself of this opportunity.

In August, 1900, I was ordered from Matanzas to Havana. The night before my transfer to Havana I was entertained at the quarters of the officers of the 2nd Cavalry stationed at Matanzas; there I met a Major Cartwright, who informed me that he also had been ordered to Havana, as he was an immune, having had the fever in '98 at Santiago. Two weeks after my arrival at the yellow fever camp the ambulance brought a patient from General Lee's headquarters, and as I stepped forward to give directions in regard to him I recognised Major Cartwright. After some conversation he stated that he could not possibly have yellow fever, as he certainly had a genuine case in '98. However, on the sixth day after his arrival he died of black vomit. Major Peterson also thought that he had had the fever, but he was taken ill again with it, and his wife, hearing of his illness, two hours after his death, committed suicide by shooting herself through the temple in our quarters at Las Animas.

The only nurse with me who had yellow fever was one that claimed to be an immune; she was sent to Major Edmund's residence at Quemados the night before his death; she returned to the camp and four days after was taken with a mild case. We had no mosquitoes in our camp.

Quarantine was very strict, but we continued to have yellow fever among the soldiers and officers; we were poorly equipped at Columbia Barracks Detention Camp, and yet the mortality was not so great as in this country. A few officers and privates from the Palace in Havana were taken to Las Animas, a Cuban hospital for civilians under Major Gorgas' supervision; he called on our chief surgeon for help and I was ordered there for ten days. At this place they were well equipped, the nurses being well cared for as well as the patients. We lost that week Major Peterson, Captain Page, the quartermaster sergeant, one soldier, and one civilian employé. Major Gorgas was very successful in the treatment of the fever, and upon my return to Camp Columbia I determined to imitate his directions.

In September I nursed Dr. James Carroll, a member of Major Reed's staff of Commissioners, and he told me he experimented upon himself with the mosquito; while he had a severe case he did not have hemorrhages, but even to the whites of his eyes he was as yellow as saffron. A few days after Dr. Carroll's chill Dr. Jesse Lazear was stricken with the fever. He also was a member of the board and was brought on a litter to our camp about eleven A.M. He knew what his illness was and informed me that he had his chill about six P.M.; he had not been in bed all night, as he was busy writing up their experiments in regard to yellow fever and the mosquito. His temperature was 103°, his pulse 80; he lived five days; the black vomit would spurt from his mouth up through the bar over his cot. I had just relieved the day nurse and gone on for the night; my efforts to keep him in bed failed and I called for help, but before assistance reached me we had made several turns around the room in his efforts to get out. All night it took two men to hold him, and he died the next morning.

In December I met Major Reed, and it was at this time that they had begun in earnest to erect buildings for the special experiments to prove that the mosquito was the only source of infection. Major Reed was an officer to whom we were all devoted; he liked best to be called "Doctor." I was always glad on my daily visits to the laboratory to catch him there; he had won the friendship and esteem of the entire corps, having the most genial manners and was so considerate and kind to everyone. I do not feel that I could speak in too high terms of Major Reed. At all times he was so willing to go into details with any part of the experiment I did not comprehend, and was patient enough to give me a peep through the different microscopes and give a full explanation. I told him of our '78 epidemic, and he informed me that Surgeon-General Sternberg was in Memphis at that time. The experimental camp was called after Dr. Lazear. In a statement I heard Major Reed make, he said that Dr. Lazear's efforts in this work had been of vast importance. Major Reed was strong in his friendships, as Dr. Carroll can readily testify. I recall an incident which gives an insight into the kind of man he was. On one occasion he moved his mess quarters because he heard his brother officers use language at the table which was very ungentlemanly. It was due to his indefatigable efforts that we owe our success with yellow fever at Camp Lazear, as we never lost a case experimented upon.   *1906*

V

THE PREVENTION OF YELLOW FEVER

WALTER REED AND JAMES CARROLL

It would be difficult to determine with accuracy the loss of life occasioned by the ninety-five invasions of our territory by yellow fever during the past two hundred and eight years. We have endeavoured to collect from the most available sources the mortality caused by the disease, but have been unable to obtain any reliable data for the earlier epidemics. If we confine ourselves to the epidemics which have occurred since 1793, we find that there have not been less than 100,000 deaths from this cause. The greatest sufferer has been the city of New Orleans, with 41,348 deaths, followed by the city of Philadelphia with 10,380 deaths. The epidemics of 1855, 1873, 1878, and 1879 claimed 7759 victims in the city of Memphis, Tenn. From 1800 to 1876 Charleston lost 4565 of its citizens by attacks of yellow fever. New York during the earlier and later invasions of this disease has had 3454 deaths, while the later epidemic of 1855 in Norfolk, Va., caused over 2000 deaths. During our brief occupation of the Island of Cuba (July, 1898-December, 1900), with every precaution brought into exercise to ward off the disease, there have occurred among the officers and men of our army 1575 cases of yellow fever, with 231 deaths. If we reckon the average mortality at 20 per cent there have not been less than 500,00 cases of yellow fever in the United States during the period from 1793 to 1900.

1901

The Inside Story of a Great
Medical Discovery

ARISTIDES AGRAMONTE

THE construction of the Panama Canal was made possible because it was shown that yellow fever, like malaria, could be spread only by the bites of infected mosquitoes.

The same discovery, which has been repeatedly referred to as the greatest medical achievement of the twentieth century, was the means of stamping out the dreaded scourge in Cuba, as well as in New Orleans, Rio de Janeiro, Vera Cruz, Colon, Panama and other cities in America.

This article is intended to narrate the motives that led up to the investigation and also the manner in which the work was planned, executed and terminated. No names are withheld and the date of every important event is given, so that an interested reader may be enabled to follow closely upon the order of things as they occurred and thus form a correct idea of the importance of the undertaking, the risk entailed in its accomplishment and how evenly divided was the work among those who, in the faithful performance of their military duties, contributed so much for the benefit of mankind; the magnitude of their achievement is of such proportions, that it loses nothing of its greatness when we tear away the halo of apparent heroism that well-meaning but ignorant historians have thrown about some of the investigators.

The whole series of events, tragic, pathetic, comical and otherwise, took place upon a stage made particularly fit by nature and the surrounding circumstances.

Columbia Barracks, a military reservation, garrisoned by some fourteen hundred troops, distant about eight miles from the city of Havana, the latter, suffering at the time from an epidemic of yellow fever, which the application of all sanitary measures had failed to check or ameliorate and finally, our experimental camp (Camp Lazear), a few army tents, securely hidden from the road leading to Marianao, and safeguarded against intercourse with the outside world; the whole setting portentously silent and gloriously bright in the glow of tropical sunlight and the green of luxuriant vegetation.

Two members of a detachment of four medical officers of the United States Army, on the morning of August 31, 1900, were busily examining under microscopes several glass slides containing blood from a fellow officer who, since the day before, had shown symptoms of yellow fever; these men were Drs. Jesse W. Lazear and myself; our sick colleague was Dr. James Carroll, who presumably had been infected by one of our "experiment mosquitoes."

It is very difficult to describe the feelings which assailed us at that moment; a sense of exultation at our apparent success no doubt animated us; regret, because the results had evidently brought a dangerous illness upon our coworker and with it all associated a thrill of uncertainty for the reason of the yet insufficient testimony tending to prove the far-reaching truth which we then hardly dared to realize.

As the idea that Carroll's fever must have been caused by the mosquito that was applied to him four days before became fixed upon our minds, we decided to test it upon the first non-immune person who should offer himself to be bitten; this was of common occurrence and taken much as a joke among the soldiers about the military hospital. Barely fifteen minutes may have elapsed since we had come to this decision when, as Lazear stood at the door of the laboratory trying to "coax" a mosquito to pass from one test-tube into another, a soldier came walking by towards the hospital buildings; he saluted, as it is customary in the army upon meeting an officer, but, as Lazear had both hands engaged, he answered with a rather pleasant "Good morning." The man stopped upon coming abreast, curious no doubt to see the performance with the tubes, and after gazing for a minute or two at the insects he said: "You still fooling with mosquitoes, Doctor?" "Yes," returned Lazear, "will you take a bite?" "Sure I ain't scared of 'em," responded the man. When I heard this, I left the microscope and stepped to the door, where the short conversation had taken place; Lazear looked at me as though in consultation; I nodded assent, then turned to the soldier and asked him to come inside and bare his forearm. Upon a slip of paper I wrote his name while several mosquitoes took their fill; William H. Dean, American by birth, belonging to Troop B, Seventh Cavalry; he said that he had never been in the tropics before and had not left the military reservation for nearly two months. The conditions for a test case were quite ideal.

I must say we were in great trepidation at the time; and well might we have been, for Dean's was the first indubitable case of yellow fever about to be produced experimentally by the bite of purposely infected mosquitoes. Five days afterwards, when he came down with yellow fever and the diagnosis of his case was corroborated by Dr. Roger P. Ames, U. S. Army, then on duty at the hospital, we sent a cablegram to Major Walter Reed, chairman of the board, who a month before had been called to Washington upon another duty, apprising him of the fact that the theory of the transmission of yellow fever by mosquitoes, which at first was doubted so much and the transcendental importance of which we could then barely appreciate, had indeed been confirmed.

STATE OF THINGS BEFORE THE DISCOVERY OF MOSQUITO TRANSMISSION

Other infectious diseases, tuberculosis, for instance, may cause a greater death-rate and bring about more misery and distress, even to-day, than yellow fever has produced at any one time; but no disease, except possibly cholera or the plague, is so tragic in its development, so appalling in its action, so devastating in its results, nor does any other make greater havoc than yellow fever when it invades non-immune or susceptible communities. . . .

The mystery which accompanied the usual course of an epidemic, the poison creeping from house to house, along one side of a street, seldom crossing the road, spreading sometimes around the whole block of houses before appearing in another neighborhood, unless distinctly carried there by a visitor to the infected zone who himself became stricken, all this series of peculiar circumstances was a never-ending source of discussion and investigation.

In the year 1900, Surgeon H. R. Carter, of the then Marine Hospital Service, published a very interesting paper calling attention to the interval of time which regularly occurred between the first case of yellow fever in a given community and those that subsequently followed; this was never less than two weeks, a period of incubation extending beyond that usually accorded to other acute infectious diseases. The accuracy of these observations has later been confirmed by the mosquito experiments hereinafter outlined.

FACTORS WHICH LED TO THE APPOINTMENT OF THE BOARD

One may well believe that such a scourge as yellow fever could not have been long neglected by medical investigators, and so we find that from the earliest days, when the germ-theory of disease took its proper place in modern science, a search for the causative agent of this infection was more or less actively instituted.

The year before the Spanish-American war, an Italian savant, who had obtained a well-deserved reputation as bacteriologist while working in the Institute Pasteur of Paris, came out with the announcement from Montevideo, Uruguay, that he had actually discovered the much-sought-for cause of yellow fever; his descriptions of the methods employed, though not materially different from those followed by Sternberg many years before, bore the imprint of truth and his experimental inoculations had apparently been successful. Sanarelli—that is his name—for about two years was the "hero of the hour," yet his claims have been proved absolutely false. . . .

In the meantime the city of Havana was being rendered sanitary in a way which experience had taught would have overcome any bacterial infection, and, in fact, the diseases of filth, such as dysentery, tuberculosis, children's complaints and others, decreased in a surprising manner, while yellow fever seemed to have been little affected if at all.

Evidently, a more thorough overhauling of the matter was necessary to arrive at the truth, and while the question of Sanarelli and his claims was practically put aside, Surgeon-General Sternberg, recognizing the importance of the work before us and that its proportions were such as to render the outcome more satisfactory by the cooperation of several investigators in the same direction, wisely decided to create a board for the purpose. . . .

Major Reed, the first member in the order of appointment, was the ranking officer and therefore the chairman of the board. He was a regular army officer, at the time curator of the Army Medical Museum in Washington and a bacteriologist of some repute. He deservedly enjoyed the full confidence of the surgeon general, besides his personal friendship and regard. Reed was a man of charming personality, honest and above board. Every one who knew him loved him and confided in him. A polished gentleman and a scientist of the highest order, he was peculiarly fitted for the work before him.

Dr. James Carroll, the second member of the board, was a self-made man, having risen from the ranks through his own efforts: while a member of the Army Hospital Corps he studied medicine and subsequently took several courses at Johns Hopkins University in the laboratory branches. At the time of his appointment to the board he had been for several years an able assistant to Major Reed. Personally, Carroll was industrious and of a retiring disposition.

Dr. Jesse W. Lazear was the fourth member of the board. He had graduated from the College of Physicians and Surgeons (Columbia University) in the same class as the writer, in 1892, and had afterwards studied abroad and at Johns Hopkins. Lazear had received special training in the investigation of mosquitoes with reference to malaria and other diseases. Stationed at Columbia Barracks, he had been in Cuba several months before the board was convened, in charge of the hospital laboratory at the camp. A thorough university man, he was the type of the old southern gentleman, kind, affectionate, dignified, with a high sense of honor, a staunch friend and a faithful soldier.

The writer was the third member of the Army Board. Born in

Cuba during the ten years' war, while still a child, my father having been killed in battle against the Spanish, I was taken to the United States and educated in the public schools and in the College of the City of New York, graduating from the College of Physicians and Surgeons in 1892. At the breaking out of the war I was assistant bacteriologist in the New York Health Department. The subject of yellow fever research was my chief object from the outset, and, at the time the board was appointed, I was in charge of the laboratory of the Division of Cuba, in Havana.

FIRST PART OF THE WORK OF THE BOARD

. . . On the afternoon of June 25, 1900, the four officers met for the first time in their new capacity, on the veranda of the officers' quarters at Columbia Barracks Hospital. We were fully appreciative of the trust and aware of the responsibility placed upon us and with a feeling akin to reverence heard the instructions which Major Reed had brought from the surgeon general; they comprised the investigation also of malaria, leprosy and unclassified febrile conditions, and were given with such detail and precision as only a man of General Sternberg's experience and knowledge in such matters could have prepared. After deciding upon the first steps to be taken, it was unanimously agreed that whatever the result of our investigation should turn out to be, it was to be considered as the work of the board as a body, and never as the outcome of any individual effort; that each one of us was to work in harmony with a general plan, though at liberty to carry out his individual methods of research. We were to meet whenever necessary, Drs. Reed, Carroll and Lazear to remain at the Barracks Hospital and I to stay in charge of the laboratory in Havana, at the Military Hospital, where I also had a ward into which yellow-fever cases from the city were often admitted.

Work was begun at once. Fortunately for our purpose, an epidemic of yellow fever existed in the town of Quemados, in close proximity to the military reservation of Camp Columbia. Even before the arrival of Reed and Carroll, Lazear and I had been studying its spread, following the cases very closely. . . .

In the meantime a rather severe outbreak of yellow fever had occurred in Santa Clara, a city in the interior of the island, having invaded the garrison and caused the death of several soldiers. . . . The infection of the city of Santa Clara had evidently taken place from Havana, distant only one night's journey by train. Captain

Stone, a particularly able officer, had already instituted effective quarantine measures before my arrival, so that I only remained there a few days.

But as to the actual cause of the disease we were still entirely at sea; it helped us little to know that a man could be infected in Havana, take the train for a town in the interior and start an outbreak there in the course of time.

Upon rejoining my colleagues (July 2) we resumed our routine investigations; not only in Quemados, where the disease was being stamped out, but also in Havana, at "Las Animas" Hospital and at Military Hospital No. 1, where my laboratory (the division laboratory) was located. There was no scarcity of material and the two members who until then had never seen a case of yellow fever (Reed and Carroll) had ample opportunity, and took advantage of it, to become acquainted with the many details of its clinical picture which escape the ordinary practitioner, the knowledge and the appreciation of which, in their relative value, give the right to the title of "expert."

Since the later part of June, reports had been coming to headquarters of an extraordinary increase of sickness among the soldiers stationed at Pinar del Rio, the capital of the extreme western province, and very soon the great mortality from so-called "pernicious malarial fever" attracted the attention of the chief surgeon, Captain A. N. Stark, who, after consulting with Major Reed, ordered me to go there and investigate. A man had died, supposedly from malaria, just before my arrival on the afternoon of July 19. The autopsy which I performed at once showed me that yellow fever had been the cause of his death, and a search through the military hospital wards revealed the existence of several unrecognized cases being treated as malaria; a consultation held with the medical officer in charge showed me his absolute incapacity, as he was under the influence of opium most of the time (he committed suicide several months afterwards)....

Conditions in the hospital were such as to demand immediate action; the commander of the post refused to believe he had yellow fever among his 900 men and was loath to abandon his comfortable quarters for the tent life in the woods that I earnestly recommended. In answer to my telegram asking for official support, I received the following:

CHIEF SURGEON'S OFFICE
HDQRS. DEPT. HAVANA AND PINAR DEL RIO,
QUEMADOS, CUBA, July 21, 1900
SURGEON AGRAMONTE,
Pinar del Rio Barracks,
Pinar del Rio, Cuba
Take charge of cases. Reed goes on morning train. Wire
for anything wanted. Nurses will be sent. Instructions wired
commanding officer. Other doctors should not attend cases.
Establish strict quarantine at hospital. You will be relieved
as soon as an immune can be sent to replace you. Report daily
by wire.

STARK,
Chief Surgeon

When Major Reed came to Pinar del Rio (July 21) I had, the
day before, established a separate yellow-fever hospital, under
tents, attended by some of the men who had already passed an
attack and were thus immune. The Major and I went over the
ground very carefully, we studied the sick report for two months
back, fruitlessly trying to place the blame upon the first case.
I well remember how, as we stood in the men's sleeping quarters,
surrounded by a hundred beds, from several of which fatal cases
had been removed, we were struck by the fact that the later
occupants had not developed the disease. In connection with this,
and particularly interesting, was the case of a soldier prisoner
who had been confined to the guard-house since June 6; he
showed the first symptoms of yellow fever on the twelfth and
died on the eighteenth; none of the other eight prisoners in the
same cell caught the infection, though one of them continued
to sleep in the same bunk previously occupied by his dead com-
rade. More than this; the three men who handled the clothing and
washed the linen of those who had died during the last month
were still in perfect health. Here we seemed to be in the presence
of the same phenomenon remarked by Captain Stone in reference
to his case at Santa Clara, and before that by several investigators
of yellow-fever epidemics; the infection at a distance, the harmless condition of bedding and clothing of the sick; the possibility
that some insect might be concerned in spreading the disease
deeply impressed us and Major Reed mentions the circumstance
in his later writings. This was really the first time that the

mosquito transmission theory was seriously considered by members of the board, and it was decided that, although discredited by the repeated failure of its most ardent supporter, Dr. Carlos J. Finlay, of Havana, to demonstrate it, the matter should be taken up by the board and thoroughly sifted.

The removal of the troops out of Pinar del Rio was the means of at once checking the propagation of the disease.

On the first day of August the board met and after due deliberation determined to investigate mosquitoes in connection with the spread of yellow fever. As Dr. Lazear was the only one of us who had had any experience in mosquito work, Major Reed thought proper that he should take charge of this part of the investigation in the beginning, while we, Carroll and I, continued with the other work on hand, at the same time gradually becoming familiar with the manipulations necessary in dealing with the insects.

A visit was now made to Dr. Finlay, who, much elated at the news that the board was about to investigate his pet theory, the transmission of yellow fever from man to man by mosquitoes, very kindly explained to us many points regarding the life of the one kind he thought most guilty and ended by furnishing us with a number of eggs which, laid by a female mosquito nearly a month before, had remained unhatched on the inside of a half empty bowl of water in his library.

Much to our disappointment and regret, during the first week of August, Major Reed was recalled to Washington that he might, in collaboration with Drs. Vaughan and Shakespeare, complete the report upon "Typhoid Fever in the Army." Thus we were deprived of his able counsel during the first part of the mosquito research. Major Reed was detained longer than he expected and could not return to Cuba until early in October, several days after Lazear's death.

The mosquito eggs obtained from Dr. Finlay hatched out in due time; the insects sent to Washington for their exact classification were declared by Dr. L. O. Howard, entomologist to the Agricultural Department, to be *Culex fasciatus*. Later, they have been called *Stegomyia fasciatus* and now go under the name of *Stegomyia calopus* (*Aedes cal.*).

Lazear applied some of these mosquitoes to cases of yellow fever at "Las Animas" Hospital, keeping them in separate glass tubes properly labeled, and every thing connected with their

THE TURN OF THE CENTURY—AND BEYOND

bitings was carefully recorded; the original batch soon died and the work was carried on with subsequent generations from the same.

The lack of material at Quemados caused us to remove our field of action to Havana, where cases of yellow fever continued to appear. We met almost every day at "Las Animas" Hospital, where Lazear was trying to infect his mosquitoes, or now and then I performed autopsy upon a case, and Carroll secured sufficient cultures to last him for several days of bacteriological investigation.

Considering that, in case our surmise as to the insect's action should prove to be correct, it was dangerous to introduce infected mosquitoes amongst a population of 1,400 non-immunes at Camp Columbia, Dr. Lazear thought best to keep his presumably infected insects in my laboratory at the Military Hospital No. 1, from where he carried them back and forth to the patients who were periodically bitten.

Incidentally, after the mosquitoes fed upon the yellow fever patients, they were applied, at intervals of two or three days, to whoever would consent to run the risk of contracting yellow fever in this way; needless to say, current opinion was against this probability and as time passed and numerous individuals who had been bitten by insects which had previously fed upon yellow fever blood remained unaffected, I must confess that even the members of the board, who were rather sanguine in their expectations, became somewhat discouraged and their faith in success very much shaken.

No secret was made of our attempts to infect mosquitoes; in fact many local physicians became intensely interested, and Lazear and his tubes were the subject of much comment on the part of the Havana doctors, who nearly twenty years before had watched and laughed at Dr. Finlay, then bent apparently upon the same quest in which we were now engaged. Dr. Finlay himself was somewhat chagrined when he learned of our failure to infect any one with mosquitoes, but, like a true believer, was inclined to attribute this negative result more to some defect in our technique than to any flaw in his favorite theory.

Although the board had thought proper to run the same risks, if any, as those who willingly and knowingly subjected themselves to the bites of the supposedly infected insects, opportunity did not offer itself readily, since Major Reed was away in Wash-

ington and Carroll, at Camp Columbia, engrossed in his bacteriological investigations came to Havana only when an autopsy was
on hand or a particularly interesting case came up for study. I
was considered an immune, a fact that I would not like to have
tested, for though born in the island of Cuba, I had practically
lived all my life away from a yellow-fever zone; it was therefore
presumed that I ran no risk in allowing mosquitoes to bite me, as
I frequently did, just to feed them blood, whether they had
previously sucked from yellow-fever cases or not. And so, time
passed and several Americans and Spaniards had subjected themselves in a sporting mood to be bitten by the infected (?) mosquitoes without causing any untoward results, when Lazear
applied to himself (August 16, 1900) a mosquito which ten days
before had fed upon a mild case of yellow fever in the fifth day
of his disease; the fact that no infection resulted, for Lazear continued in excellent health for a space of time far beyond the usual
period of incubation, served to discredit the mosquito theory in
the opinion of the investigators to a degree almost beyond re-
demption, and the most enthusiastic, Dr. Lazear himself, was
almost ready to "throw up the sponge."

I had as laboratory attendant a young American, a private
belonging to the Hospital Corps of the Army, who more than once
had bared his arm to allow a weak mosquito a fair meal with
which to regain its apparently waning strength; Loud, for that
was his name, derided the idea that such a little beast could do so
much harm as we seemed ready to accuse it of, although he was
familiar with the destruction caused by bacteria, but then, he used
to say, "bacterias work in armies of more than a million bugs
at the same time and no one would be d—— fool enough to let
more than one or two gnats sting him at once."

This state of things, the gradual loss of faith in the danger
which mosquitoes seemed to possess, led Dr. Lazear to relax a
little and become less scrupulous in his care of the insects, and
often, after applying them to patients, if pressed for time, he
would take them away with him to his laboratory at Columbia
Barracks, where, the season being then quite warm, they could
be kept as comfortably as at the Military Hospital laboratory.
Thus it happened that on the twenty-seventh of August he had
spent the whole morning at "Las Animas" Hospital getting his
mosquitoes to take yellow-fever blood: the procedure was very
simple; each insect was contained in a glass tube covered by a
wad of cotton, the same as is done with bacterial cultures. As the

mouth of the tube is turned downwards, the insect usually flies towards the bottom of the tube (upwards), then the latter is uncovered rapidly and the open mouth placed upon the forearm or the abdomen of the patient; after a few moments the mosquito drops upon the skin and if hungry will immediately start operations; when full, by gently shaking the tube, the insect is made to fly upwards again and the cotton plug replaced without difficulty. It so happened that this rather tedious work, on the day above mentioned, lasted until nearly the noon hour, so that Lazear, instead of leaving the tubes at the Military Hospital, took them all with him to Camp Columbia: among them was one insect that for some reason or other had failed to take blood when offered to it at "Las Animas" Hospital.

This mosquito had been hatched in the laboratory and in due time fed upon yellow-fever blood from a severe case on August 15, that is, twelve days before, the patient then being in the second day of his illness; also at three other times, six days, four days and two days before. Of course, at the time, no particular attention had been drawn to this insect, except that it refused to suck blood when tempted that morning.

After luncheon that day, as Carroll and Lazear were in the laboratory attending to their respective work, the conversation turning upon the mosquitoes and their apparent harmlessness, Lazear remarked how one of them had failed to take blood, at which Carroll thought that he might try to feed it, as otherwise it was liable to die before next day (the insect seemed weak and tired); the tube was carefully held first by Lazear and then by Carroll himself, for a considerable length of time, upon his forearm, before the mosquito decided to introduce its proboscis.

This insect was again fed from a yellow fever case at "Las Animas" Hospital on the twenty-ninth, two days later, Dr. Carroll being present, though not feeling very well, as it was afterwards ascertained.

We three left the yellow-fever hospital together that afternoon; I got down from the doherty-wagon where the road forks, going on to the Military Hospital, while Carroll and Lazear continued on their way to Camp Columbia. On the following day, Lazear telephoned to me in the evening, to say that Carroll was down with a chill after a sea bath taken at the beach, a mile and a half from Camp, and that they suspected he had malaria; we therefore made an appointment to examine his blood together the following morning.

When I reached Camp Columbia I found that Carroll had been examining his own blood early that morning, not finding any malarial parasites; he told me he thought he had "caught cold" at the beach: his suffused face, blood-shot eyes and general appearance, in spite of his efforts at gaiety and unconcern, shocked me beyond words. The possibility of his having yellow fever did not occur to him just then; when it did, two days later, he declared he must have caught it at my autopsy room in the Military Hospital, or at "Las Animas" Hospital, where he had been two days before taking sick. Although we insisted that he should go to bed in his quarters, we could only get him to rest upon a lounge, until the afternoon, when he felt too sick and had to take to his bed.

Lazear and I were almost panic-stricken when we realized that Carroll had yellow fever. We searched for all possibilities that might throw the blame for his infection upon any other source than the mosquito which bit him four days before; Lazear, poor fellow, in his desire to exculpate himself, as he related to me the details of Carroll's mosquito experiment, repeatedly mentioned the fact that he himself had been bitten two weeks before without any effect therefrom and finally, what seemed to relieve his mind to some extent, was the thought that Carroll offered himself to feed the mosquito and that he had held the tube upon his own arm until the work was consummated.

I have mentioned before that, as Lazear and I, vaguely hoping to find malarial parasites in Carroll's blood, sat looking into our microscopes that morning, the idea that the mosquito was what brought him down gradually took hold of our minds, but as our colleague had been exposed to infection in other ways, by visiting the yellow fever hospital "Las Animas," as well as the infected city of Havana, it was necessary to subject that same mosquito to another test and hence the inoculation of Private Dean, which is described in the opening chapter of this history.

TERMINATION OF THE FIRST SERIES OF MOSQUITO EXPERIMENTS. DEATH OF LAZEAR

The month of September, 1900, was fraught with worry and anxiety: what with Carroll's and Private Dean's attacks of yellow fever and Major Reed's inability to return, Lazear and I were well-nigh on the verge of distraction. Private Dean was not married, but Carroll's wife and children, a thousand miles away, awaited in the greatest anguish the daily cablegram which told them the condition of the husband and father, who was fighting for life, sometimes the victim of the wildest delirium caused by consuming fever, at others almost about to collapse, until one day, the worst of the disease being over, the wires must have thrilled at our announcement, "Carroll out of danger."

Fortunately both he and Dean made an uninterrupted recovery, but we were still to undergo the severest trial, a sorrow compared to which the fearful days of Carroll's sickness lose all importance and dwindle almost into insignificance.

On the morning of the eighteenth my friend and classmate Lazear, whom in spite of our short intercourse I had learned to respect and in every way appreciate most highly, complained that he was feeling "out of sorts." He remained all day about the officers' quarters and that night suffered a moderate chill. I saw him the next day with all the signs of a severe attack of yellow fever.

Carroll was already walking about, though enfeebled by his late sickness, and we both plied Lazear with questions as to the origin of his trouble; I believe we affectionately chided him for not having taken better care of himself. Lazear assured us that he had not experimented upon himself, that is, that he had not been bitten by any of the purposely infected mosquitoes.

After the case of Dean so plainly demonstrated the certainty of mosquito infection, we had agreed not to tempt fate by trying any more upon ourselves, and even I determined that no mosquito should bite me if I could prevent it, since the subject of my immunity was one that could not be sustained on scientific grounds; at the same time, we felt that we had been called upon to accomplish such work as did not justify our taking risks which then seemed really unnecessary. This we impressed upon Major Reed when he joined us in October and for this reason he was never bitten by infected mosquitoes.

Lazear told us, however, that while at "Las Animas" Hospital the previous Thursday (five days before), as he was holding a test-tube with a mosquito upon a man's abdomen, some other insect which was flying about the room rested upon his hand; at first, he said, he was tempted to frighten it away, but, as it had settled before he had time to notice it, he decided to let it fill and then capture it; besides, he did not want to move in fear of disturbing the insect contained in his tube, which was feeding voraciously. Before Lazear could prevent it, the mosquito that bit him on the hand had flown away. He told us in his lucid moments, that, although Carroll's and Dean's cases had convinced him of the mosquito's rôle in transmitting yellow fever, the fact that no infection had resulted from his own inoculation the month before had led him to believe himself, to a certain extent, immune.

How can I describe the agony of suspense which racked our souls during those six days? It seemed to us as though a life was being offered in sacrifice for the thousands which it was to contribute in saving. Across the span of thirteen years the memory of the last moments comes to me most vividly and thrilling, when the light of reason left his brain and shut out of his mind the torturing thought of the loving wife and daughter far away, and of the unborn child who was to find itself fatherless on coming to the world.

Tuesday, the twenty-fifth of September saw the end of a life full of promise; one more name, that of Jesse W. Lazear, was graven upon the portals of immortality. And we may feel justly proud for having had it, in any way, associated with our own.

The state of mind in which this calamity left us may better be imagined than described. The arrival of Major Reed several days after in a great measure came to relieve the tensity of our nerves and render us a degree of moral support of which we were sorely in need.

Lazear's death naturally served to dampen our fruition at the success of the mosquito experiments, but, this notwithstanding, when the facts were known we were the subjects of much congratulation and the question whether the theory had been definitely demonstrated or not was the theme of conversation everywhere, about Havana and Camp Columbia particularly. We fully realized that three cases, two experimental and one accidental, were not sufficient proof, and that the medical world was sure to look with doubt upon any opinion based on such meager evidence; besides, in the case of Carroll, we had been unable to exclude the possibility of other means of infection, so that we really had but one case, Dean's, that we could present as clearly demonstrative and beyond question. In spite of this, we thought that the results warranted their presentation in the shape of a "Preliminary Note," and after all the data were carefully collected from

Lazear's records and those at the Military Hospital, a short paper was prepared which the Major had the privilege to read at the meeting of the American Public Health Association, held on October 24, in the city of Indianapolis.

For this purpose Major Reed went to the States two weeks after his return to Cuba, and Carroll also took a short leave of absence so as to fully recuperate, in preparation for the second series of inoculations which we had arranged to undertake, after the Indianapolis meeting.

These inoculations, according to our program, were to be made upon volunteers who should consent to suffer a period of previous quarantine at some place to be selected in due time, away from any possibility of yellow fever.

It so happened then that I was left the only member of the board in Cuba and, under instructions from Major Reed, I began to breed mosquitoes and infect them, as Lazear used to do, wherever cases occurred, keeping them at my laboratory in the Military Hospital No. 1. Major Reed had also asked me to look about for a proper location wherein to continue the work upon his return.

ORIGIN AND DEVELOPMENT OF THE MOSQUITO THEORY

The possible agency of insects in the propagation of yellow fever was thought of by more than one observer, from a very early period in the history of this disease. For instance, Rush, of Philadelphia, in 1797, noticed the excessive abundance of mosquitoes during that awful epidemic. Subsequently, several others spoke of the coincidence of gnats or mosquitoes and yellow fever, but without ascribing any direct relation to the one regarding the other. Of course, man-to-man infection through the sole intervention of an insect was a thing entirely inconceivable and therefore unthought of until very recently, and in truth the discovery, as far as yellow fever is concerned, was the result of a slow process of evolution of the fundamental fact, taken in connection with similar findings, in other diseases. . . .

. . . In 1879, the first conclusive proof of the direct transmission of a disease from man-to-man was presented by the father of tropical medicine, Sir Patrick Manson, with regard to filaria, a blood infection that often causes the repulsive condition known as elephantiasis and which the mosquito takes from man and after

a short time gives over to another subject. This discovery attracted world-wide attention and many looked again towards the
innumerable species of biting insects that dwell in the Tropic
Zone, as possible carriers of the obscure diseases which also prevail in those regions.

In 1881, Dr. Carlos Finlay, of Havana, in an exhaustive paper
read before the Royal Academy of Sciences, gave as his opinion
that yellow fever was spread by the bites of mosquitoes "directly
contaminated by stinging a yellow fever patient (or perhaps by
contact with or feeding from his discharge)." This latter view
he held as late as 1900, which, although correct in the main fact
of the transmission of the germ from a patient to a susceptible
person by the mosquito, the *modus operandi*, as he conceived it,
was entirely erroneous.

Dr. Finlay, unfortunately was unable to produce experimentally
a single case of fever that could withstand the mildest criticism,
so that at the time when the Army Board came to investigate the
causes of yellow fever in Cuba, his theory, though practically the
correct one, had been so much discredited, in a great measure by
his own failures, that the best-known experts considered it as an
ingenious, but wholly fanciful, one and many thought it a fit
subject for humorous and sarcastic *repartee*. Finlay also believed,
erroneously, that repeated bites of contaminated insects might
protect against yellow fever and that the mosquitoes were capable
of transmitting the germ to the next generation.

The wonderful discoveries of Theobald Smith, as to the agency
of ticks in spreading Texas fever of cattle, and those of Ross and
the Italian investigators who showed conclusively that malaria
was transmitted by a species of mosquito, brought the knowledge
of these various diseases to the point where the Army Board took
up the investigation of yellow fever.

SECOND AND FINAL SERIES OF MOSQUITO
EXPERIMENTS

Major Reed came back to Havana in the early part of November, Carroll following a week after.

During their absence, I had been applying mosquitoes to
yellow-fever patients at "Las Animas" Hospital, keeping them
in my laboratory, as it was done at the beginning of the investigation; the season being more advanced, now and then a cold
"norther" would blow and my insects suffered very much
thereby, so that I had the greatest trouble in preventing their

untimely death: to this may be added the difficulty met in feeding them blood, for now that I knew their sting was dangerous, unto death perhaps, I could not allow any indiscriminate biting, but had to select for the purpose individuals who had suffered an attack of the disease and were therefore immune.

The necessity for an experimental camp became more imperative as time passed, not only where proper quarantine and isolation could be established, but also where the insects intended for the inoculations might receive better care. This entailed considerable expense.

Fortunately for us, the military governor of the island at that time, Brigadier General Leonard Wood, was a man who had received a thorough medical training; broad and clear-minded, he fully appreciated the importance of what might be the outcome of our researches. We found in him the moral support which we so much needed and, further, he promptly placed at the disposal of the board sufficient funds with which to carry on the experiments to the end. I firmly believe that had other been the circumstances, had a more military and less scientific man been at the head of the government, the investigation would have terminated there and then, and many years would have passed, with hundreds of lives uselessly sacrificed, before we could have attained our present remarkable sanitary triumphs.

We immediately set about choosing a location for our camp. I had already looked over the ground, preferring the proximity of Camp Columbia, from where supplies could be easily obtained and because the Military Hospital there could be used for treating the cases that we intended to produce; I was therefore favorably impressed with the seclusion offered by a spot situated a short distance from the main road, in a farm, named San José, belonging to my friend Dr. Ignacio Rojas, of Havana. Major Reed decided upon this place after looking at many others in the neighborhood, so that on the twentieth of November we inaugurated our camp, which we named Camp Lazear, in honor to the memory of our dead colleague, consisting then of seven army tents, guarded by a military garrison, composed of men who had been carefully selected by virtue of their previous good record and their interest in the work to be undertaken.

Feeling that we had proved, to ourselves at least, the agency of the mosquito in yellow fever, it became our duty to disprove the theory, until then held as a certainty by many authorities, to the effect that the soiled bedding and clothing, the secretions and excreta of patients, were infectious and in some way carried the germ of the disease. We therefore designed a small wooden building, to be erected a short distance from the tents, with a capacity of 2,800 cubic feet. The walls and ceiling were absolutely tight, the windows and vestibuled door screened and all precautions taken to prevent the entrance of insects.

Into this, called the "infected clothing building," three beds and a stove, to maintain a high tropical temperature, were introduced; also mattresses and pillows, underwear, pajamas, towels, sheets, blankets, etc., soiled with blood and discharges from yellow fever cases: these articles were put on the beds, hung about the room and packed in a trunk and two boxes placed there for the purpose.

The building was finished and equipped on November 30. That Friday evening, Dr. Robert P. Cook, U. S. Army, with two other American volunteers, entered it and prepared to pass the night: they had instructions to unpack the boxes and trunk, to handle and shake the clothing and in every way to attempt to disseminate the yellow fever poison, in case it was contained in the various pieces. We watched the proceedings from the outside, through one of the windows. The foul conditions which developed upon opening the trunk were of such a character that the three men were seen to suddenly rush out of the building into the fresh air; one of them was so upset that his stomach rebelled; yet, after a few minutes, with a courage and determination worthy only of such a cause, they went back into the building and passed a more or less sleepless night, in the midst of indescribable filth and overwhelming stench.

For twenty consecutive nights these men went through the same performance; during the day they remained together, occupying a tent near their sleeping quarters. Dr. Cook, by voluntarily undergoing such a test, without remuneration whatsoever, proved his faith in the mosquito theory; his demonstration of the harmless character of so-called infected clothing, in yellow fever, has been of the greatest importance. The other six men (two of them with Dr. Cook) who were subjected to this test, received each a donation of one hundred dollars for his services.

Many days even before the establishment of the experimental camp, the board had heard that several men who knew of our work were willing to submit to the inoculations and thus aid in clearing up the mystery of yellow fever. Two of these require special mention, John R. Kissinger, a private in the Hospital Corps of the·Army, was the first to offer himself most altruistically, for as he expressed it, his offer was made without any desire for pecuniary or other consideration and solely "in the interest of humanity and the cause of science," the other, J. J. Moran, a civilian employee, also stipulated as a condition that he was to receive no pay for his services. Both these men, in due time, suffered from yellow fever and until very recently had never obtained any reward for the great risk which they ran so voluntarily and praiseworthily. . . . The names of Kissinger and Moran should figure upon the roll of honor of the U. S. Army.

On the day the camp was definitely organized, Kissinger, who had not gone outside the military reservation for more than a month, moved into Camp Lazear and received his first bite from a mosquito which evidently was not "loaded" for, again on November 23, he was stung by the same insect without result. On December 5, five mosquitoes were applied, which brought about a moderate infection in three days. Moran was also bitten by mosquitoes which were supposed to be infected on November 26 and 29, both times unsuccessfully. As will be seen, he was infected later on.

By this time we had decided, the weather having cooled considerably, that it was better to keep the mosquitoes at a higher temperature and nearer to the men who were to be inoculated; therefore it was planned to put up another small wooden structure, which was to be known as the "Mosquito Building" in which an artificial temperature could be maintained; at my suggestion, the building was so designed that it might serve to infect individuals; by liberating infected mosquitoes on the inside and exposing some person to their stings, we could try to reproduce the infection as we felt it occurred in nature. Another reason for the mosquito house was the need to obviate the transportation of the insects from the Military Hospital, where I kept them, to our camp, which could not be easily done without subjecting them to severe injury.

Upon one occasion I was taking four infected mosquitoes in the pocket inside my blouse from the laboratory in Havana to the experimental camp, accompanied by my attendant Private Loud; the horse which pulled my buggy, a rather spirited animal, becoming frightened at a steam roller, as we went around the corner of Colon Cemetery, started to race down the hill towards the

Almendares River: Loud was thrown out by the first cavortings of the horse, who stood on its hind legs and jumped several times before dashing away, while I held tightly to the tubes in my pocket, as the buggy upset and left me stranded upon a sand pile in the middle of the road; the mosquitoes were quite safe, however, and upon my arrival at Camp Lazear I turned them over to Carroll for his subsequent care.

Another difficulty afterwards encountered was the scarcity of material susceptible to infection, for, although several men had expressed a willingness to be inoculated, when the time came, they all preferred the "infected clothing" experiment to the stings of our mosquitoes. We then thought best to secure lately landed Spaniards, to whom the probable outcome of the test might be explained and their consent obtained for a monetary consideration. Our method was as follows; as soon as a load of immigrants arrived, I would go to Tiscornia, the Immigration Station across the Bay of Havana, and hire eight or ten men, as day laborers, to work in our camp. Once brought in, they were bountifully fed, housed under tents, slept under mosquitoe-bars and their only work was to pick up loose stones from the grounds, during eight hours of the day, with plenty of rest between. In the meantime, as the days of observation passed, I carefully questioned them as to their antecedents, family history and the diseases which they might have suffered; those who had lived in Cuba or any other tropical country before were discarded at once and also those who were under age or had a family dependent upon them. When the selection was finally made, the matter of the experiment was put to them. Naturally, they all felt more or less that they were running the risk of getting yellow fever when they came to Cuba and so were not at all averse to allow themselves to be bitten by mosquitoes: they were paid one hundred dollars for this, and another equal sum if, as a result of the biting experiment, they developed yellow fever. Needless to say, no reference was made to any possible funeral expenses. A written consent was obtained from each one, so that our moral responsibility was to a certain extent lessened. Of course, only the healthiest specimens were experimented upon.

It so happened that some reporter discovered what we were about, or perhaps some invidious person misrepresented the facts; at any rate, on the twenty-first of November a Spanish newspaper appeared with flaring headlines denouncing the American doctors who were taking advantage of the poor immigrants and experimenting with them by injecting all sorts of poisons! It called upon the Spanish consul to look after his subjects. In view of this we felt that if such a campaign continued, in a short time it would either make it impossible to secure subjects or cause diplomatic pressure to be exerted against the continuance of our experiments. It was thought best to "beard the lion in his den" so the three of us called upon the consul the following day. He was surprised to hear one of us address him in his own language, having taken us all for Americans on first sight, and when I explained to him our method of procedure and showed him the signed contracts with the men, being an intelligent man himself, he had no objections to offer and told us to go ahead and not bother about any howl the papers might make.

The first three cases (two of them Spaniards) which we produced came down with yellow fever within a very short period, from December 8 to 13; it will therefore not surprise the reader to know that when the fourth case developed on December 15, and was carried out of the camp to the hospital, it caused a veritable panic among the remaining Spaniards, who, renouncing the five hundred pesetas that each had in view, as Major Reed very aptly put it, "lost all interest in the progress of science and incontinentally severed their connection with Camp Lazear."

But there was a rich source to draw from, and the unexpected stampede only retarded our work for a short time. Our artificial epidemic of yellow fever was temporarily suspended while a new batch of susceptible material was brought in, observed and selected. The next case for that reason was not produced upon a Spaniard until December 30.

In the face of the negative experiments with supposedly contaminated articles, it rested with us to show how a house became infected and for this purpose the main part of the "mosquito building" was utilized.

This chamber was divided into two compartments by a double wire-screen partition, which effectually prevented mosquitoes on one side from passing to the other; of course there were no mosquitoes there to begin with, as the section of the building used for breeding and keeping them was entirely separated from the other, and there could be no communication between them.

On the morning of December 21, a jar containing fifteen hungry mosquitoes, that had previously stung cases of yellow fever, was introduced and uncovered in the larger compartment, where a bed, with all linen perfectly sterilized, was ready for occupancy.

A few minutes after, Mr. Moran, dressed as though about to retire for the night, entered the room and threw himself upon the bed for half an hour; during this time two other men and Major Reed remained in the other compartment, separated from Moran only by the wire-screen partition. Seven mosquitoes were soon at work upon the young man's arms and face; he then came out, but returned in the afternoon, when five other insects bit him in less than twenty minutes. The next day, at the same hour of the afternoon, Moran entered the "mosquito building" for the third time and remained on the bed for fifteen minutes, allowing three mosquitoes to bite his hands. The room was then securely locked, but the two Americans continued to sleep in the other compartment for nearly three weeks, without experiencing any ill effects.

Promptly on Christmas morning Moran, who had not been exposed to infection except for his entrance into the "mosquito building" as described, came down with a well-marked attack of yellow fever.

The temperature in this room, where these mosquitoes had been released, was kept rather high and a vessel with water was provided, where they might lay their eggs if so inclined, but notwithstanding all these precautions, it was subsequently found that the insects had been attacked by ants, so that by the end of the month only one of the fifteen mosquitoes remained alive.

It is hardly necessary to detail here how seven other men were subjected to the sting of our infected mosquitoes, of which number five developed the disease, but it may be interesting to note that two of these men had been previously exposed in the "infected clothing building" without their becoming infected, showing that they were susceptible to yellow fever after all.

The evidence so far seemed to show that the mosquito could only be infected by sucking blood of a yellow-fever patient during the first three days of the disease; to prove that the parasite was present in the circulating blood at that time we therefore injected some of this fluid taken from a different case each time, under the skin of five men: four of these suffered an attack of yellow fever as the result of the injection. The other one, a Spaniard, could not be infected either by the injection of blood or the application of mosquitoes which were known to be infected, showing that he had a natural immunity or, more likely, that he had had yellow fever at some previous time.

While selecting the Spaniards, it was often ascertained that they had been in Cuba before, as soldiers in the Spanish army usually, and the natural conclusion was that they had undergone infection; it was very seldom that any escaped during the Spanish control of the island.

Thus terminated our experiments with mosquitoes which, though necessarily performed on human beings, fortunately *did not cause a single death*; on the other hand, they served to revolutionize all standard methods of sanitation with regard to yellow fever. They showed the uselessness of disinfection of clothing and how easily an epidemic can be stamped out in a community by simply protecting the sick from the sting of the mosquitoes and by the extensive and wholesale destruction of these insects. . . .

Besides keeping a sharp lookout against the importation of yellow fever cases, these are the simple rules that have kept the Panama Canal free and prevented the slaughter of hundreds of foreigners, so generally expected every year, in former times.

Since we made our demonstration in 1901, our work has been corroborated by various commissions appointed for the purpose, in Mexico, Brazil and Cuba, composed variously of Americans, French, English, Cuban, Brazilian and German investigators. Nothing has been added to our original findings; nothing has been contradicted of what we have reported, and to-day, after nearly thirteen years, the truths that we uncovered stand incontrovertible; besides, they have been the means of driving out yellow fever from Cuba, the United States (Laredo, Texas, 1903 and New Orleans, La., 1905), British Honduras and several cities of Brazil.

Of the Army Board only I remain. Lazear, as reported, died during the early part of our investigations; Reed left us in 1902 and Carroll only five years later. The reader may wonder of what benefit was it to us, this painstaking and remarkable accomplishment which has been such a blessing to humanity! See what the late Surgeon General of the U. S. Army had to say in his report (Senate Document No. 520, Sixty-first Congress, second session):

1. Major Walter Reed, surgeon, United States Army, died in Washington, D. C., from appendicitis, November 23, 1902, aged 51. His widow, Emilie Lawrence Reed, is receiving a pension of $125 a month.

2. Maj. James Carroll was promoted from first lieutenant to major by special act of Congress, March 9, 1907. He died in Washington, D. C., of myocarditis, September 16, 1907. His widow, Jennie H. Carroll, since his death, has received an annuity of $125 a month, appropriated from year to year in the Army appropriation bill.

3. Dr. Jesse W. Lazear, contract surgeon, United States Army, died at Camp Columbia, Cuba, of yellow fever, September 25, 1900. His widow, Mabel M. Lazear, since his death, has received an annuity of $125 a month appropriated from year to year in the Army appropriation bill.

4. Dr. Aristides Agramonte is the only living member of the board. He is professor of bacteriology and experimental pathology in the University of Habana and has never received, either directly or indirectly, any material reward for his share in the work of the board.

It is not for me to make any comments: the above paragraphs have all the force of a plain, truthful statement of facts. Perhaps it is thought that enough reward is to be found in the contemplation of so much good derived from one's own efforts and the feeling it may produce of innermost satisfaction and in forming the belief that one had not lived in vain. In a very great measure, I know, the thought is true.

1915

Joseph Goldberger and Pellagra

ROBERT P. PARSONS

,GASPAR CASAL, physician to Philip V of Spain, was such an astute observer of the diseases of his day that his commentators have called him the Asturian Hippocrates. In 1735 Casal began to record his observations on a malady termed by him *Mal de la Rosa* because of the reddened skin associated with it. He thought he was describing a new disease, and indeed his descriptions of it are the earliest known in literature, although there is now every reason to believe that it prevailed at periods throughout many centuries before the time of Casal.

He considered *Mal de la Rosa* a peculiar form of leprosy and also compared it to scurvy, another greatly dreaded plague of his time. It was caused, he believed, by humidity, fogs, temperature changes, winds, and faulty diet.

From 1735 to 1914 countless observers and investigators speculated on the nature of this strange malady. For nearly two hundred years they advanced their theories concerning its cause. . . . While some of the theories were quite "warm," bordering very closely on the general truth of the matter, they amounted to little more than mere presumptions, lacking the support of experimental evidence. They might be compared to some of the early guesses made on the mode of transmission of yellow fever, which, though accurate enough, were impossible of acceptance until proved beyond question.

In 1914 [Joseph] Goldberger entered the field. He probably would never have selected pellagra for the final work of his career. He had had no previous experience with the disease, and knew nothing about it except that two centuries of investigation had been entirely unrewarded. Pellagra seemed to have nothing akin to the diseases whose mysteries he had unraveled. How, then, could he approach it with any enthusiasm or hope of success? Before he even started on the problem, he was discouraged and pessimistic. He feared his precious time might be wasted.

But one consideration deterred him from throwing up the whole thing before he had a good look at it. Since 1908 about a hundred thousand among the poorest classes in our Southern states were being attacked every year by this ghastly disease. They were suffering, helpless, hopeless. Thousands were dying of it. In such circumstances, the least he could do would be to make every possible effort, give the job everything he had before he would cry quits. . . .

In 1909 a disturbing number of cases appeared at the Illinois State Insane Asylum, and Governor Deneen appointed an investigative commission that included some of the leading minds in American medicine of that day. With Ricketts one of these, there was excellent promise that some light would be thrown on the cause of pellagra. But his death, just after the commission was organized, was a loss which quite probably had much to do with its failure. . . .

Their investigations, which disclosed about 500 cases in Illinois, most of them in the state asylums, revealed the fallacies of the theories launched in the past. In two years, after looking into many ramifications of the problem, they completed a vast amount of work. They were hot on the trail of the truth at times, but ultimately arrived at this erroneous conclusion: "According to the weight of evidence, pellagra is a disease due to infection with a living microorganism of unknown nature." Thus they had added one more to the already large collection of false notions concerning the cause of the disease.

In 1912 the alarming spread of pellagra in the South, and its particular ravages in Southern textile-mill villages, led two philanthropists, R. M. Thompson and J. H. McFadden, to finance another commission for its study. This group, known as the Thompson-McFadden Pellagra Commission, functioned under the auspices of the New York Post-Graduate Medical School, and was composed of J. F. Siler and W. J. MacNeal, who had served on the Illinois commission, and Dr. P. E. Garrison, U.S.N.

They set up their field headquarters at Spartanburg, South Carolina, in June 1912, and worked on until the end of 1914 . . . compiling a most impressive collection of data on the epidemiological and other phases of the problem—but going constantly farther in a direction where the hunt was sure to be fruitless. The infection they were seeking did not exist. But despite their failure to uncover any substantial proof that it played any part in the cause of the disease, the idea had somehow become so riveted in their minds that they had the temerity to state in the summary of their report: "Pellagra is in all probability a specific infectious disease communicable from person to person by means at present unknown.". . .

Again Goldberger was ready to assume the role of Sherlock Holmes, treading cautiously along each intricate path of the mystery, turning the spotlight into every dark corner until all sections of the puzzle were pieced together into a perfect fit. This was a horrible crime that nature had been committing, as we learn by reading the vivid lines with which Lombroso opened his treatise of 1892. He is speaking here of pellagrins suffering from the mental symptoms commonly associated with the disease:

> If you should traverse the hills of Brianza and Canavese, you would most likely meet some pitiable wrecks of humanity, with eyes fixed and glassy, with pale and sallow faces and

arms fissured and scarred as by a burn or large wound. You would see them advancing with trembling head and staggering gait like persons intoxicated or indeed, as though impelled by an invisible force, now falling on one side, now getting up and running in a straight line like a dog after its quarry and now again falling and uttering a senseless laugh or sob which pierces the heart—such are the pellagrins . . .

Such then was the mystery to which Goldberger had been assigned. . . .

He left for the South, for a great many points South. He wanted to look at the disease, not read about it. What he saw with his own piercing eyes he could believe.

He got off the train at Spartanburg, South Carolina. At the little pellagra hospital that had been established there by the United States Public Health Service he asked the doctors and the patients a thousand questions. He walked around the town, looked in the stores and homes, drove all over the hills of Spartanburg County, poked around in several mill villages. Cotton was growing everywhere. It grew right up to the steps of the miserable huts of its growers. Here and there was a corn patch, but the rest was cotton. Those who were not raising it were working with it in the mills. Everyone in the mill villages and in the surrounding countryside was trying to live by cotton, but no one was quite making the grade. The price of cotton was low, mill wages were low, families were trying to live on fifteen dollars a week—and they all looked it. If they paid rent and bought the barest necessities in clothes and one or two other items there was not half enough left for minimum food requirements. It was pitiful; it touched him. Worst of all was the amount of pellagra Goldberger saw. Emaciated bodies, sallow sunken faces, hands, feet and faces covered with cracked and reddened skin, insane cases.

He scraped the red clay of Spartanburg from his shoes, and boarded a train for Milledgeville, Georgia. Here the picture was the same—cotton mills, cotton fields, poverty, pellagra. At the Georgia State Sanitarium for the Insane there were several hundred pellagrins. What struck him as being of particular interest, perhaps of great significance, was the fact that none of the 293 nurses, attendants and other employees who had been in daily close contact with the pellagra patients had ever developed the disease. That was pretty strong evidence against contagion. He would look into this matter further.

He went on to Jackson, Mississippi. Here at the Methodist Orphan Asylum, among the 211 children, 168 had pellagra. The place was sorrowful, but it was a good place in which to make observations. He watched everything, questioned everyone, made hundreds of notes.

He went to asylums in Virginia, Alabama, Florida, Kentucky, and then returned to Spartanburg. He found two young men in the Service who just suited him as assistants in the line of investigation he was formulating. They were D. G. Willets and C. H. Waring. Willets was to collect the data at the Georgia State Asylum, Waring was to do the watching and collecting at the orphanage in Jackson.

Goldberger now went to northern asylums to compare conditions with the southern institutions. After a tour in Illinois, Pennsylvania, New Jersey, Ohio and Wisconsin, he went back to Savannah, Spartanburg, Milledgeville and Jackson. He made several trips between these points, watching developments along the new trails of inquiry he had opened.

At every institution the same great glaring fact impressed him: the employees never contracted pellagra. What could there be about this malady that made it so discriminating? Why had the investigators of the past taken no more than casual interest in this point? Many of them had noticed and mentioned it; apparently none had attached any particular significance to it. No other communicable disease behaved in this way. To use Goldberger's words: "This peculiar exemption or immunity was inexplicable on the assumption that pellagra is communicable." He thought there must be some essential, and perhaps discoverable, difference in the living conditions of these two classes of institutional residents that was responsible for this very important epidemiological phenomenon.

Now he concentrated on the orphanage at Jackson, for here there was a strangely interesting distribution of cases. Practically all the pellagrous children were between the ages of six and twelve. Among the 25 orphans under six years, only two cases had appeared; among the 66 over twelve years only one had pellagra. But 65 of the middle group—six to twelve years—were pellagrins. How was this peculiarity to be explained?

Such an age distribution of the disease did not obtain among children outside the asylum. The answer was not long in coming. There was one distinct difference in the living conditions of the three age groups in the orphanage. It had to do with food. The little ones got milk; the two older groups got almost no milk; the oldest group got a much greater meat supply than the middle group. Otherwise the children were living under identical conditions. The dietary difference was much more real than apparent. The older children found ways of supplementing their allowed ration. They were hungry. They grabbed food and they stole it.

Goldberger and Waring and Willets found that the diet upon which the middle group of children was trying to live was essentially the same as that used wherever pellagra was prevalent. Biscuits, hominy grits, corn mush, sirup, molasses, gravy, sowbelly—but little or none of the fresh animal components, such as milk, eggs, butter, lean meats: a diet adequate in caloric value but greatly overbalanced in carbohydrate elements and almost entirely lacking in the animal protein elements.

The clue looked good enough to follow. Goldberger was not convinced, but he said the thing was "darned suspicious" and "warranted careful investigation." If his hypothesis was sound, he should be able to demonstrate its soundness. He should be able to prevent pellagra, to cure it perhaps, by dietary means. . . .

He proposed putting his idea to a test at the orphanage. The trustees were sympathetic, co-operative, but said they couldn't afford it. The forlornness of the children kept bringing to him recollections of the picture of Oliver Twist, a character who had each time he read the novel aroused his deepest sense of compassion. The orphanage trustees, it seemed to him, might have spent less money on fine buildings and a little more on nourishing the children. He hinted that it might be well to invest in a herd of cows, some beef cattle, a flock of chickens. He submitted the proposition that for a period of two years the Government should put up the extra money needed for the extra feeding. Everyone agreed.

About a mile from the Methodist orphanage was a Baptist orphanage. Here 130 of the boys and girls had pellagra. The conditions in respect to diet were the same as those at the Methodist orphanage. Goldberger made here the same arrangements for a two-year diet experiment.

Beginning in September 1914, at both orphanages every child under twelve years got fourteen ounces of milk a day, and those under six years were given twenty-one ounces. Eggs—previously unknown on the orphanage dining tables—were now on the daily menus. Fresh meat—formerly served once a week—was now served four days a week.

Within a few weeks Goldberger and Waring saw pellagra fading away from the orphanages. It seemed miraculous. A decent color was returning to the orphans' cheeks. No new cases had appeared since the change in diet. It looked great to Goldberger, but he kept it quiet. He would await the developments of the coming year before reporting his results. Most new cases and recurrences of old ones appeared in the spring—a regular phenomenon at the Baptist orphanage since its founding in 1897. They would watch for this in the coming spring of 1915.

In October a similar experiment was started at the asylum in Milledgeville. Goldberger and Willets placed 36 white female pellagrins in a separate ward, and 36 colored female pellagrins in another ward. They instituted dietary changes for these 72 women as they had done for the orphans. As a control group, 32 other pellagrous women—17 colored and 15 white—were continued on their former diet.

Willets watched everything at the asylum to see that all conditions of the experiment remained in operation. Waring did the watching at the Jackson orphanages. Goldberger kept going back and forth between Jackson and Milledgeville, with frequent side trips to other affected centers in the South.

The spring of 1915 arrived. Not a sign of pellagra at the orphanages. According to the usual rate of recurrence among children there should have been 33 such cases at the Methodist orphanage and 52 at the Baptist orphanage. But there were no recurrences, and no new cases.

At the Milledgeville asylum 15 of the control group showed recurrences. The 72 pellagrins on the new diet had fully recovered. According to the usual recurrence rate for women, 27 of the 72 should have shown recurrences. But there was not one. They had all remained entirely free from pellagra.

Now Goldberger was certain that he was on the right track. But he was far from satisfied. His theory had to be proved in other ways. He had to know much more about the dietary deficiencies that could cause pellagra, and the elements that could prevent and cure it. There were practical problems of application to be worked on. The medical profession had to be convinced. The job was just beginning.

Although he published nothing on the diet experiments until October 1915 the news of his success was leaking out. Recognition, honors, congratulations were beginning to arrive. Harvard chose him to deliver the Cutter lecture for 1915. Rosenau sent the news of this appointment, and Goldberger replied to him:

> . . . I need not say how pleased I am, nor how deeply I appreciate the compliment, but I am at the same time completely "flabbergasted"; this comes "so sudden" that it takes my breath away.
>
> If decently possible I would decline, for I am too busy with field work.
>
> If luck is with us, we shall have the ground work of pellagra securely fastened before July 1st.

The "field work" he had in mind for "securely fastening the ground work" was a thrilling experiment. He reasoned that if a suitable diet could cure and prevent pellagra, an unsuitable one should produce it in strong, healthy persons. If he could get some volunteers, he would attempt to produce the disease experimentally. But who would volunteer to be a subject in such a test? It meant several months of confinement to insure constant observation, and constant surveillance lest any of the conditions of the experiment be broken. It meant several months on a poor diet, one that was thought capable of producing a serious, dangerous illness. Who would sell his health and his time for such a period and in such a fashion? The inducements would have to be substantial.

Goldberger had a scheme. Convicts would be just right—if he could get them. Time meant nothing to them—at least, if they were doing life terms. Their only interest in time was to pass it. Life meant little to them—if they had to spend it in prison. As for being watched and restricted, they had nothing to lose in that respect. If pardons could be offered to them, they would snap at the proposition.

Earl Brewer was the Governor of Mississippi. There was nothing narrow-minded about his politics. He was a "big" man, a very intelligent and understanding man. Dr. E. H. Galloway, a close friend of the Governor, was secretary of the State Board of Health. He knew of Goldberger's work at the orphanages. . . .

When Goldberger went to Galloway and explained his scheme, he found a ready listener. He wanted a dozen convicts—absolute control over them for six months. Galloway took him to call on the Governor, who listened to their story, saw the point, and was with them. . . . By January 23 the preliminary difficulties were smoothed out, and twelve convict volunteers stood ready for the test. They had seen their lawyers, and the agreements were signed. Each was to get his pardon if he remained in Goldberger's special-diet squad and under the stipulated conditions of the experiment for six months. The volunteers were tough customers —murderers, embezzlers, forgers, highwaymen—all serving long terms, several for life. They were big healthy fellows. All were white. Goldberger wanted white men because they were at that time considered less susceptible to pellagra than Negroes. And that would make his proof even stronger—if he succeeded.

On February 4 they went into camp, in the center of the 3,200-acre prison farm, eight miles east of Jackson. . . . A real prize for the assignment was found in Dr. G. A. Wheeler, who had every qualification for the work. . . .

Before the new diet could be started a hundred details must be arranged. There had to be controls, and for this purpose eighty convicts in a working squad on the farm were to be kept under the same conditions as the volunteers—except for diet. None of the convicts had had pellagra. It was unknown at the prison, where the large farm supplied an abundant variety of fresh foods.

The volunteers were to live much better than the controls in that they were to do much lighter work. They occupied clean and screened quarters. During the preliminary period of observation they kept in fine health.

At noon on April 19 the new diet went into effect. During the first few days the men thought it was a joke. The food was well-cooked, tasted fine, and every man had all he wanted. It looked like a soft road to freedom for them. The menu was essentially that used by most of the poorer classes of the South:

BREAKFAST: Biscuits, fried mush and sirup, grits and brown gravy, coffee with sugar.
DINNER: Corn bread, cabbage, sweet potatoes, grits, sirup.
SUPPER: Fried mush, biscuits, rice, gravy, corn sirup, coffee with sugar.

After a few weeks the convict volunteers began to doubt that they had made such a fine bargain. They began to feel queer—headache, dizziness, stomach-ache, backache. Their mouths didn't feel just right, their tongues were tender and reddened. Goldberger and Wheeler kept watching for pellagra skin rashes. None appeared. Even by midsummer there were no skin developments. Goldberger figured that it would take several months for the red marks to develop, and was hopeful that something would turn up by September.

The fourth month slipped by. September came. The volunteers looked haggard; they were weak, had quit working. But their skins revealed nothing—and you couldn't make a positive diagnosis of pellagra without the skin signs.

The six months had nearly expired. With less than six weeks remaining, Goldberger and Wheeler were worried. One of the volunteers had left the squad. He fell ill with another disease, and was excused from the experiment. The other eleven kept kicking along, for the period would terminate on October 19, and liberty that near to them looked pretty sweet.

On September 12 the thing happened. Wheeler found the rash he was watching for on one of the men. He telegraphed the news to Goldberger, who took the first train for Jackson. Then it began to show on the others. By September 24 five of them had the marks. It began on their scrota, then blossomed out on the neck of one and on the hands of two.

Goldberger sent for some expert dermatologists and authorities in the diagnosis of pellagra. He was afraid the medical world might not accept his own verdict. He got his friend Galloway and Dr. Nolan Stewart, Superintendent of the Mississippi State Hospital for the Insane—both experts in the disease. They looked at the five convicts and said: "Pellagra." Two professors of dermatology, Dr. Marcus Haase of the University of Tennessee Medical College, and Dr. M. F. Engman, of the Washington University Medical School, St. Louis, came to look at the skins of the men. There was no doubt about it, they agreed—typically pellagrous.

The convicts were pardoned and released. They could have remained for treatment and quick cures, but they were too frightened about the place, and anxious to leave it.

When the success of the experiment was completely established, when Goldberger had the verdicts of Haase and Engman, he felt the elation of a great victory. . . .

The publication of this experiment did not appear until November 12, but the news leaked out and the congratulations began to pour in. Goldberger commented in particular on the letters from Carter and Rosenau and Reid Hunt. Of the letter from Carter, he said: "One is repaid for many things by such a letter from such a man. I can't tell you how much pleasure it has given me.". . .

JACKSON, MISS.
October 30, 1915

Confidential.

MY DEAR ROSENAU:

This is a deep dark secret. It is not to be "released" for yet awhile. Five of our eleven men have developed pellagra. No other case in the camp.

We have succeeded in preventing it by diet, and in producing it in not less than 45 per cent of the men submitted to the "pellagra-producing" diet.

I write you this because of your very kind interest. Please keep it tight.

Love,

JOE G

Rosenau's reply did not catch up with the now rapid traveling Goldberger for several weeks. It read, in part:

BOSTON, MASS.
November 4, 1915

. . . I almost danced for joy when I read that you had succeeded in producing pellagra through diet in volunteers. I feel that your achievement in this disease is the equal to any contribution to medical science made in America. If I said more you would get a swelled head, but really it's great. . . .

MILTON

This provoked the following from Goldberger:

WASHINGTON, D. C.
December 13, 1915

MY DEAR MILTON (If you will have it that way!)

. . . Your "delirious" letter followed me around the landscape as I have done some considerable travelling since our "stunt" came off. I need not tell you how deeply I appreciate your generous enthusiasm over the results of my work. Such enthusiasm goes far to repay me for many sacrifices of my family and myself that the work has extorted from me. Yet, after all, it's just in the day's work. . . .

I can hardly describe the feeling that I experienced as I go through our wards at the asylum and see the poor insane women who a year ago had pellagra but who this year are perfectly well—so far as pellagra is concerned. . . .

That we can prevent pellagra there can be no doubt; that we can produce pellagra at will, I'm equally certain. If there are any who doubt the latter, I think I can offer them lodging and "meals" free if they have the courage of their convictions and would like to try it. . . .

I'd like to get your cold-blooded opinion of just how the whole thing, with its details, looks to you.

Faithfully,

JOE G

Einstein comments on the satisfaction that comes to a man of science when he receives the applause of those who understand his work and its importance.

"Anyone," says Einstein, "who finds a thought which brings us closer to nature's eternal secrets partakes of a great grace. If, at the same time, he receives the recognition and assistance of the leaders of thought of his time he falls heir to more good fortune than any one can bear." . . .

During the progress of the prison experiment, when Wheeler was doing the watching and waiting and hoping and praying with the convict squad, Goldberger was in many places—and up to his neck in pellagra at all of them. He persuaded the superintendents of many institutions in the South to adopt the diet changes that he and Waring had made in the Jackson orphanages. He kept visiting these places and watching developments—watching the pellagra melt away as it had done at the orphanages.

He was doing missionary work. What good was all this new gospel about diet unless the people knew of it? He conferred with local health authorities in all the Southern towns he was visiting—told them the essential facts of the matter; addressed county and state medical societies, wrote articles. His audiences caught his enthusiasm, saw his faith, were electrified by his appeal. The more intelligent they were, the greater their thrill in following the logic of his presentation of his case. . . .

The job grew and spread in many directions. Goldberger was planning new experiments, new angles of approach. Eventually they would get down to the refined chemical and biological aspects, but now there were great practical phases that called for quick answers, urgent matters of application that were crying for attention. Goldberger was now the military general, the busy executive, as much as the sequestered scientist.

He put Edgar Sydenstricker to work. Sydenstricker was the expert statistician of the Public Health Service—if you wanted an exact survey expressed in exact figures, he was the man. Goldberger kept chasing him all over the South, principally in the Carolinas, tracking down economic data on labor, family budgets, family dietaries, food prices. Sydenstricker collected and compiled and calculated, made tables, charts, curves, of all these things. He dug into the figures of cold and precise government reports. He and Goldberger studied them, arranged them, started off on fresh hunts for more.

By the end of 1915 sufficient data had been collected to show that, among the poorer classes, the lower the economic status became, the greater was the sacrifice in animal protein foods. This condition had become intensified since the industrial depression of 1907. The increase in prices of animal protein foods was 40 per cent more than for other foods. Sydenstricker's figures showed that the economic status of wage earners' families was much lower in the Southern states, especially in the cotton-mill towns, than in other sections of the country. Certain factors, it was found, had restricted the supply of protein foods in Southern industrial centers.

For all these reasons, the poorer Southern families were living —or trying to live—on a lower proportion of protein and a higher proportion of carbohydrates than was found in the dietaries of Northern families. Such findings fitted neatly into the geographical distribution of pellagra and into the general pattern of facts that Goldberger had already established.

But he was running into trouble elsewhere. Not all of the medical profession had accepted his discoveries about the disease. Several of the "infectionists" were dying hard. They clung religiously to their belief in the theory that pellagra is a contagious malady.

In May 1915 an august body of representatives from the state and provincial boards of health of North America met in conference in Washington. Pellagra was scheduled as one of their principal subjects for consideration, and Goldberger was present. The chairman was the Public Health Officer of South Carolina. He said he wished to "enunciate certain beliefs concerning pellagra, these beliefs being backed by the exhaustive research done by good American citizens, such as Siler, Garrison and MacNeal." He then stated that it was "a specific infectious disease, communicable from person to person by unknown means." He spoke at some length, with the air of a man who was bringing much enlightenment to the delegates.

Goldberger was asked to speak. . . .

In a few minutes' talk, he then epitomized the results of his work to that date.

As for the Thompson-McFadden Commission itself, the news of the prison experiment findings had been something of a blow to it. Garrison was at Spartanburg when the report reached him. He packed his suitcase forthwith, and went home. He knew Goldberger. He was through with the Commission, and with problems in pellagra. . . .

Despite the conversion of Siler and Garrison and many other former "infectionists," there were a large number left who would not see the light. These reactionaries talked and wrote—and rankled Goldberger. He was becoming sensitive and irritable, and losing patience with such people. He planned another experiment, one calculated to convince anybody capable of even feeble cerebration. . . .

On April 26 at the Spartanburg hospital the experiment began. Goldberger selected a pellagrin suffering from an acute first attack of the disease, and drew about an ounce of blood from the patient's vein. Five cubic centimeters of this blood he injected into the muscle of Wheeler's shoulder. Wheeler then took the syringe and shot six cubic centimeters of the blood into Goldberger's shoulder. But that wasn't enough. They swabbed out the secretions from the patient's nose and throat, then applied these swabs to their own noses and throats. They waited a few days. Nothing happened.

On April 28 Goldberger went to the South Carolina State

Asylum at Columbia. The next step, experiment No. 2, was a tough one, so he tried it first on himself. He selected two pellagrins with scaling sores, and another with diarrhea. He scraped the scales from the sores, mixed the scales with four cubic centimeters of urine from the same patients, added an equal amount of liquid feces from the patient with the diarrhea—and rolled the mixture up into little dough balls by the addition of a few pinches of flour.

Lest the acid in his stomach kill any infection that might be present in the dough balls, Goldberger took a dose of sodium bicarbonate. Now he swallowed the little cakes. A half-hour later he took some more soda—he was quite worried about that acid in the stomach. Again nothing happened. There was a mild diarrhea for a few days, but this completely disappeared. It may have been a "nervous diarrhea"—if it was, no one could blame him.

On May 7 experiment No. 3 was performed at the Spartanburg hospital. There were six volunteers—Goldberger, Sydenstricker, Wheeler, Willets, Dr. W. F. Tanner and Mrs. Goldberger. Repeating the experiment of April 26, they pooled the blood from three pellagrins and each of the volunteers received seven cubic centimeters of it by hypodermic injection.

A nurse became hysterical when Mrs. Goldberger was taking her "shot." The idea of infection still prevailed in Spartanburg, and the nurse was sure that Mrs. Goldberger would contract pellagra.

Nasal secretions obtained from four patients were applied to the throats of the five men volunteers. They then partook of the "Columbia mixture"—scales, urine, feces, flour—contributed by four patients. This little meal was preceded and followed by doses of soda as in the previous experiment. But still nothing happened—no pellagra; not even diarrhea this time.

On June 7 a fourth experiment was performed with five volunteers, including Goldberger and McCoy. A similar meal was prepared, the elements this time obtained from a pellagrin in the Washington asylum. This time, cracker crumbs, as well as flour, were added to the mixture, and the material was placed in gelatine capsules. No effects were experienced by any of the group.

A fifth experiment was a repetition of the fourth, the volunteers being Goldberger, Sydenstricker and one other man. No symptoms developed in any of the three. In New Orleans Goldberger made still another of the meal tests, using himself and four other volunteers.

On June 25, no symptoms having yet appeared in any of the subjects, a final experiment was completed at Spartanburg. This time they pooled material from seven patients suffering from pellagrous attacks of varying grades of severity. Goldberger now considered that they had given the infection idea a sufficient test. And he was not sorry that this experiment was finished. He wrote:

> We had our final "filth party"—Wheeler, Sydenstricker and I—this noon. If anyone can get pellagra that way, we three should certainly have it good and hard. It's the last time. Never again.

Publication of these experiments was withheld until November. No signs of pellagra having developed in any of the volunteers, the complete report was delivered by Goldberger in an address before the Southern Medical Society at Atlanta, November 16. The following day, his paper was released in the *Public Health Reports*. No mention was made of the identity of the volunteers. They were simply called "fifteen men and a housewife." The report was quoted throughout the world's medical press, and served very effectively in quieting the "infectionists"—at least most of them. A few remain even today, adhering to their belief in a fanatical manner.

Toward the end of 1916, Goldberger was ready to work on a new phase of the problem. There was little that could be done about the economic side of it. He could discover and present the facts—but he could not adjust the wage troubles of mill-workers. He could recommend the keeping of cows and chickens and the planting of gardens, but others would have to execute these ideas.

In his search for a cheaper way out, he saw that he would need some expert advice, consultations with the country's best minds in the fields of nutrition and food chemistry. . . .

He went to Baltimore and knocked one morning on the laboratory door of E. V. McCollum, at Johns Hopkins. . . . Well loaded with McCollum's advice, Goldberger went on to New York. There he spent a day with Alfred Hess, talking vitamins, seeing some of Hess's brilliant work with scurvy at the Children's Hospital, and listening to him expound the relationship of beriberi and scurvy. Calling next on Graham Lusk at the Russell Sage

Foundation, he found Lusk revising his book on nutrition and making the chapter on pellagra conform to the concepts that Goldberger had introduced. At New Haven he talked for a day with Mendel and Osborne and their associates. . . . From New Haven he went to Boston and discussed the problem at length with Hunt and Rosenau.

Now the work became principally a matter of chemistry and experimental studies in nutrition. . . .

Goldberger kept making the rounds. He traveled almost continuously through 1917 until November, never stopping in any town for more than a day or two. At some institutions he was using somewhat different diets, and it was necessary to visit all these places frequently to check over the results and to be sure that the dietaries were being followed exactly. . . .

In 1918 Goldberger opened a ten-year chapter that was devoted almost entirely to one line of investigation. Each small step took weeks and months, sometimes years. It had to be repeated and checked in many ways. There never was any turning back. But each completed step was a certainty, a milestone that brought Goldberger closer to his goal. This work consisted principally of using a diet deficient in some certain element and seeing whether it would produce pellagrous symptoms in animals, or in using a diet rich in certain elements and noting whether it would cure or prevent human pellagra or the pellagrous symptoms of animals.

A great stimulus to these efforts was supplied by an observation that Chittenden and Underhill at Yale reported in 1917. A peculiar disease in dogs had been known to veterinarians for about seventy years, under many names but generally in America as "black tongue." Chittenden and Underhill were able to produce it in dogs by feeding them a diet that would cause pellagra in man. It had so many similar characteristics that it might reasonably be looked upon as the canine analogue of pellagra.

In this field of research Goldberger found a rich opportunity. At the end of four years of experiments he and Wheeler were able to show that pellagra and black tongue not only had almost identical clinical features, but that they acted exactly alike—they could be produced and cured by the same method.

Once they were satisfied as to the identity of the two conditions, the work went much faster. They could easily and quickly try dozens of different dietary experiments on dogs and then confirm certain curative results by giving pellagrins the same food elements that had cured the animals. . . .

When Goldberger found that diets which produced black tongue failed to do so if dried brewer's yeast was mixed with them, it was a short step to demonstrate that this yeast, in proper quantities, would cure the disease and also cure and prevent pellagra.

But he was not satisfied with knowing that the pellagra preventive was present in yeast, which also contained other vitamin factors. He was not sure whether the P-P* factor was something quite distinct from these others. It was known that the others could be destroyed by heating in an autoclave. He autoclaved the yeast and found that it still prevented and cured pellagra and black tongue. He also found that the P-P factor could be separated out of the yeast by absorption with fuller's earth. . . .

Behind the main building of the United States Hygienic Laboratory in Washington there were several accessory buildings, the largest of which presented a unique interior. Part of it was a huge kitchen, as spacious as that of a large hotel—containing no china or silverware, but many pots and pans, stoves, barrels of foodstuffs, and scales for weighing every item of food prepared. The other part of the building resembled a zoo.

During 1927 and 1928 the place looked and sounded and smelled like a dog pound. More than forty dogs were there among the other animals. Their meals were prepared in this elaborate kitchen. This was Goldberger's laboratory. He and Wheeler, Tanner, Rogers, Lillie and Sebrell worked here.

Most of the dogs were being fed on what was known as Basic Diet 123, which contained definite weights of corn meal, cowpeas, casein, sucrose, cottonseed oil, cod-liver oil, sodium chloride and calcium carbonate. It was a sure-fire producer of black tongue. Dogs living exclusively on "123" show signs of the disease within about sixty days. But if in addition to this basic diet they are given foods containing the P-P vitamin in sufficient quantity, black tongue does not appear. Also, having developed the disease while on the basic diet, they are quickly cured if given the P-P foods.

Working on these principles, Goldberger and his men were able to make during those two years a great variety of experiments in nutrition. They tested sixteen common foodstuffs, and

* Pellagra-Preventive—Eds.

found which of these were the richest in the P-P factor, then confirmed their black-tongue results by using the same foods on pellagrins at Milledgeville.

Goldberger thought in 1928 that in three years more he could complete the work as far as he cared to carry it. Given that much time, he would be able to determine the P-P values of most of the common foods and uncover several new incidental points of information bearing on the general problem of pellagra.

But there was to be no such time at his disposal.

On October 31, 1928, he addressed the American Dietetic Association. He could scarcely talk above a whisper. Perhaps he knew that he was speaking in public for the last time.

His concluding remark was:

> Now it so happens that, conservatively estimated, there were some 120,000 people in the United States last year who suffered an attack of pellagra. One may ask, therefore, why, if the matter is so simple, do so many people continue to be stricken with the disease? The answer lies in the fact . . . that the problem of pellagra is in the main a problem of poverty.
>
> Education of the people will help; but improvement in basic economic conditions alone can be expected to heal this festering ulcer of our people. This, obviously, can not be accomplished in a day, but that day will be hastened by the cooperative action of all whose vision enables them to see the great social and economic advantages to be derived from the eradication of the disease.

Today, there is scarcely a grown person, black or white, in the pellagrous regions of the South who does not know, in a general way, the cause and prevention and cure of pellagra.

But the medical profession still numbers a few members who steadfastly ignore all the proofs that Goldberger adduced. As late as 1929 an eminent physician of New Orleans concluded the leading article in a prominent American medical publication with this statement:

> All the evidence of which I have personal knowledge, to which I am able to attach much weight, favors the opinion that it [pellagra] is due to an infection. I am content to remain with the minority who have not been convinced by supposed proof of other causes, and still believe that a specific infection will be found to be the true cause.

Some thirteen years have passed since Goldberger died. During those years many men have been working in many places adding this and that little refinement to our knowledge of the dietary factors concerned in pellagra, and thus to the weapons for fighting it. At this writing, they have even isolated a pure substance, nicotinic acid, which very probably is the chief dietary factor and is remarkably effective in curing pellagra though also very probably not the entire answer to the food-deficiency complex in the disease.

Years after Goldberger's death, and in his honor, his "P-P" (pellagra preventive) was renamed vitamin G.

1943

Anemia

GEORGE RICHARDS MINOT

ANEMIA is a relatively common disorder of the blood. Although the pale individual is usually anemic, pallor is not synonymous with anemia. For a person with a normal supply of good red blood may be pale simply because of circumstances which prevent the blood from coming near the surface of his body. But a person with anemia either has an actual undersupply of red blood cells, or these cells do not contain as much as they should of the red coloring matter called hemoglobin.

The patient with anemia does not exhibit outstanding symptoms until the hemoglobin is reduced by nearly one-half. Even when the red cells and hemoglobin are reduced to about one-quarter of their normal volume, patients may have little discomfort while at complete rest.

When an advanced condition exists, however, there are many symptoms that occur with anemias of different types. These symptoms are fundamentally due to the fact that an insufficient amount of hemoglobin is present in the blood to carry the proper supply of oxygen to the tissues. Headache, faintness, palpitation, irritability, abnormal fatigue and muscular weakness and increased sensitivity to cold are common indications of this effect of anemia. Other symptoms are sometimes present, and in more advanced stages of anemia still further and more serious symptoms appear.

However, modern medicine has discovered that proper doses of iron, in certain cases, or liver preparations, to patients in need of this material, often result in the dramatic transformation of a definitely sick person into a well one.

One of the numerous ways in which anemia may be produced is by loss of blood. Normally the human body is continuously producing new blood and destroying old. When a proper state of balance between these two functions does not exist, the blood ceases to contain its normal supply of red cells and of hemoglobin, and then anemia results.

One of the more common types, namely, iron deficiency anemia, is often caused by a recurrent abnormal loss of blood. The condition of iron deficiency anemia is more common in women, due to a number of causes. In the first place, women require, at least until about the age of fifty, approximately four times as much iron as the average man. The period of rapid growth and adolescence of girls makes special demands on their supply of blood. Motherhood also carries with it some risk of iron deficiency anemia; for the development of a supply of blood for the unborn child creates a real and substantial loss for the mother. Furthermore, the baby born of an anemic mother is itself liable to develop anemia within a year after birth. The answer to this situation lies in full doses of iron administered to the expectant mother, a cure which has been found to alleviate her condition and prevent the recurrence of anemia in the future infant as well. A more frequent use of iron for expectant mothers today would considerably lower the present rate of those cases of anemia which are associated with childbirth.

A well-balanced, natural diet provides a normal amount of iron, but when an iron deficit exists, it has been found that full doses of iron taken by mouth, either as pills or fluid, will correct the condition rapidly, and will return the victim of iron deficiency anemia to a full state of health.

Pernicious anemia, another of the major varieties of anemia, was first described by Thomas Addison of Guy's Hospital, London, in 1849. It has since been found to be due to a deficiency in the body of certain material which should normally be derived from food; and it manifests itself as an anemia associated with disturbances of the digestive system, and frequently of the nervous system as well. Pernicious anemia is somewhat more likely to develop in middle-aged patients with blue eyes and prematurely grey hair. In this variety of anemia the red blood cells are not pale, and average abnormally large, in contrast to iron deficiency anemia where the cells are pale and average abnormally small.

Recurrent burning and soreness of the tongue is apt to occur early in pernicious anemia, and gradually the tongue becomes smooth and shiny. Symptoms related to the nervous system sometimes develop early but usually develop later if the disease is not arrested. There may occur symmetrical numbness and tingling of the hands and feet. Eventually all degrees of limp and jerky paralyses, especially of the legs, occur and sometimes the patient cannot even walk. If untreated, the disease will progress by relapses and remissions for about four years with ultimately fatal results. But comparable to the case of iron deficiency anemia, there has been discovered a way to permanently alleviate this previously terrible disease.

Treatment for this variety of anemia requires, in fact, the application through life of adequate amounts of an appropriate preparation of liver or liver extract. Under this treatment the digestive symptoms vanish and no progress or development of the lesions of the nervous system occurs. Originally the patient was required to eat large amounts of animal liver daily. Today the effective countermeasure for pernicious anemia is supplied in an extract which may be swallowed daily in doses of several tablespoonfuls or, much better, injected into the muscles in very small quantities every one to four weeks. It is necessary, however, for this treatment to continue for life. Normally the stomach secretes a substance which is essential for the production of material, from particular sorts of food, that eventually becomes liver extract. In pernicious anemia, this substance is virtually lacking both before and after treatment. Thus, the patient with this disease, even though he eats the right foods, may be said to be starving in the land of plenty. He is never able to manufacture his own liver extract and, therefore, he must continue to get it through his physician.

The regular treatment with liver promptly alleviates the condition of the pale, frequently grapefruit-colored, individual whose red cells are often found to be reduced by two-thirds. Within days, the sick individual has a return of color to his cheeks, and he develops a ravenous appetite. Young red cells are poured into the circulation from the bone marrow where they are made.

The red cells increase about two and one-half million per cubic millimeter in about four weeks, and the last million required cells are made more slowly. The patient's tongue becomes normal again and the nervous symptoms of pernicious anemia are arrested.

Omission of treatment sooner or later causes the patient to feel sick again and the neural symptoms to progress quite unnecessarily. The properly treated patient, however, will lose all symptoms except those caused by some nervous system changes. Thus, contrary to its name, this disease is not to be looked upon as a pernicious one.

You may well ask how long we have known of the use of iron and of liver for the treatment of anemia. Iron has been used for this purpose since an English physician, Sydenham, introduced it about 1670 because from ancient days it had been considered a source of strength. This was some years before iron was demonstrated in the blood. In France, Pierre Blaud in 1831 indicated the importance of large doses of iron for the treatment of chlorosis, a form of what today is called iron deficiency anemia. About 1890 various scientific results led to the use of only small doses of iron with little effect on the anemia. Recently the value of large doses of iron has been emphasized anew, indeed thirty times the amount advised by some experts in 1900.

Liver treatment is entirely modern. The similarity of certain symptoms and signs of pernicious anemia to those of known dietary deficiency disease led to wondering whether pernicious anemia might be of this nature. Something seemed to be needed to make the primitive red cells, that crowd the bone marrow, grow to normal cells and make blood. Liver had been found to promote the growth of animals and thus, perhaps, the growth of red cells. It was effective in certain diseases that resembled, somewhat, pernicious anemia. Whipple had demonstrated that liver could regenerate blood in dogs. This was proved, later on, not to be due to the factor in pernicious anemia, therefore liver extract should not be given indiscriminately. In 1926 a report was made of the striking effect of feeding liver to forty-five patients with pernicious anemia. Effective extracts were soon made.

The individual with a normally good digestion and a proper diet need not ordinarily fear the presence of iron deficiency or pernicious anemia as long as any blood loss is stopped and any factors which inhibit nutrition are removed. But for those of us not so fortunate, modern medicine has provided effective cures in the form of iron and liver which have brought the formerly serious effects of these anemias I have discussed to a virtual standstill.

1947

The Story of the Glands
of Internal Secretion

WALTER TIMME

THERE are scattered throughout the body a number of small masses of tissue each of whose function it is to produce one or several highly important secretions. The secretions consist of powerful biochemical substances which are given to the blood stream or other circulating media to be distributed to the body generally, and by their action to maintain the normal activity and reactivity of the entire organism. Therefore all life and its continuity depend upon them. Because they give off their products directly to the circulation they are known as the glands of internal secretion as distinct from those glands that deliver theirs through the medium of a duct or channel. Hence they were also known as the "ductless" glands. But it was then discovered that some of the glands with ducts had an internal secretion in addition—such as the pancreas and the testicle—and the name "glands of internal secretion" or "incretory glands" was substituted. Their number is still somewhat in doubt because of the lack of unanimity among investigators in recognition of the specificity of the secretions of a few of these structures. . . .

. . . The anatomists began to give us real knowledge in the matter of the internal glands. . . . Vesalius in 1543 described and named the pituitary gland although it was known to Galen in the second century A.D. as was also the thyroid. Vesalius also described the thyroid in 1543 . . . Not only were the anatomists engaged in these studies, but many interesting correlations of disease of the glandular mechanisms with symptoms began to appear. Thus in 1705 Raymond Vieussens stated that epileptiform seizures were associated with pituitary disease in the case of a prominent Cardinal treated by him.

Even at this day the connection between some forms of epilepsy and pituitary disease is recognized and many papers by prominent physicians are in evidence. In 1761 de Haen associated amenorrhœa—a lack of menstruation—with pituitary disease; and the most modern theories of the anterior lobe of the pituitary gland agree with this statement. The famous John Hunter of London experimented in 1762 with transplants of testes into fowls noting their effect on the secondary sex characteristics. But it remained for a Frenchman, Theophile de Bordeu, to present for the first time in 1776 a clear statement of the function of the glands of internal secretion. He published the doctrine that each gland or organ produces a specific substance which is passed into the blood and that the entire organism is dependent upon these specific substances for its maintenance. This is the idea expressed by the modern term *hormone*, derived from the Greek ὁρμάνειν meaning, "I excite." That is to say, a hormone excites other tissues of the body to maintain their activity. Bordeu also described the bodily changes that take place in eunuchs, capons and spayed females as a result of the deprivation of sexual secretions.

THE THYROID GLAND

It might be well at this point to indicate the gradual trend of medical thought by taking up the discussion of the thyroid gland. (Thyroid from the Greek θυρεός, shield.) Even the Romans knew that endemic goiter existed in the Alps and it is mentioned both by Juvenal and Pliny. Goiter as you probably know simply means a swelling of the thyroid gland. Paracelsus in the sixteenth century recognized endemic goiter in Salzburg, Austria, and attributed it to the mineral constituents of the water. Interesting to note is the fact that he associated cretinism with goiter. And the use of iodine in goiter was possibly known to the early Chinese as it was certainly in the Mediterranean regions as early as the twelfth century, for they used burnt sponges and seaweed, both charged with iodine, in its cure. Of course, they did not know the particular ingredient of the ash which accomplished the result. But it remained for several European physicians to describe goiter, during the first half of the nineteenth century. The Englishman Parry collected eight cases of the disease up to

1815. The findings were published in 1825, ten years after his death. But while he described them fully, he did not affix a name to the malady and hence the honor of the discovery seems to have passed him by. It is much like the discovery of America with the name-labeler, Amerigo Vespucci, carrying the honor instead of Columbus. In 1835 Robert Graves of Dublin published a classical description of exophthalmic goiter with especial reference to the exophthalmos, the bulging of the eyes; and in 1840 Basedow, a German physician, described the cardinal symptoms of the disease so thoroughly that, at least in Germany, it has been ever since called by his name—Basedow's Disease. The three symptoms were: the thyroid swelling, the eyeball protrusion, and the rapidity of the heart. Earlier in the century, 1802, an Italian—Flajani—described a condition called *bronchocele* in which goiter and rapidity of the heart were combined. The Italians consider him the discoverer and so in Italy the name of *morbo di Flajani* is pinned to exophthalmic goiter. England and America, when using a name for the disease invariably turn to Graves. And so we have Graves' Disease, Basedow's Disease and Flajani's Disease, depending upon one's patriotic predilection. Parry is all but forgotten.

To go a step further in thyroid history, the first excision of the thyroid was performed by Theodore Kocher of Berne, Switzerland, in 1878. Within four years he discovered that 30 per cent of his cases suffered from a cachexia following the operation, that is to say, from a progressive decline in health, to death in many instances. Reverdin of Geneva a year later showed death to be due to the loss of thyroid function by the complete removal of the gland.

Maritz Schiff of Frankfort completed the explanation when he showed that although all his dogs with thyroid removal died of cachexia, yet if he grafted thyroid tissue beneath their skin, or gave thyroid juice, or raw thyroid by mouth after the operation, the dogs survived. In 1891, G. R. Murray of London recognizing that myxedema (the name given to the disease caused by deficiency of thyroid activity) was one form of thyroid deficiency, gave a woman patient thyroid both by mouth and subcutaneous injection. She improved and lived until a few years ago. Sir William Osler, in reporting the successful use of thyroid by oral administration in myxedema wrote that "not the magic wand of Prospero or the brave kiss of the daughter of Hippocrates ever affected such a change." To-day these various steps seem far apart and long drawn out, but it simply goes to show how slowly, methodically, judicial, logical advance is made. But well made, it rests permanently upon solid foundations.

The next step in the thyroid evolution is to determine what the important ingredient is that produces so many important consequences—positive by its presence—negative by its absence. Many investigators have taken up this problem. At one time it was thought that the iodine content of the thyroid was its most important constituent, but iodine alone in animals deprived of their thyroid is not efficacious in the restoration from their cachexia. After many years of trial, it was finally determined by E. C. Kendall of the Mayo Clinic in 1914 that there is an active principle in the thyroid gland which he extracted in an exceedingly pure state and which he believes to contain all the properties of thyroid extract. This hormone he called *thyroxin*. It is interesting to note that the discovery was almost accidental . . . .

However, the importance, nay, even the necessity for thyroid activity of the presence of iodine is well recognized. There are certain regions in the world in which there is a marked lack of iodine in the soil, the water, and the atmosphere. Throughout these regions many individuals develop, as a result of this lack, inadequate thyroid activity. As a consequence, the thyroid gland, unable to furnish thyroxin to the body, retains its secretions and becomes a boggy, enlarged mass. This is seen as goiter, and does not mean an overactive thyroid as many supposedly believe, but an underactive one . . . .

I was in Seattle in 1920 and in one half hour in a busy shopping district counted one hundred and fifty goitrous individuals. That situation has, however, been practically eradicated. Because it was recognized that the absence of iodine was responsible for the thyroid enlargement, Dr. David Marine, then of Cleveland, proposed that small quantities of iodine be given to all persons living in those districts. This has been accomplished in various ways. In one city iodine is put into the reservoir; in one state the use of iodized table salt is said to be compulsory; in the schools of one city children receive iodine as a medicament for two weeks twice yearly; and as the medical knowledge relating to the dependence of goiter upon a lack of iodine has spread, many are using iodine voluntarily. As a result, goiter is fast disappearing as an endemic disease in the United States . . . Some two or three years ago I again visited Seattle, and the goiters to be seen were few and far between. The success attendant upon the general use of iodine is strikingly evident.

Later on I shall describe the change that takes place in the individual when his thyroid underactivity gives place to normality. In conclusion, it may be stated that the thyroid gland produces a substance which is absolutely necessary to the individual, in that its presence produces proper oxidation within every cell of the body. Without it, this oxidation is prevented and slowness of all bodily processes results . . . therefore the hypothyroid individual, that is, one with an underactive gland, is sluggish in his physical and mental make-up. His weight increases, his secretions all diminish so that his skin remains dry, his nails become brittle, his hair falls out and he loses interest in his surroundings. There is a lowered body temperature, a slowness of the pulse rate, and a disinclination to move or work— no novelty to-day! It is difficult for him to arise early and he goes through the day in a lethargic manner. Fatigue is his constant companion. How different the hyperthyroid individual! He is always on the move; his pulse rate is increased; his heart's action is accelerated, he is constantly in a state of mental and bodily overactivity. There is a tendency to loss of weight, a warmness of the skin, a flushing of the face and a condition of excessive perspiration. Indeed, because of the fact that his hands are moist constantly, he gets into the habit of washing them frequently and occasionally will give this habit as his most prominent symptom. With all this activity he shows usually— although this is not at all always the case—a fullness of the thyroid gland and perhaps an undue prominence of the eyeball. Restlessness is the keynote of his existence; he keeps the world moving—not always in the proper direction nor with the proper rhythm—but moving . . . .

THE PITUITARY GLAND

Taking the next glandular element in the order of historic importance we shall discuss the pituitary gland. As you may know, this organ is situated in the base of the skull and is almost completely surrounded by a bony framework, known as the sella turcica—Turkish saddle. It is less than a half inch in length, almost a third of an inch in height and a half an inch wide— about the size of a filbert nut—and weighs about ten grains.

Think of it! And it controls practically all the other glands, it controls growth, development, sexual maturity, blood pressure, pregnancy, menstruation, the water exchange of the body, many of the biochemical ingredients of the blood, and probably also mental activity. Nature, endowing it with so much power and responsibility likewise took care to protect it adequately. The bony cavity in which it is, is actually a skull itself within the real skull, and so, far from harm's way. It is surrounded on all sides by the most remarkable circular blood stream in the entire body —called the circle of Willis—so that it is almost impossible to deprive it of blood. Because it is almost hidden away, little mention is made of it by early writers for they hardly knew of its existence, or, knowing it, gave it scant courtesy on account of its size.

. . . In 1838 Rathke, the German anatomist showed that the anterior part of the pituitary gland is derived from the mucous membrane of the upper pharynx and was gradually closed out from its origin by the development of the sphenoid bone of the skull which finally resulted in the almost complete inclusion of this part of the gland within the skull. This part of the pituitary gland is known as the anterior lobe. At its inclusion within the skull it joins a process coming down from the brain to which it becomes attached. This latter part derived from the brain is known as the posterior lobe. The actual division of the pituitary gland is a good deal more complicated than here appears but need not require detailed description at this time. And only two years later (1840) appears the account of an autopsy by a German physician of Würzburg, Bernhard Mohr, of a woman who had had a curious and massive obesity accompanied by mental and physical sluggishness, loss of memory and eye symptoms, and cessation of menstruation. The autopsy disclosed a tumor mass of the pituitary gland with neighborhood pressure on the adjacent cerebral parts. This was the first description of what later was to be known as the Froehlich syndrome—characterized by adiposity with sexual inadequacy. Curiously enough, this report appeared in the same medical volume that carried the first report of exophthalmic goiter by Basedow.

Further studies show us that giantism is due similarly to disturbances in the activity of the pituitary gland. So that clinically, up to this time, we have thus far had described to us as a result of pituitary disturbance: growth abnormality, sexual deficiency, abnormal obesity, mental aberration, and sluggishness with somnolence. All these from a small mass of tissue of an average weight of *ten grains!*

And the story is only begun. Harvey Cushing with his associates at Harvard, Herbert Evans of California, Philip E. Smith and Carl T. Engle of Columbia, Collip of Montreal, Riddle of the Carnegie Institution, and many others in practically all the laboratories of the world have been and are now engaged on the many complex problems offered by this most perplexing gland. And as a result of their endeavors we are gradually beginning to get a faint idea of the multitudinous activities of this gland.[1] Not only have these investigators with their associates shed much light upon the specific properties of the secretions of the pituitary but they have found out furthermore that the gland elaborates biochemical materials that control almost all the other glands in addition thereto. That is to say, there is in the anterior lobe of the pituitary a controlling substance without which the thyroid gland would deteriorate, one without which the adrenal gland would diminish its activity, one without which the parathyroid would cease functioning and finally one without which there could be no sex function. That is paramount to saying that the pituitary gland is a master gland.

To explain succinctly its specific functions: It controls growth, so that dwarfism or giantism or acromegaly are all of them its products when the growth factor indulges in vagaries. The sexual function is also one of its chief underlying charges and when it is in any way modified so that menstruation is delayed or too frequent or profuse or even absent, the pituitary anterior lobe is immediately suspect. Non-descent of the testicle in the male, or impotence, or lack of the secondary sexual characteristics may all be impugned either entirely or at least in part to the anterior pituitary. Many of the occurrences in labor, such as the contraction of the uterus preventing hemorrhage, are due to pituitary activity. Obversely, when disturbances in sexual organs occur such as disease or the removal of the testes in the young male or the ovaries in the female, the pituitary gland becomes involved and curious after effects are noticed such as abnormal growth— witness the eunuchs—a change in the voice so that it becomes high-pitched, and an abnormal growth of hair in the female, together with other pituitary effects such as increase in fat and weight, and sluggishness of mind and body. Many of these symptoms, however, can now be prevented by application of modern methods of treatment whereby substitutes for the disturbed glandular secretions are available for introduction into the body.

As before noted, the anterior lobe of the gland also has to do with the proper conversion of the fats and starches of our food. If this factor is lacking, then these food materials, instead of being utilized, simply produce additional weight of the body— obesity reigns. As the gland also controls the balance between the intake and outgo of fluids from the body, its deficiency produces too great a retention of fluid within the body and this still further increases the weight.

Another one of the newer principles discovered in the anterior lobe of the pituitary gland has been called *prolactin* by Riddle, its discoverer. This principle seems to be the one governing the production of milk. His work was done on pigeons. Both male and female birds have crop glands in the neck which secrete milk for the young squab. These crop glands develop only at maturity. But if this anterior lobe principle is injected into the very young birds many weeks before maturity, then the crop glands develop as an immediate result. . . . But one important thing still remains to be said about the anterior pituitary. It is that when all its functions cease, a condition of cachexia results— the individual becomes weak and emaciated and his vitality is lowered to a point at which life becomes impossible. Such a condition has been brought about by Philip E. Smith of Columbia artifically in monkeys by destruction of the pituitary gland. It is known as Simmond's Disease. . . .

The pituitary individuals are always with us. The hypoactive ones show a mental hebetude that is quite characteristic. They acquire fat, are somewhat easygoing; they don't face their problems but go the paths of least resistance; there is no self-denial or self-abnegation. The Fat Boy in Dickens' *Pickwick Papers* is a classical example. But there is a group of hypopituitary cases that is extremely important. These cases don't get fat, but they do show markedly the trait of mental subservience. They are easily led by stronger minds. As a result and because they have no self-control they become addicts to many habits. They drink to excess or they take drugs and this latter fact makes them more and more amenable to masters who control their entire life and destiny; while under the influence of the drug they will commit any and all types of crime. The hypopituitary case cannot fix his mind properly upon his work or problems— he cannot concentrate. In youth this leads to mental deficiency. In general it may be stated that the many factors of development of stature, sex, intelligence, behavior are all held in abeyance by a deficient pituitary gland.

The other side of the picture—the hyperpituitary, is of extreme interest. The individual develops in all phases of life, he is intelligent, keen, active both mentally and physically, body well grown and well proportioned and has powers of judgment and ratiocination beyond the normal. But if the overactivity persists we get a curious let-down and a gradual picture of hypopituitarism is engrafted upon the previous state. Many so-called wonder-children belong to this group. They begin life as marvels in some activity of mind or body. In a few years, they gradually become less and less marked and then gradually decline to a normal level or even lower, and are soon lost to view. The slightly overactive pituitaric, however, is the one that leads the world, the one that bends others to his will—the one that has his plan and carries it through. Usually he pays the price through his high blood sugar and high blood pressure with a comparatively early death.

THE PARATHYROID GLANDS

We are now brought to the consideration of the next glandular element of the body—the parathyroid glands. These small bodies eluded investigators until quite recently for they are exceedingly small—but two grains in weight each. Fifty years ago they were first described by Sandström. There are four of them and they are imbedded in the thyroid gland. Curiously enough, from time to time some parathyroid tissue is also found in the thymus gland. Their function until quite recently was unknown. When the thyroid surgeons some years ago removed the entire gland in diseased states they, of course, unknowingly removed the parathyroids also. It was found out that shortly thereafter the patient, while relieved of his thyroid symptoms, began to show evidences of a condition of spasm, of muscular twitchings and then bodily convulsions occurred; and finally death took place. It was thought that meat eating produced the condition in the absence of the thyroid and as a matter of fact, meat-free diet helped the condition materially. To determine this, thyroid glands of *herbivoræ* were removed. And no convulsions occurred in them as a result of the operation. It seemed clear that meat eating was the cause. But upon closer investigation it was found that in the *herbivoræ*, the thyroid gland is distinct from the parathyroids and its removal did not include these smaller organs; therefore the conclusion was not warranted.

And so the parathyroids as a possible cause of the difficulty were studied. It was found that when they were removed in animals, even though the thyroid was left in place, the animals entered into convulsive states. A study of the blood chemistry in these animals determined the fact that their blood was very poor in calcium. And so calcium was injected into the veins of the animal whose parathyroids were removed, after which no convulsions occurred. Repetition of the experiment with various controls soon showed that the parathyroid glands determined the calcium level of the blood. It was known that the condition of body spasm called tetany was due to a lack of calcium utilization, and now the main reason of the lack was proven to lie in parathyroid underactivity. While marked diminution of calcium in the blood causes these convulsions of tetany, there are a great many states produced by a slight lessening of the calcium level below the normal which are not convulsive but which are intensely disturbing.

The action of calcium in the body is not only to supply the material out of which bone is made, but further, to act upon the muscular and nervous systems. Its presence makes the nerve currents more stable and keeps them checked and reined. As soon as it diminishes in quantity, these nerve currents become intensified and much more easily stimulated. As a result, the person with a low blood calcium perceives the most minute external stimulus which ordinarily is not appreciated. He hears the slightest sounds and is aware of the slightest environmental change. As a result he is constantly on the qui vive and hence is never in complete repose. This means that he is always at tension. He cannot relax. Therefore he sleeps poorly, is easily awakened and not sufficiently refreshed by sleep. Because of the incessant irritation of the environmental stimuli and lack of calcium control of the nerve currents, his reaction to these stimuli is quick and out of all proportion to the cause. A chance remark, a mere disapproving

glance, any admonitory observation, and he is goaded to fury
and gives vent to it violently. Many criminal acts are thus
initiated. One of my patients, a fine intelligent boy, thus afflicted,
took up a shotgun that was near him, and shot his mother because
of some minor fault she was finding with him. Immediately the
explosion is over, contrition enters, but too late.

Proper treatment for the utilization of calcium helps this condition immediately. This consists in giving not only calcium itself
to the patient but also, in addition, parathyroid extract. In the
past decade an active extract of the parathyroid gland has been
isolated and prepared for general use. Both Collip and Hanson
are credited with its preparation. With parathyroid overactivity,
we see a disturbance produced which is highly dangerous particularly to the bony framework of the body. Because these
glands increase the blood calcium this calcium must be forth-
coming from some source and as the food is insufficient as a base
of supplies when the glands are overactive the calcium is taken
from the bones of the body. This results in a demineralization
of the skeleton with cyst formation and marked weakness of the
bones. As a result, spontaneous fractures result or else are produced by very slight trauma. If the parathyroid gland that is at
fault can be removed surgically then the trouble is mitigated, but
occasionally even after the removal of all four glands no improvement has been found. Later a large diseased parathyroid
may be discovered elsewhere than in the thyroid—frequently in
the thymus gland. The entire subject of the parathyroids forms
one of the newer, highly important chapters, still incomplete, of
the glands of internal secretion.

THE ADRENAL GLANDS

The adrenal glands next engage us. These are two in number
and are found in the abdomen above the kidneys. They are composed of two distinct portions, the interior or medulla, and the
shell or covering, called the cortex. It is the medulla which produces the important biochemical product "adrenalin," originally
discovered simultaneously by the Japanese Takamine and
Professor Abel of Johns Hopkins. This product is of the most
extreme importance. It is found to increase, to at least maintain,
blood pressure—to increase blood sugar, to stimulate the heart
action and above all, to stimulate the sympathetic nervous system.
As this nerve system controls all the involuntary activity of the

body it is at once apparent that life itself depends upon the adrenal secretion. All the abdominal organs—stomach, intestines, liver, pancreas; with the organs of the thorax—heart and lungs; and the pelvic system with its genital and urinary organs are under the control of some part of this involuntary nervous system. There is some discussion as to whether adrenalin is constantly being produced and utilized or whether it is given out only in emergencies, such as shock, extreme fatigue, fright and other emotional states, as described by Cannon. One important characteristic is that it controls hemorrhage by causing contraction of the capillaries, and so may be used for such purpose in small operations. It is efficient in the smallest, almost imperceptible quantities. Abel of Johns Hopkins has shown that its presence may be detected in solution of a strength of one part in four hundred million!

The cortex of the gland furnishes one of the most recent examples of an active principle—or hormone—controlling a heretofore incurable condition known as Addison's Disease. Addison described this condition as long ago as 1849. It is characterized by bronzing of the skin and mucous membranes, progressive weakness, emaciation and finally death. No cure has been known for it. For a decade or two, however, it was surmised that the cortex of the adrenal glands was the tissue responsible for the condition and while the active principle had not been isolated it was referred to as "hormone X." Finally, however, it was given to two investigators almost simultaneously to discover and produce it. Hartmann of Buffalo and Swingle of Princeton both succeeded in isolating the principle—now called *cortin*, from the adrenal cortex, some five years ago. This active agent when injected into sufferers from Addison's Disease causes an almost immediate response. From being moribund, they almost immediately begin to sit up and take notice, acquire an appetite and improve in all their symptoms. As this result is fairly temporary, however, cortin must be given daily or even oftener. It is a very expensive preparation and beyond the means of many sufferers, and so much time and thought are being given to prepare a more simple and cheap method of treatment.

From this short synopsis of the work done by the adrenal glands, one can readily see that without them, life would be impossible. One extremely interesting fact is that the cortex of the glands is composed of the same kind of cellular element as goes to the structure of the genital organs—notably, the ovary. And as a result, disturbance of the cortex, such as inflammation or tumor, produces a change in the secondary sexual characteristics. In the female particularly, there is an abnormal growth of hair— even to the formation of a mustache or beard—and finally the entire body becomes covered with coarse hair. At the same time, menstruation ceases, and with these events a marked personality change enters, masculinity being its keynote. It is curious to note that practically all the glandular elements of the body have many functions to perform, not only to maintain biochemical balances but to maintain as well external appearances and psychic reactions. Probably all three are correlated functions of an underlying principle and the combinations of all these underlying glandular principles make up the complexity of the individual—no wonder no two human beings are alike!

THE GONADS

We are now led almost directly to the consideration of the genital glands. As stated earlier in this discussion, from time immemorial these glands were the object of the greatest solicitude for they were recognized as the basic tissue for the continuation of the race. And when it was apparent that they were not functioning normally, all means were taken to correct the disturbance. And almost invariably these means were to utilize the sex tissue of animals as correctives. These tissues were prepared in all possible ways: decoctions, broths, tinctures, extracts, and even the raw material was used as food, and curiously enough with frequently favorable results. This one glandular treatment of a glandular deficiency has come down to us through the ages and was utilized by all peoples. It remained for a one-time professor of Harvard, Dr. Brown-Sequard toward the end of the nineteenth century to place this treatment on a more or less rational basis. He prepared a solution of testicular material from animals and injected this into himself. He had gradually been becoming tired and jaded with oncoming age and believed he could thus fortify himself against too rapid senility. The results apparently justified all his theories for his mental and physical stamina returned and renewed vigor asserted itself. This date of his report to the French medical world, May 31, 1889, is now regarded as the birth of modern endocrinology. Much water has gone over the dam since then and the genital organs, or gonads as they are termed,

have become the center of the recent intensive investigation
into the glandular system. To go into details of these investigations would exhaust the reader's interest and patience but in so
far as results are concerned these are epochal.

In the first place, two American physicians, Allan and Doisy,
discovered almost a decade ago, 1929, the active principle of
one of the component tissues of the ovary—the follicular tissue.
This active principle named *folliculin* or *theelin* is that which pre-
pares the living membrane of the uterus for the reception of the
ovum after it is fertilized. In a general way it stimulates the entire
genital tract. Should the ovum not have been fertilized, then this
living membrane is shed in the next menstrual flow. After the
ovum is discharged from the ovary where it has been developed,
a small blood clot remains in the site of rupture. This blood clot
becomes organized and then is known, because of its yellow-
ing color, as the corpus luteum, which has an effect to prevent
the shedding of the uterine membrane. That is to say it is
in a measure antagonistic to theelin (from the Greek θῆλυς,
"female," and "*in*"). When the ovum, however, is fertilized, then
the activity of the corpus luteum is prolonged for practically
the entire length of time necessary to the complete development of the ovum into the fetus and finally into the child, ready
to be delivered into the world. And this activity of the corpus
luteum prevents the menstrual flow and shedding of the uterine
membrane during the entire gestational period, and therefore con-
serves the race. From it, the ovarian principle, "progestin" is
prepared. When this ceases to function at full term, then the
uterus empties itself and a newcomer is ushered in. While this all
seems to be an activity of the ovary, yet it has been found that the
anterior lobe of the pituitary gland is sponsor for the initiation
of much, if not all of the ovary's activity.

Without the presence of this pituitary anterior lobe gonadal
hormone, these events would not occur. Now comes a highly
interesting corollary to the whole matter. Should the ovum become fertilized and there is no further use for ovarian activity
during pregnancy, what becomes of the secretions, theelin and
that gonadal principle of the anterior lobe of the pituitary gland
which are now not needed? They are excreted largely in the
urine. Therefore, if we examined the urine of pregnant women
we ought to find evidence of such gonadal extracts in it. And
they ought to produce their effects on ovaries in other individuals

if they were injected into them. And this is exactly what we find they do. Therefore, if we examine the urine of a woman in whom we wish to diagnose the presence or not of pregnancy and find that it contains these ovary stimulating properties, then pregnancy is practically positively assured. How is the test made? Injections of the urine are made into immature rats and if within a few days these rats show in their ovaries the results of stimulation, seen in the enlargement and maturity of the glands and the bleeding points of the corpora lutea, then the test for pregnancy is positive. This test can be made in the first few weeks of the suspected pregnancy and is almost completely satisfactory. The test is known as the Aschheim-Zondek test. A few years ago the diagnosis for pregnancy could not be positively made before the third month. It has always been a most interesting subject for debate as to the time when the rupture of the ovum from the ovary takes place for it is at this time or very shortly thereafter that fertilization must take place. Most recently this time has been partially fixed as about midway between two menstrual periods. This represents the most promising time for the fertilization of the ovum. The remainder of the month is known among women as the "safe period."

When it comes to the male gonads we have a somewhat different and simpler arrangement. There are two types of tissue, one being the sperm and the other known as the interstitial tissue producing an active principle which controls the secondary sexual characteristics of the male. We need not dwell upon the activity of the spermatozoa—they take all too good care of themselves! But the interstitial tissue needs some explanation. It is this tissue which is assumed to be at the basis of man's virility and youth, and it is this tissue to which he directs himself for the delights of rejuvenation. All possible methods for extracting and utilizing its active principles are in vogue and none up to the present time has given much promise. The so-called Steinach operation which engaged so much attention in recent years, is an attempt to increase the activity of the interstitial tissue by irritating it through tying off the duct through which the spermatozoa leave the testicle. This results in retention of the sperm cells within the gland causing irritation and congestion with resulting stimulation of the interstitial cells. This causes presumably increased vigor and mentality and generally a rejuvenation. Some cases have apparently shown improvement in these respects, even to the restoration of youthful hair coloring. Nothing is said, however, of the danger of overburdening old arteries through increasing vigor and activity. One hears much less nowadays of this much advertised operative procedure than of yore.

Interesting is the experimental work on the gonads by which through transplantation of female ovaries into males with removal of the testes, and the transplantation of testes into females with removal of the ovaries, the complete transformation into the other sex of these operated animals can be brought about. Thus Oscar Riddle speaks of a case in which a fowl, originally a mother and laying eggs, became later a father with the production of male germ cells. And there are several not thoroughly authenticated cases of like character that have been reported as occurring in humans. Even the possibility of parthogenesis in humans has been shown to exist. What determines the sex of an individual originally is as yet not known but in all probability this is fixed at the moment of fertilization.

PANCREAS AND INSULIN

A short description must now of necessity be given of the gland, the pancreas (Greek: πᾶς, all, plus κρέας, meat) which is not ductless but has an internal secretion. This organ, situated just below the stomach, has a duct through which it supplies the intestinal contents with several of the digestive juices that have to do with the conversion of starches, fats and proteins. While experimenting on dogs deprived of their pancreas, an attendant in the laboratory of Minkowski noticed that large swarms of flies were attracted to the urine passed by these dogs and not to that of the other control animals. This led to a chemical examination of this urine which was found filled with sugar. Thus the effect of the pancreas as a whole on sugar control was immediately suspected and later established. By methods of elimination it was soon proven that the part of the pancreas concerned in this sugar metabolism was the groups of cells known as the Islands of Langerhans.

Many investigators then set themselves to the task of deriving from these cells their active principle. It was finally accomplished in the laboratory of Professor McLeod of the University of Toronto by Dr. F. G. Banting and C. H. Best in 1921. They were assisted in the work and partially directed by Dr. McLeod and

Dr. J. B. Collip. This active principle, called *insulin*, was the result of their labors. It is supererogatory to tell you of the importance of this discovery. It not only helped thousands of human beings that had been suffering from the condition known as diabetes from an early and certain death (in which disease there is an inability to oxidize and utilize sugar), but it immediately placed the entire subject of internal glandular disease upon a high physiological plane. It quieted many of the scoffers and antagonists of this "quasi-medical" science and led them into the fold. It has been said that the original paper published by the Toronto group was refused at first by almost all medical journals as too sensational for belief. The Nobel Prize was awarded to them nevertheless and their names will go down in medical history as among the greatest benefactors of mankind. It must be remembered, however, that insulin is not a "cure" for diabetes, but simply a substitutive treatment for the lack of proper pancreative principle.

THE THYMUS

Finally, we reach in our march the thymus gland. Actually this gland ought to be considered first in our course for it is preëminently the gland that is active during our early years. It is situated within the thorax above the heart and in close relationship to it. It weighs about one ounce at birth and gradually increases in size to the tenth year, after which it gradually involutes. At times, small rests may be found during life but so far as we now know its activity practically ceases at puberty. Its recognition as a gland has been and still is widely disputed, for experiments in feeding, in removal and by injection have often had paradoxical—not to say negative—results. Its removal in dogs has been shown to produce disturbances in skeleton growth, resembling rickets, so that the legs became bowed and the dogs stunted. To confirm this result, similar experiments were made a decade ago at Johns Hopkins, and almost completely negative results were produced—no change in the skeleton resulted! As for feeding, Gudernatsch fed thymus to tadpoles and produced marked increase in growth so that he had actual giant tadpoles—but they did not develop into frogs. So that the conclusion was drawn that the thymus produced growth but hindered development. Later on, an Italian, Soli, showed that fowl with the thymus removed produced eggs without a shell. If these same fowl were fed with thymus gland the egg again had the shell. Riddle showed similar results in doves.

From these experiments it became evident that the thymus gland had to do with lime or calcium metabolism and therefore the idea that it produced growth again arose. In the last three years Rowntree, with an active principle of the thymus prepared by Hanson succeeded in accelerating the growth of white rats in a surprising way when given to successive generations. And in addition, and in contradiction to previous investigators these rats also developed much more rapidly. Their eyes opened earlier, and their genitals matured in half the normal time.

Interesting to note was the fact that the pituitary gland in these rats showed an increase in the size and number of the sex cells, the basophiles, as well as the growth cells, the acidophiles. The thymus evidently produced a pituitary activity. However, these experiments of Rowntree as yet lack complete confirmation by others. When we consider the thymus gland in man and its apparent effect clinically on him we witness partial confirmation of animal experimentation. Thus in children with large thymus glands, growth in height is usually abnormal, but development in them is retarded. They remain children in many respects longer than the average, and they show these childhood traits in many ways. Their skin is velvety and smooth—peaches and cream in character. Their hair is soft and silky, no mustache hairs make their appearance until very late, if at all—and the body hair is almost absent. The genitals remain small and undeveloped and sometimes take on the character of the other sex.

However, intelligence is not usually in abeyance and later, when proper compensations in the glandular system arise, these children develop into adults of usually superior quality although their arrival at complete development is much later than normal. But during their childhood, and even later, if proper compensation does not occur, they suffer from the lack of proper development in many important organs. The heart and blood vessels are too small, the pituitary and adrenal glands are too small and they are inefficient. These factors make for great fatigability. The sex glands are undeveloped. And because the body growth is so great and its proportions incorrect, their joints are loose and they are subject to all manner of dislocations—so-called double-joints. Because the joints of the arch of the foot are so pliable, flatfoot results; and because of the laxness of the joint between spine and pelvis, backache on undue exercise is produced; and so we have an individual that in many ways is incapable of competing with his fellows. This changes his psychological aspect and he becomes shy, cannot meet his problems, and therefore becomes a mere follower and never an aggressor. These is no actual proof that the thymus overactivity produces such individuals, but these individuals do possess enlarged thymus glands and the involution of the gland is delayed.

In early life the thymus gland may be so large that it impedes proper breathing and if it is drawn into the upper entrance into the chest, it may so interfere with the nerves and blood vessels there situated that death may ensue rapidly. This is the so-called mors-thymica. Children with large thymus glands may have all the appearance of perfect health. Upon sudden undue exertion, they become cyanotic and collapse. It has been found, however, that because of the small and thin blood vessels in this condition, such exertion may produce a rupture in one of the blood vessels in some important vital organ, such as the brain, or the suprarenal gland or even in the artery supplying the heart, and the sudden death is then attributable to this cause rather than to the actual size of the thymus gland. Between the children that die this early death and the mature, thoroughly compensated adult that began life with a large thymus, there are hosts of individuals that only partially compensate and carry their troubles, due to this lack of complete maturity, throughout life. They are always tired, cannot concentrate well, have fugacious pains involving the back, or the foot, or the heart; have low blood pressure, don't react well to cold or exercise, and in general have such a wrong mental attitude to life that they are dubbed neurasthenic or hysterical or are even found among the psychically disturbed. Many of our shell-shocked cases in the war belong to this group.

Then there are individuals that have too small a thymus gland and while the diagnosis is difficult, it has been shown that these cases are quite the reverse of those just cited. They mature early, but remain small in stature and are of the old-young type. Mustache and beard and early general maturity occur and they show a curious mental attitude of precocity without the basis of knowledge or experience. Because of these characteristics they prove a bane to society.

GENERAL

There are several other important organs that have so-called internal secretions but because of the highly technical character of the biochemistry involved or because of the failure to prove the presence of one as yet unrecognized active principle—they are omitted in this paper. These are the pineal gland, the liver, the intestinal mucosa, the spleen.

Finally we may note that the span of human life may be divided logically into three great epochs: the first, from birth to maturity; the second, from maturity to the prime; and lastly, from the prime through senescence to death. During each of these periods, because the goal of each is different from the others, a different equipment is necessary. During the first period, when maturity is the objective, all the glandular elements that make for growth and accretion are in the ascendant. When maturity is attained, and all man's powers are to be utilized in the procreation of his kind and in the struggle for existence in sharp competition, then the glandular activity of the pituitary, the thyroid, the adrenals, and the gonads is called forth in the highest degree. When this second period has reached its acme, no further biological reason exists for man's further survival and he gradually, with his glandular mechanism, fades into the composite picture of the human race.

The Johns Hopkins Hospital

JOHN SHAW BILLINGS

THE hospital should contribute to Charity, Education and Science. First to Charity. It is to furnish the best possible care and treatment to the sick. Its patients are to have the benefit of the best medical and surgical skill which can be procured, of properly trained nurses, of pure air and proper food, and they are not to be subjected to any annoyances or depressing influences by being made a show of in any way.

Their treatment by the Hospital authorities is to be in the same spirit in which they would be treated in their own homes.

I wish to make my views on this point distinctly and clearly understood, even at the risk of being tedious. A sick man enters the Hospital to have his pain relieved—his disease cured. To this end the mental influences brought to bear upon him are always important, sometimes more so than the physical. He needs sympathy and encouragement as much as medicine. He is not to have his feelings hurt by being, against his will, brought before a large class of unsympathetic, noisy students, to be lectured over as if he were a curious sort of beetle. Some men, and even women, are perfectly indifferent to being thus displayed, in fact rather like it, but there are many who regard it with aversion and fear, and will undergo much privation and suffering in their miserable homes rather than subject themselves to the exposure above referred to.

In this Hospital I propose that he shall have nothing of the sort to fear . . .

This Hospital should advance our knowledge of the causes, symptoms and pathology of disease, and methods of treatment, so that its good work shall not be confined to the city of Baltimore or the State of Maryland, but shall in part consist in furnishing more knowledge of disease and more power to control it, for the benefit of the sick and afflicted of all countries and of all future time.

It should be remembered that our buildings and machinery are simply tools and instruments, that the real Hospital, the moving and animating soul of the Institution, which is to do its work and determine its character, consists of the brains to be put in it. Whether it shall be a truly great Hospital and a charity such as was intended by its founder, is not a matter solely of arrangement and plan of buildings, it depends upon not more than half a dozen men and one or two women . . .

We can much more certainly secure men who will minutely and patiently investigate individual cases, noting every abnormal appearance or sound, testing every excretion, recording the precise effects of each plan of medication, in short doing everything that science can suggest to understand the condition of the patient and the best method of relieving him; by showing them that they shall have space and apparatus to work with, that the resources of modern science and mechanical skill shall be at their command, and that any discoveries which they make shall be properly published, than by simply offering double pay . . .

After we have got our good men we want to keep them good. For our purposes there is no such thing as a man who "knows enough." They are to improve steadily, to grow mentally, and for this growth we must provide nutriment and space just as certainly as we must provide them for the trees which we propose to plant, or else expect stunting, impaired vitality, and absence of fruit. The buildings are to be arranged with reference to these considerations . . .

But there are other objects for a Medical School which do not at all enter into the plan of existing institutions. One of these is to train men to be original investigators, to bring them face to face with the innumerable problems relating to life, disease and death, which are yet to be solved; to inspire them with the desire to investigate these questions; and to give them the training of the special senses, of manual dexterity, and, above all, of clearness and logical scientific precision of thought, which are required to fit them to be explorers in this field.

To do this, I think, should be one of the objects of this Medical School.

1876

My Professional Colleagues

JOHN MILLER TURPIN FINNEY

I HAVE already referred repeatedly to my professional teachers, colleagues, assistants and students, but I should not feel that this autobiography had fulfilled its purpose without a more intimate personal sketch of some of these men, from the close association with whom I have gained so much both in knowledge and inspiration. I shall begin with the "Big Four" of the Johns Hopkins Hospital, Dr. William H. Welch, Sir William Osler, Dr. William S. Halsted and Dr. Howard A. Kelly,[1] who had so much to do with the development and early progress of this institution, and who exerted so profound an influence, not only upon myself and all others who worked with them, but also upon the science and art of medicine.

Everyone who was privileged to work under Dr. William H. Welch, the first of the "Big Four," felt much the same way about him, and everyone now feels that there can never be another Dr. Welch. He died without descendants; the mold was broken with his death, to the great loss of the medical profession and the world of science and humanity in general. What Dr. Welch meant to scientific medicine and public health is beyond computation.

William Henry Welch was a native of Connecticut. He was

[1] Died in 1943.

born in 1850, the son of a doctor, descended from a line of distinguished medical ancestry. He was graduated from Yale in 1870, after which he taught for a year and then took an extra year in chemistry before entering the College of Physicians and Surgeons in New York. He was graduated in 1875. He then interned for a year and a half in Bellevue Hospital . . .

Stimulated and guided by this remarkable group of men, Dr. Welch then went abroad and was fortunate enough to come into contact with many of the leaders of the German school of thought, which then led the scientific world. This was, of course, the most wonderful period in the evolution of the medical sciences. The great discoveries of Pasteur were preparing the way for the new science of bacteriology, and Virchow had just established cellular pathology on a sound basis. Some of the most famous of the German school were just at the height of their activity. What a wonderful opportunity for a young man of Dr. Welch's capability! He at once became a convert to the new pathology. About this time the opening of the Johns Hopkins Hospital afforded an ideal opportunity for developing in America a school of pathology that would follow the German lead. Dr. Welch was quick to take advantage of this opportunity, and in 1885 he began his epoch-making work in Baltimore, and here played a highly important role in the establishment of a new era in medical education.

From the time of his arrival in Baltimore, several years before the opening of the Johns Hopkins Hospital, Dr. Welch's laboratory became the center around which the prospective hospital revolved. Here was gradually assembled a group of eager students and investigators attracted by his personality and by the unequalled opportunity afforded for advanced work. Dr. John S. Billings was the one primarily responsible for the actual planning and construction of the Hospital, and President Daniel C. Gilman furnished the motive power for the whole University. But all will agree that Dr. Welch was chiefly responsible for the selection of the original staff of the Hospital and for providing the initial tone, atmosphere, or scientific spirit, whatever you may choose to call it, that has characterized the Johns Hopkins Hospital and Medical School from the beginning. Yes, it was Dr. Welch who set the pace, and those who later became associated with him. recognized at once his extraordinary qualities of leadership and were only too glad to follow him. He exerted a commanding influence in the formative period of the Hospital and Medical School.

One is forced to deal in superlatives in order to give any proper estimate of what Dr. Welch accomplished in scientific medicine. In this country he stood in a class by himself in almost everything pertaining to a scientific knowledge of disease processes. He had an encylopedic mind, and his fund of knowledge was simply inexhaustible. He could discuss intelligently and constructively any question, medical or otherwise, that came up, and he did it in so pleasant a way, never condescendingly or patronizingly, but always in so interesting a manner that one learned much from merely associating with him and listening to him. He seemed to have read everything, and he remembered all that he had read or heard, and furthermore, could use it at any time. There seemed to be no subject that came up in conversation about which he was not well informed.

Once I operated upon a man for an intestinal obstruction, the nature of which I had been unable to determine before the operation. On opening the abdomen, I found the obstructing mass to be composed of multiple small cysts filled with gas, which looked for all the world like soap suds. I had never seen or heard of anything like it, nor could I find anyone who had until I went to see Dr. Welch. He sat smoking a cigar and listening carefully while I described what I had found. Then he said that he himself had never seen anything of the kind, but that he remembered reading some years previously in Virchow's *Archives of Pathology* a report of such a condition. He walked over to his library, and after thinking a moment, pulled out a certain volume. He opened the book and turned a few pages, and then said, "Yes, here it is. I thought it must be in this number." On the page he indicated was the description of a case of "Gas Cysts of the Intestine," similar to mine, and as I recall, the only one in a human being that had been reported in the literature up to that time.

I looked at the date of the volume and saw that it had been published about ten years previously. Dr. Welch had found the report of the case without even looking at the Index. To be able to remember the report of a single case after ten years, to pick out the correct volume, and then to turn to the right page without looking at the Index surpassed anything I had ever seen. Furthermore, he went on to say that he thought John Hunter (one of the fathers of scientific medicine) had, about a century ago, described the same condition in the intestines of sheep and hogs, and that I might find his specimens in the Hunterian Museum of Anatomy in London. As it happened, I was going to London shortly thereafter. The first place that I visited after arriving there was the Museum, and, sure enough, there I found several specimens of gas cysts of the intestine of both sheep and hogs, mounted by John Hunter and described in his own handwriting.

Never was there a more stimulating or better beloved teacher than Dr. Welch. His lectures were clear, concise and logical, and at the end of them each point he had made stood out so plainly that the student could not miss it. . . . He was never too busy, nor was it ever too much trouble for him, burdened as he was with so many matters of importance, to stop what he was doing and take the time to answer questions, discuss problems and give advice to anyone who came to him for counsel. He was as courteous to the student who wanted to ask him a question as he was to a member of the faculty. Thus it was that he received the nickname of "Popsie," by which he was affectionately known to all of the students, for he was indeed a father to them all. . . .

But Dr. Welch was a father to more than the students; members of the faculty as well used to consult him on all manner of problems. He seemed to be equally well informed about them all, and his advice and suggestions were found by experience to be invariably sound. No wonder then that he came to be mentor of the Johns Hopkins School of Medicine, to whom everyone turned and whom everyone delighted to honor. At the time of his death he was the unquestioned Nestor of American medicine.

Dr. William Osler, afterward Sir William Osler, or "The Chief," as he was affectionately known among his students and associates, was the first Physician-in-Chief to the Johns Hopkins Hospital and the first occupant of the Chair of Medicine in the Johns Hopkins Medical School. As a member of the Surgical Staff of the Hospital, I was not privileged to serve under him. However, during his fifteen years of service at the Johns Hopkins Hospital I came to know him well and, like every other earnest student fortunate enough to have been attached to the staff of the Johns Hopkins Hospital in any capacity whatsover during these golden years of opportunity, could not fail to come to some degree under the magic spell of his influence, so potently manifested wherever he happened to be, whether in Toronto, Montreal, Philadelphia, Baltimore or Oxford. This was an influence so subtle, and yet so compelling, that one could not remain in his immediate environment for any length of time without experiencing in some form or other its lasting effect.

William Osler was born in Ontario, Canada, July 12, 1849, and, like so many distinguished men, was the son of a clergyman. His early education was received in Toronto, and he was graduated from Trinity College in 1868. He took his medical degree at McGill University, Montreal, in 1872. He studied abroad for two years, chiefly in London, Berlin, and Vienna. On his return in 1874, he was made Professor of Medicine at McGill University. Here he remained until 1884, when he accepted a call to the Professorship of Clinical Medicine at the University of Pennsylvania.

When the Medical Department of the Johns Hopkins University was inaugurated in 1889, he became Professor of the Theory and Practice of Medicine and Physician-in-Chief to the Johns Hopkins Hospital. Here he was one of the famous "Big Four" of the Faculty, and the credit for the organization and development of the Hospital, and the far-reaching effect which it has had on medical education in this country is largely shared by him.

In the fall of 1904 he accepted a call to become Regius Professor of Medicine in the University of Oxford, England, where he remained until his death on December 29, 1919—fifteen years crowded with manifold activities, especially during the World War, when his counsel and advice were continually in demand, both by military and civil authorities.

His career in the various institutions he served is too well known by the public and the profession to require extended comment. He was the recipient of many honors, too numerous to recount. Institutions of learning were eager to honor themselves in honoring him. The list of universities conferring degrees upon him would include practically all the leading ones of this country, and many of those of Great Britain. In addition to all this, in 1911 he was created a Baronet of the United Kingdom by King George V. An unusual distinction completed this list of honors when in 1918 Sir William was made President of the British Classical Association, a rare honor indeed to be conferred upon a physician, a member of a profession without special classical training. This is but an additional evidence of the wide range of his interest and of his scholarship.

On May 7, 1889, when the doors of the Johns Hopkins Hospital were first thrown open to the public, there had gathered a distinguished assemblage containing many notable personages, both lay and medical, representing the élite of the profession at home and abroad. Among the prominent figures who were present, Osler perhaps more than any other focused the attention and the interest of the assemblage: a man of rather spare figure, a little below the average height, dressed immaculately with a flower in the buttonhole of his Prince Albert coat. He had coal black hair, just beginning to turn a little gray at the temples and to grow a little thin over a high forehead, which showed signs of intellectuality of a high order; a flowing black mustache; bright piercing eyes, in which lurked almost constantly a most engaging twinkle; and a complexion rather sallow, yet suggesting good health. His manner was debonair, his movements quick and agile, indicating great nervous energy. Altogether he gave the impression of a body under excellent control, a mind endowed with great mental acumen and poise, and a well-developed sense of humor.

But let us follow him a little later, after he had begun his work at the Hopkins, as he made his ward rounds, where we can observe the effect of his personality upon his patients. He had a cheery word of greeting for each one, a characteristic wave of the hand, a friendly pat on the back or perhaps a momentary grasp of the hand. He would make a bright sally, usually at the expense of the patient, but leaving no sting behind, as unfortunately witty sayings so often do, but rather leaving on the mind of the patient an effect which was both pleasing and salutary. It would be difficult to imagine a personality more human, more engaging or more inspiring of hope and confidence. He seemed to put into operation without knowing it the best that there is in psychotherapy. There was developed in him to an unusual degree the capacity of making each patient feel that he was personally interested in his or her individual case. This was not merely an assumed interest; it was genuine. His patients fairly worshiped him.

But if his patients were so profoundly affected by Dr. Osler's personality, what of his students and staff? The relationship between him and them was intimate and cordial. Never was leader more loyally followed or more devotedly worshiped by his subjects than was Dr. Osler by his associates. The following verses were penned by one unknown to me, undoubtedly a member of the Medical Staff of the Hopkins. They reflect very well the respect that prevailed around the Hospital with regard to Dr. Osler's ability to show up what a medical student did not know as well as what he did:

WHEN WILLIAM OSLER MAKES HIS ROUNDS

Haste! Haste! ye clerks,* make breakfast brief,
And follow close your lord and chief:
With paper blank and pen in fist,
Let not a single note be missed,
When William Osler, K. C. B., F. R. S., F. R. C. P.,
    Makes his rounds.

No matter how much work may be
Awaiting you beneath Ward 'G,'
When on the bridge he's heard to sing
Drop all, and wait upon the king,
For William Osler, K. C. B., F. R. S., F. R. C. P.,
    Is making rounds.

See how the double doors swing back,
And in he comes with all his pack!
From North and South, from West and East,
They flock like vultures to a feast
When William Osler, K. C. B., F. R. S., F. R. C. P.,
    Is making rounds.

All sorts of folk are in the pack,
From city swell to country hack,
Swine-like they crowd each empty space,
Crowd clerk and interne out of place
When William Osler, K. C. B., F. R. S., F. R. C. P.,
    Is making rounds.

Now when he's seen your case perchance,
And done his little song and dance,
A cunning trap he lays for you
And holds four fingers up to view,
Does William Osler, K. C. B., F. R. S., F. R. C. P.,
    In making rounds.

* The medical internes whose duty it was to take the histories of the patients were known as "clinical clerks," an old English term, pronounced "clarks."

Says: "Mr. Blank, tell us what points
About the swelling of the joints
Have been impressed upon your brain
Since you have followed in our train?"
Says William Osler, K. C. B., F. R. S., F. R. C. P.,
    While making rounds.

You glibly give the list of points
He made upon those self-same joints
When last he talked upon the case.
You stop, and smile into the face
Of William Osler, K. C. B., F. R. S., F. R. C. P.,.
    Who's making rounds.

Poor lad! Pride antedates a fall,
For when you're sure you've named them all,
From out his sleeve he'll draw two more
Which you have never heard before,
Will William Osler, K. C. B., F. R. S., F. R. C. P.,
    . While making rounds.

Cheer up, sad heart, you're not alone,
For ere this morning's work is done,
Unless some marvel come to pass
He'll prove each clerk in turn an ass,
Will William Osler, K. C. B., F. R. S., F. R. C. P.,
    While making rounds.

But in order to get a glimpse of the real "Chief," of the many
sides of his character; his wonderful memory for cases, the inexhaustible storehouse of medical lore with which his mind was
filled, his remarkable insight into human nature, his intimate
knowledge of disease and its protean manifestations; in order to
feel the magic of his personality, one must watch him by the
bedside of his patient, surrounded by his students, the ideal clinician and teacher. There he sits in characteristic pose in the midst
of them, his exquisite hands palpating the patient or toying with
a stethoscope, of thoughtful mien, his mind alert, never missing
an opportunity to direct attention to some point of interest illustrated by the case or to point out to the students some way in
which by study and research additions could be made to existing

knowledge. Nor does he fail to take advantage of the opportunity to try in his own delightful way to stimulate in the minds of his students the desire for real accomplishment in their work. . . .

. . . Dr. Osler was the best loved of men. His patients recognized in him a trusted friend who at the same time could be confidently relied upon to employ every agency that science afforded for their benefit. Dr. Osler was the embodiment of St. Luke, "The Beloved Physician" of Holy Writ. His life illustrated the fine balance that should be maintained between the scientific and the practical in medicine, between the head and the heart. Like Abou ben Adhem, he loved his fellowmen despite their faults and frailties, toward which he was always willing to turn a blind eye or a deaf ear.

Dr. Osler was an extraordinary physician and beyond question a great diagnostician, but a few at least of his patients were perhaps at times inclined a bit to take exception to his treatment, especially of minor ailments. He had the reputation in certain quarters of being more or less of a therapeutic nihilist. It was said rather jokingly of him that "he rarely used more than a half-dozen drugs, all of which were poisons." On one occasion I happened to be calling on a well-known physician of Baltimore who was well advanced in years. He had been suffering for some time from angina pectoris and was a patient of Dr. Osler. While I as a friend was visiting the old doctor, Dr. Osler happened to come in. As soon as the doctor-patient saw him, he began berating him because he was doing so little for him, insisting that he had been having a lot of pain and wanted more medicine to make him comfortable. Dr. Osler, in his characteristic manner, began twitting him about what poor patients doctors make, but the old doctor was insistent. "What's the use," said he, "of having the supposedly best doctor in the country as your physician when he doesn't do anything for you? I'd rather have a fifty-cent doctor from South Baltimore who would do something to relieve my pain than the best in the land who just comes in and jokes and pats you on the back, and then goes out without leaving you any medicine to make you feel better." As Dr. Osler went out, he called the nurse and told her to be sure to give the doctor-patient the medicine, which he then prescribed, and to give him enough to keep him comfortable.

Dr. William Stewart Halsted, the third of the "Big Four" and the one of the group with whom, since I was in the Surgical Department, I had most contact, was the first Professor of Surgery in the Johns Hopkins University and the first Surgeon-in-Chief to the Johns Hopkins Hospital.

William Stewart Halsted was born in the city of New York on September 23, 1852. He was graduated from Yale University with the A. B. degree in 1874. He studied medicine in the College of Physicians and Surgeons, now a department of Columbia University, and was graduated in 1877 at the head of his class, for which he received the first prize of one hundred dollars. He then served as Surgical Interne and House Surgeon in Bellevue Hospital.

He began the practice of surgery in New York in the fall of 1880. From the beginning he limited his practice to surgery, and in all probability was the first in this country to confine himself exclusively to this specialty. About the same time he was appointed Attending Surgeon to the Presbyterian and the Bellevue Hospitals and Assistant Attending Surgeon to the Roosevelt Hospital. From 1881 to 1888 he was also Chief Surgeon to the Dispensary of Roosevelt Hospital. In addition to all this, he was Surgeon to numerous other hospitals in the city. Indeed this period of Dr. Halsted's career seems to have been characterized by a mad rushing from one hospital to another, in which his time was fully taken up by operating, seeing patients, teaching and lecturing on anatomy and by his private quiz; one wonders how he accomplished so much. To one who knew Dr. Halsted only in the latter half of his active professional life, when time was taken for a leisurely study of each problem as it came up, when the element of haste was entirely out of the picture, it seems utterly incomprehensible that he could ever have masqueraded as a "Dr. Jekyll-Mr. Hyde" type of person. But such undoubtedly was the case. He used to refer in a deprecating manner now and then to this period of hyperactivity. As a direct result of the character and extent of his work during this period, his health suffered, and he was compelled to relinquish his duties for a time.

Another contributing factor to Dr. Halsted's breakdown in health, which I should not refer to had it not already been mentioned by others, was his unfortunate addiction to cocaine, which began about this time. The habit was acquired quite innocently by Dr. Halsted and several of his assistants who were working with him at the time. The discovery of cocaine, announced by Koller in 1884, stimulated great interest in the use of this new local anesthetic. Dr. Halsted and his assistants were among the most active in studying its therapeutic action, so much so that they experimented on themselves and some of their students. As an outcome of these experiments Dr. Halsted made the interesting and important discovery that cocaine could be injected into the trunk of a sensory nerve and thus anesthetize the area supplied by that nerve. So insidious and exhilarating was the action of this drug that for a time it was a common practice to snuff it up the nostrils in order to experience its rather pleasant physiological effect. All unconscious of the habit-forming nature of the drug, they continued its use until the dreadful habit had fastened itself upon several of them, Dr. Halsted among the number. To the very great credit of Dr. Halsted, he was one of the few who were able to overcome its disastrous effect. This required herculean effort upon his part and necessitated his retirement from active work for a time. But he persisted in his efforts and finally overcame it, and subsequently made some of his most brilliant contributions to scientific surgery. Curiously enough, his whole manner of life underwent a complete change after this experience.

His health having improved, Dr. Halsted in 1887 came to Baltimore as one of that brilliant coterie of men who had been attracted thither by the unequalled opportunities offered in the newly opened Pathological Laboratory of the Johns Hopkins University, under the inspiring leadership of Dr. Welch. Here Dr. Halsted became at once identified with and a leading spirit in the New Johns Hopkins School of Scientific Medicine, then in the process of development . . .

In the conduct of his Clinic Dr. Halsted was an ardent admirer and exponent of the best in the German school in which he had been trained. His students and assistants were not spoon-fed. His idea was to help a man to help himself, not destroy the assistant's initiative by continually telling him what he should do next and then showing him how to do it, but rather to leave him to follow largely his own lead, only helping him here and there with a word of advice or warning as occasion required. Dr. Halsted's influence on the group of younger surgeons trained by him was an unconscious rather than a conscious one. He taught by example, the best of all methods, rather than by precept. His associates were (much more than they realized) deeply impressed by his habits of thought and work; his enthusiasm, his painstaking accuracy, his close observation and his never-failing interest in studying problems with characteristic and indefatigable industry until he had at last mastered them. His methods were less striking than those of some of his confreres because less spectacular, but they did not suffer thereby in effectiveness. . . .

A man of comparatively few words himself, he was an excellent listener. He was a better writer than speaker, as he was a better surgeon than operator. As an original thinker and investigator interested in the larger problems of scientific surgery, he was without a peer. As a contributor to surgical progress, no one was more active or fruitful. Few surgeons of his own or preceding generations have by their original contributions so enriched surgery and in such varied ways. The versatility of his genius was quite as striking as its originality. While the science rather than the art of surgery appealed the more strongly to him, the latter was not wholly neglected, as witness the several valuable contributions that he has made in this particular field. Nevertheless, he should be classed as a "head" surgeon rather than a "hand" one. He was much more interested in thinking surgery than in doing it, happier in his laboratory than in the operating room. He recognized and frequently referred to the fact in conversation with members of his staff that operating was not his forte and he was always glad to be relieved of its great responsibilities. Yet his associates will be able to recall many occasions when he has performed unusual and dangerous operations, requiring a high degree of courage and dexterity, with consummate skill. . . .

Dr. Halsted was the most modest of men. Caring little for the applause of the multitude, he preferred to be left undisturbed to follow the even tenor of his way, his mind intent upon the special problem which for the time being engaged his attention, yet ever alert to grasp new ones as they presented themselves. Because of his scholarly tastes and studious habits, it was hard to see in him the athlete he had been in his earlier years. He shunned publicity and applause and shrank from everything that savored of notoriety. He did his best work in the quiet of his study or his laboratory, never before a crowded gallery, where he was always ill at ease. His apparent reticence, misinterpreted at times by some who did not know him as coldness or lack of interest, was but a natural defense reaction for his shyness. But let his attention be attracted by some phenomenon observed or by some remark made in the course of conversation, and instantly the barriers were down. He at once became so much absorbed in the possibilities the thought suggested that the shyness vanished and instead was revealed the interested scientist.

I have said that Dr. Osler was known as "The Chief" and Dr. Welch as "Popsie," nicknames which were given them by the students, according to the almost universal custom of students with their teachers. These names were taken up by others until they became definitely attached to each and superseded all other titles. Dr. Halsted too had a nickname, and the story of how this came about is of some interest. One day soon after the opening of the Medical School Dr. Halsted had a small boy as a patient. It was an interesting case, and he was using the boy as the subject of his morning clinic before a room full of students. The father of the boy was present. He was one of these smooth and rather offensively obsequious types. He was forever butting in with "Professor" this and "Professor" that, bowing and scraping along with it. I had noticed that Dr. Halsted was getting a little bored, and I expected something to happen. Presently after one of these interruptions, he turned on the father and said in a very bored tone, "Oh, don't call me 'Professor.' I am no dancing master." From that time on the title of "The Professor" was permanently attached to Dr. Halsted. I think he did not like it, but that made no difference to the boys.

The members of his staff regretted that with few exceptions he could not establish an intimate personal relationship with them. His younger associates felt keenly the loss of his comradeship, and Dr. Halsted himself was heard to remark more than once that he wished he knew how to get as close to the individual members of his staff as, for instance, Dr. Osler appeared to be able to do with his. This atmosphere of aloofness with which Dr. Halsted surrounded himself was, I believe, largely temperamental and to a certain extent artificial, but he never seemed quite able to overcome it. No chief ever had more loyal or devoted followers than were the members of Dr. Halsted's staff, and if their genuine affection for him was not more demonstratively manifested, it was simply because they felt that he preferred it so.

Dr. Halsted was extremely particular in most things, and it was difficult at times to know just what to do when anything new came up for decision. I had learned early the kind of person he was and how to take him. As long as he felt that one was doing one's best, there was little comment, either praise or criticism. He was chary with both, but one always had this satisfaction, that so long as he had no comment to make one way or the other, one could be reasonably sure the work was satisfactory. However, Dr. Halsted was not by any means always an easy man to get along with. At times he was difficult and unreasonable, or so he appeared to some of his assistants. At least one of his Residents resigned and left because of inability to get along with him . . .

The same rules to a certain extent applied to the nurses. If Dr. Halsted liked a particular nurse, she usually got along pretty well. . . . the use of rubber gloves in surgical technique came about as a result of Dr. Halsted's interest in Miss Caroline Hampton, the operating room nurse, and his efforts to protect her hands from the antiseptic solutions then in use. His attention had been attracted to her because he recognized in her an efficient nurse, but this interest, at first entirely platonic, developed into affection and a courtship which the entire Surgical Staff watched with interest. After a time they were married, establishing a precedent to be followed later by other members of the staff, including myself . . .

Dr. Halsted was an adept in making sarcastic remarks. His sarcasm was sometimes so keen and subtle that the individual toward whom it was directed did not always fully appreciate it. He had one of the best "come-backs" of anyone whom I have known. Only once have I heard him fail to get the better of his adversary in such an exchange. The victorious party on that occasion was a little red-headed, snub-nosed nurse. The circumstances were of sufficient interest to relate here.

In the early days of the Hospital Dr. Halsted was in the habit of doing most of the surgical dressings himself. Ward rounds were formal affairs. On such occasions Dr. Halsted was attended by a retinue of staff members and nurses, who stood around at respectful attention while he was making the dressing. At that time he was fond of using the so-called crinoline, or starched, bandage for his dressings. He had developed a regular technique to be followed by the nurse: first wetting the bandage, then removing all loose threads from either end by winding them on her finger before handing it to the surgeon. Otherwise the loose threads were apt to get tangled up and interfere with the application of the bandage.

This time we were all standing around watching what was going on. The nurse had gone through the prescribed formula perfectly, and had handed Dr. Halsted the moistened bandage in proper fashion, but in putting on the bandage somehow or other one or two loose threads had developed and interfered with Dr. Halsted's application of the bandage. I could see that he was becoming more and more annoyed as he proceeded, and presently, when he became hopelessly entangled in the threads, he held up the bandage so that everybody could see it, and in very impressive fashion said, "In New York, where I was brought up surgically, a nurse would blush to hand a doctor a bandage such as this."

Quick as a flash the little nurse, with a toss of her head, exclaimed, "Ah, but we are more brazen than they!"

The effect was electrical. Dr. Halsted appeared stunned. I was standing just behind him and could see the blood mounting up to the bald spot on the top of his head until he became livid. He held the bandage for a moment or two, not knowing what to do or say, then quickly broke the loose threads and without a word finished applying the bandage as rapidly as possible. He then turned and walked out of the ward without completing his rounds. This was the only time I ever knew Dr. Halsted by word or deed to acknowledge defeat.

In an encounter of wits Dr. Halsted usually had the better of it. Once I had been called out of town, and my associate, Dr. Pancoast, had been called in the night to see a woman patient with an acute abdomen. He had not been able to make a definite diagnosis, and as she seemed to be quite ill, he sent her into the hospital. In the morning, her condition not having improved, he asked Dr. Halsted to see her in consultation with him. Neither of them was able to make a definite diagnosis, even after a careful physical examination. As I was due back shortly and the patient had asked for me originally, Dr. Pancoast decided that he would "pass the buck" to me and wait until I had seen her.

He called me up by telephone on my return and told me the situation. The patient, a middle-aged, unattractive woman (this fact is pertinent to the diagnosis), was a practical nurse. Dr. Pancoast said that her patient, whom she had nursed for some time, was a man who was a paralytic and bedridden. In answer to my questions as to her symptoms, he said she had given a history of having missed her period, and in order to bring it on again, had brewed herself a cup or two of tansey tea, and in addition had taken three compound cathartic pills before retiring. She had waked up during the night with sharp abdominal pain and diarrhea as a result of her medication, and after going to the toilet had fainted. Then, Dr. Pancoast explained, he had been sent for and found her in a condition of shock with a tense and tender abdomen.

"What is the diagnosis?" I asked Pancoast.

"Neither Dr. Halsted nor I could satisfy ourselves as to just what was the trouble," he replied.

"Pancoast," said I, "are you as innocent as you seem, or is this all a bluff?"

"What do you mean?"

"I mean just what I say." (This, of course, was all over the telephone).

"I don't understand you."

"Well," I said, "what was her object in brewing and taking several cups of tansey tea with the three compound cathartic pills?"

"Well," said Pancoast, "I don't know."

"Why," said I, "there could be but one reason, to re-establish her menstrual flow."

"We discussed that," said Pancoast, "but could not arrive at a definite conclusion. What do you think is the diagnosis?"

"Why, of course," said I, "there can be but one diagnosis; at least that was her diagnosis."

"What is that?" asked Pancoast.

"Why, a pregnancy," said I, "probably a ruptured tubal pregnancy."

"Oh! But you haven't yet seen the patient. Wait until you see her, and you'll agree that it can't be that."

"Well, I'll have to be shown. I'll be right along."

By the time I got there the picture had changed somewhat, and the patient now showed definite evidence of hemorrhage, pallor, rapid pulse, and sighing respiration. We took her to the operating room and operated as soon as possible, and found what I had suspected, a ruptured tubal pregnancy with the abdominal cavity filled with blood.

Dr. Halsted, when told by Dr. Pancoast that I had "made a diagnosis right away over the telephone without even seeing the patient," asked in astonishment, "Did Finney do that? Make a diagnosis right off over the telephone without seeing the patient?"

"He certainly did," said Pancoast.

"Well," said Dr. Halsted, "come to think it over, after all it isn't so astonishing as it might appear. Of course, you and I,

Pancoast, wouldn't be expected to know the significance of the administration of tansey tea and cathartics, but Finney, with his knowledge of the world, he would know." I might add that I don't claim any special credit for the diagnosis, it was too easy. . . .

During the last few years of Dr. Halsted's life, he developed attacks of severe pain in the chest and abdomen, which resembled very closely those of typical angina pectoris. He would be incapacitated for days at a time so that he could not even get over to the Hospital. Occasionally he would have an attack during an operation and would be compelled to stop and have the Resident finish it for him. He was a typical doctor-patient, for during all this time he would not consult a medical man. The only doctor he would see for a good while was Dr. Welch, who never had been a clinician.

He managed to get along this way for some time, feeling sure all the time that his attacks were anginal in character and that any one might be the last, until one day after an especially severe attack he developed jaundice. As this put a new interpretation on his attacks, he finally consented to have a physician, Dr. Thomas Boggs, called in. Dr. Boggs diagnosed the trouble at once as gall stones, and since the jaundice continued with increasing intensity, Dr. Halsted finally entered the Hospital and was operated on. This happened, much to my relief, while I was off on my summer vacation. Dr. Richard Follis performed the operation and found stones in the common duct. Considerable relief was afforded for a time by this operation, but subsequently the jaundice and pain returned, and a second operation was necessitated. This time Dr. George Heuer officiated, as I was again out of the city, and another stone was removed from the common duct. However, by this time Dr. Halsted's resistance had been so lowered by his illness that a post-operative pneumonia developed, from the effects of which he died on September 7, 1922.

In the death of Dr. Halsted surgery lost one of its most illustrious leaders. He was a great teacher and trainer of surgeons, and the founder of a distinct school. I feel I owe him as my chief a debt of gratitude that can never be paid. I have to thank him for whatever measure of success I may have attained in my chosen profession. He left a lasting imprint not only on the surgery of his own time, but of all time. Measured by all recognized professional standards, he was a great surgeon, but he was more than this. He was a great scientist and a great humanitarian as well. No one man possesses in his character all of the elements of greatness. Such a man would be a superman. Each individual in varying proportion has his elements of strength and weakness. Such is human nature. Dr. Halsted was only human, and like all mortals, he possessed characteristics of both. But to those who were privileged to work under him long enough to come really to know him, and to the chosen few of his intimates who were permitted to enter the inner circle of his life, he will always stand out in memory as the commanding figure that he was—teacher, investigator, master surgeon and benefactor of mankind . . .

Dr. Kelly came to Baltimore from Philadelphia, where already, while still a young man, he had made for himself a name in his chosen specialty of gynecology; indeed, it may be truthfully said that he put that specialty on the surgical map. When asked by President Gilman to suggest someone for the Chair of Gynecology at Hopkins, Dr. Osler is said to have replied in his characteristic manner that he was "backing a dark horse for the new post, the Kensington colt." Kensington was the Hospital that Dr. Kelly had started, first as a private hospital, in Philadelphia. It has since become the well-known Kensington Hospital for Women.

Dr. Kelly was known by his own Staff generally as "The Chief," but as that title had already been pre-empted by Dr. Osler, it did not spread to the members of the other services.

As a surgeon Dr. Kelly was the despair of those who watched his extraordinary operative technique. The facility with which he used his hands and handled his instruments, the assurance with which he successfully attacked and solved hitherto unsolved surgical problems, quickly established a reputation that drew visitors to the Hospital from all parts of this country and abroad. The skill and finesse with which he could perform the most difficult surgical procedures were astonishing. They were disheartening as well, for few could hope to equal him. He was one of the few surgeons whom I have known who could watch the clock while operating and get away with it. Ordinarily the patient suffers as a consequence of such a procedure, for the average surgeon, in his haste to beat the clock, is apt to slur over or omit some important detail of the operation. Not so with Dr. Kelly. His operations were models of skill and thoroughness as well as brevity.

His many contributions to his own specialties, gynecology, urology and abdominal surgery in general, have been epoch-making and have left for him a lasting name in the annals of surgery.

1940

From the Writings
of William Osler

THE MASTER WORD IN MEDICINE

I PROPOSE to tell you the secret of life as I have seen the game played, and as I have tried to play it myself. You remember in one of the Jungle Stories that when Mowgli wished to be avenged on the villagers he could only get the help of Hathi and his sons by sending them the master-word. This I propose to give you in the hope, yes, in the full assurance, that some of you at least will lay hold upon it to your profit. Though a little one, the master-word looms large in meaning. It is the open sesame to every portal, the great equalizer in the world, the true philosopher's stone, which transmutes all the base metal of humanity into gold. The stupid man among you it will make bright, the bright man brilliant, and the brilliant student steady. With the magic word in your heart all things are possible, and without it all study is vanity and vexation. The miracles of life are with it; the blind see by touch, the deaf hear with eyes, the dumb speak with fingers. To the youth it brings hope, to the middle-aged confidence, to the aged repose. True balm of hurt minds, in its presence the heart of the sorrowful is lightened and consoled. It is directly responsible for all advances in medicine during the past twenty-five centuries. Laying hold upon it Hippocrates made observation and science the warp and woof of our art. Galen so read its meaning that fifteen centuries stopped thinking, and slept until awakened by the *De Fabrica* of Vesalius, which is the very incarnation of the master-word. With its inspiration Harvey gave an impulse to a larger circulation than he wot of, an impulse which we feel to-day. Hunter sounded all its heights and depths, and stands out in our history as one of the great exemplars of its virtue. With it Virchow smote the rock, and the waters of progress gushed out;

while in the hands of Pasteur it proved a very talisman to open to us a new heaven in medicine and a new earth in surgery. Not only has it been the touchstone of progress, but it is the measure of success in every-day life. Not a man before you but is beholden to it for his position here, while he who addresses you has that honour directly in consequence of having had it graven on his heart when he was as you are to-day. And the master-word is *Work*, a little one, as I have said, but fraught with momentous consequences if you can but write it on the tablets of your hearts, and bind it upon your foreheads.

1903

PERSONAL IDEALS

I have three personal ideals. One, to do the day's work well and not to bother about the morrow. It has been urged that this is not a satisfactory ideal. It is; and there is not one which the student can carry with him into practice with greater effect. To it, more than anything else, I owe whatever success I have had—to this power of settling down to the day's work and trying to do it well to the best of one's ability, and letting the future take care of itself.

The second ideal has been to act the Golden Rule, as far as in me lay, towards my professional brethren and towards the patient committed to my care.

And the third has been to cultivate such measure of equanimity as would enable me to bear success with humility, the affection of my friends without pride, and to be ready when the day of sorrow and grief came, to meet it with courage befitting a man . . .

From "Farewell Address," May 2, 1905

BED-SIDE LIBRARY FOR MEDICAL STUDENTS

A liberal education may be had at a very slight cost of time and money. Well filled though the day be with appointed tasks, to make the best possible use of your one or of your ten talents, rest not satisfied with this professional training, but try to get the education, if not of a scholar, at least of a gentleman. Before going to sleep read for half an hour, and in the morning have a book open on your dressing table. You will be surprised to find how much can be accomplished in the course of a year. I have put down a list of ten books which you may make close friends. There are many others; studied carefully in your student days these will help in the inner education of which I speak.

    I. Old and New Testament.
   II. Shakespeare.
  III. Montaigne.
  IV. Plutarch's *Lives.*
   V. Marcus Aurelius.
  VI. Epictetus.
 VII. *Religio Medici.*
VIII. *Don Quixote.*
  IX. Emerson.
   X. Oliver Wendell Holmes—Breakfast-Table Series.

From Aequanimitas, edition of 1932

Medical Practice

HANS ZINSSER

HE LEARNS THAT IT TAKES MORE THAN PROFESSIONAL KNOWLEDGE TO MAKE A GOOD DOCTOR

FOR the young physician, there is no more painful experience than the sudden transition from the proud dignity of House Physician or House Surgeon to the desolate situation of young doctor without a practice. Yesterday, he was absolute ruler over two hundred patients. Assistants reported to him, laboratory workers carried out his orders, nurses rose when he entered a ward. There were, in my time, no residents between the Senior Interne and the Consulting Staff, and when the latter had made their daily rounds, the House Physician was the responsible head of an active service. The two happy years over, his last midnight rounds made on the last day of June or December, he woke up the following morning a man without a job.

In my case, I had entered medicine only with the eventual hope of becoming an investigator of infectious disease. But the fascination of practical medicine is a powerful one. Once in a hospital, the feeling of power, the contact with patients, the opportunities to console, to comfort, and—not infrequently—actually to help, made a deep appeal to all that is best in youngsters of that age. Moreover, in those days, laboratory opportunities were rare. The scientific departments of medical schools and hospitals were small, and budgets at a minimum. There was room for a very few only; and even if one obtained entrée to a well-equipped laboratory, the wages for a beginner ranged somewhat lower than those of a scullery maid—from two hundred and fifty to four hundred dollars a year.

True to my early determination, I applied for one of these positions in the Bacteriological Department of my old Medical School, which was presided over by two dignified, but stern gentlemen known to the students—because of their superior aloofness—as "The Jesi." The Jesi received me kindly, and after much questioning and careful scrutiny of my record gave me a job representing a good deal of work but no pay. It included, however, a working place, the use of apparatus, and a free hand to do as I pleased in my spare time. Together with this, I picked up another job, which yielded $400 a year in real money, as Bacteriologist to a hospital where I obtained, in addition, the title of Assistant Pathologist, unlimited pathological material, and the instruction of a man who was unusually erudite and a born teacher. These two jobs might easily have filled my time, but I was ambitious—I think quite properly—of contributing more adequately to my own support. For this reason, as well as because of a growing reluctance to lose all contact with practical medicine, I opened an office in West 80th Street, together with a classmate, K.

K. was a born doctor. He was somewhat older than I was, and appeared much older. He had the not unimportant asset of a blond moustache that looked as though it belonged to his face naturally, and not like the red and downy stage whiskers that were the best my face could bring forth on one or two vacations during which I had abjured the razor, hoping that I might look more like a doctor. K. was the kind of man to whom patients were drawn in admiring and confiding awe. He has amply proved all this since then, in his large practice in a New England city. Thanks to him, our office started with considerable éclat. Older physicians, knowing K.'s qualities, began to send him patients. What little I had to do, at first, was in the form of laboratory examinations. But every now and then, even I picked up a neighborhood emergency or some case that no one else wanted—chronic leg ulcers, delirium tremens, old people without money, and such.

It was dull, keeping office hours. When the doorbell did interrupt my one-handed chess game (I didn't dare to play the piano), it was more often than not a book agent, or someone visiting my wife, or the grocer delivering vegetables. At first, this was exciting. On the sound of the bell, I would put on my coat, straighten my necktie, and seat myself behind my desk with a serious expression. When it really was a patient, I didn't believe it until I had him safely sitting in my office, with the door closed and myself between him and the door.

My great fault, apart from my youthful appearance, was my excessive thoroughness. Most patients in those days wanted immediate directions and a prescription, after a bit of conversation. A physical examination they didn't mind if they felt very sick. But I never let it go at that.

The great Dr. J. had once said to me, after rounds on the private corridor: "My boy, you seem to know your stuff; but you'll never make a good doctor unless you pay a little more attention to the psychology of your patients. Now, that last woman is a damn fool. There's nothing much the matter with her, but she wants to be taken seriously. All patients, especially women, expect the doctor to act as though they were really sick—but bearing up bravely. Never act as though you took them lightly, and never seem in a hurry. Whatever else you may not do, never fail to sit down in the sick room as though all your time were for this particular case. Pat the hand, and say 'Brave little woman,' or something like that. Act thoughtful; and if you don't know what to say, say nothing; but say nothing deliberately and slowly, with an air of withholding a great deal. Then give them a good overhauling, with a lot of laboratory examinations."

This might have worked with the Fifth Avenue practice that crowded Dr. J.'s office. It is also possible that I overdid it. Anyway, I lost the few good patients that were referred to me, by just this technique.

First, I sat them down and looked at them penetratingly. Then, pad in hand, I began to ask them questions. The patient might be bursting to tell me about a pain in his foot. "Just a minute, just a minute! We'll get to that presently," I'd say. Then, still fixing him with an accusing eye, I'd begin to ask questions. "Taking the history," we called it.

"How old are you? What is your occupation? Were your parents healthy? Is there any tuberculosis in your family? What did your father die of? And your mother? How old were they when they died? Have you any brothers or sisters? Are they healthy? Have you had any children? Are they healthy? Have you ever had any venereal disease? What! Are you sure? Do you drink? How much? Do you sleep well? How is your appetite? Do you sweat at night?"

By this time, many of them showed signs of fatigue or indignation. Some of them asked for a drink of water. But I gazed at them with disapproving severity, and began on their childhood.

"What diseases did you have as a child? Were you precocious? Did you ever notice any swollen glands in the neck? Were you premature? Did you ever have a rash on your skin? Do your bowels move regularly? Do you have to take medicine for it? What do you take? Do you suffer from colds? Do you cough in the morning? Do you bring up anything when you cough? Do you have to get up at night?"

All the time, I was taking notes. If any of the answers were unfavorable, I would appear to prick up my ears—the patient could see it in my face. Some began to look anxious. One got up and left at this point, the best prospect I had—she had driven up in a victoria. Old Dr. "Monkey" Jackson had told her I was a very thorough youngster. She believed it, but didn't like it in practice.

Those that lasted that long I would then proceed to examine. First, down the throat with a light and a hand mirror. The tongue was pushed down. "Say Eeeeh!"[1] They gagged. Then into the ears with a speculum. Then up the nose, ditto. And the ophthalmoscope! I was proud of that. It had cost twenty-five dollars, and I could see the eye grounds with it. It might disclose bad kidney, or diabetes. Then, "Will you undress, please?" The heart—thump, thump! I outlined it with a blue pencil. The stethoscope. No murmurs. The lungs. "Say one, two, three. Again! Whisper ninety-nine, ninety-nine. Well, fine! That's all right."

"But, doctor—"

"Lie on this couch, please. Pull up your knees." I percussed the liver. I pushed for the spleen. I palpated the gall bladder, and McBurney's point, and the ovaries. "Does that hurt?"

"You push so hard, doctor."

[1] The force of habit is powerful. A friend of mine, a throat specialist, was called upon to make a rectal examination in a case of lues of the larynx. He exclaimed, "Say Eeeeh!" while gazing at the wrong aperture, and lost a wealthy patient who thought him flippant.

"You can dress now. But first, step behind that screen and let me have a specimen of the urine."

Meanwhile, I'd be getting my things ready to take blood. A drop from the ear, for cell counts and a differential. A syringe, for the vein. I had just learned to do the Wassermann reaction. It was great fun, and I was proud of it. Every case must have a Wassermann done. No one tells the truth about such things.

Few lasted through. Those few got their money's worth—largely, perhaps, because they never paid my modest bills. Most of them walked out at one stage or another, because we didn't get down to the sore foot. Some even slammed the door as they walked out.

This was unquestionably the wrong technique, certainly for a young practitioner. K. was wiser. He allowed the patient to unburden himself, asked a few pertinent questions, examined as far as necessary, and prescribed.

Some years later, in a very busy office in a provincial town, a colleague showed me a large bottle into which all the left-over remains of dispensed mixtures were spilled together. In that town, twenty years ago, the doctors still dispensed their own medicines. The big bottle was marked "Bill Kelly," after a patient who was an insatiable medicine tippler. When anyone who had nothing obvious the matter with him, but had a lot of symptoms to show for it, came in, he was given a four-ounce bottle filled from "Bill Kelly," to take a teaspoonful three times a day, after meals. It tasted atrociously and, of course, was different every day. But it cured a lot of cases.

Apropos of medicine tippling, the elevator boy in my apartment, who also cleaned out the wastepaper baskets, used to take all the medicine that came to me from drug houses as samples. I found on one occasion that he had swallowed a quart of a preparation that was recommended for irregular menstrual periods. He said it made him feel fine.

We "fired" a negro cook at this time who left behind such a dirty kitchen that, being still young and helpful, I decided to clean it out myself. In a closet I found a whole case of empty bottles labeled: "Stimulates the reproductive organs and prevents tumors." I never found out for which of these effects she was dosing herself. It smelled like bad whiskey. Thus have some of our largest American fortunes been acquired.

The old practitioner adapts his method to the situation, with psychological insight. Dr. J., who gave me all that advice about making a big fuss over every patient, did not follow this out with all of them by any means. His assistant, who occasionally sent me a case, told me of an old lady who had come to Dr. J. faithfully, twice a year, for twenty years or more. When admitted to the inner sanctum, she never gave the doctor a chance to say even "How do you do?" She burst into the room with a "Now, doctor—don't move. I don't want you to examine me. Don't ask me any questions. Just write me a prescription for that brown tonic you gave me last year." She always got it, paid her money, and went out satisfied. Another, a younger woman who adored Dr. J., —as most of them did,—he dismissed one day, after a short conversation and a look at her tongue, saying: "Don't worry, my dear. You'll be all right. Just keep your bowels open and always wear mauve."

I might, of course, have learned this sort of thing if I had stuck at it long enough. But in the two years that I was a private practitioner I never got over the fear that if I didn't go into every possibility I might be overlooking some hidden danger that hung over my patient's unsuspecting head. And often the patient, who may have come in for the simplest kind of advice, sensed my own nervousness and rushed off to another physician for just the kind of overhauling I was about to give him.

Nevertheless, my method was professionally correct—if I had only been more adroit about it. It certainly saved me from the kind of thing that happened to a friend of mine who leaned rather too much toward "snap diagnosis." A middle-aged man, a coachman, came to see him one day, complaining of a stiffness and soreness in the throat. My friend looked into his mouth, saw a little redness, and prescribed a gargle. The next day, the man was back. His throat was still sore, and much more stiff on swallowing. Again the look in, a painting of the throat with iodine in glycerine, and a reassuring pat on the back. Two days went by, and back came the coachman. This time, he said he had difficulty in opening his mouth for examination. "You know, doctor," he said, "if you didn't say I was all right, I'd think I might have lockjaw." "Good God, man!" cried my friend in consternation. "Why didn't you tell me that in the first place?" ...

I had done my reluctant duty as an accoucheur with a considerable number of ambulance and hospital babies, and felt that I had mastered at least the first principle, the Fabian strategy of "watch and wait," with reasonable skill in the rudiments of manipulation. There is quite a difference, psychologically at any rate,—which the institutionalized doctor will never understand,—between that sort of thing and handling one's first private case.

Obstetrics is not the pleasantest of medical occupations, although it pays well and is one of the things that the young physician with any kind of practice can count on as a financial backlog. Yet it takes a great deal of time and means a lot of night work. While the statement may not be statistically correct, it does seem to the medical man as though the large majority of all babies were born at night. An observant medical student in my class once asked one of our instructors about this. "Dr. V., why is it that most children are born at night?" Dr. V., who was something of a wag, replied: "Well, my boy, that's simple. It takes just nine months." . . .

My own first obstetrical case . . . was sent me by a colleague who was still himself taking all the obstetrics that came to him with money. Those who had little or nothing and wouldn't go to a hospital, he referred "for experience," as he called it, to beginners like myself. This one lived in a two-family frame house in East 173rd Street. My office was in 80th Street on the West Side. There were no automobiles—and if there had been, I could not have afforded one. To make my visits, I had to take the streetcar from 80th Street to 59th Street, another one across to the Third Avenue Elevated Railroad and proceed on this to 166th Street, whence I walked north and west fifteen minutes up a steep hill. I mention these details because the case, a "first delivery," was very nervous, although not more so than I was myself. In consequence, there were a great many false alarms during the two weeks preceding the actual event. Every time there was the slightest twinge, the grandfather was sent out to the neighboring drugstore to call me on the telephone. His usual formula was, "I don't think it's anything, but maybe you'd better come up." I made three round trips within twenty-four hours a week before the child was born. The unusual thing about the case was that both father and mother were deaf and dumb. They spoke to each other with their hands, making weird sea-lion noises, and it was only from the expressions on their faces that I could gather that I seemed far too young, that they didn't think much of me anyway, but that they couldn't afford anything better. When there was finally no doubt that things were beginning to happen, they were very much frightened; and the gesticulations and the noises of animal panic added to my tension. During the last forty-eight hours, I canceled all other engagements and lived there, snatching an occasional nap on a horsehair sofa that seemed stuffed with steel wire and had leaked. In the early stages, when pains were not too frequent, I soothed my disturbed nerves by walking around the block, accompanied by the grandfather. He—good man—was much sorrier for me than he was for his daughter, and consoled me by saying: "Now, doctor, don't worry. Everything's going to come out all right. There've been lots of babies in our family, and nothing ever happened." Towards the end, I felt that the final stage was lasting much too long. I prepared a forceps by boiling it on the kitchen stove, and then went out to telephone to K. to come up and help me. He was out. It took five or six telephone calls in various directions to locate him. When I finally got back to the house, I was met in the hall by the beaming grandfather, who said: "Hurrah, doctor! It's a fine big boy! He was born about five minutes after you left."

When I made up my books, such as they were, I found that I had averaged about twenty-three cents a call on this case. Each trip back and forth cost me thirty cents in carfare. . . .

Early in my medical career I developed a deep and lasting admiration for the old-fashioned, self-reliant country practitioner, the "horse and buggy doctor" so sympathetically described in the recent book by Dr. Hertzler. While a medical student in New York, I was accustomed to recuperate from strenuous days and nights under a lamp by spending occasional week ends on my father's farm in Westchester County. I slept in a cold house, with a wood stove in my bedroom, stoked till the lid glowed red, with my collie dog keeping my feet warm. All day and into the night I would ride the horses—each one in turn—across country over the snow-covered hills. Those were unforgettably lovely vacations. The utter loneliness of the big house (the farmer lived at the other end of a beech wood), the nights silent except for the cracking of the frozen branches of the big trees in the wind, the brittleness of the air and the incandescent brilliance of the stars! And the rides! Physical fitness that could spend itself on three successive unexercised horses, and the spiritual peace that only a good horse or a small boat at sea can give—the white landscape, woods and fields crisp, cold, and lifeless except for the silent testimony of tracks in the snow, an occasional squirrel and, once in a while, a flock of crows angrily clamoring away from a leafless perch. I knew all the paths and openings and the hidden spots in the birch woods where, in the summers, I hunted birds; where the foxes went to earth; and where, among the big rocks on Piano Mountain, one could get a glimpse of the Hudson. I still remember those rides as among the happiest gifts of a Providence that has been munificent. Often, galloping through the fields and across the hills between snowbound villages, I would see far off on the valley roads the familiar "cutter" sleighs of our local doctors—Jenkins and Hart—answering calls that often meant hours of driving and small fees, irrespective of roads or weather, with an unfailing and expected fidelity not demanded of the rural delivery. Sometimes I would meet one of them, whiskers frosted, nose red and dripping, with not much more showing than these between the fur cap and the muffler. Always they stopped for a chat, to tell me about the case and exchange medical gossip—for they treated me as a professional equal who was getting things they wished they had time to catch up with. For their difficulties made them modest; whereas I, with the arrogance of a young and silly student (arrogance, being a state of mind, I have noticed is always intensified by sitting a horse), was just a trace patronizing. I lost all that as a matter of course when I tried to practise by myself. But a good deal of it was jarred out of me by the episode of Dr. Kerr.

Dr. Kerr is now dead. He is probably forgotten by all but a few old farmers' wives. He had neither fame nor more than a frugal living. He was probably unhappy, while he lived, not for the reasons mentioned, but because he never could do for his people as much as he wanted to do. He practised in St. Lawrence County, near Chippewa Bay. His office was a little surgery extension of a small village house. He was tall, thin, and very dark, with hairy wrists, a big nose, a bushy moustache, and kind, tired brown eyes. I was camping on my island in the bay and was known to the grocer in the village as a young doctor from New York. One day at about 4 A.M. a motorboat approaching my island aroused me and the grocer's son shouted through the fog and drizzle that Dr. Kerr needed my help in a difficult case. He landed while I dressed, and we were off four miles to the village. There Dr. Kerr was waiting for me with his buggy. I had never seen him before and he impressed me, in my young self-confidence, as probably a poor country bonesetter whom I would have to show how a case should be handled. This, however, lasted only until we were bumping along a muddy country lane and he had begun to tell me about the patient.

It was a woman, a farm hand's wife, who was having her first baby. She had developed eclampsia seven months along, and the child had died. She was having convulsions. The problem was to deliver the dead baby from a uterus with an undistended cervix, and the mother dangerously toxic. At this point, I was thoroughly scared. I had had training at the Sloane Maternity, but this was a "high forceps" under difficulties, a case for Professor Cragin in a well-equipped operating room, with an assistant and two or three nurses.

We drove about four miles into the river flats. I could see the little unpainted cottage next to a haystack a mile away. I offered no suggestion while I was trying to recover my old ambulance courage. He didn't ask me any questions.

The place was a picture of abject poverty. The husband, a pathetic little bandy-legged, redheaded fellow in torn overalls, was waiting at the door, anxious and silent. The kitchen was a mess from his efforts at housekeeping. In the next room the woman, half-conscious, her bloated face twitching, lay on a dirty double bed, on a mattress without sheets under an old quilt half kicked off, leaving her almost naked.

While I stood looking at her with frightened sympathy, Dr. Kerr unpacked his bag. Without asking me to do anything, he filled a wash boiler with hot water from a kettle, added a little lysol, and put on his forceps to boil. Then he took off his coat, rolled up his sleeves, filled a basin, and began to soap and lysol his hands. Not until he was doing this did he speak.

Then he began to give me directions. In a few minutes I was cleaning up the patient, spreading clean towels under her, preparing a chloroform cone and jumping at his words as though in Dr. Cragin's clinic. With no essential help from me, he performed as neat a cervix dilation and forceps delivery as I had ever seen. When, after the long and arduous task, with everything complete as possible, he began to clean up, he didn't even thank me. He took it for granted that, being a doctor and being in the neighborhood, I was on call. It was his only compliment, except for a friendly smile.

He asked me to stay there the rest of the day while he made his rounds, gave me a few directions, and left a sedative. Then he went out, patted the husband on the back, and drove away. The woman recovered. Dr. Kerr, I heard later, spent the first two nights after this on a rocking chair, drinking cider with the husband, and napping when he could. His fee, I also heard, accepted to please the husband, was a peck of potatoes.

Some time later, I had occasion to ask him to open a boil on my neck. He sat me down in a chair, wiped my neck with alcohol, took a knife out of a little leather case, wiped that with alcohol, and let me have it. I made no suggestion whatever. I saw him often after that, and I sincerely hope—even now—that he liked me.

One of Dr. Kerr's colleagues from up near Ogdensburg, whom I had met at this time, did a most extraordinary thing. I met him on the river one day when we were both fishing off the head of Watch Island. Just as I came in sight of him as I rounded the point, he pulled out a magnificent pickerel.

"Good for you, doctor!" I shouted to him.

"What d'ye think, young feller?" he called back. "I caught that fish with a nice fat appendix I took out this mornin'."

Speaking of Dr. T. reminds me of a case in which I was credited with saving a life under peculiar circumstances. While still House Physician at the hospital, during Dr. T.'s visiting period, we had a poor fellow on the male ward who appeared to suffer from advanced nephritis. Dr. T., as I have remarked, was a virtuoso at compounding drugs. During his short annual reign of three months, the order sheets of every patient were covered with the red ink in which medication orders were entered. They got something or other "t.i.d." (three times a day), other things with meals, something else on waking up, another before the lights went out, and a few odd pills or injections "p.r.n." (*pro re nata*). Many of them had to be waked out of sound sleep to get one of his "black draughts" or "blue pills" or "brown decoctions"—all of them proudly originated by the Chief himself, and most of them quite complicated, with strong medicaments. The particular old boy of whom I write was getting a formidable sequence of daily doses and was slipping out of our hands—taking it patiently, with good humor and courage. We all liked him, and during his month on the ward he became a favorite. One night, when he was pretty low, I was making my midnight rounds with the ward nurse. We stopped at his bed and held a whispered conversation. He was in bad condition, the nurse said, and she didn't think he'd last long. She hated to force all that medicine down his throat. It bothered him and didn't seem to be doing him any good.

"All right," I said. "He's going to die soon anyway, and we'll stop all medication. Just leave the orders on the chart, and we'll steer the old boy around him as well as we can. Give him anything he wants to eat, within reason, and a shot of my Scotch when you come on at night. I'll bring you a bottle. He might as well die happy."

From that moment, our friend began to improve. Pretty soon, by respectful and adroit suggestion, I arranged to have official sanction for the omission of one pill and "draught" after another. In two weeks our patient began to sit up in bed for extraordinarily hearty meals. In three weeks he was up—his old self, he said. In four, he was out and I forgot about him.

The sequel came one Sunday afternoon during the following winter, when I was sitting in my office. The doorbell rang, and in walked a short, fat, ruddy man of about sixty, behind him a shorter, fatter, and ruddier boy of twenty or so. Neither of them did I recognize. Yet the older man stuck out his ham of a hand and said: "God bless you, doctor, how are you?" Then I suddenly remembered him. "I hope you're not sick again," I said.

"Oh, no, doctor! I'm fine. I just brought in my son" (who, apparently in the horse business, was embarrassedly rolling a flat-topped derby in one hand while he kept adjusting a white piqué tie with a horseshoe pin) "to show him the man who saved my life. You remember, doctor, that night in the hospital when I was nigh dead? You came around about midnight with the nurse. I was feelin' awful low, an' everybody thought I was goin' to die. I was thinkin' so my own self. You thought I was sleepin', but I wasn't. I was just pretendin'. You had a long talk with the nurse in front of my bed an' then you give her some orders. From that minute, I begun to mend.

"This is the man, my boy, as pulled your Pa out of the claws of the Reaper," he said poetically.

I was at that time beginning to become deeply interested in that disease which is called by a venerable French writer "*une punition divinement envoyée aux hommes et aux femmes pour leur paillardises et incontinences désordonnées*"; by Sytz of

Pforzheim, on the other hand, "*die bösen Franzosen*"; and by Goethe, with his prophetic vision,—considering the wormlike appearance of the *Treponema pallidum,—"der Wurm in der Liebe.*" I was to spend a number of subsequent years on this malady, in an effort to gain insight into the properties of the strange microorganism which the great Schaudinn had discovered. For the time being, I was engaged in introducing the so-called "Wassermann reaction" into the laboratory practice of St. Luke's Hospital. This reaction, in its original form, was based on a principle too technical for these pages, established by the Belgian bacteriologist, Bordet, and taught to me, out of the kindness of his heart, by my friend Noguchi, in whose room at the Rockefeller Institute I sat for hours to pick up what I could. According to the old technique, one of the reagents required for this reaction was tissue from heavily infected syphilitic organs. And the most heavily infected organs known to medicine are those of stillborn, syphilitic babies.

Accordingly, I had a standing order at the Sloane Maternity Hospital that syphilitic babies were to be kept for me. And whenever one of these coveted treasures appeared, it was put into a large paper bag on which my name was written, and I was notified by telephone. I would then stop at the hospital on my afternoon journey to St. Luke's, tuck my prize under my arm, and proceed.

On the occasion of which I write, I received the happy news that "one of your babies," as the facetious head nurse called them, was ready for me. I was just about to leave my laboratory for a luncheon meeting of the newly formed Society for Cancer Research, which was to take place at a downtown hotel. It was only natural, therefore, since I was due at the hospital after this meeting, that I should stop to pick up my baby and take it to the meeting with me.

The society was not a large one. At the hotel, therefore, a convenient bedroom had been assigned for hats and coats. Arriving late, I shoved my paper bag under the bed, laid hat and coat on top of the bed, and went to my place at the table. It was not a very thrilling meeting. There were hardly any ideas, and those there were were neither new nor very intelligent. But I was very young, and proud of being present; and I listened to every word spoken by my elders with hopeful attention. One or two of the speeches were needlessly long. And when the meeting broke up I found that I was at least an hour behind my usual schedule. I rushed to the improvised cloakroom, picked up my hat and coat, and ran out to the subway. I had an incubatorful of work waiting for me, an autopsy to perform, and cultures to examine. Toward the end of the afternoon, an interesting case turned up on one of the wards, and I was asked to make several examinations, including a blood culture. It was not until 8 P.M. that I got home to a late supper, and not until 8:15 that suddenly, gazing into my soup, I exclaimed, "Good God—the baby!" When I remembered that my name was plainly written on the bag, I began to sweat. My appetite left me. It was not easy to decide what to do. I still remember to this day the number of the room. It was 217. I couldn't very well call up the clerk and say: "Look here—I forgot a dead baby under the bed at 217. Take care of it for me." If I went down there, what could I say? On the other hand, I couldn't very well leave the baby where it was, if only for aesthetic reasons. Yet if my name—good God!—had not been on the bag, this is what—in the state I was in—I might have done. It would have made a first-rate police mystery, and in the end, with sufficient publicity, might even have proved amusing. However, my name was on the bag. By this time it was 8:30.

I got into a cab and went down to the hotel. It needed all the little courage I had left to address the room clerk. I tried to be what is called nonchalant.

"I wonder whether you could let me go up to room 217," I said to the young man at the desk. "I was at the cancer meeting to-day, and I left something behind when I took my hat and coat out of that room."

The clerk, I thought, didn't seem to like my looks. Perhaps it was just my nervousness. He said that if anything had been left behind, it would have been reported by the chambermaid who had cleaned up. What was it I'd forgotten, anyway? "A package," I called it.

"Hey, Miss White," he called over his shoulder. "Was a package reported left in 217 this afternoon?"

Miss White, who sat behind a glass partition, fumbled about in a pigeonhole, read three or four paper slips, and said: "No. Nothing reported to me."

Could I see the chambermaid? It was a very important package.

"She went off duty at seven. Back in the morning."

Could I go up and have a look around the room?

"The room's been taken."

Could I ask the people now in it to let me look around?

He guessed "they went out to the theatre. Young couple from Milwaukee."

I had not stopped sweating, but now I sweated harder. The clerk looked at me suspiciously, I thought. "May I ask who you are?"

I told him. I looked pretty young for a doctor. Obviously, he didn't believe me.

"Do you mind if I call up the room and see if they're in?"

Reluctantly, he consented. Their name was Richards.

"Hello, is this Mr. Richards?" I asked.

"What do you want?" answered an excited voice.

Here I made another mistake. I should have explained what I wanted; but all I could think of was to get into that room.

"May I come up to see you a minute?"

I heard a whispered conversation,—"Ask him who it is,"—then:—

"Who are you?"

"You don't know me." I said the wrong thing again. "I just want to see you a minute." He hung up abruptly.

"He told me to come up," I reported to the clerk, and went right up. I didn't bother about the elevator, and I went three steps at a time. I knocked at the door of 217.

"Who's there?"

"It's the man who called you on the telephone."

"What do you want?"

The door was opened a crack and I saw the pale face of a frightened man with a chin beard. I shoved my foot against the crack. He pushed, but couldn't close the door.

"Better let him in, Frank. We can prove we're innocent," I heard in a woman's voice.

We stared at each other through the crack. "Stop pushing," said the man. "Don't resist him, Frank"—the woman's voice. Frank weakened. The door opened, and I slipped in.

On the bed sat a stout woman in a kimono. She was quite handsome, I noticed later, but now there were signs of recent tears and her hair was in disorder. She stared at me. At her feet on the floor was my bag. She looked at it and shuddered.

I turned and closed the door. The bellboy had followed me up. I could hear him in the hall. As I turned around, the husband confronted me. He was in his shirt sleeves, suspenders hanging.

His chin whiskers stood out like the hair on the back of a frightened cat.

"Look here," he said, "we can explain all this, though you may not believe it."

"Good Lord, man, there's nothing for *you* to explain."

They hadn't seen the name on the bag.

"Do you mind if I sit down?"—my knees were shaky. I told them my story. As I told it, I could see them gradually relax. Then, as I finished, Mrs. Richards began to laugh. First she laughed silently, with her face only. Then she began to make a noise, and the laughter spread down to her shoulders and chest. Then her whole body began to laugh, and she shrieked. She fell backward on the bed, writhing and shaking as though in a convulsion, stuffing the pillow into her mouth. Then her husband began to laugh. He leaned against the door, and his big shoulders made it rattle. At first, I didn't know whether to laugh or to cry. Then I laughed. We tried to speak, but we couldn't. There were tears in our eyes, and every time one of us stopped laughing, the sight of the others started it over again. Finally, we recovered, and Mr. Richards ordered a round of highballs. When I left, we were old friends but every time they looked at me, they started to chuckle.

As I walked out of the hotel with my "package" under my arm, I felt the clerk's eyes boring into my back. But now I didn't care. I took the subway to the hospital, clutching my baby, and—once there—I put it into the ice box.

I heard from the Richardses a year later. They had a real baby of their own. I still hear from them from time to time. They are among my most grateful patients.

My private practice did not grow. At the end of the first year my collections had amounted to about eleven hundred dollars, my uncollected bills to almost the same sum. My expenses had been about six thousand. Probably I would never have made a successful practitioner. My heart was in the laboratory. And when I was offered a full-time position in the Bacteriological Department of the University, I jumped at the chance, and felt that my true career had begun.

1939

Leprosy in the Philippines

VICTOR HEISER

HUNDREDS of thousands of lepers still exist throughout the world as social pariahs, thrust out of society because they have, through no fault of their own, contracted a repulsive disease. Far beyond their physical suffering is their terrible mental anguish. No criminal condemned to solitary confinement is confronted with such torture and loneliness. Shunned by friends and acquaintances, who are in terror of even coming within speaking distance, the unfortunate victims soon find themselves alone in a world in which they have no part. The few who come in contact with lepers instinctively draw back from them, so that normal social relationship dies at birth. Patients, when avoided by everybody, sit idle and brood; a human being devoid of hope is the most terrible object in the world.

The treatment of cases of leprosy today is sometimes as inhuman as in former times. In India a leper is often cast out by his own relatives, and has to go to the government for relief. The Karo-Bataks of the East Coast of Sumatra expel a leper from their villages, and at night surround and set fire to his hut, burning him alive. The Yakuts of Siberia, in their great terror of leprosy, force the leper to leave the community, and he must henceforth live alone unless he finds some other leper to keep him company.

Even in the United States lepers have not always been treated kindly. The people of a West Virginia town, when they once found a leper, placed him in a box car and nailed the door shut. The train departed. It was in the middle of winter, and before the door was finally opened, the man had starved and frozen to death. . . .

Leprosy never breaks fresh ground unless it has been introduced from without by a leper; and a sure and safe way of stamping it out is by isolation. For example, lepers were unknown in Hawaii until 1859, but thirty-two years later one out of thirty of the population was leprous. A Chinese introduced the disease into New Caledonia in 1865, and four thousand cases grew up in twenty-three years. The first instance in the Loyalty Islands was in 1882, and on one tiny islet six years later there were seventy cases. . . .

Leprosy begins insidiously, progresses slowly, and may last for twenty or thirty years. Aretaeus, a Greek physician of Cappadocia who came to Rome in the First Century A.D., wrote an account of the disease which holds true today:

> "Shining tubercles of different size, dusky red or livid in color, on face, ears and extremities, together with a thickened and rugous state of the skin, a diminution or total loss of its sensibility, and a falling off of all the hair except that of the scalp. The alae of the nose become swollen, the nostrils dilate, the lips are tumid; the external ears, especially the lobes, are enlarged and thickened and beset with tubercles; the skin of the cheek and of the forehead grows thick and tumid and forms large and prominent rugae, especially over the eyes; the hair of the eyebrows, beard, pubes, and axillae falls off; the voice becomes hoarse and obscure, and the sensibility of the parts affected is obtuse or totally abolished, so that pinching or puncturing gives no uneasiness. This disfiguration of the countenance suggests the idea of the features of a satyr, or wild beast, hence the disease is, by some, called satyriasis, or by others leontiasis. As the malady proceeds, the tubercles crack and ultimately ulcerate. Ulcerations also appear in the throat and nose, which sometimes destroy the palate and septum, the nose falls, and the breath is intolerably offensive; the fingers and toes gangrene, and separate joint after joint."

Anesthesia among lepers is extremely common. I have often seen a lighted cigarette burning into the fingers of a leper without his being at all aware of it. Even the odor of burning flesh did not attract his attention because the sense of smell was also gone.

Anesthetic leprosy attacks the trophic nerves, which carry impulses throughout the body, causing the blood to bring essential elements to damaged tissue. Ordinarily, if the fingers of a well person are merely drawn across a piece of paper, a few surface cells of the skin are rubbed off. But nature telegraphs by means of these trophic nerves to headquarters that tissue has been removed, and at once the blood supply opens, the repair is made, and the hand heals. But this telegraph system in lepers is completely out of order. Nature is not aware that any cells have been removed, and the result is they are not replaced, but are gone forever.

Lepers frequently have worn their hands down until they are no more than bats.

Wounds in anesthetic cases heal with great difficulty. A slight injury, such as caused by running a thorn in the foot, often starts an unhealable ulcer that produces a deep hole and discharges foul pus. We keep such wounds dressed and try to make them bleed, but the ulcers often become so bad that the bone is exposed and the feet often have to be amputated. A characteristic lesion is interosseous atrophy, where the tissue between the bones at the back of the hand is absorbed.

The anesthesia is not accompanied by paralysis, because the motor nerves are not affected and still retain their functions. The nerves of the eye are sometimes attacked, often resulting in frightful suffering from iritis. The larynx may be affected and the voice becomes hoarse.

Leprosy is horrible to live with and difficult to die with. Death seldom comes unless from some other cause. The average life of a leper is probably about ten years after the disease first becomes apparent. At Culion a pathological survey of the causes of death showed that twenty-four percent died of tuberculosis and sixteen percent of nephritis. The mortality at the colony was high, but it was believed to be materially lower than it would have been among these people in their homes. Many of them had been beggars and wholly dependent upon public charity for their living. The great majority of cases during the early years were so far advanced when admitted that they were practically beyond human aid.

There are usually two male for one female leper. Why this is so no one has been able to tell. When I visited any leper colony for the first time, I used to ask, "How many men have you?"

"We have two hundred."

"Then you have one hundred women."

The invariable reply was, "Yes."

Gerhard Armauer Hansen, a Norwegian doctor of Bergen, in the early 1870's first proved leprosy due to a bacillus. This microbe, which usually grows in bundles of rectilinear sticks resembling the Chinese puzzle, is too small to be seen with the naked eye. Whenever this bacillus can be demonstrated in the tissues, it may be stated beyond question that leprosy is present. Scientists have tried to advance the study of leprosy by attempting to transmit it to guinea pigs, Japanese dancing mice, rats, and monkeys, but without success because no animal contracts it. They have also attempted to isolate and cultivate the lepra bacillus in the test tube. Many have claimed to have succeeded, but their claims so far are open to question because the experiment could not be satisfactorily repeated by others. . . .

When I became Director of Health of the Philippines I realized that one of my most important duties would be to isolate the lepers whose numbers were estimated anywhere from ten to thirty thousand, although officially a little less than four thousand were recorded. There were twelve hundred new cases developing every year and practically nothing was being done about them.

Segregation is always cruel. We did not want to separate husband and wife or children and parents. But segregation is cruel to relatively few whereas non-segregation threatens an entire people. I believed that isolation not only protected others from contracting leprosy but, furthermore, was the most humane solution for the leper himself. Instead of being shunned and rebuffed by the world, he could have an opportunity to associate with others of his kind in pleasant relationship. In the Philippines the lepers were sensitive and proud and quick to notice any infringement upon their human rights.

Among the Filipinos family ties are unbelievably strong. Every step would have to be taken most tactfully; otherwise the Filipinos would conceal their lepers, or even actively oppose segregation. First, the colony would have to be prepared, and, then, the Islanders would have to be educated to the benefits of the plan.

Almost at the very inception of the civil government, negotiations had been carried on which led to the setting aside of Culion Island for a leper colony. Culion is one of the Calamianes group between the Sulu and China Seas, two hundred miles southwest of Manila. It is twenty miles long and twelve miles at its widest point. The population was then about eight hundred; more than half were harmless, wild Tagbuanas, without fixed abode or title to land beyond that of possession. Outside the town of Culion there were only eight small houses. . . .

The problem of Culion was one of the most arduous which faced me when I took office. I became wholly responsible for the undertaking, which proved more difficult than I could ever have anticipated, even in my wildest dreams. The actual building began in 1905. Every imaginable type of social question presented itself. Not only houses and a hospital had to be constructed and separate quarters for the non-lepers built, but streets had to be laid out, wharves constructed, buoys planted, a sewer system installed, amusement halls and a postoffice planned. Arrangements had to be made for public order, for municipal ordinances, for banking, and for disinfecting letters. . . .

In May, 1906, we prepared to transfer the three hundred and sixty-five inmates of the San Lazaro Hospital at Cebu to Culion. Often, before and afterwards, we had to contend with fear. A government boat had been set aside for the purpose, but as we were about to sail the entire crew deserted. Only the chief engineer and the skipper, a Maine Yankee named Tom Hilgrove stuck to the ship. Even after a new crew had, with great pains, been assembled, I had qualms about setting forth over the treacherous waters of the China Sea, because the skipper had fortified himself with such huge quantities of alcohol. But he was so good a navigator that he was equal to all emergencies, and we arrived safely at Culion, where Father Valles, a Jesuit priest, and four Sisters of the order of St. Paul de Chartres were on hand to receive the lepers.

I wanted to popularize Culion so that the lepers who were at large would come there willingly. I had photographs taken of the colony, and even moving picture reels made, a great achievement in those days, showing how attractive it was. I invited leaders of public thought to come to the Island, trusting they would write home about it to their friends. Agents were sent to the various towns to explain the purpose of Culion, and tell the lepers what they would find there, the type of house they woud live in, the food they would eat, and the facilities for treatment. The Filipino is cautious, and not many came at first. But those who were persuaded found they were much better off than at home. The first two years we received enough volunteers to tax all our resources. . . .

In the early days the very word leprosy struck unreasoning terror into the hearts of those suspected, and a number went into hiding. There was a young leper girl in Cebu whom the local authorities were never able to produce when we arrived. Finally her brother was stricken and taken to Culion. On our next visit she gave herself up voluntarily. When I asked her how she had eluded us so long, she explained that the telegraph operator was her friend, and had informed her in advance when we were due. She would then speed away to a cave back in the hills where she had always had enough food cached to last her until we had gone.

I have never seen remorse that equaled hers. Her heart was broken. I used to talk with her each time I visited Culion, and each time she would say to me, "I thought I was fooling you and all the time the only person I fooled was myself. I infected my brother, and if only I had given myself up it would never have happened."

One of our most prolific sources of information as to evaders was the anonymous communication. If a Filipino wants to secure revenge on an enemy, he spies upon him until he discovers some evidence to report to the authorities. Curiously enough such delations as we received were, in the main, correct. On one occasion we were told that if we were to go to a certain house in the center of Manila, and knock three times, and then again once, a trap door in the ceiling would open, and there we would find a leper. We followed these instructions, and found the leper. Somebody had a grudge against his family, and was trying to get even. . . .

The Filipino is also likely to be unscrupulous when he is attempting to secure a political advantage. When I arrived one day at a small town, the mayor reported he had all the local lepers ready in waiting. On the way to the detention building one of the prominent citizens approached me and asked me to help him, saying his daughter, who was perfectly healthy, had been shut up with the lepers. Since this was a very common story, I was not particularly impressed, but told him I would look into it.

I was somewhat surprised to find that he was right. His daughter, a beautiful girl, had been herded into camp with real lepers, although she had not the slightest sign of the disease. I ordered her released and then demanded of the local health officer, "Why did you lock her up?"

"The mayor told me to, and I have to obey his orders."

"But what reason did he have?"

"Her father is a candidate. The present mayor thought he could win the election if he could brand his rival's daughter with the stigma of leprosy."

At the very inception of gathering up the lepers it became our fixed policy not to confine anyone at Culion from whom leprosy bacilli could not be recovered and demonstrated by microscopial examination. Filipinos had so many skin diseases that an occasional mistake might easily have been made in diagnosing non-lepers as lepers. We never placed anyone on the ship until from three to five leprosy experts, acting as a Board, were unanimously satisfied that the man or woman had leprosy. If we erred it was on the side of safety, but, as far as I know, no mistake was ever made. The reason more cases are now being found is that since those days many refinements in diagnosis have been made. The more recent complete knowledge is of great value because the early stages of the disease are the most infective.

For the clinical examination of the anesthetic form the suspect was blindfolded. Then his skin was touched with a cotton swab, a feather, a camel's hair brush, or a paper spill, and he was asked to indicate where he had been touched. The head and the point of a pin were pressed alternately against suspected spots, and the patient was asked which caused the more pain. Test tubes, one filled with hot water and the other with cold, were held against his skin, and he was asked to tell which was warm and which was cold. Finally, a scraping was taken from the septum of the nose with a blunt, narrow-bladed scalpel, and put under the microscope. . . .

Often lepers had been confined in a barbarous manner by the local officials at the outskirts of towns. Once when we arrived in a province we found them in an abandoned warehouse, where they had been shut up for weeks pending our arrival. Some were literally rotting away. I had several doctors with me, most of them long experienced in work of this kind, but they became so nauseated by the foul stench from the gangrenous, putrescent ulcers that they could hardly bring themselves to handle the patients. One old woman in particular was no more than a mass of decaying flesh, rotten as a corpse long exposed; she looked as though she were going to fall to pieces. It was with the utmost difficulty that I finally summoned the courage to gather her up and carry her on board in a basket.

There was always, of course, the danger of infection. On one occasion cholera broke out on the *Basilan* in the midst of a collection trip in the Southern Islands. I ordered the boat to make for Culion as quickly as possible, but at best it would take several days, and the quarters on board were too small for effective isolation. After we arrived at Culion, I immediately segregated the lepers in groups of ten, so that if one group should become infected, it alone would have to be quarantined. One leprous woman was not only violently insane, but also came down with cholera. She would keep no clothing on and, since she was completely uncontrollable, she was a deadly menace to everyone. It required a physical struggle, but I finally succeeded in pinioning and imprisoning her. In the process she scratched me so deeply in the arm that I still bear the scar. It is extremely unpleasant to be scratched by an insane leper with cholera, and I lost no time in drenching the wound with disinfectant, though I could not be certain that it would prove effective. There is no way to tell who have and who have not immunity to leprosy, but my mind is now at rest, because the twenty years of possible incubation have passed, and I have not yet evidenced any signs of leprosy. . . .

It must be said to the credit of the Filipinos that the effort to segregate lepers was never seriously opposed. In the majority of cases they cooperated, even though this often involved the life-long separation of wife from husband, sister from brother, child from parents, and friend from friend. Only in comprehending this can it be realized what forbearance was exercised by the Filipinos.

I can still hear ringing in my ears the cries of anguish of the relatives and friends who used to follow us down to the boat drawn up on the open beach. As we rowed out to the *Basilan*, and the *Basilan* steamed out to the open sea, I could see them standing there, and hear faint echoes of their grief. It was an experience to which I never became hardened. I knew that even as the *Basilan* was hull down on the horizon they would still be there, straining for a last glance at those whom they never expected to see again.

The *Basilan* had no sooner landed its first grim cargo at Culion than I realized that my responsibilities toward the lepers whom I had uprooted from their homes had only begun. Transporting them there and providing them with food and lodging was merely a prelude to the real work.

After the novelty of their surroundings had ceased to attract and divert the lepers, they often became homesick, and yearned for their old associations. In every way we tried to make their life as nearly as possible like that of their own villages, always remembering Culion was a town of invalids. We put Tagalog with Tagalog, Ilocano with Ilocano, Visayan with Visayan, Moro with Moro; they would mix during the day but at night liked to be with their own kind.

Little by little we beautified the place with trees, palms, and shrubbery. I designed a semi-open air theatre, with Chinese spirals and other roof decorations, but the workmen were unable to follow my intention so that when finished it resembled no known style of architecture. It served its purpose, however. It was so constructed that those who needed protection could sit under the roof, and the rest in chairs around the outside.

Filipinos are born actors and the lepers took eagerly to dramatics. Besides putting on plays of their own, they enjoyed greatly the films with which generous motion picture companies kept me supplied.

Filipinos are natural musicians also. I have always believed it would be possible to hand fifty band instruments at random to fifty Filipinos and hear sweet music at once. The Filipinos have made music for the entire East. I have heard the rhythm of their Spanish melodies echoing from dance floors and theatres at Calcutta, Bombay, Singapore, and everywhere else in the Orient.

The lepers were no exception. Culion took great pride in its band and practised faithfully. This we encouraged, because the music cheered them enormously. The lepers at San Lazaro at Manila had a particularly good stringed orchestra which used to greet me on every visit. Once after a long absence I was welcomed as warmly as ever but observed with surprise that no music was on hand. "Why don't you play?" I asked.

"We can't."

"Why not?"

In dumb reply they held up their hands; they had literally played their fingers off.

Our first collections of lepers were composed of those who were so ill as to be nearly helpless. The disease had produced such contractions of limbs, destruction of tissues, losses of fingers and toes, impairment of muscular power, and general debility, that only a few could perform the heavy work connected with agriculture, which we hoped would divert them as well as contribute toward their support. Also, many had fever several days during the month, and more were entirely bedfast.

It was not easy to keep the semi-well occupied and distracted. Because of the public's great fear of infection, they could not weave hats of palm or dresses of jusi cloth, carve knickknacks or hammer brass ash trays for general sale. We did not even advocate the manufacture of these handicrafts because the innate Filipino disposition to take life easy, while deplorable for the healthy, is not at all a bad thing for lepers. They did little work other than that entailed by their own domestic requirements.

At first we tried serving cooked food in a cafeteria, but when our Occidental methods of preparation obviously did not please our patrons, we gave them raw food and let them prepare it to suit their own tastes. Some years later Miss Hartley Embrey, an able food chemist, went to Culion as a volunteer to devise ways of combining proper dietary with Filipino gustatory preferences. The most advanced cases had been collected earlier; the later comers were in the initial stages of the disease, and consequently not so badly incapacitated. Basing his action on Miss Embrey's advice, General Wood arranged for the employment of competent gardeners. Ubi tubers were introduced from the Batanes and leafy vegetables were grown with great success. They started tiny sugar plantations, the output of which was purchased by the government and reissued as food to the lepers.

Cattle raising was started. We also encouraged them to fish, and they paddled little balsas of lashed bamboo to the huge fenced fish traps and to other waters. They did well at fishing, and daily we purchased large quantities. In addition to buying their produce we gave them a gratuity of twenty cents a week, and established a store at which small comforts were sold. In order to avoid all risk of infection outside, special money was used, which circulated only in the colony. . . .

The comparative contentment of the lepers was in great measure due to the Sisters of St. Paul de Chartres, who had dedicated their lives to the care of these unfortunates. Outwardly calm and happy, the Sisters spread an atmosphere of cheer around them that was truly magnificent. Whenever the *Basilan* came into port, they would have to dress the nauseating, disgusting wounds of the newcomers, and each day thereafter throughout every year, this routine had to be repeated with never a break. In emergencies they had to perform amateur surgical operations. . . .

I asked the Sisters to promise me solemnly that when they entered the hospital from their quarters in the clean part of the colony, they would remove their clothes in a room provided for that purpose before walking into the next room, where disinfected clothing would be waiting. When they left, they were to reverse the process, bathing themselves with disinfecting soap, stepping into the clean room, and there putting on their own clothes. Some of these nurses have been at Culion almost thirty years and not one has contracted leprosy. I have always ascribed this to the faithful manner in which they have carried out my initial instructions.

Among the loyal band of nurses Sister Calixte Christen was out-standing. As a young woman she had left Chartres and her family and friends to devote her life to lepers, the most friendless of human beings. With her own gaiety she lightened the burden of the hopeless. She had an extraordinary facility for languages, which she cultivated so that she might bring to each of the patients under her care added cheer. In June, 1926, General Wood and his staff attended the ceremony of presenting her a gold medal, cast especially for the occasion and given in recognition of her remarkable services over this long period of time. . . .

Each time I paid a visit to Culion there was usually a public reception, complete with banners, a band, and an impressive parade. The duty of presenting petitions weighs heavily upon all Filipinos, no matter how unimportant the subject matter may be. My coming offered an unexampled opportunity to fulfill this obligation. Such petitions I was usually able to handle with a fair degree of diplomacy, but once I found myself obliged to retreat ingloriously from a mass attack of the woman of Culion on the question of segregation of the sexes.

We had provided separate sleeping quarters for men and women but did not forbid them to mingle by day. Certain well-meaning persons who had interested themselves in the lepers were horrified. They brought pressure to bear on the government, and the Governor General issued orders. One part of the Island was to be set aside for the women and surrounded with a very high barbed wire fence. It was all finished and prepared for occupation when I arrived on my next trip. But I found that the sequestration had not been carried out in accordance with the decree. "Why hasn't this been done?" I asked the doctor in charge.

"The women simply won't go," he replied. "Short of a couple of regiments of constabulary we can't do anything with them. If you think you can persuade them, you go ahead and try."

"Let's call a meeting," I suggested. I had often addressed them before and anticipated no trouble. When the women were assembled, I climbed up on a soap box and stood under the blazing hot noonday sun, looking down on the bobbing mass of black umbrellas, tipped back to frame the furious faces. I explained to them that separation was believed to be for their own good, and that in any event the instructions of the Governor General must be carried out.

The Filipino women are even better orators than the men.

One of them rose and delivered a fervent harangue to the effect that the rest of the world, after having segregated them, had not before seemed to concern itself with their welfare, and why should it take this unpleasant interest in them now? The women of Culion had asked for no protection from the men and did not want any.

Another rebel followed with an even more impassioned address. She worked upon the audience, already aroused, until they began to shout, "Kill him! Kill him!"

The umbrellas shut with a loud concerted swish, and with steel points sparkling, they converged toward my midriff. As the rush began, there flashed through my mind a picture of the igno-minious fate which awaited me—punctured to death by um-brellas.

I held up my hand and shouted at the top of my lungs. "Wait a minute! Wait a minute!"

Fortunately one of the leaders heard me, and with a stentorian voice repeated, "Wait a minute! Let him talk! Let's hear what he has to say."

The umbrellas were poised in mid-air, steel points still aimed at me.

"If you feel so strongly about this, I promise you will not be isolated until I have had a talk with the Governor General! I give you my word that no further attempts will be made to carry out the order until after we have had this conference!"

Slowly the points were lowered, and the women disbanded. I was saved. I went to the Governor General as I had promised. "It's no longer the responsibility of the Director of Health to carry out such orders. I've made every reasonable effort, and I'm not going to risk my life again."

He agreed that other means should be found to meet objec-tions. The women continued to live as they had done formerly, but ultimately homes were established for the young girls. The Sisters took charge of them, and saw that the doors were securely locked at night, although a rumor was current that a Sabine raid had once been planned and executed.

We had discouraged marriage because we did not want the lepers to contract lasting relationships which might entail suffer-ing later if one partner should be cured and dismissed from Culion. But when they produced offspring without benefit of clergy, moral necessities obtruded upon medical ones, and our religious advisers insisted they must marry. Our concern before had been to prevent propagation, but now the birth rate began to increase.

Leprosy is most easily contracted in childhood; the earliest age at which it can be detected is about two, although generally it evinces its presence at from three to four years. Possibly the contraction of the disease in infancy is due to the close contact of leprous parents and children. Statistics show that if babies are not removed from their mothers before they are six months old, approximately half of them will become leprous. . . .

The problem of what should be done with the children born at Culion offered great difficulties. No law existed, as in Hawaii, whereby we could take them from their parents. The duty seemed to devolve upon me of persuading the mothers of Culion to surrender their babies. I used to get them together and harangue them for hours, appealing to their mother love, and explaining how their children would almost certainly contract leprosy unless they were put in a safe home outside the colony. After having my pleas fall on deaf ears time after time, on one occasion my persuasive powers must have become transcendental, because twenty-six mothers, inspired with the spirit of self-denial, offered me their children.

. . . The plan ultimately adopted was to allow the babies to remain with their mothers for six months, and then place them for two years in a nursery situated outside the leper limits. Those who became afflicted with the disease during that period were returned to their parents; those who remained free of it could be sent, with their parents' approval, to Welfareville near Manila. Only a small percentage of the children treated in this manner became leprous. . . .

Many treatments for leprosy, like those for tuberculosis, seemed to cause some improvement. Furthermore, under better hygienic conditions and hospital care, or for other reasons not understood, the disease is often arrested; in a few instances improvement results, so that occasionally apparent cures may take place without any treatment. . . .

It has long been known to the natives of India that chewing the leaves and the twigs of the chaulmoogra tree has a beneficial effect on leprosy. There was a pre-Buddhist legend, centuries old, that a leprous king of Burma had entered the forest and cured himself by eating the raw seeds. Eventually the Indians deduced that it was the oil of the chaulmoogra tree, and this is found most abundantly in the nut, which contains the curative substance.

In 1907, Dr. Isadore Dyer, Professor of Dermatology at Tulane University, brought the properties of chaulmoogra oil arrestingly to the attention of the scientific world by reporting its successful use at the Louisiana colony for leprosy in Iberville Parish. I visited there the following year and gained a most favorable impression of the treatment.

As soon as I had returned to the Islands Dr. Dyer's treatment was given a thorough trial. The drug had to be taken by mouth, and most patients became so nauseated that only one out of three hundred could retain the oil over a period long enough to be effective. The poor lepers would say, "Doctor, I'd rather have leprosy than take another dose!"

Then began an extended series of experiments to develop some method of administering the remedy without the resulting nausea. Chaulmoogra capsules were coated with salol or other substances so that they would pass through the stomach without digesting. Enemas were tried. Most of all we wanted to inject chaulmoogra hypodermically, but the oil would not absorb.

At this point a letter was written to Merck & Company, in Germany, in which we asked whether they could suggest any substance to add to the chaulmoogra oil which might cause it to absorb when injected hypodermically. They replied that they had no practical knowledge, but theoretically it was possible that the addition of camphor or ether might give the desired result. The testing of this possibility was done by Elidoro Mercado, the house physician at San Lazaro. He added camphor to Unna's old oral prescription of resorcin and chaulmoogra oil. To our great joy we found that this combination was readily absorbed.

Many came forward to volunteer for the new treatment. In fact, had I announced to the lepers of Culion, "If your right arm is cut off, you will be cured," dozens would have stepped forward.

The camphor-resorcin solution proved a great advance. After the first year we were able to announce to the world that a number of cases had become negative. We promised that if any patient remained so for two years we would release him. When this actually happened, for the first time in history hope was aroused that a permanent cure might be found for this most hopeless disease.

Few can imagine with what a thrill we watched the first case to which chaulmoogra was administered in hypodermic form, how we watched for the first faint suspicion of eyebrows beginning to grow in again and sensation returning to paralyzed areas. We took photographs at frequent and regular intervals to compare progress and to check on our observations, fearing our imagination might be playing tricks upon us, because in hundreds of years no remedy had been found which had more than slight influence on this disease.

But I was not satisfied. The treatment was still so slow in bringing about improvement or recovery that, after the first flush of excitement, the interest of doctors, nurses, and patients all began to wane. To remedy this and to discover more effective preparations of the oil, we brought over chemists from America. They failed. As we went deeper into the subject it became more and more clear that the world's knowledge of leprosy was still very primitive. If further progress were to be made, the resources of science should be coordinated.

In 1915 I visited Calcutta and there met Sir Leonard Rogers, who had just succeeded in curing amoebic dysentery with the emetine treatment. I endeavored to interest him in our research work, telling him we were on the first rung of the ladder but, strive as we would to reach the next one, we could not secure a footing.

Although Sir Leonard was interested he said, "I've been in India many years now, and I feel I'm entitled to a rest. I'm just about to retire and return to England." But he had made a mistake in having me as his guest. I kept after him hammer and tongs until he agreed to postpone his retirement and work on my problem. In only a few months, with the assistance of an Indian chemist, he was able to make a chaulmoogra oil preparation which halved the time of treatment. . . .

The earlier a case of leprosy can be detected, the greater the likelihood of recovery. In Zamboanga live two girls who were paroled in 1911 when they were ten and twelve years old. I have been watching them since their childhood. They are grown up and married, and have children of their own. They bear a few scars which will never disappear, but they are well, and show no signs of leprosy.

Several thousand lepers have now been freed from Culion after having the treatment, but one of the great unsolved problems is what to do with those who have recovered but who are badly disfigured. Many were deeply conscious of the stigma attached to them when they returned to their old homes. Often they begged to be allowed to stay at Culion, and a clean section of the Island was set apart for them where they could earn their living. . . .

Too many disappointments in the past prevent us from becoming excited about a supposed new remedy until it has been completely tested. So far none has proved more efficacious than chaulmoogra ethyl esters. But meanwhile the quest goes on. . . .

"In his nipa hut, high on the hill of the Leper City, old Lazaro de Paerusza sits in the little bamboo doorway staring seaward with eyes that leprosy has long since blinded. He turns over and over in gnarled patient fingers a battered pair of binoculars. One of the padres gave them to him when his sight first began to fail to help his dimming eyes grope seaward towards the ships—the little trudging coastwise ships that, once in three weeks, in four, in six, come tacking through the reefs with help for Culion. Each day he waits, listening, for the new ship that is to bring America's mercy to those who live beyond the grave. 'No ship today, *matanda?*' they ask him at the end of an empty day. He listens. He hears the night. The reefs chant under the moon. The wild dogs howl in the hills as they rummage among the shallow graves. He shakes his old head and smiles, wisely and believingly as children smile, '*Darating. Darating din Bukas,*' he says in the vernacular—says it for all the patient, buried thousands at Culion—'tomorrow. Tomorrow it will come.' "

1936

On the Edge of the
Primeval Forest

ALBERT SCHWEITZER

I GAVE up my position of professor in the University of Strasbourg, my literary work, and my organ-playing, in order to go as a doctor to Equatorial Africa. How did that come about?

I had read about the physical miseries of the natives in the virgin forests; I had heard about them from missionaries, and the more I thought about it the stranger it seemed to me that we Europeans trouble ourselves so little about the great humanitarian task which offers itself to us in far-off lands. The parable of Dives and Lazarus seemed to me to have been spoken directly of us! We are Dives, for, through the advances of medical science, we now know a great deal about disease and pain, and have innumerable means of fighting them: yet we take as a matter of course the incalculable advantages which this new wealth gives us! Out there in the colonies, however, sits wretched Lazarus, the coloured folk, who suffers from illness and pain just as much as we do, nay, much more, and has absolutely no means of fighting them. And just as Dives sinned against the poor man at his gate because for want of thought he never put himself in his place and let his heart and conscience tell him what he ought to do, so do we sin against the poor man at our gate. . . .

The Lambaréné mission station is built on hills, the one which lies farthest upstream having on its summit the buildings of the boys' school, and on the side which slopes down to the river of the storehouse and the largest of the mission houses. On the middle hill is the doctor's little house, and on the remaining one the girls' school and the other mission house. Some twenty yards beyond the houses is the edge of the forest. We live, then, between the river and the virgin forest, on three hills, which every year have to be secured afresh against the invasion of wild Nature, who is ever trying to get her own back again. All round the houses there are coffee bushes, cocoa trees, lemon trees, orange trees, mandarin trees, mango trees, oil palms, and pawpaw trees. To the negroes its name has always been "Andende." Deeply indebted are we to the first missionaries that they took so much trouble to grow these big trees.

The station is about 650 yards long and 110 to 120 yards across. We measure it again and again in every direction in our evening and Sunday constitutionals, which one seldom or never takes on the paths that lead to the nearest villages. On these paths the heat is intolerable, for on either side of these narrow passages rises the forest in an impenetrable wall nearly 100 feet high, and between these walls not a breath of air stirs. There is the same absence of air and movement in Lambaréné. One seems to be living in a prison. If we could only cut down a corner of the forest which shuts in the lower end of the station we should get a little of the breeze in the river valley; but we have neither the money nor the men for such an attack on the trees. The only relief we have is that in the dry season the river sandbanks are exposed, and we can take our exercise upon them and enjoy the breeze which blows upstream. . . .

The number of people with heart complaints astonishes me more and more. They, on the other hand, are astonished that I know all about their trouble as soon as I have examined them with the stethoscope. "Now I believe we've got a real doctor!" said an old woman to Joseph not long ago. "He knows that I can often hardly breathe at night, and that I often have swollen feet, yet I've never told him a word about it and he has never even looked at my feet." I cannot help saying to myself that there is something really glorious in the means which modern medicine has for treating the heart. I give digitalis according to the new French method (daily doses of a tenth of a milligram of digitalin continued for weeks and months) and am more than pleased with the results obtained. It must be said that it is easier to treat heart disease here than it is in Europe, for when patients are told that they must rest and keep quiet for weeks, they are never obliged to object that they will lose their wages and perhaps their work. They simply live at home and "recruit," and their family, in the widest sense of that word, supports them.

Mental complaints are relatively rarer here than in Europe, though I have already seen some half-dozen such. They are a great worry as I do not know how to dispose of them. If they are allowed to remain on the station they disturb us with their cries all the night through, and I have to get up again and again to quieten them with a subcutaneous injection. I can look back on several terrible nights which resulted in my feeling tired for many a day afterwards. The difficulty can be surmounted in the dry season, for then I can make the mental patients and their friends camp out on a sandbank about 600 yards away, although getting across to see them twice a day consumes a great deal both of time and of energy.

The condition of these poor creatures out here is dreadful. The natives do not know how to protect themselves from them. Confinement is impossible, as they can at any time break out of a bamboo hut. They are therefore bound with cords of bast, but that only makes their condition worse, and the final result almost always is that they are somehow or other got rid of. One of the Samkita missionaries told me once that a couple of years before, while sitting one Sunday in his house, he had heard loud cries in a neighbouring village. He got up and started off to see what was the matter, but met a native who told him it was only that some children were having the sand flies cut out from their feet; he need not worry, but might go home again. He did so, but learnt the next day that one of the villagers, who had become insane, had been bound hand and foot and thrown into the water.

My first contact with a mentally-diseased native happened at night. I was knocked up and taken to a palm tree to which an elderly woman was bound. Around a fire in front of her sat the whole of her family, and behind them was the black forest wall. It was a glorious African night and the shimmering glow of the starry sky lighted up the scene. I ordered them to set her free, which they did, but with timidity and hesitation. The woman was no sooner free than she sprang at me in order to seize my lamp and throw it away. The natives fled with shrieks in every direction and would not come any nearer, even when the woman, whose hand I had seized, sank quietly to the ground as I told her, and offered me her arm for an injection of morphia and scopolamin. A few moments later she followed me to a hut, where, in a short time, she went to sleep. The case was one of an attack of recurrent maniacal disturbance, and in a fortnight she was well again, at least for a time. In consequence of this the report spread that the doctor was a great magician and could cure all mental diseases.

Unfortunately, I was soon to learn that there are forms of maniacal disturbance here with which our drugs can do little or nothing. The second case was an old man, and he, too, was brought with hands and feet bound. The ropes had cut deeply into his flesh, and hands and feet alike were covered with blood and sores. I was amazed at the small effect produced by the strongest doses of morphia, scopolamin, chloral hydrate, and bromide of potassium. On the second day Joseph said to me: "Doctor, believe me, the man is out of his mind because he has been poisoned. You will make nothing of him; he will get weaker and wilder, and at last he will die." And Joseph was right; in a fortnight the man was dead. From one of the Catholic fathers I learnt that he had robbed some women, and, therefore, had been followed up and poisoned by their relatives.

A similar case I was able to study from the beginning. One Sunday evening there arrived in a canoe a woman who was writhing with cramp. I thought at first that it was simple hysteria, but the next day maniacal disturbance supervened, and during the night she began to rave and shriek. On her, too, the narcotics had hardly any effect, and her strength rapidly diminished. The natives surmised that she had been poisoned, and whether they were right or not I am not in a position to decide.

From all I hear it must be true that poison is much used in these parts, and further south that is still oftener the case: the tribes between the Ogowe and the Congo are notorious in this respect. At the same time there are, among the natives, many inexplicable cases of sudden death which are quite unjustifiably regarded as the result of poison.

Anyhow, there must be many plants the juices of which have a peculiarly stimulating effect on the system. I have been assured by trustworthy persons that there are certain leaves and roots which enable men to row for a whole day without experiencing either hunger, thirst, or fatigue, and to display at the same time an increasingly boisterous merriment. I hope in time to learn something more definite about these "medicines," but it is always difficult to do so, because the knowledge about them is kept a strict secret. Any one who is suspected of betraying anything about them, and, above all, if it is to a white man, may count with certainty on being poisoned.

That the medicine men employ poison to maintain their authority I learnt in a peculiar way through Joseph. About the middle of the dry season his village went off to a sandbank about three hours upstream from here, on a fishing expedition. These fishing days are not unlike the Old Testament harvest festivals, when the people "rejoiced before Yahweh." Old and young live together for a fortnight in "booths" made with branches of trees and eat at every meal fresh fish, broiled, baked, or stewed. Whatever is not consumed is dried and smoked, and if all goes well, a village may take home with it as many as ten thousand fish. As Joseph's eyes nearly start from their sockets whenever the conversation turns on fish, I proposed to allow him to go out with his village for the first afternoon, and asked him to take a small tub in which to bring back a few fishes for the doctor. He showed, however, no enthusiasm at the prospect, and a few questions put me in possession of the reason. On the first day there is no fishing done, but the place is blessed. The "elders" pour rum and throw tobacco leaves into the water to put the evil spirits into a good humour, so that they may let the fish be caught in the nets and may injure no one. These ceremonies were once omitted several years ago, but the following year an old woman wrapped herself up in a net and let herself be drowned. "But—why? Most of you are Christians!" I exclaimed; "you don't believe in these things!" "Certainly not," he replied, "but any one who spoke against them or even allowed himself to smile while the rum and tobacco were being offered, would assuredly be poisoned sooner or later. The medicine men never forgive, and they live among us without any one knowing who they are." So he stayed at home the first day, but I allowed him to go some days later.

Besides the fear of poison there is also their dread of the supernatural power for evil which one man can exert over another, for the natives here believe that there are means of acquiring such powers. Whoever has the right fetish can do anything; he will always be successful when hunting, and he can bring bad luck, sickness, and death on any one whom he wishes to injure. Europeans will never be able to understand how terrible is the life of the poor creatures who pass their days in continual fear of the fetishes which can be used against them. Only those who have seen this misery at close quarters will understand that it is a simple human duty to bring to these primitive peoples a new view of the world which can free them from these torturing superstitions. In this matter the greatest sceptic, did he find himself out here, would prove a real helper of mission work.

What is fetishism? It is something born of the fears of primitive man. Primitive man wants to possess some charm to protect him from the evil spirits in nature and from those of the dead, as well as from the power for evil of his fellow men, and this protecting power he attributes to certain objects which he carries about with him. He does not worship his fetish, but regards it as a little bit of property which cannot but be of service to him through its supernatural powers.

What makes a fetish? That which is unknown is supposed to have magical power. A fetish is composed of a number of little objects which fill a small bag, a buffalo horn, or a box; the things most commonly used are red feathers, small parcels of red earth, leopard's claws and teeth, and . . . bells from Europe! Bells of an old-fashioned shape which date from the barter transactions of the eighteenth century! Opposite the mission station a negro has laid out a small cocoa plantation, and the fetish which is expected to protect it hangs on a tree in a corked bottle. Nowadays valuable fetishes are enclosed in tin boxes, so that they may not be damaged by termites, from whose ravages a wooden box gives no permanent protection.

There are big fetishes and little ones. A big one usually includes a piece of human skull, but it must be from the skull of someone who was killed expressly to provide the fetish. Last summer at a short distance below the station an elderly man was killed in a canoe. The murderer was discovered, and it is considered to have been proved that he committed the crime in order to secure a fetish by means of which he hoped to ensure the fulfilment of their contracts by people who owed him goods and money!

A few weeks later my wife and I took a walk one Sunday through the forest to Lake Degele, which is about two hours distant. In the village in which we took a midday rest the people had nothing to eat because for several days the women had been afraid to go out to the banana field. It had become known that several men were prowling about the neighbourhood who wanted to kill someone in order to obtain a fetish. The women of Lambaréné asserted that these men had also been seen near one of our wells, and the whole district was in a state of excitement for several weeks.

I am myself the possessor of a fetish. The most important objects in it are two fragments of a human skull, of a longish oval shape and dyed with some sort of red colouring matter; they seem to me to be from the parietal bones. The owner was ill for many months, and his wife also, both suffering tortures from sleeplessness. Several times, however, the man heard in a dream a voice which revealed to him that they could only get well if they took the family fetish he had inherited to Mr. Haug, the missionary in N'Gômô, and followed Mr. Haug's orders. Mr. Haug referred him to me, and made me a present of the fetish. The man and his wife stayed with me several weeks for treatment, and were discharged with their health very much improved.

The belief that magical power dwells in human skulls which have been obtained expressly for this purpose, must be a quite primitive one. I saw not long ago in a medical periodical the assertion that the supposed cases of trephining which have often been recognised during the excavation and examination of prehistoric graves were by no means attempts at treatment of tumours on the brain or similar growths, as had been assumed, but were simply operations for the securing of fetish objects. The author of the article is probably right.[1]

In the first nine months of my work here I have had close on two thousand patients to examine, and I can affirm that most European diseases are represented here; I even had a child with whooping-cough. Cancer, however, and appendicitis I have never seen. Apparently they have not yet reached the negroes of Equatorial Africa. On the other hand, chills play a great part here. At the beginning of the dry season there is as much sneezing and coughing in the church at Lambaréné as there is in England at a midnight service on New Year's Eve. Many children die of unrecognised pleurisy.

In the dry season the nights are fresher and colder than at other times, and as the negroes have no bedclothes they get so cold in their huts that they cannot sleep, even though according to European standards the temperature is still fairly high. On cold nights the thermometer shows at least 68 degrees F., but the damp of the atmosphere, which makes people sweat continually by day, makes them thereby so sensitive that they shiver and freeze by night. White people, too, suffer continually from chills and colds in the head, and there is much truth in a sentence I came across in a book on tropical medicine, though it seemed at the time rather paradoxical: "Where the sun is hot, one must be more careful than elsewhere to avoid chills." Especially fatal to the natives is the camp life on the sandbanks when they are out on their summer fishing expeditions. Most of the old folk die of pneumonia which they have caught on these occasions.

Rheumatism is commoner here than in Europe, and I not infrequently come across cases of gout, though the sufferers cannot be said to bring it on by an epicurean diet. That they eat too much

[1] In Keith's *Antiquity of Man* (Williams & Norgate, 1915), p. 21, is a picture of a prehistoric skull in which there is a hole made by trephining, as is shown by the fact that the edges are bevelled off. The condition of the bone shows further that the wound had healed prior to death.

flesh food cannot possibly be alleged, as except for the fish-days in summer they live almost exclusively on bananas and manioc.

That I should have to treat chronic nicotine poisoning out here I should never have believed. At first I could not tell what to think of acute constipation which was accompanied by nervous disturbances and only made worse by aperients, but while treating a black Government official who was suffering severely I came to see clearly, through observation and questioning, that the misuse of tobacco lay at the root of it. The man soon got well and the case was much talked of, as he had been a sufferer for years and had become almost incapable of work. From that time, whenever a case of severe constipation came to me, I asked at once: "How many pipes a day do you smoke?" and I recognised in a few weeks what mischief nicotine produces here. It is among the women that cases of nicotine poisoning are most frequent. Joseph explained to me that the natives suffer much from insomnia, and then smoke all through the night in order to stupefy themselves.

Tobacco comes here from America in the form of leaves, seven of which form a head (*tête de tobac*). It is a plant which is frightfully common and also frightfully strong (much stronger than that which is smoked by white people), and it largely takes the place of small coins: e.g., one leaf, worth about a halfpenny, will buy two pineapples, and almost all temporary services are paid for by means of it. If you have to travel, you take for the purchase of food for the crew, not money, for that has no value in the forest, but a box of tobacco-leaves, and to prevent the men from helping themselves to its valuable contents you make it your seat. A pipe goes from mouth to mouth during the journey; and anybody who wants to travel fast and will promise his crew an extra two leaves each, is sure to arrive an hour or two sooner than he otherwise would.

Abdominal tumours are very common here with the women. My hope that I should not need to perform any major operation before the medical ward was ready for use was disappointed. On August 15th I had to operate on a case of strangulated hernia which had been brought in the evening before. The man, whose name was Aïnda, begged me to operate, for, like all the natives, he knew well enough the dangers of his condition. There was, in fact, no time to lose, and the instruments were brought together

as quickly as possible. Mr. Christol allowed me to use his boys'
bedroom as an operating theatre; my wife undertook to give the
anaesthetic, and a missionary acted as assistant. Everything went
off better than we could have expected, but I was almost staggered by the quiet confidence with which the man placed himself
in position on the operating table.

A military doctor from the interior, who is going to Europe on
leave, tells me that he envies me the excellent assistance I had for
my first operation on hernia! He himself, he said, had performed
his with one native prisoner handing him the instruments and
another administering the chloroform by guesswork, while each
time they moved the fetters on their legs rattled; but his regular
assistant was ill and there was on one who could take his place.

The aseptic precautions were, naturally, far from perfect, but
the patient recovered. . . .

At the end of January and the beginning of February my wife
and I were in Talagouga busy looking after Mr. Hermann, a missionary, who was suffering from a bad attack of boils with high
fever, and at the same time I treated the sick of the neighbourhood. Among the latter was a small boy who, with every sign of
extreme terror, refused to enter the room, and had to be carried
in by force. It transpired later that he quite thought the doctor
meant to kill and eat him! The poor little fellow had got his
knowledge of cannibalism, not from nursery tales, but from the
terrible reality, for even to-day it has not been quite extirpated
among the Pahouins. About the area over which it still prevails
it is hard to say anything definite, as fear of the heavy penalties
attached to it make the natives keep every case as secret as possible. A short time ago, however, a man went from the neighbourhood of Lambaréné into some outlying villages to collect
arrears of debt, and did not come back. A labourer disappeared
in the same way from near Samkita. People who know the country say that "missing" is often to be interpreted as "eaten."

The hut for the sleeping sickness victims is now in course of
erection on the opposite bank, and costs me much money and
time. When I am not myself superintending the labourers whom
we have secured for grubbing up the vegetation and building the
hut, nothing is done. For whole afternoons I have to neglect the
sick to play the part of foreman there.

Sleeping sickness prevails more widely here than I suspected at first. The chief focus of infection is in the N'Gounje district, the N'Gounje being a tributary of the Ogowe about ninety miles from here, but there are isolated centres round Lambaréné and on the lakes behind N'Gômô.

What is the sleeping sickness? How is it spread? It seems to have existed in Equatorial Africa from time immemorial, but it was confined to particular centres, since there was little or no travelling. The native method of trade with the sea coast was for each tribe to convey the goods to the boundary of its territory, and there to hand them over to the traders of the adjoining one. From my window I can see the place where the N'Gounje enters the Ogowe, and so far only might the Galoas living round Lambaréné travel. Any one who went beyond this point, further into the interior, was eaten.

When the Europeans came, the natives who served them as boats' crews, or as carriers in their caravans, moved with them from one district to another, and if any of them had the sleeping sickness they took it to fresh places. In the early days it was unknown on the Ogowe, and it was introduced about thirty years ago by carriers from Loango. Whenever it gets into a new district it is terribly destructive, and may carry off a third of the population. In Uganda, for example, it reduced the number of inhabitants in six years from 300,000 to 100,000. An officer told me that he once visited a village on the Upper Ogowe which had two thousand inhabitants. On passing it again two years later he could only count five hundred; the rest had died meanwhile of sleeping sickness. After some time the disease loses its virulence, for reasons that we cannot as yet explain, though it continues to carry off a regular, if small, number of victims, and then it may begin to rage again as destructively as before.

The first symptom consists of irregular attacks of fever, sometimes light, sometimes severe, and these may come and go for months without the sufferer feeling himself really ill. There are victims who enter the sleep stage straight from this condition of apparent health, but usually severe headaches come during the fever stage. Many a patient have I had come to me crying out: "Oh, doctor! my head, my head! I can't stand it any longer; let me die!" Again, the sleep stage is sometimes preceded by torturing sleeplessness, and there are patients who at this stage get mentally deranged; some become melancholy, others delirious.

One of my first patients was a young man who was brought because he wanted to commit suicide.

As a rule, rheumatism sets in with the fever. A white man came to me once from the N'Gômô lake district suffering from sciatica. On careful examination, I saw it was the beginning of the sleeping sickness, and I sent him at once to the Pasteur Institute at Paris, where French sufferers are treated. Often, again, an annoying loss of memory is experienced, and this is not infrequently the first symptom which is noticed by those around them. Sooner or later, however, though it may be two or three years after the first attacks of fever, the sleep sets in. At first it is only an urgent need of sleep; the sufferer falls asleep whenever he sits down and is quiet, or just after meals.

A short time ago a white non-commissioned officer from Mouila, which is six days' journey from here, visited me because, while cleaning his revolver, he had put a bullet through his hand. He stayed at the Catholic mission station, and his black boy accompanied him whenever he came to have his hand dressed, and waited outside. When the N.C.O. was ready to go, there was almost always much shouting and searching for his attendant, till at last, with sleepy looks, the latter emerged from some corner. His master complained that he had already lost him several times because, wherever he happened to be, he was always taking a long nap. I examined his blood and discovered that he had the sleeping sickness.

Towards the finish the sleep becomes sounder and passes at last into coma. Then the sick man lies without either feeling or perception; his natural motions take place without his being conscious of them, and he gets continually thinner. Meanwhile his back and sides get covered with bed-sores; his knees are gradually drawn up to his neck, and he is altogether a horrible sight. Release by death has, however, often to be awaited for a long time, and sometimes there is even a lengthy spell of improved health. Last December I was treating a case which had reached this final stage, and at the end of four weeks the relatives hurried home with him that, at least, he might die in his own village. I myself expected the end to come almost at once, but a few days ago I got the news that he had recovered so far as to eat and speak and sit up, and had only died in April. The immediate cause of death is usually pneumonia.

Knowledge of the real nature of sleeping sickness is one of the latest victories of medicine, and is connected with the names of

Ford, Castellani, Bruce, Dutton, Koch, Martin, and Leboeuf. The first description of it was given in 1803 from cases observed among the natives of Sierra Leone, and it was afterwards studied also in negroes who had been taken from Africa to the Antilles and to Martinique. It was only in the 'sixties that extensive observations were begun in Africa itself, and these first led to a closer description of the last phase of the disease, no one even suspecting a preceding stage or that there was any connection between the disease and the long period of feverishness. This was only made possible by the discovery that both these forms of sickness had the same producing cause.

Then in 1901 the English doctors, Ford and Dutton, found, on examining with the microscope the blood of fever patients in Gambia, not the malaria parasites they expected, but small, active creatures which on account of their form they compared to gimlets, and named Trypanosomata, i.e., boring-bodies. Two years later the leaders of the English expedition for the investigation of sleeping sickness in the Uganda district found in the blood of a whole series of patients similar little active creatures. Being acquainted with what Ford and Dutton had published on the subject, they asked whether these were not identical with those found in the fever patients from the Gambia region, and at the same time, on examination of their own fever patients, they found the fever to be due to the same cause as produced the sleeping sickness. Thus it was proved that the "Gambia fever" was only an early stage of sleeping sickness.

The sleeping sickness is most commonly conveyed by the *Glossina palpalis*, a species of tsetse fly which flies only by day. If this fly has once bitten any one with sleeping sickness, it can carry the disease to others for a long time, perhaps for the rest of its life, for the trypanosomes which entered it in the blood it sucked live and increase and pass in its saliva into the blood of any one it bites.

Still closer study of sleeping sickness revealed the fact that it can be also conveyed by mosquitoes, if these insects take their fill of blood from a healthy person immediately after they have bitten any one with sleeping sickness, as they will then have trypanosomes in their saliva. Thus the mosquito army continues by night the work which the *glossina* is carrying on all day. Poor Africa![1]

[1] I must, however, in justice add that the mosquito does not harbour the trypanosomes permanently, and that its saliva is poisonous only for a short time after it has been polluted by the blood of a sleeping sickness victim.

In its essential nature sleeping sickness is a chronic inflammation of the meninges and the brain, one, however, which always ends in death, and this ensues because the trypanosomes pass from the blood into the cerebro-spinal fluid. To fight the disease successfully it is necessary to kill them before they have passed from the blood, since it is only in the blood that atoxyl,[1] one weapon that we at present possess, produces effects which can to any extent be relied on; in the cerebro-spinal marrow the trypanosomes are comparatively safe from it. A doctor must, therefore, learn to recognise the disease in the early stage, when it first produces fever. If he can do that, there is a prospect of recovery.

In a district, therefore, where sleeping sickness has to be treated, its diagnosis is a terribly complicated business because the significance of every attack of fever, of every persistent headache, of every prolonged attack of sleeplessness, and of all rheumatic pains must be gauged with the help of the microscope. Moreover, this examination of the blood is, unfortunately, by no means simple, but takes a great deal of time, for it is only very very seldom that these pale, thin parasites, about one eighteen-thousandth ($\frac{1}{18000}$) of a millimetre long, are to be found in any considerable number in the blood. So far I have only examined one case in which three or four were to be seen together. Even when the disease is certainly present one can, as a rule, examine several drops of blood, one after another, before discovering a single trypanosome, and to scrutinise each drop properly needs at least ten minutes. I may, therefore, spend an hour over the blood of a suspected victim, examining four or five drops without finding anything, and even then have no right to say there is no disease; there is still a long and tedious testing process which must be applied. This consists in taking ten cubic centimetres of blood from a vein in one of the sufferer's arms, and keeping it revolving centrifugally for an hour according to certain prescribed rules, at the same time pouring off at intervals the outer rings of blood. The trypanosomes are expected to have collected into the last few drops, and these are put under the microscope; but even if there is again a negative result, it is not safe to say that the disease is not present. If there are no trypanosomes to-day, I may find them ten days hence, and if I have discovered some to-day, there may be none in three days' time and for a consider-

---

[1] Atoxyl (meta-arsenic anilid) is a compound of arsenic with an aniline product.

able period after that. A white official, whose blood I had proved to contain trypanosomes, was subsequently kept under observation for weeks, in Libreville, without any being discovered, and it was only in the Sleeping Sickness Institute at Brazzaville that they were a second time proved to be there.

If, then, I wish to treat such patients conscientiously, a couple of them together can tie me for a whole morning to the microscope while outside there are sitting a score of sick people who want to be seen before dinner-time! There are also surgical patients whose dressings must be renewed; water must be distilled, and medicines prepared; sores must be cleansed, and there are teeth to be drawn! With this continual drive, and the impatience of the waiting sick, I often get so worried and nervous that I hardly know where I am or what I am doing.

Atoxyl is a frightfully dangerous drug. If the solution is left for some time in the light it decomposes, just like salvarsan, and works as a poison, but even if it is prepared faultlessly and is in perfect condition, it may cause blindness by injuring the nerves of sight. Nor does this depend on the size of the dose; small ones are often more dangerous than large ones, and they are never of any use. If one begins with too small a dose, in order to see whether the patient can take the drug, the trypanosomes get inured to it; they become "atoxylproof," as it is called, and then can defy the strongest doses. Every five days my sleeping sick come to me for an injection, and before I begin I always ask in trepidation whether any of them have noticed that their sight is not as good as usual. Happily, I have so far only one case of blinding to record, and that was a man in whom the disease had already reached a very advanced stage. Sleeping sickness now prevails from the east coast of Africa right to the west, and from the Niger in the north-west to the Zambesi in the south-east. Shall we now conquer it? A systematic campaign against it over this wide district would need many doctors and the cost would be enormous. . . . Yet, where death already stalks about as conqueror, the European States provide in most niggardly fashion the means of stopping it, and merely undertake stupid defensive measures which only give it a chance of reaping a fresh harvest in Europe itself.

As to operations, one undertakes, naturally, in the forest only such as are urgent and which promise a successful result. The one I have had to perform oftenest is that for hernia, a thing which afflicts the negroes of Central Africa much more than it does white people, though why this should be so we do not know. They also suffer much oftener than white people from strangulated hernia, in which the intestine becomes constricted and blocked, so that it can no longer empty itself. It then becomes enormously inflated by the gases which form, and this causes terrible pain. Then after several days of torture death takes place, unless the intestine can be got back through the rupture into the abdomen. Our ancestors were well acquainted with this terrible method of dying, but we no longer see it in Europe because every case is operated upon as soon as ever it is recognised. "Let not the sun go down upon your—strangulated hernia," is the maxim continually impressed upon medical students. But in Africa this terrible death is quite common. There are few negroes who have not as boys seen some man rolling in the sand of his hut and howling with agony till death came to release him. So now, the moment a man feels that his rupture is a strangulated one—rupture is far rarer among women—he begs his friends to put him in a canoe and bring him to me.

How can I describe my feelings when a poor fellow is brought me in this condition? I am the only person within hundreds of miles who can help him. Because I am here and am supplied by my friends with the necessary means, he can be saved, like those who came before him in the same condition and those who will come after him, while otherwise he would have fallen a victim to the torture. This does not mean merely that I can save his life. We must all die. But that I can save him from days of torture, that is what I feel as my great and ever new privilege. Pain is a more terrible lord of mankind than even death himself.

So, when the poor, moaning creature comes, I lay my hand on his forehead and say to him: "Don't be afraid! In an hour's time you shall be put to sleep, and when you wake you won't feel any more pain." Very soon he is given an injection of omnipon; the doctor's wife is called to the hospital, and, with Joseph's help, makes everything ready for the operation. When that is to begin she administers the anæsthetic, and Joseph, in a long pair of rubber gloves, acts as assistant.

The operation is finished, and in the hardly-lighted dormitory I watch for the sick man's awaking. Scarcely has he recovered consciousness when he stares about him and ejaculates again and again: "I've no more pain! I've no more pain!" . . . His hand feels for mine and will not let it go. Then I begin to tell him and the others who are in the room that it is the Lord Jesus who has told the doctor and his wife to come to the Ogowe, and that white people in Europe give them the money to live here and cure the sick negroes. Then I have to answer questions as to who these white people are, where they live, and how they know that the natives suffer so much from sickness. The African sun is shining through the coffee bushes into the dark shed, but we, black and white, sit side by side and feel that we know by experience the meaning of the words: "And all ye are brethren" (Matt. xxiii, 8). Would that my generous friends in Europe could come out here and live through one such hour!

1931

Contemporary Medicine

Contemporary Medicine

SYNOPSIS

WE *are at the contemporary period in medical research. In hundreds of laboratories every phase of the problem of health and disease is being minutely examined. Thousands of workers, billions of dollars and the discoveries of most of the sciences are being united in the work. In our preface, we noted that the problems of life and growth await their Newton and their Einstein. Perhaps future generations will decide that the twentieth century was the period in which the solutions were discovered. For already the veil begins to lift, the skein to be unraveled. The Russian Oparin formulated a theory for the origin of life on this planet, based on the production of proteins through the action of electricity (lightning) on the primordial broth which existed on the face of the earth when it was young. The theory is being tested by experiments both here and abroad, and the results are encouraging. The problems of growth are being attacked on a dozen different biological fronts. Of great immediate importance for health and disease is the study of those submicroscopic particles, the viruses, which are responsible for some of the most fearful diseases of mankind, such as scarlet fever, poliomyelitis and possibly cancer. One of the pioneer researchers in the field is the Nobel laureate Wendell M. Stanley, whose article "On the Nature of Viruses, Cancer, Genes and Life—a Declaration of Independence" is here reprinted. Stanley has shown that viruses are giant molecules, that they occupy a position in the scale of size between the nonliving molecules and the smallest of the living bacteria. Moreover, they react sometimes as if alive and sometimes as if nonliving. In their activities lies a clue not only to problems of disease but to mysteries even more basic. Stanley's paper was addressed to an audience of scientists, and the lay reader will find much of it difficult. He is urged, however, to persevere—the thoughts presented are pregnant with the widest philosophical implications.*

The investigation of viruses and their effects is taking place in laboratories throughout the world. One of the most significant of these investigations has been the study of influenza viruses. F. M. Burnett of Melbourne University in Australia is, like Stanley, a winner of the Nobel Prize, for the "discovery of acquired immunological tolerance." He has done extensive work in the isolation and classification of the several influenza viruses. His article on "Influenza" is a classic description of techniques of solving problems in this submicroscopic field.

Perhaps the most widely publicized of the medical problems of the last decade has been the search for a method for the prevention of polio. "Organized Medicine and Polio Control with Sabin Vaccine" is reprinted not only for the interest of its material but also as an example of the controversies which have arisen throughout the history of medicine and of the other sciences as well. Sometimes questions of priority have been involved, as in the amicable dispute between Darwin and Wallace. Sometimes, more fundamental problems of theory and method have been at stake. In many cases like the present one, they have resulted in recrimination and bitterness.

This paper was presented under the sponsorship of the American Medical Association. It was immediately challanged by Dr. Jonas A. Salk, the originator of vaccination with killed polio virus. Salk and Sabin had been engaged in a race for prior adoption of their respective methods, which Salk, of course, had won. Salk claimed that the A. M. A. endorsement of the Sabin vaccine was made on "embarrassingly uncertain scientific grounds" and that his own vaccine could result in complete elimination of polio. The last word in the controversy remains to be spoken.

"A Pig from Jersey," by Berton Roueché is a true detective story of the New York City Health Department. It documents and dramatizes an extremely important development in modern medical science: the rise of public health services, tracking down diseases to their source and preventing their spread in the population.

On a thousand different fronts, the search for a cure for cancer goes on. It may be on the basic study of growth—for cancer is a manifestation of growth gone wild. It may be through chemical research—tens of thousands of compounds have been tested. And on the clinical level, in hospitals and sick rooms all over the world, the most seemingly insignificant clues are being followed. A reading of "The New Weapons Against Cancer" by Steven M. Spencer explains why the disease has so far evaded cure, why it may be that not one but many cures will be found necessary, and what the most promising lines of investigation now are. The article is written in language that laymen can understand. It is completely authentic and has been distributed by the American Cancer Society.

So accustomed are we to the use of antibiotics that we find it difficult to believe that the discovery of the first of them took place within recent memory and that only during World War II, as the result of the most intensive activity, did they come into widespread use. Sir Alexander Fleming, the discoverer of penicillin, evaluated the various new drugs in his article "Chemotherapy," written in 1946. Since then there have of course been enormous strides in the development of both antibiotics and sulfa drugs. "Chemotherapy" is included here, however, because it is a classic statement by the dominant figure in the field.

In "Surgery," the well-known English writer John Thwaites offers a round-up of the most interesting recent developments. As we read his description of the handling of shock and infection, of repairs to damaged hearts, of the accomplishments of plastic surgery, of repairs to deeply injured tissue, of the growing use of blood banks and spare parts for organs of the body, we are reminded of incredibly skillful automobile mechanics who clean valves, replace carburetors, repair fouled gasoline and oil lines and perform almost unbelievable feats to keep damaged machines in working order.

One of the most interesting examples of this kind of surgical substitution is the transplantation of the kidney, described in detail by John P. Merrill, director of the cardiorenal section at the Peter Bent Brigham Hospital. Such a kidney transplant is especially difficult because the body is normally "immune" to the graft and rejects it; in certain cases, however, the immune response of the body can be circumvented. This article is significant not only because of the achievement it records, but

*but also because it dramatizes the challenges and frustrations that
so often precede triumph in medical research.*

*Operations play their part in the new techniques for dealing
with strokes, but just as important are new methods of diagnosis of the various types of stroke. Doctors hope that in the
future they may prevent strokes before they occur. Meanwhile
new methods can, in some cases, restore the injured to health. A
specialist in the field, Dr. Robert A. Kuhn, describes these new
developments in "Hope for Victims of Stroke."*

*One of the most dramatic of recent happenings has been the
sharp reduction in the number of patients in hospitals for the
mentally ill. Insanity, to use the word which has now fallen into
disrepute, has been one of the great human afflictions in every
age of which we have any record. In his article on "The Medicine Man" Logan Clendening points out that "skulls with round
trephine openings in them have been found in prehistoric human
excavations all over the world." These openings must have
been made for the purpose of relieving headaches or curing
insanity by permitting the devils which caused them to escape.
Surgery has been only one of the methods of cure and care,
and the record of these methods has been one of the most
grisly and inhuman in all human history. One has but to read
the "Memorial to the Legislature of Massachusetts" by Dorothea
Lynde Dix, on page 385, to realize the horrifying methods in
use even in comparatively modern times. Now, almost overnight,
that picture has been altered by chemical therapy. Instead of
the comparatively ineffective techniques of the surgeons and
the psychiatrists, many drugs, some of which have been known
but not fully understood for years, are helping to empty our
asylums and restore former mental incompetents to useful,
normal existence. This is the story that Robert S. de Ropp tells
in "Sick Minds, New Medicines."*

*One of the most important new tools of medicine is also the
greatest threat to the survival of the human race. In "The Therapeutical Use of Radioactive Isotopes," Fernand Lot shows how
radioactive tracers are used in the diagnosis and exact location
of disease, and how they have been used to cure certain types
of cancer. This is the positive and hopeful aspect of a development whose more somber implications are known to us all. These
implications have to do not only with the gross effects of the
atomic bomb but also with the long-term dangers which are*

described in "Radiations and the Genetic Threat" by Warren Weaver. Dr. Weaver has been active in the administration of medical research both in government and as an officer of the Rockefeller Foundation. The facts he states are the authentic results of elaborate investigation. Failure to take due heed of them may penalize generations yet unborn.

On the Nature of Viruses, Cancer, Genes and Life—A Declaration of Independence

WENDELL M. STANLEY

EACH of the four topics mentioned in the title of this lecture is substantial enough to warrant having an entire lecture devoted to it alone. Actually a proper and full discussion of viruses, of cancer, of genes or of life would require many hours. It may, therefore, appear quite presumptuous to have included all four in the title of a single lecture. But let me hasten to indicate that I do not propose to attempt to develop these topics as such, but that I do propose to sketch in certain basic information and then to devote most of my time to a discussion of new relationships of these four subjects, relationships which I believe to be of the utmost importance.

Recent scientific discoveries, especially in the virus field, are throwing new light on the basic nature of viruses and on the possible nature of cancer, genes and even life itself. These discoveries are providing evidence for relationships of these four subjects which indicate that one may be dependent upon another to an extent not fully appreciated heretofore, and hence the time is appropriate for a declaration of the nature of the dependence that may be involved. Too often one works and thinks within too narrow a range and hence fails to recognize the significance of certain facts for other areas. Sometimes the important new ideas and subsequent fundamental discoveries come from the borderline areas between two well-established fields of investigation. I trust, therefore, that this declaration of dependence will result in the synthesis of new ideas regarding viruses, cancer, genes and life, and that these ideas in turn will result in new experiments which may provide the basis for fundamental discoveries in these fields so important to every one of us.

I suppose there is no doubt that, of the four topics, life is the one most people would consider to be of the greatest importance. One would think that the nature of life would be easy to define since we are all experiencing it. However, just as life means different things to different people, we find that in reality it is extremely difficult to define just what we mean by life or by a living agent in its most simple form. There is no difficulty in recognizing an agent as living or nonliving as long as we contemplate structures such as man, cats and dogs or even small organisms such as the bacteria or, at the other extreme, structures such as a piece of iron or glass, an atom of hydrogen, or even a molecule of water, sugar or of our blood pigment, hemoglobin. The former are examples of animate or living agents, whereas the latter are examples of inanimate or nonliving things. But what is the true nature of the difference between a man and a piece of iron, or between a bacterial organism and a molecule of hemoglobin? The ability to grow or reproduce and to change or mutate has long been regarded as a special property characteristic of living agents. Certainly mankind and bacteria have the ability to assimilate and metabolize food, respond to external stimuli and reproduce their kind— properties not shared by bits of iron or by molecules of hemoglobin. Now, if viruses had not been discovered, all would have been well. The organisms of the biologist would have ranged from the largest of animals, whales and elephants and the like, all the way down to the smallest of the bacteria, which are about 200 mμ or a few millionths of an inch in diameter. There would have been a definite break with respect to size, since the largest molecules known to the chemist were less than 20 mμ in size. Life and living agents would have been represented solely by those structures which possessed the ability to reproduce themselves and to change or mutate, and all of these were about 200 mμ or larger in size, thus more than ten times larger than the largest known molecule. This would have provided a comfortable area of separation or discontinuity between living and nonliving things and would have provided ample justification for considering life as something set distinctly apart and perhaps unapproachable and unexplainable by science.

Then about 1900 came the discovery of the viruses—first the plant virus of tobacco mosaic, then the foot-and-mouth disease virus of cattle and then the first virus affecting man, the yellow fever virus. These infectious, disease-producing agents are characterized by their small size, by their ability to grow or reproduce within specific living cells, and by their ability to change or mutate during reproduction. Their inability to grow or reproduce on artificial or nonliving media did not cause too much concern and their reproductive and mutative powers were enough to convince most people that viruses were merely still smaller ordinary living organisms. However, about 1930 the sizes of different viruses were determined with some precision, and it was found that some viruses were indeed quite small, actually smaller than certain protein molecules. Then in 1935 the first discovered virus, the tobacco mosaic, which is a middle-sized virus, was isolated in the form of a crystallizable material which was found to be a nucleoprotein, that is, a substance composed of nucleic acid and protein. This nucleoprotein molecule was found to be 15 mμ in cross-section and 300 mμ in length and to possess the unusually high molecular weight of about 50,000,000. It was, therefore, larger than any molecule previously described, yet it was found to possess all of the usual properties associated with larger protein molecules. The same material could be obtained from different kinds of mosaic-diseased plants, such as tomato, phlox, and spinach plants, whereas plants diseased with different strains of tobacco mosaic virus yielded slightly different nucleoproteins. Many tests indicated that the new high molecular weight nucleoprotein was actually tobacco mosaic virus, and it was concluded that this virus could, in fact, be a nucleoprotein molecule. Here, therefore, was a molecule that possessed the ability to reproduce itself and to mutate; hence, the distinction between living and nonliving things which had existed up to that time seemed to be tottering and soon a full-scale intellectual revolution was in progress.

Today the revolution is past and we know that the gap between 20 and 200 mμ has been filled in completely by the viruses—so much so that there is actually an overlapping with respect to size at both ends. Some larger viruses are larger than certain well accepted living organisms, whereas some small viruses are acutally smaller than certain protein molecules. We have, therefore, a continuity with respect to size as we go from the electrons, mesons, atoms and molecules of the physicist and the chemist to the organisms of the biologist and on, if you please, to the stars and galaxies. Nowhere is it possible to draw a line in this continuity of structures and say that all above this size are living and all below are nonliving. There appears to be a gradual transition with respect to size and complexity of structure as one goes from things that are normally considered to be alive to things that are generally considered to be nonliving. One is reminded of the quotation attributed to Aristotle more than 2,000 years ago to the effect that nature makes so gradual a transition from the animate to the inanimate that the boundary line between the two is doubtful and perhaps nonexistent. Much scientific knowledge has been accumulated since Aristotle's time, but the essence of his statement is as true today as it was when he made it. But does this mean there is really no difference between the animate and the inanimate? I do not believe that it does. However, we must be willing to define what we mean by life and then we must be willing to accept as living any structure possessing properties fulfilling such a definition.

The essence of life is the ability to reproduce. This is accomplished by the utilization of energy to create order out of disorder, to bring together into a specific predetermined pattern from semi-order or even from chaos all the component parts of that pattern with the perpetuation of that pattern with time. This is life. Now, there is another very basic property which seems to be characteristic of living things and that is the ability to mutate, to change or to respond to a stimulus. I do not believe this property is absolutely necessary for life, but it certainly lends grandeur to life, for not only is it responsible for the whole evolutionary process and thus for the myriad kinds of life we have on earth but, most importantly for mankind, it permits one to dare to aspire. It is presumably responsible for man, his conscience and his faith. It is obvious that I believe that mutation merits much, much study.

The discovery of viruses has permitted us to contemplate the nature of life with new understanding. It has enabled us to appreciate in a new light the inherent potentialities of chemical structure, whether that of a single molecule or that produced by the interaction of two or more molecules. Viruses were discovered by virtue of their ability to replicate, and in the last analysis this ability to reproduce remains today as the only definitive way in which they can be recognized. We may purify and isolate preparations from virus-diseased tissues, but it is only when a reasonably pure material is obtained and units of this are found to possess the ability to reproduce themselves that we are privileged to refer to the material as virus. Since the isolation of tobacco mosaic virus in the form of a crystallizable nucleoprotein 15 by 300 mμ in size, many other viruses have been obtained in pure form and characterized in part by their chemical and physical properties. My colleagues Arthur Knight, Robley Williams and Howard Schachman have made major contributions to the biochemical, electron-microscopical, and biophysical knowledge of viruses. Until two years ago all viruses studied had been found to be at least as complex as a nucleoprotein. However, some appear to have lipide, carbohydrate and, in some cases, a limiting membrane in addition to nucleic acid and protein. Whereas some viruses, like tobacco mosaic, are crystallizable nucleoproteins which have the usual molecular properties, other viruses, such as vaccinia, have a degree of morphological differentiation which can hardly be called molecular in nature and which is rather more organismal or cell-like in nature. Some of the bacterial viruses have a very complex morphology, with a head and a tail somewhat similar to the sperm of higher organisms.

For a long time many investigators thought that the plant viruses differed basically from viruses affecting animals and man. This idea stemmed mainly from the fact that for twenty years all of the crystallizable viruses were plant viruses. This idea had to be relinquished two years ago when my colleagues Carlton Schwerdt and Frederick Schaffer obtained poliomyelitis virus, which is a typical animal or human virus, in crystalline form. Since then at least one other animal or human virus has been crystallized. This is crystalline Coxsackie virus, obtained by Doctor Mattern of the National Institute of Health. Hundreds of viruses are known, and more are being discovered every month; yet only a dozen or so have been obtained in purified form. In view of the possibility that these may represent the more stable and more readily purified viruses, one cannot be certain that a true picture of the chemical and physical properties of viruses as a whole has been obtained as yet. However, I believe that we have sufficient sampling to be significant for the purposes of the present discussion, for we already know that viruses may range from small crystallizable animal, human or plant viruses which are nucleoprotein molecules, through intermediate structures consisting of nucleoprotein, lipide and carbohydrate, to large structures possessing a morphology and composition similar to that of accepted cellular organisms. All of these diverse structures are bound together by one all-important property, that of being able to reproduce their own characteristic structure when placed within certain living cells. They are all in short, by definition, alive.

Now, I am only too fully aware of objections that some may have to considering a crystallizable nucleoprotein molecule a living agent. Some may feel that life is a mystery which is and must remain beyond the comprehension of the human mind. With these I must disagree. Some may believe that a living molecule is contrary to religion. Here again I must disagree, for I see no conflict whatsoever between science and religion, and I see no wrong in accepting a molecule as a living structure. To many scientists the diverse expressions of chemical structure represent miracles, and our expanding knowledge of the wonders of nature provides ample opportunities to express our faith and only serves to make us full of humility. Some may prefer to regard a virus molecule in a crystal in a test tube as a potentially living structure and to restrict the term "living" to a virus during the time that it is actually reproducing. I would have no serious objection to this, for I am reminded of the fact that certain tapeworms a foot or so in length can live and reproduce only in certain hosts and that even man himself can be regarded as requiring rather special conditions for life. Yet no one objects to accepting man and tapeworms as examples of life. I am also reminded that we are taught that the essence of a thing is not what it is, but what it does, and the doing of something involves time; hence there may be good reason always to consider the virus with time. Regardless of certain mental restrictions that may differ from person to person, I think there is no escape from the acceptance ultimately of viruses, including the crystallizable viral nucleoprotein molecules, as living agents. This must be done because of their ability to reproduce or to bring about their own replication. Certainly the essence of life is the ability to reproduce, to create a specific order out of disorder by the repetitive formation with time of a specific predetermined pattern. This the viral nucleo-protein molecules can do.

Of course, it would have been dull indeed if the first formed living agent had been restricted to exact duplicates of itself. The logical reasoning provided in schemes such as those outlined by Calvin, Haldane, Horowitz, Oparin and Urey by means of which relatively complex organic substances could have arisen from inorganic matter provides justification for assuming that a chemical structure, perhaps something like nucleic acid, which possessed the ability to replicate, did come into being once upon a time. It needed to have happened only once, and thereafter without the great phenomenon of mutation it merely would have kept going until it had filled the world with replicates of this precise structure or until it had exhausted the starting materials. However, nature has provided a built-in error, so that the replication process is not perfect, and about one in every million or so replicates is slightly different. This change, which has been of tremendous fundamental importance, we now recognize as mutation; and as these errors or differences were accumulated by replicating structures it became necessary to make formal recognition of them. These differences or markers we now call genes. We do not recognize genes directly but only by differences. Needless to say, some physical structure had to be responsible for the accumulation, preservation and potential exhibition of these differences, and this assembly of genes we call a chromosome. The incorporation of one or more assemblies of genes into a structure possessing a limiting membrane, which we now call a cell, then made possible gene interchanges between these cellular assemblies. This genetic interchange by the fusion of two cells, a sexual process, also represents a phenomenon of the greatest fundamental importance, for this permitted genetic recombination, a factor that has served to speed up the evolutionary process immeasurably. Therefore, life as we know it today is dependent not only upon reproduction but also upon mutation and genetic recombination.

Now let us consider for a moment the relationships between genes and viruses, since we see that both are related to life. Muller's estimate of the maximum size of a gene would place it just below tobacco mosaic virus, near the middle of the viruses. Both genes and viruses seem to be nucleoproteins, and both reproduce only within specific living cells. Both possess the ability to mutate. Although viruses generally reproduce many times within a given cell, some situations are known in which they appear to reproduce only once with each cell division. Genes usually reproduce once with each cell division, but here also the rate can be changed as, for example, in the case of polyploidy resulting from treatment with colchicine. Actually the similarities between genes and viruses are so remarkable that viruses very early were referred to as "naked genes" or "genes on the loose." Two great discoveries, one in 1928 and the other in 1952, have provided experimental evidence for an exceedingly intimate relationship between viruses and genes. In 1928 Griffith found that he could transform one specific S type of pneumococcus into another specific S type by injecting mice with nonvirulent R forms together with large amounts of heat-killed S pneumococci of a type other than that of the organisms from which the R cells were derived. Living, virulent S organisms of the same type as the heat-killed S forms were then recovered from the animals. Later, Dawson and Sia as well as Alloway found that the addition of an extract of one type of capsulated pneumococcus to a culture of a noncapsulated rough form would convert the latter into the type of capsulated pneumococcus that provided the extract. It was obvious that something was being transferred, and in 1938 I discussed the possibility that this something might be a virus. In 1944 Avery and his colleagues at the Rockefeller Institute proved that this something was a transforming principle consisting of deoxyribonucleic acid (DNA). Muller in 1947 discussed the possibility that the DNA might correspond to still viable parts of bacterial chromosomes loose in solution which, after entering the capsuleless bacteria, undergo a kind of crossing over with the chromosomes of the host, but this suggestion was not widely accepted. That the phenomenon was not an isolated one was demonstrated in 1953 by Leidy and Alexander, who obtained similar results with an influenza bacteria system. The close relationship to genetics was further emphasized by the work of Hotchkiss and by Ephrussi-Taylor who, as well as Leidy and Alexander, showed that drug resistance and other genetic factors could be so transferred. This work provided evidence that genetic factors or genes, if one prefers such a designation, can be represented by DNA and can be obtained in chemically pure solution.

This information as well as our knowledge of viruses was soon fortified by the very important discovery by Zinder and Lederberg in 1952 of transduction in Salmonella by means of a bacterial virus. It was found that genetic factors could be carried from one type of Salmonella cells to another type by means of a bacterial virus. In this type of transformation the genetic fragment is not free but is carried within the structure of the bacterial virus. It is, for example, not affected by the enzyme deoxyribonuclease, and in this respect is unlike the DNA pneumococcus transforming principle. However, it is not necessary for the virus actually to possess virus activity, for killing of the virus by ultraviolet light does not prevent the transduction of other traits. The closeness of the relationship between the virus and the genes of the host is emphasized by the fact that the transducing ability of any bacterial virus is determined strictly by the character of the cells on which the virus was most recently grown. Virus grown on Serotype E_2 Salmonella cells will, when added to Serotype E_1 cells, convert a fraction of these cells into Serotype E_2 cells. It is of interest to note that the virus in filtrates of toxin-forming bacterial strains will convert non-toxin-forming cells into toxin-forming cells. In transduction, a fragment of a chromosome, which might be regarded as a gene or a collection of a few or even many genes, can be transferred from one kind of donor cell to another kind of receiver cell and be incorporated into the genetic apparatus of the receiver cell. In the pneumococcus or influenza bacterium this can be caused by a DNA preparation which can be separated and isolated as such, and in Salmonella this gene or gene collection rides within the bacterial virus, presumably with the viral DNA, which is added to the cell to be transduced. Here one hardly knows what to call a virus and what to call a gene, for it is obvious that at times the two merge completely.

The persistence of a bacterial virus in an apparently concealed form or prophage in lysogenic strains of bacteria, extensively investigated by Lwoff, provides further evidence in this direction. Lysogenic bacteria perpetuate in what may be considered a hereditary manner the property of being able to produce a bacterial virus. The term "prophage" is used to describe the form in which the potentiality to produce a bacterial virus is perpetuated in lysogenic bacteria. Prophage is non-pathogenic and noninfectious in the usual sense but, since it is multiplied at least once with each cell division, it may be regarded as infectious in the sense that genes or chromosomes are infectious. In other words, the prophage might be considered as a temporary part of the genetic apparatus of the cell, the genetic element that differentiates a lysogenic from a sensitive cell, and at the same time as the noninfectious form of a bacterial virus. There are times, therefore, when a virus may not exhibit its normally infectious nature but have its potentially unlimited reproductive capacity under genetic control, so that it replicates only once with each cell division. There are times when a specific genetic element of a cell can be freed of the normal controlling mechanism of the cell and go forth in viable form in solution or associated with a virus, enter a different cell, replace a homologous chromosomal segment and resume its original specific function in the new cell. It is obvious that the latter phenomenon could readily be considered an infectious process, and that viruses can act as genes and genes as viruses under certain circumstances.

I should now like to discuss the relationships which involve cancer. You probably know that cancer or abnormal, uncontrolled cellular growth may occur in all kinds of organisms and that cancer is second only to heart disease as a killer of mankind; hence I need say no more about the relationship between cancer and life. Cancer originates when a normal cell for reasons—some known and some unknown—suddenly becomes a cancer cell, which then multiplies wildly and without apparent restraint. Cancer may originate in many different kinds of cells, but the cancer cell usually continues to carry certain traits of the cell of origin. The transformation of a normal cell into a cancer cell may have more than one kind of cause, but there is good reason to consider the relationships that exist between viruses and cancer. Viruses have been implicated in animal cancers ever since Peyton Rous, in 1911, transmitted a chicken sarcoma from animal to animal by means of a cell-free filtrate. Despite the fact that today viruses are known to cause cancer or tumors in chickens, pheasants, ducks, mice, frogs, rabbits, deer and other animals, and even in certain plants, there exists a great reluctance to accept viruses as being of etiological importance in human cancer. However, basic biological phenomena generally do not differ strikingly as one goes from one species to another, and I must say that I regard the fact, now proved beyond contention, that viruses can cause cancer in animals to be directly pertinent to the human cancer problem. It should be recognized that cancer is a biological problem and not a problem that is unique for man.

Since there is no evidence that human cancer as generally experienced is infectious, many persons believe that because viruses are infectious agents they cannot possibly be of etiological importance in human cancer. However, this is not a valid conclusion for several reasons. It is well known from the work of Bryan and of Beard that animal cancer viruses may alternately be filterable and hence infectious and then nonfilterable and hence appear noninfectious, apparently because of great variations in the actual amount of virus present in the cancer. It is also well known that viruses may be highly specific, so specific in fact that a given virus may infect and cause disease only in one kind of cell in one kind of animal, and hence, under all other conditions, appear noninfectious. For example, the kidney carcinoma virus of the leopard frog studied in this city by Lucké would appear to be such a virus. Then there is the possibility that man may be carrying viruses of etiological importance for cancer which for one reason or another have not yet been discovered. The possibility of mutation of latent viruses into a new strain of etiological importance must also be kept in mind. Pertinent to both of these possibilities is the discovery during the past few years of dozens upon dozens of hitherto unknown viruses in human beings. These consist of the ECHO viruses isolated from the human intestinal tract, the adenoviruses isolated from the upper respiratory tract and eyes of man and a group of viruses isolated from human sera. New viruses of man are discovered almost every week. Thus we now have many more human viruses than we know what to do with, and there is no reason to shy away from giving consideration to viruses as causative agents in human cancer for lack of viruses.

During the past few years there has been an almost unbelievably rapid development of techniques by means of which it is now possible to grow almost all kinds of human and animal cells in the test tube. As a consequence, vast new opportunities for experimentation on human cells without danger to man have opened to us. These cells are also providing means for the isolation of new viruses, since many kinds of cells are very susceptible to many viruses. The human amnion cell, which my colleagues Elsa Zitcer, Jørgen Fogh and Thelma Dunnebacke first obtained from the full-term amnion in cell culture, is proving of great use in this connection as well as in studies on the transition from a normal to a potentially malignant cell. For example, we are finding interesting changes in chromosome number and in ability to grow in cortisone or X-ray treated animals as these human amnion cells are passed in culture. It is also of interest that one of the adenoviruses has been found to destroy human cancer cells both in the human being and in the test tube. Thus a virus may cause a cancer and a virus may destroy a cancer. Unfortunately in the case of Huebner's studies on carcinoma of the human cervix not all of the cancer cells were destroyed and the cancer eventually progressed. However Huebner, as well as others, is attempting to train a series of viruses to grow on cancer cells, so this approach may not be too hopeless. In the same way it is possible to train cells to respond to viruses, and this may provide even better test systems for human viruses as yet undiscovered. Even if eventually one should find no cancer virus among the large number of human viruses, the fact that man carries so many viruses within his cells and that these are continually passing from person to person means that we should be ever alert to the possibility of transduction by these viruses. Of course, there is no confirmed case of transduction in higher organisms as yet. However, human cancer is a fact and there is certainly something within every human cancer cell that insures its reproduction whether we call it a gene or a chromosomal fragment, and as long as human viruses are so abundant we certainly have the possibility of transduction.

There are many examples of latent viruses that may remain hidden for a lifetime or even for generations, only to come to light as a result of some treatment or change. Most human beings acquire the virus of herpes simplex quite early in life, and in many persons the evidence for the persistence of this virus throughout their lifetime is quite good. Traub has found that infection of a mouse colony with the virus of lymphocytic choriomeningitis can result, with time, in an unapparent infection of all animals. The virus is apparently transmitted *in utero* and remains with the animal throughout its life; hence this virus persists throughout generation after generation of mice. Injection of such mice with sterile broth can revive the pathogenicity of the virus and bring it to light. Certain potato viruses such as potato X virus, also known as the healthy potato virus or the latent mosaic of potato virus, can be passed from generation to generation without causing an apparent disease. This virus is not present in several varieties of potato grown in Europe, but it is thought to be present in all, or almost all, potato plants grown in the United States. Needless to say, it was only by virtue of the fact that potato plants without this virus are known to exist and the fact that this virus causes obvious disease symptoms when inoculated into certain other plants that it was possible to establish the actual existence of this virus. In the absence of such information this latent mosaic virus would have to be regarded as a normal constituent of the potato plant.

Since viruses can mutate, and examples are known in which a virus that never kills its host can mutate to form a new strain of virus that always kills its host, it does not seem unreasonable to assume that an innocuous latent virus might mutate to form a strain that causes cancer. The great wealth of newly discovered viruses of man, plus our knowledge of the latent virus phenomenon, provide ample justification to re-examine quite carefully the relationships between viruses and human cancer.

Another fact which may prove of the greatest importance in this connection is that treatment of certain lysogenic strains of bacteria with physical and chemical agents, such as X rays, ultraviolet light, nitrogen mustard, certain chemical-reducing agents or iron-chelating agents, results, after a latent period, in the lysis of the bacterial cells and the release of large amounts of bacterial virus particles. These agents are called "inducers," and you may recognize some as carcinogenic agents for man and animals. Non-lysogenic bacteria are unaffected by these "inducers" insofar as the production of a bacterial virus is concerned. Is it possible that this activation of a prophage by certain chemical or physical agents with development into a fully infectious bacterial virus and the consequent destruction of the bacterial cells provides a biological example of a process which occurs in man? I believe that this activation of phophage as well as the phenomenon of transduction by free deoxyribonucleic acid in the pneumococcus and by bacterial viruses in Salmonella is pertinent to the human cancer problem, especially so in view of the recent discovery of dozens upon dozens of new viruses of man. Certainly the experimental evidence now available is consistent with the idea that viruses, as we know them today, could be the etiological agents of most if not all cancer, including cancer in man. I have been urging the acceptance of this idea as a working hypothesis because it will result in the doing of experiments that might otherwise be left undone, experiments that could result in the solving of the cancer problem. Needless to say, what we do in the way of experimentation depends in large measure upon what we think, and I am sure the time has come when we should change our thinking with respect to the nature of cancer.

I hope that by this time it is obvious that viruses, cancer, genes and life are tied together by a whole series of relationships, that viruses can act as genes and genes as viruses under certain circumstances, that viruses can cause cancer and that viruses are structures at the twilight zone of life, partaking both of living and of molecular properties. Let us now see whether there is a common thread of understanding permeating all of these relationships. We know that viruses have been thought to be at least as complex as a nucleoprotein, but we also know that the transforming agent of the pneumococcus has been found to be a deoxyribonucleic acid. However, until recently no gene or chromosome or any of the ordinary viruses had been isolated as such in the form of nucleic acid; hence the "stuff of life," as well as the viruses, has been considered to be nucleoprotein in nature, with considerable doubt as to whether the protein or the nucleic acid or the combination of the two was really the biologically active structure.

A recent very important discovery made in our laboratory by Doctor Fraenkel-Conrat has changed the situation considerably and now makes it seem certain that nucleic acid is the all-important structure. It was reported by Fraenkel-Conrat and also shortly thereafter by Gierer and Schramm in Germany that special treatment of tobacco mosaic virus yielded a nucleic acid preparation possessing virus activity. It would now appear necessary to recognize that a nucleic acid structure of around 300,-000 molecular weight can possess coded within its 1,000 or so nucleoteids not only all of the information that is necessary to bring about in the host cell the production of more of this same nucleic acid, but also apparently the *de novo* synthesis of its own characteristic and highly specific protein with which it eventually coats itself. This work provides wonderful evidence for a direct relationship between specific nucleic acid and specific protein synthesis and makes it possible to consider virus and gene action, including their relationships to cancer and to the nature of life, in terms, not of nucleoprotein structure, but in terms of nucleic acid structure. We see, most importantly, that viruses, cancer, genes and life are all directly dependent upon the structure of nucleic acid.

It may be calculated that a thousand-unit polynucleoteid linear chain consisting of a coded repeat of only four different components, adenine, guanine, cytosine and uracil, in the same ratio as exists in tobacco mosaic virus, nucleic acid could form about 10^{590} different arrangements. This number is so large that it is incomprehensible. Even a 100-unit polynucleoteid chain of this composition could exist in about 10^{57} different arrangements. This number is vastly larger than the total of all living things on earth and in the oceans. We have therefore in this structure, consisting of the four chemicals—adenine, guanine, cytosine and uracil (thymine in the case of deoxyribonucleic acid)—repeated many times over, in unique fashion, the code for every bit of life on earth and in the sea. When a normal cell becomes a cancer cell there is undoubtedly a change in this structure within the cell. It is of interest to note that many anti-cancer compounds are anti-metabolites for these chemical components of nucleic acids. And in our laboratory Litman and Pardee made the very important observation that the incorporation of 5-bromouracil into a bacterial virus in place of thymine resulted in the production of the highest percentage of mutants ever recorded. Certainly all of this information, plus the discovery that virus activity can be a property of nucleic acid, and our knowledge of relationships between viruses, cancer, genes and life now make it obvious that the common thread upon which all of these depend is specific nucleic acid structure. Therefore this declaration of dependence revolves around nucleic acid.

I believe that the elucidation of the structure of nucleic acid in all of its aspects is the most important scientific problem we face today. It is vastly more important than any of the problems associated with the structure of the atom, for in nucleic acid structure we are dealing with life itself and with a unique approach for bettering the lot of mankind on earth. It is possible that the solution of this scientific problem could lead eventually to the solution of major political and economic problems. Never before has it been possible to realize so fully our utter dependence upon the structure of nucleic acid. Eventually chemists should be able to synthesize a small polynucleoteid specifically arranged; hence one may now dare to think of synthesizing in the laboratory a structure possessing genetic continuity and of all of the tremendous implications of such an accomplishment.

1957

Influenza

F. M. BURNETT

SOMETIME in most winters and not infrequently at other seasons large numbers of people suffer from a sharp, short-lasting fever associated with signs of infection in the air passages. Every few years such epidemics are much more widespread, involving 10 or 20 percent of the population, and once only in the history of epidemics what seemed to be an enormously more virulent prevalence of the same type swept over the world—in 1918-19. All these conditions are popularly called influenza. It is still impossible to give a name that means anything to many of these acute respiratory infections, but we can say that all the extensive epidemics of what is called typical influenza that have occurred since 1933 have been due to one or other of two well-defined viruses known among virologists as influenza viruses A and B. The nature of the great pandemic of 1918-19 has never been established, but most authorities would probably agree—at least there is nothing to disprove the hypothesis—that is was due primarily to influenza viruses resembling the modern A types.

Once the viruses have been isolated, their ability to grow readily in the chick embryo and to agglutinate red blood cells make them particularly easy to handle, and a great deal is known about their properties. This same ease of handling has also stimulated the study of influenza as it occurs in man and of the experimental disease produced by infecting animals with the virus.

The first isolation of a virus from human influenza was made in 1933 by an English team of research workers headed by the late Sir Patrick Laidlaw. Two years previously, however, a virus now known to be very closely related to influenza virus A was isolated from pigs with the disease known in America as swine influenza or "hog flu."

The events leading to the isolation of human influenza virus are worth mentioning, Ever since the great influenza epidemic of 1890 bacteriologists had been interested in discovering the organism responsible for the disease. In 1893 Pfeiffer, a German bacteriologist, had claimed that a bacterium now called Haemophilus influenzae was the cause. Extensive investigations of the 1918-19 epidemic showed that no special types of bacteria were consistently present, and there was a considerable body of opinion in favour of the view that the primary agent must have been a virus. No one succeeded, however, in demonstrating that a virus was present, even with the use in some cases of human volunteers. By the end of 1932 techniques for virus study were much more advanced than in 1919, and in particular Laidlaw and Dunkin had just completed a successful study of the virus disease dog distemper which many people regarded as essentially similar to human influenza. When a fairly severe influenza epidemic hit London in December, 1932, Laidlaw, Andrewes and Wilson Smith undertook primarily to see whether, by injection of material from the throats of patients with influenza, anything resembling influenza could be produced in experimental animals. They were prepared to try all available animals, from white mice to horses, but in fact almost the first animals they tried gave them their answer. During the work on distemper Laidlaw had found that, in addition to dogs, ferrets were highly susceptible, usually dying of the experimental disease. They had proved convenient experimental animals, and methods for handling ferrets so as to prevent any accidental unwanted infections had been worked out. The whole experimental set-up for this work was still available, so it was natural to test the susceptibility of ferrets to the material that they hoped contained the virus of influenza.

I can vividly remember the excitement that went around the National Institute of Medical Research at Hampstead when the ferrets developed symptoms unmistakably similar to human influenza. Two days after a throat washing from a human patient had been dropped into their noses they developed a high fever, lost their appetites, and curled up miserably. Their noses began to run and they even sneezed! It was a relatively mild disease and, as in human beings, the fever abated in four or five days, and the animals recovered completely. There was hardly any doubt right from the beginning that it really was influenza that had been given to the ferrets, and all subsequent work has supported this conclusion. It was found, for instance, that when a patient had recovered from influenza his blood serum contained antibody that would, when mixed with virus, render it incapable of producing influenza on inoculation into a ferret.

Ferrets, however, are not the most convenient laboratory animals; they are expensive, difficult to breed, and they bite. The next step in influenza virus research was to show that mice could also be infected, although not with virus direct from the human patient. If the virus had gone through a few "passages" in ferrets, i.e. transferring nasal material from an infected ferret to a new one in sequence, it could then infect mice, and after a few passages through them gave rise to a fatal pneumonia. The degree to which the lungs became solid, airless, and deep plum colour could be used as a measure of the amount of virus that had been inoculated. In the years 1935-40 most experimental work on influenza viruses was carried out on mice and many important results were obtained. In the two years 1940-41 there was a rather dramatic change in the experimental approach. In 1940 I showed that influenza virus would grow freely and produce visible changes in the chick embryo if it were inoculated into the amniotic cavity. This method of inoculation could be used to isolate influenza virus directly from human throat washings, and it soon became the standard method of isolation. Following on this several people showed in 1941 that the much simpler method of inoculation into the more superficial allantoic cavity was equally effective for influenza virus once it had been successfully isolated. The method was, however, of no use for isolating the virus from human patients. In the same year Dr. George Hirst of the Rockefeller Foundation laboratories made the all-important discovery that fluids from chick embryos infected with influenza virus would clump the red blood cells of chickens or men. Since then most work on problems of influenza virus has been done by a combination of chick-embryo culture and haemagglutination. I have told elsewhere how this type of work has thrown a great deal of light on the nature of virus action on the cell. It has been equally productive in regard to the problems of influenza as a human disease.

The first essential to the understanding of any infectious

disease is to be able to recognize it. This is often by no means easy. For very many years the two diseases typhoid fever and typhus fever were indistinguishable by physicians, although we would now regard them as utterly different in almost every essential. It was not long before it was found that not all infectious fevers labled influenza by doctor and patient were due to the virus that had infected the ferrets in 1933. Out of the hotchpotch of acute respiratory infections it became necessary to sort out those which, on the basis of laboratory tests, were "true influenza," i.e. infections due to the newly isolated virus. By 1937 it was possible to say that influenza virus characteristically produced the sort of influenza that occurs in acute widespread epidemics. When only occasional cases were occurring during a winter these gave no evidence of being due to influenza virus. However, even this generalization did not always hold. There was for instance a typical large epidemic in America in 1936, which was not due to the virus that Laidlaw and his colleagues had isolated. Then from a similar American epidemic in 1940 Dr. Thomas Francis isolated another sort of virus obviously resembling the first but with no immunological relationship to it. This virus is now known as influenza B, in contrast to the influenza A virus isolated in 1933. A third type of influenza virus was found in 1948 and is known as influenza C. It is apparently widespread in most countries but produces only the most trivial of symptoms. It is certainly of no great importance in comparison with influenza A and B, and will not be mentioned again.

In investigating any outbreak of the general nature of influenza the first practical job is to find whether it is due to A or B virus, or to neither. This is now a fully standardized procedure. First one locates a few patients in the first acute stage of the disease with a temperature of at least 100°F. These are given an ounce of salt solution to gargle; this is then returned to a test tube, where it is mixed with a solution "serum-broth" that helps preserve the virus. At the same time a sample of blood is taken from a patient's veins. This is allowed to clot, the fluid serum separated, labelled "Serum I," and placed in the refrigerator. A fortnight later the same patient is bled again to provide "Serum II." These three fluids are the raw materials for the laboratory tests.

The throat washings are filtered through sterilized ordinary

filter paper to get rid of particles of food, etc., and then penicillin and streptomycin are added to prevent the growth of
bacteria. A few drops are then inoculated into the amniotic
cavity of each of six chick embryos that have been incubated
for thirteen days. The eggs are sealed and put back into an
incubator for five days. The amniotic fluid and the lungs are
then removed from each embryo and tested for their ability
to agglutinate human or guinea-pig red cells. If influenza virus
is present the cells will show typical clumping. After this it is
usual to "adapt" the virus to growth in the allantoic cavity
before testing whether it is of A or B type. This is very simple
in theory, although in practice there are some complications.
If it is type A, a known anti-A serum will inactivate it so that
it will not agglutinate red cells; an anti-B serum will have no
such action.

It is a much simpler matter to determine from the two samples
of serum whether the patient has had true influenza and whether
it was type A or B. Tests are made to see how active each
sample is in inactivating given amounts of standard A and B
viruses. We can express that activity in numerical fashion as
so many units of antibody, and we may tabulate the kind of
result one would expect from a case of influenza A as follows:

	Antibody against	
	Influenza A	Influzena B
Serum I	10	20
Serum II	500	20

There is a rise in antibody between first and second bleeds
of the type corresponding to the virus involved. In most
laboratories a second kind of test, a complement fixation reaction
that depends on a somewhat different principle, is also used to
differentiate A and B infections. It has definite advantages over
the simple neutralization test, but the theory of the reaction
is too complicated to be discussed here.

In dealing with an actual epidemic it is usual to be content
with isolating a small number of samples of virus, but to obtain
first and second samples of serum from large numbers of typical
cases, doubtful cases, and people who have been exposed but
have shown no symptoms. When these are worked out we know
pretty accurately the nature and extent of the epidemic.

We can now say something about the behavior of influenza A and B in Europe, America and Australia since 1933. On the basis of studies in various laboratories a diagram could be presented which would show the main epidemics. It would be seen that epidemics are always at least two years apart, influénza A tending to be at two- or three-year intervals, whereas major influenza B epidemics are usually four to six years apart. In recent years many isolations of A and B virus have been made in intermediate years or from small outbreaks unassociated with a typical widespread epidemic. Influenza A has consistently tended to be more frequent and more important than B. Much more work has been done with A, and general concepts of how influenza epidemics arise and spread have been developed mainly around influenza A. Also, there is a little circumstantial evidence that the great influenza epidemic of 1918-19 was due to influenza A viruses.

If for the time being we omit influenza before 1933 and concentrate on influenza A, the picture that emerges is something like this.

Influenza A virus is wholly a human parasite in the sense that infection is always derived fairly directly from another infected human being. Epidemics occur only when seasonal conditions are appropriate, almost wholly in winter and spring, and when there is a large enough population of individuals nonimmune to the particular virus active at the time. In between epidemic periods the virus survives as trickling streams of infection in nonimmune individuals, often without actual symptoms being produced. When a typical big influenza epidemic has passed through a country most nonimmunes have probably been infected either with fever or without symptoms and have become immune. This immunity gradually fades, but it is probable that, if the virus remained constant in character the great majority of people would retain an effective immunity for at least five or six years. It is gradually becoming certain, however, that the virus does not remain constant. Influenza virus is a highly labile organism prone to mutation of many types, including mutation in immunological character. Such inheritable changes in character have never been so great as to render an A virus unrecognizable as A or convert it to B, but they have been sufficient to allow an animal immune to one type to be susceptible to the changed form. It appears that to survive an as agent of human disease influenza A virus needs to be undergoing a more or less steady sequence of changes in its immunological character. The form that immunized a city population two years earlier cannot provoke an epidemic there, but if one of its descendants has changed by mutation so that antibody against the old form is no longer effective, this descendant virus can initiate an epidemic. The facts are that each new epidemic of influenza A seems to be due to virus differing to a greater or lesser extent from all previous viruses in these immunological characters. It is only an assumption, but a very likely assumption, that the mutability of influenza virus is an essential requirement for its survival as a species.

THE GREAT PANDEMIC OF 1918-19

Within the last century there have been two epidemics of influenza intense enough and extending widely enough to merit the term pandemics, epidemics involving the whole of the world's population. These occurred in 1890-2 and in 1918-19. The latter was by far the more devastating of the two. In England the epidemic of 1890 broke on a population which for some reason had not experienced a definite influenza epidemic since 1857. There were extremely large numbers of cases in the three waves of the epidemic and many deaths, especially of older people. Naturally, nothing is known about the virus responsible, but one's impression is strong that the epidemic was quite similar to a modern influenza A epidemic. Its extent was probably due simply to the fact that for some unknown reason there had been an unusually long gap since the last epidemic of influenza A.

From 1890 onward there were recurrent epidemics of influenza in England which appear to have been quite similar in character to the epidemics of influenza A and B 'that have been verified since 1933. In 1918, however, something unprecedented occurred. In England an acute epidemic of influenza broke out in the second week of June. It had clearly been brought from France by soldiers on leave from the Western Front. In that week there was a sudden change in the age incidence of deaths ascribed to influenza. Instead of deaths being concentrated in the oldest age groups plus some in infancy, they involved young adults. This epidemic in early summer spread widely through the community and, considering the very large number of people who were infected, the death rate was quite

low. The disturbing feature, however, was the sinister concentration of mortality on the young adult. This was to be
characteristic of the pandemic throughout its course, both in its
early mild phase and its subsequent killing waves. The summer
epidemic died down, but in August a new wave of cases began
with a frighteningly high mortality. This wave in England
reached its acme in October. Another lull was followed by a
winter wave, also of high mortality. Influenza remained unduly
active and unduly fatal through 1919 and 1920, but gradually
reverted to normal character. The change from the young adult
incidence of fatality to the standard type involving virtually
only the old was not complete until 1929. The pandemic involved the whole world and the total death roll probably exceeded 25,000,000 persons. The greatest absolute mortality was
in India, where it was sufficient to wipe out the whole population increase over the decade 1911-21. In some small communities
where the whole population was stricken almost simultaneously
nearly 50 per cent died. In most countries with accurate vital
statistics and populations predominantly of European origin the
mortality rate was about 5 per 1,000 of the population. In countries like South Africa and New Zealand the non-European
death rate was four to ten times higher than that of whites
in the same country. Only a few very isolated places escaped
the pandemic completely. The largest was New Caledonia, and
the list also included New Guinea and some other islands in the
Southwest Pacific and St. Helena.

It is not possible to give an accurate account of the origin and
spread of the epidemic. In 1940 Miss Clark and I published a
monograph in which this was discussed in detail, and here we
can only present a brief statement of the conclusions we reached
in that monograph. Influenza of the new type first appeared
around April, 1918, in Western France, in the region where large
numbers of American troops were being poured into Europe.
There had been moderately intense epidemics of "ordinary"
influenza in both America and Europe in the immediately preceding winter and spring, and there is therefore a strong suggestion that in some way the mingling of large numbers of
Americans and Europeans, with their associated viruses, was
responsible for the genesis of the new type of influenza. From
France the epidemic passed to Spain, where it first created real
public alarm, and received the name Spanish influenza by which,

in English-speaking countries, it was generally referred to at the time. The summer epidemic spread over most of Europe, and other similar and presumably related epidemics are referred to from places as far apart as West Africa and Chungking in the heart of China. The change from the mild summer wave to the much more lethal autumn type took place close to the Western Front, where the great battles of July and August, 1918, were being fought. It spread rapidly to every major part of the globe. There are hints that the change to the lethal type took place independently at more than one point, but it seems more reasonable to assume that the change occurred in France and spread thence at the speed and in the direction of human movement.

Pandemic influenza entered America at Boston on August 12 and flared across the continent within a month. It reached Australia and New Zealand in October. In New Zealand it spread through the country at once, but in Australia stringent quarantine regulations—or perhaps some other factor unknown—prevented any outbreak until February, 1919. The peak of the Australian epidemic was in August, 1919, and it was only in that month that pandemic influenza reached Tasmania. This was the last sizable community to be reached anywhere in the world, and it is probably significant that the mortality that resulted was the lowest of any state in Australia and for that matter of any major community in the world.

There is some evidence that human beings were not the only victims. In South Africa large numbers of baboons died at the time, and it may be that the popular ascription of their deaths to influenza was correct. A much more substantial story concerns the swine influenza of Iowa and other Mid-Western American states. Dr. Richard Shope, the outstanding authority on that disease, says that there is unanimity among farmers and veterinarians that "hog flu" was unknown before 1918 and was actually first seen at the Iowa State Fair which in 1918, coincided with the time of the first experience of pandemic influenza in that state. The disease has persisted since, breaking out in the late autumn each year. In 1931 Shope and Lewis found that hog flu was a complex infection due to the association of a virus and a bacterium. A few years later it was shown that the virus was closely related to human influenza A virus. Others showed that in association with a human epidemic in 1937

pigs fed on garbage developed evidence of infection with virus
of the current human type. Most virologists would probably
agree that the weight of evidence supports Shope's contention
that the swine virus is a lineal descendant of the virus or one
of the viruses of pandemic influenza. There are, however, many
who, like myself, would regard our current influenza A viruses
as also having had the pandemic viruses in their "ancestral tree."
We can be certain of nothing in this field apart from the fact
that influenza viruses are extremely variable, and it is in no
way inconceivable that descendants of the same virus after
thirty years' passage through different hosts should differ greatly
in many important characteristics. Swine influenza virus is of
importance in relation to pandemic influenza only if there is
reason to believe that it has been maintained in the pig cycle
with less change in its immunological type than would have
occurred if it had survived by the normal course of passage from
one human being to another over the same period of years.

The pandemic of 1918-19, as I have said, was an unprecedented
occurrence, a type of epidemic which we can be quite certain
had never previously involved any community whose historical
records have survived. We do not know what were the initiating
circumstances. Immediately after the pandemic it was natural
to conclude that the situation created in Europe by the first
World War had been responsible in some way. It was not
difficult to think up a plausible story along such lines, but if
war circumstances in 1918 were responsible we should surely
have seen a similar pandemic sometime between 1940 and 1946.
In 1944-6 Europe suffered far greater social disorganization than
in 1918, and there were other factors such as crowding into air-
raid shelters that would have been expected to favor respiratory
disease. But there was no influenza to speak of until the first
months of 1949. We are left with the unsatisfying hypothesis
that the pandemic was due simply to some accident of mutation
or recombination that gave rise to a virus of unusual invasiveness
and capacity to spread. Once this step was taken, the subsequent
development of enormous amounts of virus would automatically
provide opportunities for further mutations to occur. It has recently been suggested that one series of mutations to greater
virulence may have taken place in the fighting zone itself as
a result of exposure of the virus to mustard gas. Compounds
of mustard gas type, in particular the so-called nitrogen-mustard,

are known to increase the mutation rate of a variety of organisms, and the suggestion is a logical one.

Finally, we must not forget that the evidence suggests that a great many, perhaps most, of the deaths were due not to virus infection as such, but to the activity of various bacteria which found a soil in which they could flourish in the lungs damaged by the virus.

THE PREVENTION OF INFLUENZA

In discussing the prevention of influenza the first question to be put is whether it is worth attempting to do so. Now, there is no question that influenza, even in the absence of a pandemic, is a killing disease. Whenever an influenza A epidemic appears there is a sharp temporary increase in deaths, most of which, however, are not ascribed to influenza. Deaths of old people ill for some other reason are characteristically increased by influenza. The severe epidemic of influenza in England during January, 1951, showed this clearly. In Liverpool, which was very heavily hit, the number of deaths in the worst week of the epidemic exceeded that of the worst week in the 1918-19 pandemic. In 1951, however, deaths were almost wholly among older people. There were few in persons under fifty-five, but above that age the mortality increased progressively in each five-year age group. A nineteenth-century writer pointed out that one could always deduce the presence of an influenza epidemic when the obituary columns of *The Times* became unusually crowded with deaths of the elderly and the distinguished. The death rate from tuberculosis also shows minor ups and downs, which indicate that many persons who would normally die from tuberculosis in one year will die in the previous year if that is marked by a definite epidemic of influenza. The harmless week's illness of a healthy individual is hardly worth preventing except when service men are involved. The prevention of pandemic influenza would, of course, become the greatest of all public health problems should anything of 1918 type arise in the future. As we have indicated, there is no clue whatever as to how the initiation of such a pandemic could be prevented.

Work on the prevention of influenza to date has been concentrated on an attempt to find a method of immunization that would be effective in preventing a disabling incidence of influenza in service men. Within limits these efforts have been successful. A vaccine can be produced from influenza virus grown in chick embryos, concentrated and killed by formalin. A single injection of this will protect about 80 per cent of those who would otherwise have influenza, provided the epidemic in question is due to virus of the same immunological type as is used for production of the vaccine. With such vaccines effective protection was provided against the influenza A epidemic of November, 1943, and the influenza B epidemic of spring, 1946. The same type of vaccine, however, was wholly ineffective against the American influenza A epidemic of 1947. The reason for this failure was simply that the 1947 epidemic was caused by a type of virus very different immunologically from the virus strains previously current.

This is the whole crux of the problem of immunization against influenza. As we have seen earlier, there is a progressive change in immunological type from epidemic to epidemic. Sometimes the change appears to be more rapid than at other times. This demands that if influenza vaccines are to have any hope of being effective they must be right up to date. When, for instance, there is a sharp epidemic in the Southern Hemisphere one winter, the virus concerned should be added to the vaccine to be used against influenza in the Northern Hemisphere six months later. This, however, is not an easy requirement to fulfill at the practical level. A biological supply firm with an order for, say, 5,000,000 doses of influenza vaccine to fulfill has to "tool up" for the work in a way almost analogous to a motor-car factory when it makes a change of the model. In particular it must have the viruses which are to be incorporated in the vaccine, fully adapted to grow freely in chick embryos. This is often exasperatingly difficult to attain, and a new virus may also require some modification of the large-scale techniques previously used. This all takes time and may be very expensive. In practice the maintenance of effective large-scale immunization against influenza is possible only if it is very heavily subsidized from defence funds. It can never become a straightforward standard procedure like immunization against diphtheria.

It is an interesting experience to see the functioning of a large commercial unit producing influenza vaccine. One unit that was in action in Australia during 1945 used approximately 11,000 eggs a day. These arrived at the plant from the poultry farms in the form of embryos at the eleventh day of development. The first step was to verify by a rapid candling process that the embryo had developed to the normal extent and was alive. Then the trays of eggs passed to girls who drilled a small hole in the bunt end of each egg and placed them blunt end upwards in rubber cups on a continuously moving belt. This led them first under a sterilizing ultraviolet lamp and then to the inoculators. These girls had a mechanical syringe fed from a reservoir of dilute "seed virus," i.e. a 1:10,000 solution of virus-containing fluid from previously infected eggs. One sharp jab and each egg received a tenth of a c.c. of fluid into the allantoic cavity. The next set of operators sealed the hole with a drop of sterile melted wax and transferred the eggs to incubator trays. The trays then went into a giant incubator, where they stayed forty-eight hours while the virus multiplied.

"Harvesting" of the virus was done with sterile precautions under a glass hood. Each egg was placed in a brass eggcup so arranged that it could rotate freely on a vertical axis. To remove the cap of shell at the blunt end where the air space is, the egg was spun around gently against the tip of a very fine oxy-acetylene flame set at the proper level. In this way the cap of the egg could be neatly cut off and the cut edge automatically sterilized by the heat of the flame. The operator then flipped off the top and with sterile scissors opened into the allantoic cavity, cutting the blood vessels and allowing the embryo blood to mix with the virus-containing fluid. The next girl in the sequence sucked out this bloodstained fluid with a specially guarded tube, in which a low negative pressure was maintained, into a receptacle chilled to near freezing point. Here the red cells settled, carrying down with them practically all the virus. The next step was to spin down the red cells in a refrigerated centrifuge and discard the fluid. The cells were then suspended in one-tenth the original volume of salt solution and held at body temperature until all the virus was reliberated into the solution. This tenfold concentrate was separated, checked for sterility, titrated for its virus content, and finally treated with formalin to give the vaccine.

Suppose that somewhere in the world a highly virulent form of influenza should arise with a concentration of mortality on young adults and an imminent threat of a new pandemic of 1918 type. What in the light of present knowledge could be done to minimize its effects? Attempts to block the spread by quarantine measures would undoubtedly be made, but would probably not be successful in doing more than to slow down the movement of the epidemic at certain points. Virologists and bacteriologists would, of course, provide as rapidly as possible information as to the type of virus concerned and the important associated bacteria. As the pandemic developed a constant watch for mutational changes in the virus would be necessary. Vaccines of the pandemic strain would be produced with the greatest possible speed, but I think we would need to be lucky to have large-scale production sufficiently under way to have a chance of making use of it in areas not yet reached by the pandemic. If, as is likely, new types arose during the course of the epidemics the vaccines would need to be modified accordingly.

There have been two great therapeutic advances made since 1918 which may change the whole aspect of a new pandemic. Death seemed to be largely due to bacterial infection in 1918-19, and there is at least a strong presumption that those deaths could have been prevented by the drugs now available. Penicillin could be expected to deal with pneumococcal, staphylococcal, and streptococcal infections, streptomycin and aureomycin with the Haemophilus influenza (Pfeifer's influenza bacillus), which was very common in 1918-19 and which is unsusceptible to penicillin. There is in the minds of many bacteriologists a suspicion that the 1918 virus was in itself the major cause of death and that the bacteria found had only a minor part in determining the issue. If this is so, the antibiotics might have proved completely disappointing.

There is another reason for doubting how effective the antibiotic drug would be if a 1918 type pandemic appeared in the next year or two—the existence of bacteria that are resistant to the drugs. It is notorious how rapidly the staphylococcus (the cause of many boils and other skin infections) becomes resistant to penicillin and the other commonly-used antibiotics. There are nearly always staphylococci in the nose, and it would be amusing if it were not sinister to see how uniformly hospital bacteriologists all around the world have found that a few months after any new antibiotic comes into general use in their hospital the "staphs" in the noses of the nursing staff begin to show an increasing proportion of resistant types. From our present point of view this is particularly sinister, because since 1933 most of the acute deaths from influenza in younger people have been due to a superadded staphylococcal pneumonia. Most pathologists believe the effect of the pandemic virus was to make the air passages vulnerable to any bacteria that might find access. It seems quite likely, therefore, that if a pandemic arose nowadays the free use of antibiotics would almost certainly result in the appearance of resistant and, therefore, dangerous staphylococci as the chief agent of secondary pneumonia.

The other approach to treatment which is of great theoretical interest at the present time is related to the fact we have stressed repeatedly, that the main incidence of death in 1918 was on the young adult. There are more than hints that the work now in progress on pituitary and adrenal hormones (ACTH and cortisone) will throw light on this phenomenon. From what we already know of the therapeutic action of ACTH (adreno-corticotrophic hormone), I should feel very confident that in a good hospital the combined use of ACTH and the appropriate antibiotics according to the best modern standards would have allowed the recovery of many of the young adults who died in 1918.

In view of the fact that supplies of these potent drugs and of physicians who can use them adequately are bound to be insufficient when patients are numbered in hundreds of millions, we could never hope to save more than a small proportion, but we at least should feel far less impotent than the last generation of physicians did in 1918.

1955

Organized Medicine and Polio Control with Sabin Vaccine

THOMAS F. FLETCHER, JR. and FRANK PROCOPIO

Dauphin County Medical Society, Dauphin County, Pennsylvania

Presented as a Scientific Exhibit, American Medical Association Annual Meeting, June 25-30, 1961, New York, New York

CAN THIS PROJECT BE REPEATED IN YOUR COMMUNITY?

BECAUSE the Harrisburg (Pennsylvania) Sabin Vaccine program represents a pioneer effort, successfully initiated by the doctors of the area themselves, it might well become a model for other communities to repeat as the Sabin vaccine becomes available. The impressive experience with live, attenuated vaccine fed to more than 60,000,000 people in the Soviet Union, Mexico, Singapore, Chile, Czechoslovakia, Japan and Holland is behind us; the practical problem of preventing poliomyelitis is before us. The prospect of eliminating poliomyelitis in the United States, as smallpox has been virtually eradicated, is favorable at last.

A City-wide Immunization Effort

On April 6, 1961, almost half the population of the greater Harrisburg area, turned out at 15 vaccine centers to receive the first of three doses of Sabin poliovirus vaccine. In a program sponsored by the Dauphin County Medical Society, more than 80,000 people were inoculated the first day. Additional participation in Type I inoculations on April 8, brought the total to 91,000 men, women, children and infants. Feedings of Types III and II were given at intervals of one month; Type III, on May 11 and Type II, on June 8.

Inoculations of Type I vaccine are given first because this strain is responsible for approximately 85% of paralytic poliomyelitis.

Material

The vaccine was diluted in distilled water, and was distributed to the vaccine centers in bottles with droppers designed to deliver 0.1 milliliters in two drops. Infants were given two drops of this mixture directly from the dropper. Older groups received two drops of diluted vaccine in a half ounce of distilled water in a paper cup.

Procedure

The handling of 81,746 people in a single day can involve major logistic problems. Such problems are not staggering when medical leadership and county society support are mobilized to stimulate community participation. Cooperation by civic leaders and the public is important to physicians in achieving a concerted attack on infectious disease. Such a program is accepted willingly by the community and is bound to enhance relations between organized medicine and the public it serves.

Although staff are assigned to one of three shifts, it is important that one competent individual remain at the vaccine center all day to keep efficiency at a maximum and confusion to a minimum. In addition to two physicians for each station, the experience of this trial suggests that for every 10,000 patients there be 50 registrars, 5 pharmacists, 5 nurses and 5 recorders to mark the data on cards. Three ushers, 3 door sergeants, 1 supply man and 1 man supervising the supply area should complete the personnel. The above numbers of personnel are essential for the first inoculation but can be reduced for subsequent inoculations.

Program

The initial impetus for the Harrisburg project came through the Committee on Child Health of the Dauphin County Medical Society and was fully backed along the way by the society. The vaccine was provided by Chas. Pfizer and Co., Inc. for this study. Then began the intense campaign (12 days) to educate the public using all possible media. Adequate physical means for patient management and distribution of vaccine required careful planning by the Committee to assure greatest efficiency.

PLAN OF ACTION

Physicians volunteered for active duty. From one to eight Medical Society members were on duty at every vaccine center to supervise the mixing and administering of vaccine and provide other support. Of the 14 doctors who served as captains for each unit, six were pediatricians.

Television, newspapers, radio and churches performed outstanding jobs of keeping the program constantly before the public through front page stories, broadcasts and announcements from the pulpit.

Dauphin County Medical Society Auxiliary brought out about 500 physicians' wives to handle the huge amount of paper work in registering long lines of people, completing forms and making necessary records.

Medical Assistants Association of Harrisburg helped doctors and pharmacists handle vaccine, and assisted in controlling lines of people, registering, and other paper work.

Dauphin-Cumberland-Lebanon Pharmaceutical Association provided trained pharmacists who mixed and dispensed vaccine supplies at every immunization depot, many volunteering all-day service to the neglect of their own immediate affairs.

Harrisburg Red Cross assisted in distribution of vaccine and in administrative work.

PTA and other civic organizations gave the project needed publicity and urged Harrisburg residents to come in and take the vaccine. In addition, they provided volunteers for work at various stations.

Police—municipal and state—cooperated willingly in handling traffic and controlling jams, particularly in areas where long lines formed and car traffic was heavy.

Cumberland-Perry-Dauphin District Nurses Association supplied 54 nurses to serve at stations the first day and 15 more on the second day, working directly with pharmacists and doctors.

Factors Influencing Participation*

Interviews were conducted with 300 heads of households, randomly selected in Harrisburg proper, in order to determine some of the factors influencing participation or non-participation in the vaccination program.

97 per cent of all people interviewed had heard about the Sabin vaccine and knew it was being administered in Harrisburg.

Of the people who took the first dose of vaccine (in April), 93

* *Survey conducted by National Analysts, Inc.*

per cent continued on to the second dosage (in May). An additional 15 per cent joined the program in May.

95 per cent of those who took the vaccine made a special trip to obtain it. Only a handful stopped in on their way to work, during a shopping trip, or during lunch hour.

Participation was usually a family event. Only 10 per cent went alone, 72 per cent were accompanied by their children, and 40 per cent were accompanied by their spouse.

There was a direct relation between formal education and participation. High school and college graduates participated in about the same proportions; fewer among non-graduates; and fewest among those who did not go beyond 8th grade.

Harrisburg Schedule—Sabin Vaccine

	Type I*	Type III	Type II
DATE	April 6 1961	May 11 1961	June 8 1961
PARTICIPANTS	91,000	105,000	105,000

* *Type I given first since Type I wild virus causes 85% of paralytic polio in U.S.A.*

Evaluation

Type I Conversion rates 6 weeks after vaccination of seronegative patients.

Lot
A—87%
B—95%
C—93%
D—86%
E—82%

Poliomyelitis Control

The term *eradication* has come into use recently to connote the complete elimination of the disease-producing agent from the community.

The concept *poliomyelitis control* is based on the belief that attenuated poliovirus vaccine strains when administered orally, can permanently break the fecal-oral chain of transmission of wild strains that circulate in nature.

Sabin Vaccine

Live, attenuated vaccines have certain advantages over the inactivated vaccines:

Infection with attenuated live virus leads to the development of a state of local resistance of the gastrointestinal tract that limits or prevents subsequent intestinal multiplication of virus on exposure to infection with wild virus.

Serum antibody develops quickly as a sequel to gastrointestinal infection.

Since there is rapid development of serum antibody as well as gastrointestinal resistance, attenuated live vaccine may be used during an epidemic of poliomyelitis, to prevent further spread of wild virus.

Sabin vacine is simple and painless to administer, since it is given by mouth.

The cost of administration is low as much of the work can be assigned to volunteer workers.

Conclusion

The introduction of live attenuated poliovirus vaccine brings within reach the prospect of eradication of poliomyelitis.

In a community-wide mass immunization program, almost half the population of greater Harrisburg area received oral Sabin poliovirus vaccine.

The program, sponsored by the Dauphin County Medical Society, enrolled the services of many civic and voluntary organizations.

We feel that the preliminary public educational campaign was responsible for the unparalleled attendance for the initial inoculation. The value of continuing the educational campaign is evident from the increased participation in subsequent inoculation periods.

This program can and should be repeated in other communities.

A Pig from Jersey

BERTON ROUECHÉ

AMONG those who passed through the general clinic of Lenox Hill Hospital, at Seventy-sixth Street and Park Avenue, on Monday morning, April 6, 1942, was a forty-year-old Yorkville dishwasher whom I will call Herman Sauer. His complaint, like his occupation, was an undistinguished one. He had a stomach ache. The pain had seized him early Sunday evening, he told the examining physician, and although it was not unendurably severe, its persistence worried him. He added that he was diarrheic and somewhat nauseated. Also, his head hurt. The doctor took his temperature and the usual soundings. Neither disclosed any cause for alarm. Then he turned his attention to the manifest symptoms. The course of treatment he chose for their alleviation was unexceptionable. It consisted of a dose of bismuth subcarbonate, a word of dietetic advice, and an invitation to come back the next day if the trouble continued. Sauer went home under the comforting impression that he was suffering from nothing more serious than a touch of dyspepsia.

Sauer was worse in the morning. The pain had spread to his chest, and when he stood up, he felt dazed and dizzy. He did not, however, return to Lenox Hill. Instead, with the inconsistancy of the ailing, he made his way to Metropolitan Hospital, on Welfare Island. He arrived there, shortly before noon, in such a state of confusion and collapse that a nurse had to assist him into the examining room. Half an hour later, having submitted to another potion of bismuth and what turned out to be an uninstructive blood count, he was admitted to a general ward for observation. During the afternoon, his temperature, which earlier had been, equivocally, normal, began to rise. When the resident physician reached him on his evening round, it was a trifle over a hundred and three. As is customary in all but the most crystalline cases, the doctor avoided a flat-footed diagnosis. In his record of the case, he suggested three compatible possibilities. One was aortitis, a heart condition caused by an inflammation of the great trunk artery. The others, both of which were inspired by an admission of intemperance that had been wrung from Sauer in the examining room, were cirrhosis of the liver and gastritis due to alcoholism. At the moment, the doctor indicated, the last appeared to be the most likely.

Gastritis, aortitis, and cirrhosis of the liver, like innumerable other ailments, can seldom be repulsed by specific medication, but time is frequently effective. Sauer responded to neither. His fever held and his symptoms multiplied. He itched all over, an edema sealed his eyes, his voice faded and failed, and the seething pains in his chest and abdomen advanced to his arms and legs. Toward the end of the week, he sank into a stony, comalike apathy. Confronted by this disturbing decline, the house physician reopened his mind and reconsidered the evidence. His adaptability was soon rewarded. He concluded that he was up against an acute and, to judge from his patient's progressive dilapidation, a peculiarly rapacious infection. It was an insinuating notion, but it had one awkward flaw. The white-bloodcell count is a reliable barometer of infection, and Sauer's count had been entirely normal. On Wednesday, April 15th, the doctor requested that another count be made. He did not question the accuracy of the original test, but the thought had occurred to him that it might have been made prematurely. The report from the laboratory was on his desk when he reached the hospital the following day. It more than confirmed his hunch. It also relieved him simultaneously of both uncertainty and hope. Sauer's white count was morbidly elevated by a preponderance of eosinophiles, a variety of cell that is produced by several potentially epidemic diseases but just one as formidably dishevelling as the case in question. The doctor put down the report and called the hospital superintendent's office. He asked the clerk who answered the phone to inform the Department of Health, to which the appearance of any disease of an epidemiological nature must be promptly communicated, that he had just uncovered a case of trichinosis.

The cause of trichinosis is a voracious endoparasitic worm, *Trichinella spiralis*, commonly called trichina, that lodges in the muscle fibres of an animal host. It enters the host by way of the alimentary canal, and in the intestine produces larvae that penetrate the intestinal walls to enter the blood stream. The worm is staggeringly prolific, and it has been known to remain alive, though quiescent, in the body of a surviving victim for thirty-one years. In general, the number of trichinae that succeed in reaching the muscle determines the severity of an attack. As such parasitic organisms go, adult trichinae are relatively large, the males averaging one-twentieth of an inch in length and the females about twice that. The larvae are less statuesque. Pathologists have found as many as twelve hundred of them encysted in a single gram of tissue. Numerous animals, ranging in size from the mole to the hippopotamus, are hospitable to the trichina, but it has a strong predilection for swine and man. Man's only source of infection is pork. The disease is perpetuated in swine by the practice common among hog raisers of using garbage, some of which inevitably contains trichinous meat, for feed. Swine have a high degree of tolerance for the trichina, but man's resistive powers are feeble. In 1931, in Detroit, a man suffered a violent seizure of trichinosis as a result of merely eating a piece of bread buttered with a knife that had been used to slice an infested sausage. The hog from which the sausage was made had appeared to be in excellent health. Few acute afflictions are more painful than trichinosis, or more prolonged and debilitating. Its victims are occasionally prostrated for many months, and relapses after apparent recoveries are not uncommon. Its mortality rate is disconcertingly variable. It is usually around six per cent, but in some outbreaks nearly a third of those stricken have died, and the recovery of a patient from a full-scale attack is almost unheard of. Nobody is, or can be rendered, immune to trichinosis. Also, there is no specific cure. In the opinion of most investigators, it is far from likely that one will ever be found. They are persuaded that any therapeutic agent potent enough to kill a multitude of embedded trichinae would probably kill the patient, too.

Although medical science is unable to terminate, or even lessen the severity of, an assault of trichinosis, no disease is easier to dodge. There are several dependable means of evasion. Abstention from pork is, of course, one. It is also the most venerable, having been known, vigorously recommended, and widely practiced for at least three thousand years. Some authorities, in fact, regard the Mosaic proscription of pork as the pioneering step in the development of preventive medicine. However, since the middle of the nineteenth century, when the cause and nature of trichinosis were illuminated by Sir James Paget, Rudolf Virchow, Friedrich Albert von Zenker, and others, less ascetic safeguards have become

·available. The trichinae are rugged but not indestructible. It has been amply demonstrated that thorough cooking (until the meat is bone-white) will make even the wormiest pork harmless. So will refrigeration at a maximum temperature of five degrees for a minimum of twenty days. So, just as effectively, will certain scrupulous methods of salting, smoking, and pickling.

Despite this abundance of easily applied defensive techniques, the incidence of trichinosis has not greatly diminished over the globe in the past fifty or sixty years. In some countries, it has even increased. The United States is one of them. Many epidemiologists are convinced that this country now leads the world in trichinosis. It is, at any rate, a major health problem here. According to a compendium of recent autopsy studies, approximately one American in five has at some time or another had trichinosis, and it is probable that well over a million are afflicted with it every year. As a considerable source of misery, it ranks with tuberculosis, syphillis, and undulant fever. It will probably continue to be one for some time to come. Its spread is almost unimpeded. A few states, New York among them, have statutes prohibiting the feeding of uncooked garbage to swine, but nowhere is a very determined effort made at enforcement, and the Bureau of Animal Industry of the United States Department of Agriculture, although it assumes all pork to be trichinous until proved otherwise, requires packing houses to administer a prophylactic freeze to only those varieties of the meat—frankfurters, salami, prosciutto, and the like—that are often eaten raw. Moreover, not all processed pork comes under the jurisdiction of the Department. At least a third of it is processed under local ordinances in small, neighborhood abattoirs beyond the reach of the Bureau, or on farms. Nearly two per cent of the hogs slaughtered in the United States are trichinous.

Except for a brief period around the beginning of this century, when several European countries refused, because of its dubious nature, to import American pork, the adoption of a less porous system of control has never been seriously contemplated here. One reason is that it would run into money. Another is that, except by a few informed authorities, it has always been considered unnecessary. Trichinosis is generally believed to be a rarity. This view, though hallucinated, is not altogether without explanation. Outbreaks of trichinosis are seldom widely publicized. They are seldom even recognized. Trichinosis is the chameleon of diseases.

Nearly all diseases are anonymous at onset, and many tend to resist identification until their grip is well established, but most can eventually be identified by patient scrutiny. Trichinosis is occasionally impervious to bedside detection at any stage. Even blood counts sometimes inexplicably fail to reveal its presence at any stage in its development. As a diagnostic deadfall, it is practically unique. The number and variety of ailments with which it is more or less commonly confused approach the encyclopedic. They include arthritis, acute alcoholism, conjunctivitis, food poisoning, lead poisoning, heart disease, laryngitis, mumps, asthma, rheumatism, rheumatic fever, rheumatic myocarditis, gout, tuberculosis, angioneurotic edema, dermatomyositis, frontal sinusitis, influenza, nephritis, peptic ulcer, appendicitis, cholecystitis, malaria, scarlet fever, typhoid fever, paratyphoid fever, undulant fever, encephalitis, gastroenteritis, intercostal neuritis, tetanus, pleurisy, colitis, meningitis, syphilis, typhus, and cholera. It has even been mistaken for beriberi. With all the rich inducements to error, a sound diagnosis of trichinosis is rarely made, and the diagnostician cannot always take much credit for it. Often, as at Metropolitan Hospital that April day in 1942, it is forced upon him.

The report of the arresting discovery at Metropolitan reached the Health Department on the morning of Friday, April 17th. Its form was conventional—a postcard bearing a scribbled name, address, and diagnosis—and it was handled with conventional dispatch. Within an hour, Dr. Morris Greenberg, who was then chief epidemiologist of the Bureau of Preventive Diseases and is now its director, had put one of his fleetest agents on the case, a field epidemiologist named Lawrence Levy. Ten minutes after receiving the assignment, Dr. Levy was on his way to the hospital, intent on tracking down the source of the infection, with the idea of alerting the physicians of other persons who might have contracted the disease along with Sauer. At eleven o'clock, Dr. Levy walked into the office of the medical superintendent at Metropolitan. His immediate objective was to satisfy himself that Sauer was indeed suffering from trichinosis. He was quickly convinced. The evidence of the eosinophile count was now supported in the record by more graphic proof. Sauer, the night before had undergone a biopsy. A sliver of muscle had been taken from one of his legs and examined under a microscope. It teemed with *Tri-*

chinella spiralis. On the basis of the sample, the record noted, the pathologist who made the test estimated the total infestation of trichinae at upward of twelve million. A count of over five million is almost invariably lethal. Dr. Levy returned the dossier to the file. Then, moving on to his more general objective, he had a word with the patient. He found him bemused but conscious. Sauer appeared at times to distantly comprehend what was said to him, but his replies were faint and rambling and mostly incoherent. At the end of five minutes, Dr. Levy gave up. He hadn't learned much, but he had learned something, and he didn't have the heart to go on with his questioning. It was just possible, he let himself hope, that he had the lead he needed. Sauer had mentioned the New York Labor Temple, a German-American meeting-and-banquet hall on East Eighty-fourth Street, and he had twice uttered the word *"Schlachtfest."* A *Schlachtfest,* in Yorkville, the doctor knew, is a pork feast.

Before leaving the hospital, Dr. Levy telephoned Dr. Greenberg and dutifully related what he had found out. It didn't take him long. Then he had a sandwich and a cup of coffee and headed for the Labor Temple, getting there at a little past one. It was, and is, a shabby yellowbrick building of six stories, a few doors west of Second Avenue, with a high, ornately balustraded stoop and a double basement. Engraved on the façade, just above the entrance, is a maxim: "Knowledge Is Power." In 1942, the Temple was owned and operated, on a non-profit basis, by the Workmen's Educational Association; it has since been acquired by private interests and is now given over to business and light manufacturing. A porter directed Dr. Levy to the manager's office, a cubicle at the end of a dim corridor flanked by meeting rooms. The manager was in, and, after a spasm of bewilderment, keenly coöperative. He brought out his records and gave Dr. Levy all the information he had. Sauer was known at the Temple. He had been employed there off and on for a year or more as a dishwasher and general kitchen helper, the manager related. He was one of a large group of lightly skilled wanderers from which the cook was accustomed to recruit a staff whenever the need arose. Sauer had last worked at the Temple on the nights of March 27th and 28th. On the latter, as it happened, the occasion was a *Schlachtfest.*

Dr. Levy, aware that the incubation period of trichinosis is usually from seven to fourteen days and that Sauer had presented himself at Lenox Hill on April 6th, motioned to the manager to continue. The *Schlachtfest* had been given by the Hindenburg Pleasure Society, an informal organization whose members and their wives gathered periodically at the Temple for an evening of singing and dancing and overeating. The arrangements for the party had been made by the secretary of the society——Felix Lindenhauser, a name which, like those of Sauer and the others I shall mention in connection with the *Schlachtfest*, is a fictitious one. Lindenhauser lived in St. George, on Staten Island. The manager's records did not indicate where the pork had been obtained. Probably, he said, it had been supplied by the society. That was frequently the case. The cook would know, but it was not yet time for him to come on duty. The implication of this statement was not lost on Dr. Levy. Then the cook, he asked, was well? The manager said that he appeared to be. Having absorbed this awkward piece of information, Dr. Levy inquired about the health of the others who had been employed in the kitchen on the night of March 28th. The manager didn't know. His records showed, however, that, like Sauer, none of them had worked at the Temple since that night. He pointed out that it was quite possible, of course, that they hadn't been asked to. Dr. Levy noted down their names—Rudolf Nath, Henry Kuhn, Frederick Kreisler, and William Ritter—and their addresses. Nath lived in Queens, Kreisler in Brooklyn, and Kuhn and Ritter in the Bronx. Then Dr. Levy settled back to await the arrival of the cook. The cook turned up at three, and he, too, was very coöperative. He was feeling fine, he said. He remembered the *Schlachtfest*. The pig, he recalled, had been provided by the society. Some of it had been ground up into sausage and baked. The rest had been roasted. All of it had been thoroughly cooked. He was certain of that. The sausage, for example, had been boiled for two hours before it was baked. He had eaten his share of both. He supposed that the rest of the help had, too, but there was no knowing. He had neither seen nor talked to any of them since the night of the feast. There had been no occasion to, he said.

Dr. Levy returned to his office, and sat there for a while in meditation. Presently, he put in a call to Felix Lindenhauser, the secretary of the society, at his home on Staten Island. Lindenhauser answered the telephone. Dr. Levy introduced himself and stated his problem. Lindenhauser was plainly flabbergasted. He said he was in excellent health, and had been for months. His wife, who had accompanied him to the *Schlachtfest*, was also in good health. He had heard of no illness in the society. He couldn't believe that there had been anything wrong with that pork. It had been delicious. The pig had been obtained by two members of the society, George Muller and Hans Breit, both of whom lived in the Bronx. They had bought it from a farmer of their acquaintance in New Jersey. Lindenhauser went on to say that there had been twenty-seven people at the feast, including himself and his wife. The names and addresses of the company were in his minute book. He fetched it to the phone and patiently read them off as Dr. Levy wrote them down. If he could be of any further help, he added as he prepared to hang up, just let him know, but he was convinced that Dr. Levy was wasting his time. At the moment, Dr. Levy was almost inclined to agree with him.

Dr. Levy spent an increasingly uneasy weekend. He was of two antagonistic minds. He refused to believe that Sauer's illness was not in some way related to the *Schlachtfest* of the Hindenburg Pleasure Society. On the other hand, it didn't seem possible that it was. Late Saturday afternoon, at his home, he received a call that increased his discouragement, if not his perplexity. It was from his office. Metropolitan Hospital had called to report that Herman Sauer was dead. Dr. Levy put down the receiver with the leaden realization that, good or bad, the *Schlachtfest* was now the only lead he would ever have.

On Monday, Dr. Levy buckled heavily down to the essential but unexhilarating task of determining the health of the twenty-seven men and women who had attended the *Schlachtfest*. Although his attitude was halfhearted, his procedure was methodical, unhurried, and objective. He called on and closely examined each of the guests, including the Lindenhausers, and from each procured a sample of blood for analysis in the Health Department laboratories. The job, necessarily involving a good deal of leg work and many evening visits, took him the better part of two weeks. He ended up, on April 30th, about equally reassured and stumped. His findings were provocative but contradictory. Of the twenty-seven who had feasted together on the night of March 28th, twenty-five were in what undeniably was their normal state of health. Two, just as surely, were not. The exceptions were George Muller and Hans Breit, the men who had provided the pig. Muller was at home and in bed, suffering sorely from what his family physician had uncertainly diagnosed as some sort of

intestinal upheaval. Breit was in as bad a way, or worse, in Fordham Hospital. He had been admitted there for observation on
April 10th. Several diagnoses had been suggested, including rheumatic myocarditis, pleurisy, and grippe, but none had been formally retained. The nature of the two men's trouble was no
mystery to Dr. Levy. Both, as he was subsequently able to demonstrate, had trichinosis.

   On Friday morning, May 1st, Dr. Levy returned to the Bronx
for a more searching word with Muller. Owing to Muller's de-
bilitated condition on the occasion of Dr. Levy's first visit, their
talk had been brief and clinical in character. Muller, who was
now up and shakily about, received him warmly. Since their
meeting several days before, he said, he had been enlivening the
tedious hours of illness with reflection. A question had occurred
to him. Would it be possible, he inquired, to contract trichinosis
from just a few nibbles of raw pork? It would, Dr. Levy told him.
He also urged him to be more explicit. Thus encouraged, Muller
displayed an unexpected gift for what appeared to be total recall.
He leisurely recounted to Dr. Levy that he and Breit had bought
the pig from a farmer who owned a place near Midvale, New
Jersey. The farmer had killed and dressed the animal, and they
had delivered the carcass to the Labor Temple kitchen on the
evening of March 27th. That, however, had been only part of
their job. Not wishing to trouble the cook and his helpers, who
were otherwise occupied, Muller and Breit had then set about
preparing the sausage for the feast. They were both experienced
amateur sausage makers, he said, and explained the process—
grinding, macerating, and seasoning—in laborious detail. Dr. Levy
began to fidget. Naturally, Muller presently went on, they had
been obliged to sample their work. There was no other way to
make sure that the meat was properly seasoned. He had taken
perhaps two or three little nibbles. Breit, who had a heartier taste
for raw pork, had probably eaten a trifle more. It was hard to
believe, Muller said, that so little—just a pinch or two—could
cause such misery. He had thought his head would split, and the
pain in his legs had been almost beyond endurance. Dr. Levy
returned him sympathetically to the night of March 27th. They
had finished with the sausage around midnight, Muller remembered. The cook had departed by then, but his helpers were still
at work. There had been five of them. He didn't know their
names, but he had seen all or most of them again the next night,

during the feast. Neither he nor Breit had given them any of the sausage before they left. But it was possible, of course, since the refrigerator in which he and Breit had stored the meat was not, like some, equipped with a lock . . . Dr. Levy thanked him, and moved rapidly to the door.

Dr. Levy spent the rest of the morning in the Bronx. After lunch, he hopped over to Queens. From there, he made his way to Brooklyn. It was past four by the time he got back to his office. He was hot and gritty from a dozen subway journeys, and his legs ached from pounding pavements and stairs and hospital corridors, but he had tracked down and had a revealing chat with each of Sauer's kitchen colleagues, and his heart was light. Three of them—William Ritter, Rudolf Nath, and Frederick Kreisler— were in hospitals. Ritter was at Fordham, Nath at Queens General, and Kreisler at the Coney Island Hospital, not far from his home in Brooklyn. The fourth member of the group, Henry Kuhn, was sick in bed at home. All were veterans of numerous reasonable but incorrect diagnoses, all were in more discomfort than danger, and all, it was obvious to Dr. Levy's unclouded eye, were suffering from trichinosis. Its source was equally obvious. They had prowled the icebox after the departure of Muller and Breit, come upon the sausage meat, and cheerfully helped themselves. They thought it was hamburger.

Before settling down at his desk to compose the final installment of his report, Dr. Levy looked in on Dr. Greenburg. He wanted, among other things, to relieve him of the agony of suspense. Dr. Greenburg gave him a chair, a cigarette, and an attentive ear. At the end of the travelogue, he groaned. "Didn't they even bother to cook it?" he asked.

"Yes, most of them did," Dr. Levy said. "They made it up into patties and fried them. Kuhn cooked his fairly well. A few minutes, at least. The others liked theirs rare. All except Sauer. He ate his raw."

"Oh," Dr. Greenberg said.

"Also," Dr. Levy added, "he ate two."

1950

The New Weapons
Against Cancer

STEVEN M. SPENCER

In 1898 Dr. Roswell Park, a professor of surgery at the University of Buffalo, assured the New York legislature that he could find the cause of cancer in two years and thus solve the problem for all time. All he needed was $10,000 to work with. The lawmakers, swayed by his enthusiasm, appropriated the requested amount and set up the first laboratory in the world with a full-time staff devoted to cancer research.

Today, sixty years and many millions of dollars later, the problem is still unsolved. But no one with faith in the power of medical science begrudges the funds channeled into the Roswell Park Memorial Institute, as it is now known, or into the hundreds of other laboratories searching for the cause and cure of cancer. We should use the plural form, for cancer is not one disease, but many, and more than one type of treatment will be needed to conquer it. In any event, this effort has become the largest research program in modern medical history, and the most varied. During the current year more than $50,000,000 will be spent to keep 5,500 scientists and an equal number of technicians at work on cancer in this country alone. These are combined estimates of the American Cancer Society and the National Cancer Institute, a unit of the United States Public Health Service. Cancer is also a high-priority research goal, of course, in many other countries.

Never before have so many millions of dollars and so many trained men and women converged upon that microscopic package of evil, the cancer cell. And never before, in their quest for lifesaving answers, have the searchers probed so deeply and from so many directions.

Biochemists are ingeniously synthesizing bogus compounds that resemble natural nutrients, aiming to fool the cancer cell's metabolic machinery and stall its growth. Pharmacologists have screened upward of 40,000 chemicals against human and animal cancers grown in test tubes and in animals and have found about thirty promising enough to try in human patients. In New Orleans a group of doctors has devised a method of piping a high concentration of anticancer drug through the tumor without letting it spread to sensitive organs elsewhere in the body. A combination of chemicals and surgery has shown some preliminary value and is now undergoing a large-scale test.

To study the phenomenon of immunity—a subject of interest to the Buffalo laboratory nearly fifty years ago—physicians of the Sloan-Kettering Institute and Ohio State University Medical School have been injecting live cancer cells into the arms of Ohio prison volunteers. Other researchers are prying viruses apart to see how they are put together and what causal connection they may have with cancer in man—a connection fully established in many animal cancers. Whether the prisoner studies and the virus work will lead to a vaccine against human cancer is anybody's guess.

Some of the very brightest hopes for successful treatment spring from evidence that many common cancers, notably those of the breast and prostate, and possibly others, are dependent upon a certain hormonal environment for their early growth. Medical or surgical alteration of this environment may, if begun soon enough, reverse the cell's lethal metamorphosis back toward normal.

It should not be inferred that any of these maneuvers have yet given us a sure chemical cure for malignancy. To be frank, optimism regarding this form of therapy is somewhat more restrained than it was in the 1940s, when this writer was reporting the first break-throughs with hormone and chemical treatments. Experience has brought a more realistic appreciation of the tenacity of both the leukemia and the cancer cells. Doctors have repeatedly seen them bounce back to destructive dimensions after being held in chemical check for years.

But one cannot overlook the fact that the patients treated by these new methods have gained precious intervals of comfort and fairly good health—sometimes lasting many years. This is no small achievement in the battle against otherwise hopeless malignancy. It is a bright ray of hope piercing the gloom, a sign that measurable progress is being made. On the dark side are the 250,000 who die of cancer each year in this country. But balanced against them are 800,000 men and women now living who were saved from cancer by better methods of detection and treatment. Thousands of the women in this group owe their lives to the cell-smear technique of detecting uterine cancer, devised by Dr. George N. Papanicolaou, whose seventy-fifth birthday last May 13 was marked by the American Cancer Society with a luncheon. It has been estimated that cancer of the uterine cervix would be almost 100 per cent curable if all cases were detected early. This and other practical results of research have already increased the cure rate of cancer in general to 32 per cent. And the research army is steadily amassing new knowledge that is almost sure to be fashioned into more effective therapy for the future.

To review in detail the entire research front, naming every one of the hundreds of worthy projects, would be impossible in a single article. In this report, therefore, we shall simply trace some of the main lines along which the cancer fighters are driving and indicate a few of the high points of hope.

The multiplicity of therapeutic weapons, both old and new, is in itself a valuable asset. Many patients are gratefully aware of this. During a tour of research centers conducted last spring by the American Cancer Society we visited New York's Sloan-Kettering Institute, largest of these centers, and talked to Mrs. C. An attractive, dark-haired woman of fifty-five, she had fought cancer to a standstill no less than five times in twelve years.

The first trouble occurred in her breasts, and surgeons removed both of them in 1946. Mrs. C. remained well until 1950, when severe backaches signaled a return of the cancer and its spread to the spine. X-ray treatments suppressed the condition and gave her three more years of comfort. A second recurrence in the spine was put down with a second course of X rays. But in 1954 the cancer struck again, producing intense pain in the legs. Once more she received X-ray therapy. Again a short respite. When pain and numbness in the legs returned in 1955, the physicians decided upon surgical removal of the pituitary gland. Even though the cancer was in the leg bones, it was still composed of breast-cancer cells and theoretically would respond to hormone control.

The pituitary is located on the underside of the brain, and removing it interferes with a hormone upon which the breast cancer may still be dependent. Dr. Olof H. Pearson, of the Sloan-Kettering staff, and Dr. Bronson Ray, neurosurgeon of the

Cornell Medical School faculty, have four years of evidence that excision of this gland often slows down advanced breast cancer. Mrs. C. was among their first 109 patients, a group whose progress has been recently evaluated in a follow-up study. She is one of the 50 per cent who gained relief from the operation.

It abolished her pain at once, and two months later she was able to walk again. For the past three years Mrs. C. has been employed as a secretary to a busy sales executive, she told us, and she goes to and from work on the subway. To replace some of the hormones whose output was reduced by pituitary removal, she takes cortisone and thyroid. "That's no trouble at all," she said. "I simply keep track of my medication by marking it off on my calendar day by day."

Most of the research approaches, whether in the laboratory or at the bedside, have as their target the interior of the cancer cell itself. Cancer has long been regarded by many authorities as a result of breakdown of the orderly life of the body's normal cells. The big unanswered question has been the precise nature of that breakdown, the identity of the forces that convert a good cell into a bad one. Today, with their increasingly sensitive instruments and methods—electron microscopes, radioactively-tagged atoms, ultracentrifuges, paper chromatography, even electronic computers—the researchers are obtaining a close look at the cell's inner structure.

What they hope to find is the metabolic sand that is jamming the gears or throwing the thermostat out of kilter. They want to learn just what it is that causes the useful, hard-working normal cell to get out of hand and degenerate into a lazy, worthless but highly destructive lump of protoplasm. And once the cell has become cancerous they want to know how to interfere with its metabolism in such a way as to stop its growth.

Enough is already known about some of the steps in cancer formation to permit the researchers to get a chemical toe in the door. They began to do this more than ten years ago. At that time Dr. Sidney Farber, director of the Boston Children's Hospital Cancer Research Foundation, and the late Dr. Yellapragada SubbaRow, biochemist of the Lederle Laboratories, found that certain anti-vitamins called folic-acid antagonists would gum up the metabolism of the leukemia cells. Treatment with these compounds added months and in some cases years to the lives of young patients. In 1953 another potent antileukemia medicine,

6-mercaptopurine, was developed at the Sloan-Kettering Institute with the co-operation of the Wellcome Research Laboratories.

Just recently, dramatic success with one of those first folic-acid antagonists—originally named A-methopterin, but now called Methotrexate—has been reported against a rare and usually fatal form of uterine cancer. The cancer is choriocarcinoma, and it arises in a placental membrane, either during pregnancy, in which case it destroys the fetus, or after the birth of the baby. Dr. Roy Hertz and Dr. Min Chiu Li, of the National Cancer Institute—the latter is now at the Sloan-Kettering Institute—found that heavy, almost toxic doses of Methotrexate caused the tumor to regress or disappear. Of the first fifteen women treated, ten have been entirely free of symptoms for from three months to more than two years. In some of them no evidence of cancer could be found following treatment. It is too early for a final evaluation, but the results are an unequivocal triumph for chemotherapy.

Among the variations on the Methotrexate formula is a Lederle compound called dichloroamethopterin, and current interest in it is running high because of its achievements in mouse leukemia. Dr. Abraham Goldin and his associates at the National Cancer Institute found that it is 75 per cent more effective than Methotrexate in extending the survival time of these mice. Trials in human patients are now under way, with preliminary reports expected some time this year.

Another biochemical achievement of recent date is that of Dr. Charles Heidelberger, of the McArdle Memorial Laboratory at the University of Wisconsin. He knew that cancer cells use a substance named uracil much more rapidly than do normal cells. Following the principle of fooling the cell's metabolic machinery, Doctor Heidelberger reasoned that if he could alter the uracil molecule just enough, the greedy cancer cell, mistaking the fake molecule for the real thing, might eat a lethal amount of it. The normal cell, absorbing it at a slower rate, would only get sick.

So with the aid of Dr. Robert Duschinsky, of the Hoffmann-LaRoche pharmaceutical company at Nutley, New Jersey, Doctor Heidelberger set about synthesizing an imitation uracil. They replaced a hydrogen atom of the uracil molecule with an atom of fluorine, obtaining a compound called 5-fluorouracil. After tests on animals, Doctor Heidelberger's clinical colleagues, Drs. Anthony R. Curreri and Fred J. Ansfield, tried it on patients with far-advanced cancer who had gained little or no help from other treatments. At first nothing happened. Then the doctors doubled the dose. Again no effect. They doubled it again. Finally, when the patients began to suffer from nausea and other toxic effects, such as anemia, their cancers began to shrink. This happened with cancers of the neck, breast, ovary, liver, stomach and intestine, although in some patients there was no response. And it is only fair to add that Doctors Curreri and Ansfield have had more encouraging results with 5-fluorouracil than have many other doctors.

While it is possible to slack off the dosage a little, after reaching the toxic level, the margin is slender, and 5-fluorouracil is recommended for use only by physicians experienced in cancer chemotherapy. Because of its toxicity its value is limited, the Wisconsin investigators conclude. "But attempts are now being made," they state, "to alter the structure of the drug so as to reduce its toxicity while maintaining its therapeutic effect."

Not only synthetic chemicals but compounds from natural sources are being employed. One of the most promising of the latter is a filtrate obtained from human placentas by prolonged incubation at twenty-five pounds pressure. Dr. W. Steele Livingston, formerly a practicing veterinarian and now a research associate in the School of Medicine at the University of California at Los Angeles, has been quietly working on this material ever since 1945, and made his first report on it only last February in the *Journal of the National Cancer Institute*.

"This work was stimulated," Doctor Livingston said,. "by the widespread speculation during the first quarter of this century that some product of tissue breakdown might possess growth-regulatory capacity." He also felt, from noticing how often swelling and pressure accompanied the healing of wounds in nature, that pressure might be a factor in producing the beneficial chemical, whatever it was. Hence, his use of pressure in preparing the placental extracts.

The precise chemical identity of the effective compound has not yet been determined, but the material has brought about complete or partial regression of naturally occurring cancers in twenty-one of twenty-three dogs, and more recently has shown striking effects on transplanted tumors in mice. After a week of treatment, mouse tumors are only one fifth as large as those in untreated animals, and their spread to other organs has been prevented.

Doctor Livingston's work is being supported by the California Institute for Cancer Research and by the National Cancer Institute.

While the chemical attack on cancer is receiving the strongest backing—$25,000,000 in Government funds alone this year—a number of scientists are looking for ways to strengthen the body's natural defense machinery. This is the immunity approach, and it motivates the experiments with the Ohio prisoner volunteers, begun two years ago and still continuing. They are directed by Drs. Chester M. Southam and Alice E. Moore, of the Sloan-Kettering Institute; Dr. Charles A. Doan, of Ohio State University College of Medicine, and Dr. Richard H. Brooks of Ohio State Penitentiary.

When live human cancer cells were implanted under the skin of the forearms of the healthy prisoners, there was at first a red swelling, but it disappeared in one to three weeks as the body destroyed the foreign tissue. This was a normal and expected reaction. In New York volunteers suffering from internal cancer, however, similar implants under the skin grew for many weeks —in a few cases as long as six months—before they finally degenerated and vanished. This could be explained on the basis of the generally low resistance possessed by cancer patients.

But when a second injection of cancer cells was made, both the prisoners and the cancer patients rejected the cells much more rapidly than they had the first time. This suggested to the researchers that the first inoculation had stimulated immune mechanisms which then acted more promptly on the second contact. There was even a speed-up in the rejection of a different type of cancer cell, indicating an encouraging degree of cross-immunity.

Just what is the nature of this anti-cancer response? Can it be boosted to a practical level? These questions are now under intensive study, and no one yet knows the answer. One factor which may play a part is a natural defense chemical known as properdin, discovered a few years ago by the late Dr. Louis Pillemer, of Cleveland. The blood level of properdin is well below normal in advanced cancer patients. Injections of a yeast product, zymosan, increase blood properdin levels in animals and cause disappearance of transplanted mouse tumors. Whether such treatments will raise the properdin in cancer patients remains to be seen. Preliminary tests are under way in which properdin obtained from blood albumin prepared for the Armed Forces is being administered to a few children with cancer.

Dr. Cornelius Rhoads, director of the Sloan-Kettering Institute, is enthusiastic about the immunity approach. He believes it might be possible by use of a soluble antigen—a vaccinelike preparation —to "enhance the patient's rejection of his own cancer cells."

"We here regard the cancer cell as a foreign cell," he remarked. "It behaves differently and is biochemically different. In fact, I think the failure to recognize this has retarded our own advance against cancer."

Because the whole problem is so very complex and involves so many different branches of science, efforts have been made to develop a "unified field theory" of cancer to serve as an over-all guide. This would be analogous to the "field theory" which Einstein and more recently other mathematicians have postulated for the universe as a whole.

One of the most articulate cancer theoreticians is Dr. Van R. Potter, professor of oncology (cancer science) at the University of Wisconsin. He presented his ideas, based on his own research and that of many others, in a symposium of The Biology of the Cancer Cell, at the big Philadelphia meeting of the Federation of American Societies for Experimental Biology last April.

Doctor Potter sees the normal cell as a biochemical factory with three levels of molecular function: (1) the blueprints, (2) the machine makers, or enzyme-forming system, and (3) the machines or enzymes themselves. The blueprints are molecules of heredity-controlling material known as desoxyribonucleic acid. These molecules, the hottest item in present-day biochemical research, are tiny spiral storehouses of coded information that guides the growth and destiny of the cells and the individual. The amount of information in them is fantastic. A British scientist quoted by Doctor Potter has calculated that the DNA molecules in a single fertilized human egg, much smaller than the head of a pin, carry information equal to the number of words in fifty sets of the Encyclopaedia Britannica.

The blueprint molecules direct the construction of the machine makers and they, in turn, stamp out the enzymes, in much the way that a factory die stamps out spoons. And like a kitchen spoon stirring ingredients together to make a cake, an enzyme is a catalyst which promotes a chemical reaction. The reaction may be a building up (anabolic) or a breaking down (catabolic). A familiar example of an enzyme is pepsin, which helps split our food proteins into smaller molecules called amino acids. Other enzymes build those amino acids back into human-type proteins for muscle or skin. Enzymes also assist in the cell's respiration and in its production of energy. And where reactions occur stepwise, as they usually do in the building or dismantling of large molecules, there is a specific enzyme for each step. Consider, says Doctor Potter, that hundreds of compounds are being converted into hundreds of other compounds, each via ten or twenty steps, and you can see how there can be from 3,000 to 5,000 different kinds of enzymes at work in a single cell at any one moment.

All of this goes on in the normal cells, which not only perform their assigned functions for the body but also make copies of themselves according to the information in the blueprints. Usually the system is foolproof, says Doctor Potter, but things can go wrong at any one of the three levels. For example, cells have a tendency to make errors when they try to reproduce. This occurs only about once in every million cell divisions. But when a series of errors accumulates in one cell, that cell becomes cancerous. Cancer is thus "an expression of random imperfections in the chemistry of the body."

Since the adult body contains some ten trillion cells (10,000,-000,000,000), and millions of them are continually dividing, especially in the skin, the lungs and the lining of the digestive tract, there are many opportunities for error. Not all errors give rise to cancer, but the more numerous the mistakes, the greater the likelihood. Moreover, the error rate can be increased by such external influences as radiation, carcinogenic chemicals, hormonal imbalances, and perhaps viruses.

When the errors are expressed as derangements of the enzyme-forming system, there is a loss of essential enzymes. This phenomenon has been termed the "deletion hypothesis" of cancer formation, and the enzymes most acutely missed are the catabolic or "breaking down" type. Without them the products of cell life are used for abnormal growth instead of being broken down and disposed of in a controlled manner.

"What is beginning to emerge," Doctor Potter writes, "is a picture of cells that may in some cases be near the simplest forms of life—cells in which the enzyme pattern has been reduced to near the absolute minimum."

An encouraging feature of this theory is the emphasis on accumulation of errors. To throw a normal cell into a fixed pattern of malignant growth requires not one but several metabolic mistakes. They may be spread out over years. Hence there may be opportunity to nip the cancer cell in the bud. Doctor Potter suggests that an initial injury, produced perhaps by radiation, may induce a slight but not malignant alteration in the DNA. Then, many years later when the cell is called on to divide, in response to infection or a hormone stimulus or old age, its crippled enzyme machinery produces cancer instead of normal cells.

Can the widely discussed virus theory of cancer causation fit into this general hypothesis? Some authorities believe it can, although it should be emphasized that in spite of all the discussion the only human tumor known to be caused by a virus is the common wart, which is not cancer at all. Nevertheless, much basic research on viruses is being pursued under the heading of cancer. Dr. Seymour Cohen, on a lifetime grant from the American Cancer Society, is working almost exclusively on bacteriophages, tiny viruses that infect bacteria. He and other virus investigators, including Dr. S. E. Luria, of the University of Illinois, point out that the virus particle may be regarded as a "fragment of genetic material" which can alter the characteristics of the host cell.

"The virus brings in a new set of blueprints and compels the cell to make the virus' own type of nucleic acid," Doctor Luria explains. "If a cancer cell is one which has alterations due to changes in its control system, infection with a virus is certainly one way this could happen."

The theory is quite compatible with what is being learned about the "hormone-dependent" tumors of the breast and prostate. These are among the commonest life-threatening cancers in the American population. More than 52,000 new cases of breast cancer are diagnosed annually, a figure exceeded only by skin cancer (55,000), which is relatively easy to cure. Cancer of the prostate is discovered in about 24,000 men each year. These and possibly other tumors thrive only when the hormonal environment is favorable.

Although breast cancers are primarily dependent on female sex hormones and prostate cancers on male hormones, this states the situation much too simply. In the case of the breast, normal development and function are maintained by a complex interplay of hormones from the pituitary and adrenal glands, as well as from the ovaries. Cancer apparently results from derangement of this delicate balance. Dr. Sheldon C. Sommers, of Boston University, has noted that 60 per cent of the women with breast cancer also had an underactive thyroid gland, a slowdown which may have called forth the harmful speed-up of other glands.

The physician's problem here, then, is to correct the imbalance while the cancer cells are still in their dependent phase. Otherwise they eventually become autonomous and go on growing regardless of the state of their hormonal environment.

Ideally the hormone imbalance should be corrected before the tumor is large enough to be seen or felt. But at present that is hardly possible, because there is no reliable scale to tell the doctor exactly when the endocrine system is off balance. Doctor Farber, of Boston Children's Hospital, and his associate, Dr. Jacob Furth, have proposed a hormone assay of a large number of healthy persons and cancer patients to provide better guidance on this point. In the meantime, a dozen different methods of shifting hormone balance are being employed to check dependent but far-advanced tumors.

No one is more firmly convinced of the usefulness of the hormone-dependence principle than Dr. Charles B. Huggins, of the University of Chicago, who nineteen years ago was the first to apply it in human patients. He treated cancer of the prostate by castration, which removes the tumor-supporting male hormone. Remissions in some individuals lasted up to sixteen years, which, as Doctor Huggins recently commented, "approaches the concept of cure." In a condition that usually kills within nine months after it has spread to the bones, these results are almost miraculous.

"We have come to the conclusion," Doctor Huggins said, "that hormones have nearly everything to do with cancer—its cause, progress and cure. This doesn't mean the problem is simple. There are some 2,000 hormones and related substances, and a great many have not yet been investigated."

In every adult, man or woman, there is a balance of male and female hormones. Doctor Huggins' newest theory to explain the hormone dependence of the prostate cancer is that "the male hormone surrounds the tumor and shields it from the violently active female hormone." Removing the testes takes away the male hormone protection and lets the patient's female hormone attack the cancer.

Doctor Huggins and his associates at the University of Chicago's Ben May Laboratory are employing the hormone-control approach not only against prostate cancer but in advanced breast cancer. They believe that about 45 per cent of breast cancers are hormone dependent, and the hormones may come, as we have previously indicated, from the ovaries, the adrenals or the pituitary. One or all of these glands may be removed to check the cancer. In fact, Doctor Huggins was the first to do an adrenalectomy for breast cancer, and we have already mentioned the results of pituitary surgery, as shown by Doctor Pearson and Doctor Ray.

Some physicians believe that results almost as good as those from gland surgery can be achieved through the use of counteracting hormones. Over the past five years Dr. Henry M. Lemon, of Boston University, has treated sixty women with cortisone or its relative, prednisone, to neutralize the estrogenic hormone from their adrenals and thereby arrest the spread of breast cancer. The patients under sixty-five had already had their ovaries removed. More than half of the women enjoyed definite clearing of their symptoms, and in a third of the series the remissions lasted six months or more. One woman is still well four years, and another three and a half years, after the treatment began.

"These results exceed those accomplished through surgical removal of the pituitary," Doctor Lemon pointed out. "Indeed, we feel that much of the benefit attributed to the operative procedures probably comes from the postoperative supportive medical therapy, which always includes cortisone."

Doctor Lemon even believes these studies "may be extended ultimately toward the prevention of breast cancer, since the administration of small doses of adrenal corticoids over long periods of time appears to be relatively free of hazard and very well tolerated by women in the age groups prone to develop cancer."

Among several new compounds reported at the Philadelphia meeting of the American Association for Cancer Research is an orally active chemical of the female-hormone class. It is 9-alphabromo-11-eta-ketoprogesterone, known for convenience as Broxoron, or just BOP. Dr. Ulfar Jonsson, Dr. Ralph Jones, Jr., and their associates at the University of Miami School of Medi-

cine, in Florida, reported measurable improvement—shrinking of
the tumor and recalcification of cancerous bone—in seven of
thirty-four women with advanced breast carcinoma.

One of their first patients, Mrs. S., on her own initiative, wrote
to me in glowing terms about the help it had brought her, after
hormone and X-ray treatment had failed. "I weighed less than
eighty pounds," she said, "was in constant, terrible pain, and
completely helpless—unable to even lift my hand to my face."
After treatment started, the pain disappeared, weight and strength
improved and she was able to sit up and get around in a wheel
chair, and then to walk with a cane, supported on her husband's
arm. "Doctor Jonsson was so happy to show me off," she wrote,
"that he looked as if a light were turned on inside him. . . .
Believe me, today, 'God's in His heaven—all's right with the
world.' " Unhappily, this was not, as Mrs. S. had hoped, the long-
sought-for cure. Its holding power eventually waned, and a few
months after her letters to me she suffered a relapse and died. But
as Doctor Jones remarked at the cancer meeting, "She had six
extra months of pleasant life as a result of the therapy."

Six more months of life may seem like a slight accomplishment.
But to the patient and her family they are of immeasurable importance, assuming they were comfortable months, as they often
are. And the results are also valuable for the light they throw
into the dark interior of the cancer cell and upon its many links
with the glands.

Let us examine further those complex connections with the
pituitary. This master of the endocrine system produces several
hormones. One of them stimulates lactation. Now there is an old
theory, hardly more than folklore, that a nursing mother can't
get breast cancer, that there is some antagonism between lactation and malignancy. Recently a group of Texas physicians, after
an accidental observation that gave some support to this theory,
made practical use of it to help several women in the late stages
of breast cancer.

Dr. Nylene E. Eckles, research physician at the M.D. Ander-
son Hospital and Tumor Institute, at Houston, was caring for a
Negro woman who had had a breast removed but whose cancer
had so honeycombed her bones that she could not stand or walk.
It had invaded her legs, pelvis, spine, ribs and skull. As a last
resort, Dr. George Ehni, a neurosurgeon, performed what is
called a pituitary stalk section, leaving the pituitary gland in

place and supplied with blood vessels but severing the stalk that joins it to the hypothalamus, a part of the brain.

The patient immediately gained strength and weight. She was able to return to her job as a domestic and she actually grew fat. Her remaining breast filled out and, curiously, seven months after the operation, she noticed milk oozing from it, although she had not borne a child.

When this occurred in a second patient, Doctor Eckles recalled the old theory about the antagonism between lactation and cancer and reasoned that something like the following had happened: (1) Cutting the pituitary stalk had interrupted brain messages which normally inhibit pituitary production of lactogenic hormone; (2) this hormone therefore flowed, via blood vessels, from the pituitary to the normal breast and to breast-cancer cells now scattered through the bones; (3) the lactation hormone stimulated the normal breast to produce milk and redirected the breast-cancer cells away from the malignant growth pattern back toward functional differentiation—that is, a more breastlike cell.

Impressed by the results in the first two patients, Doctor Eckles and Doctor Ehni prescribed the operation for fifteen more women with disseminated cancer of the breast. Five of the seventeen died within two months of the operation, but twelve had regression of their tumors, including strong healing of bone lesions, and four lactated. Here again, the relief was temporary. The longest survival was twenty-two months, this patient dying last January of Asian flu.

Because of space limitations we have been able to discuss only a few of the advances being made by such clinical investigators as Doctor Huggins and Doctor Sommers and Doctor Eckles. There are many others, and so long as sensitive and imaginative doctors are confronted with suffering cancer patients they will continue to find new and better ways to help them. We have room here to mention only three more.

First, several blood specialists are transfusing bone-marrow suspensions in an effort to improve the treatment of leukemia, in which the patient's own blood-forming tissues are defective. Dr. Leandro Tocantins, of Jefferson Medical College, who combines the marrow transfusions with conventional X-ray therapy, obtains the marrow from the contributors to a "walking bone bank." These volunteers permit one or two ribs to be removed surgically for their marrow content. The ribs grow back if the membranous bone sheath is left in place. Dr. William Dameshek, professor of clinical medicine at Tufts and director of the New England Center Hospital's blood-research laboratory, also has the co-operation of donors, usually members of the patient's family. He infuses the marrow after super doses of antileukemic chemicals.

Doctor Tocantins explains that the X ray and the bone-marrow transfusions complement each other. The X ray not only attacks the leukemia cells but also depresses the normal immune reaction which would otherwise destroy the foreign marrow. The marrow, on its part, bolsters the patient's supply of blood-forming material. Neither Doctor Tocantins nor Doctor Dameshek, however, feels that a definite evaluation of the method can yet be made.

At Tulane University School of Medicine, in New Orleans, surgeons have worked out a method of isolating the cancer-ridden part of the body—an arm, leg, lung or even the pelvic area—and flowing a high concentration of anticancer chemical through it. This perfusion technique protects vital organs from the toxic effects of the drug. The surgeons, Drs. James N. Winblad, Robert F. Ryan, Oscar Creech and Edward T. Krementz, developed the method as an offshoot of their work in blood-vessel surgery. It requires the careful tying-off of large blood vessels and the use of a heart-lung machine to pump blood through the perfused part. The cancer medicine is then injected into this circuit. A number of patients with far-advanced cancer have experienced marked relief with this treatment, and their tumors have diminished in size.

Finally, a nationwide program has been organized to determine whether anticancer chemicals which have to date given only palliative results might produce real cures if used earlier in the course of the disease. A number of authorities have had a theory, recently voiced by Dr. Louis Lasagna, director of clinical pharmacology at Johns Hopkins University School of Medicine, that we are missing a bet by limiting cancer chemotherapy to the "terminal" stages. Why not, they have asked, give the chemicals at the time the cancer is operated upon? This seems an appropriate moment, because there is evidence that the operation itself may jar some of the cancer cells loose from the primary tumor and send them drifting through the circulation to set up new growths elsewhere in the body. Additional evidence, mainly in animals, shows that not all such circulating cells do take root, and that fairly large clusters are necessary. Thus, if chemicals could be injected early enough they might mop up all of the floating fragments of malignancy and prevent the metastatic tumors which are so often the cause of death.

It was on these premises that the Cancer Chemotherapy National Service Center, a Government group, set up a statistically controlled study known as the Adjuvant Use of Chemotherapy in the Surgical Treatment of Cancer. Surgery departments of twenty-seven medical schools and twenty-one Veterans' Administration hospitals are participating and will pool their results. Dr. Michael B. Shimkin, chief of the biometry branch of the National Cancer Institute, and Dr. George E. Moore, director of the Roswell Park Memorial Institute in Buffalo, are supervising the program, which is starting off with two projects: (1) the administration of Thio-TEPA to patients at the time of surgical removal of stomach cancer, and (2) the use of nitrogen mustard in connection with surgery for lung cancer. Additional studies of other types of cancer and other drugs, as well as radioisotopes, are under consideration.

Although the first patients in this investigation were treated in November, 1956, those in charge feel that a total of 500 patients in each of the two studies—with half receiving the drug and half getting surgery only—will be necessary before final conclusions can be drawn. Early statements, however, are hopeful. Doctor Shimkin and Doctor Moore, in an article soon to appear in the *Journal of The American Medical Association*, say that "a review of pertinent experimental work suggests that a moderatively effective agent against an advanced tumor may be curative against smaller tumors and unestablished cancer cells." And Dr. Warren H. Cole, of the University of Illinois, who has been combining chemicals with surgery for some time, has said, "It is too early to evaluate the results, but my whole impression to date is favorable. The next three years will tell the story."

No one expects that the story will be that of 100 per cent cure. Cancer isn't going to give up that easily. But as I thumb back through my foot-thick pile of notes and reports, covering as they do the work of hundreds of talented and dedicated research scientists, I cannot help but feel encouraged. For we now have many different procedures which can hold cancer in check for varying lengths of time. Each method alone may produce only moderately good results. But the total effort assumes important dimensions. It is worth noting that this is a war in which every new weapon pushes the enemy that much farther back. Our own movement is always forward. There is every reason to believe that the terror and heartache will in time be driven away.

1958

Chemotherapy

ALEXANDER FLEMING

Scientific chemotherapy dates from Ehrlich and scientific chemotherapy of a bacterial disease from Ehrlich's Salvarsan, which in 1910 revolutionized the treatment of syphilis. The story of Salvarsan has often been told, and I need not go further into it except to say that it was the first real success in the chemotherapeutic treatment of a bacterial disease. Ehrlich originally aimed at "Therapia magna sterilisans," which can be explained as a blitz sufficient to destroy at once all the infecting microbes. This idea was not quite realized, and now the treatment of syphilis with arsenical preparations is a long-drawn-out affair. But it was extraordinarily successful treatment, and stimulated work on further chemotherapeutic drugs. While they had success in some parasitic diseases the ordinary bacteria which infect us were still unaffected.

Some aniline dyes were shown by Churchman many years ago to have remarkable selective properties as antibacterial agents, and they became prominent as antiseptics in septic wounds after Browning in 1917 described the action of acriflavine. This substance has been recommended as a chemotherapeutic agent for intravenous injection, but it proved to have some toxicity for the liver. When it is injected it very rapidly disappears from the blood and all the tissues are stained except the nervous system. The following figures give the antibacterial power of the blood before and at intervals after an intravenous injection of acriflavine, and these are contrasted with the result obtained after an intravenous injection of hypertonic sodium chloride:

*Bactericidal power of blood after intravenous
injection (in rabbit)*

A. Acriflavine 20 c.c. of 1/1000	No. of colonies	B. NaCl 3 c.c. of 10%	No. of colonies
Before injection	87	Before	25
1 min. after injection	62	2 min. after	28
3 min. after injection	87	30 min. after	8
45 min. after injection	92	2 hr. after	0
		6 hr. after	0

Whereas the increased antibacterial power after acriflavine was slight and evanescent, there was a very considerable increase after sodium chloride which lasted for hours. This could not be due directly to the sodium chloride, which in itself was not antibacterial, and the only change that could be discovered was some rise in the opsonic power of the serum. This could not be true chemotherapy, but it illustrates another of the factors which have to be borne in mind in the investigation of the action of these drugs.

Then Sanocrysin was introduced as a chemotherapeutic agent against the tubercle bacillus, and it was said that after administration so many tubercle bacilli were destroyed that an antitubercular serum had to be given to prevent poisoning with the toxins of the dead bacilli. This was another failure; Fry showed that Sanocrysin in the concentrations used had no action on the growth of the tubercle bacillus, but it is still used for the treatment of tuberculosis, although it is not with the idea of direct chemotherapeutic action.

Long before this it had been noticed that some microbes were antagonistic to others—Pasteur himself was the first to show this—and some microbic substances or antibiotics had been used for local treatment for their direct effect on the infection. Notable among these was pyocyanase—a product of *B. pyocyaneus*—which was introduced early in the century. It was not very successful and fell into disuse. . . .

Now we have to go on to a consideration of the chemotherapeutic happenings of to-day, and by to-day I mean the last decade. Things have moved indeed, and it is safe to say that in the last ten years more advances have been made in the chemotherapy of bacterial infections than in the whole history of medicine.

It was in 1932 that a sulphonamide of the dye chrysoidine was prepared, and in 1935 Domagk showed that this compound (Prontosil) had a curative action on mice infected with streptococci. It was only in 1936, however, that its extraordinary clinical action in streptococcal septicaemia in man was brought out. Thus just 10 years ago and 26 years after Ehrlich had made history by producing Salvarsan, the medical world woke up to find another drug which controlled a bacterial disease. Not a venereal disease this time, but a common septic infection which unfortunately not infrequently supervened in one of the necessary events of life—childbirth.

Before the announcement of the merits of the drug Prontosil, the industrialists concerned had perfected their preparations and patents. Fortunately for the world, however, Téfouel and his colleagues in Paris soon showed that Prontosil acted by being broken up in the body with the liberation of sulphanilamide, and this simple drug, on which there were no patents, would do all that Prontosil could do. Sulphanilamide affected streptococcal, gonococcal and meningococcal infections as well as B. coli infections in the urinary tract, but it was too weak to deal with infections due to organisms like pneumococci and staphylococci.

Two years later Ewins produced sulphapyridine—another drug of the same series—and Whitby showed that this was powerful enough to deal with pneumococcal infections. This again created a great stir, for pneumonia is a condition which may come to every home.

The hunt was now on and chemists everywhere were preparing new sulphonamides—sulphathiazole appeared, which was still more powerful on streptococci and pneumococci than its predecessors, and which could clinically affect generalized staphylococcal infections.

Since then we have had sulphadiazine, sulphamerazine, sulphamethazine and others. But of these we need not go into detail, so much has already been written about them. Meantime there had appeared other sulphonamide compounds, such as sulphaguanidine, which were not absorbed from the alimentary tract, and these were used for the treatment of intestinal infections like dysentery.

The sulphonamides were very convenient for practice, in that they could be taken by the mouth. The drug was absorbed into the blood, where it appeared in concentration more than was necessary to inhibit the growth of sensitive bacteria. From the blood it could pass with ease into the spinal fluid, so it was eminently suited for the treatment of cerebrospinal infections. The sulphonamides were excreted in high concentration in the urine, so that although they were unable to control generalized infections with coliform bacilli they rapidly eliminated similar infections of the urinary tract. In contrast to the older antiseptics they had practically no toxic action on the leucocytes. There were disadvantages in that they were not without toxicity to the patient. Many suffered from nausea and vomiting, in some the bone marrow was affected with resultant agranulocytosis, and in others the drug was excreted in such a concentration that it crystallized out in the kidney tubules with serious results.

However, for the first time we had something which did control many common bacterial infections.

It was found, however, that the action was inhibited by certain substances. Early in the work on sulphanilamide it was noticed that, *in vitro*, complete bacteriostasis was obtained with a small inoculum, while if the inoculum was large the microbes grew freely. . . .

It was shown that haemolytic streptococci, one of the most sensitive organisms, contained a substance which inhibited the action of sulphanilamide. Then it was found that pus, peptone, and products of tissue breakdown, would inhibit the action. For these reasons the local application of the sulphonamides to septic areas has not been quite so successful.

The following experiment illustrates the effect of streptococci in inhibiting the action of sulphanilamide. A large number of haemolytic streptococci, sensitive to sulphanilamide, were suspended in a 1% solution of the drug and allowed to extract for an hour or two. They were then centrifuged out and the supernatant fluid was boiled to kill any remaining organisms. Serial dilutions of this fluid were made and incubated with blood infected with a small number of the same haemolytic streptococci. (If the streptococci grew, the blood was haemolysed and served as an indicator.) In the strongest concentrations of the fluid the streptococci grew freely, but after it was diluted growth was completely inhibited, and this inhibition was manifest until the dilution reached 1 in 200,000. This was the dilution at which the original solution of sulphanilamide would have failed to inhibit if it had not been treated with streptococci.

The streptococci, therefore, produced something which did not destroy the sulphanilamide but merely inhibited its action.

This experiment furnishes an instance of a watery fluid which is not in itself antibacterial, but which becomes strongly bacteriostatic by the simple process of dilution with water.

Soon after the sulphonamides came into practice, also, it was discovered that some strains of what were generally sensitive microbes were resistant to their action. The result of widespread treatment was that the sensitive strains were largely displaced by insensitive strains. This was especially noticeable in gonococcal infections, and after a few years something like half of the gonococcal infections were sulphonamide insensitive.

This could be due to one of two things; the sensitive organisms might have been eliminated by treatment with the drug, while the insensitive ones persisted and were passed on from one individual to another; or that by insufficient treatment with the drug a sensitive microbe might have acquired a resistance or "fastness" to the drug.

It is not difficult in the laboratory to make sensitive bacteria resistant to the sulphonamides, but this is not peculiar to the sulphonamides. There is probably no chemotherapeutic drug to which in suitable circumstances the bacteria cannot react by in some way acquiring "fastness."

In the first year of the war the sulphonamides had the field of chemotherapy of septic infections to themselves, but there were always the drawbacks I have mentioned. Later another type of sulphonamide, "Marfanil", was introduced in Germany which for systemic administration had relatively little potency, but which was not inhibited by pus or the usual sulphonamide inhibitors. This was largely used in Germany throughout the war, but there is no doubt from what was seen in German hospitals when they were overrun that their methods of dealing with sepsis were far behind ours.

The sulphonamides did not directly kill the organisms—they stopped their growth, and the natural protective mechanisms of the body had to complete their destruction. This explained why

in some cases of rather long-continued streptococcal septicaemia
sulphanilamide failed to save the patient, although the *Streptococcus* was fully sensitive to the drug; the protective mechanism
of the body—the opsonic power and phagocytes—had become
worn out and failed.

Fildes introduced a most attractive theory of the action of
chemotherapeutic drugs. It was that these drugs had a chemical
structure so similar to an "essential metabolite" of the sensitive
organism that it deluded the organism into the belief that it was
the essential metabolite. The organism therefore took it up, and
then its receptors became filled with the drug so that it was unable
to take up the essential metabolite which was necessary for its
growth. Thus it was prevented from growing and died or was an
easy prey for the body cells. This theory had been supported by
many experimental facts and may give a most profitable guide to
future advances in chemotherapy.

But another completely different type of chemotherapeutic
drug appeared, namely, penicillin. This actually was described
years before the sulphonamides appeared, but it was only concentrated sufficiently for practical chemotherapeutic use in 1940.

The story of penicillin has often been told in the last few years.
How, in 1928, a mould spore contaminating one of my culture
plates at St. Mary's Hospital produced an effect which called
for investigation; how I found that this mould—a *Penicillium*—
made in its growth a diffusible and very selective antibacterial
agent which I christened Penicillin; how this substance, unlike the
older antiseptics, killed the bacteria but it was non-toxic to
animals or to human leucocytes; how I failed to concentrate this
substance from lack of sufficient chemical assistance, so that it was
only 10 years afterwards, when chemotherapy of septic infections
was a predominant thought in the physician's mind, that Florey
and his colleagues at Oxford embarked on a study of antibiotic
substances, and succeeded in concentrating penicillin and showing its wonderful therapeutic properties; how this happened at
a critical stage of the war, and how they took their information
to America and induced the authorities there to produce penicillin on a large scale; how the Americans improved methods of
production so that on D day there was enough penicillin for every
wounded man who needed it, and how this result was obtained
by the closest co-operation between Governments, industrialists,
scientists and workmen on both sides of the Atlantic without

thought of patents or other restrictive measures. Everyone had a near relative in the fighting line and there was the urge to help him, so progress and production went on at an unprecedented pace.

Penicillin is the most powerful chemotherapeutic drug yet introduced. Even when it is diluted 80,000,000 times it will still inhibit the growth of *Staphylococcus*. This is a formidable dilution, but the figure conveys little except a series of many naughts. Suppose we translate it into something concrete. If a drop of water is diluted 80,000,000 times it would fill over 6000 whisky bottles.

We have already seen that all the older antiseptics were more toxic to leucocytes than to bacteria. The sulphonamides were much more toxic to bacteria than to leucocytes, but they had some poisonous action on the whole human organism. Here in penicillin we had a substance extremely toxic to some bacteria but almost completely nontoxic to man. And it not only stopped the growth of the bacteria, it killed them, so it was effective even if the natural protective mechanism of the body was deficient. It was effective, too, in pus and in the presence of other substances which inhibited sulphonamide activity.

Penicillin has proved itself in war casualties and in a great variety of the ordinary civil illnesses, but it is specific, and there are many common infections on which it has no effect. Perhaps the most striking results have been in venereal disease. Gonococcal infections are eradicated with a single injection and syphilis in most cases by a treatment of under 10 days. Subacute bacterial endocarditis, too, was a disease which until recently was almost invariably fatal. Now with penicillin treatment there are something like 70% recoveries.

So far in this country penicillin has been under strict control, but soon it will be on sale in the chemists' shops. It is to be hoped that it will not be abused as were the sulphonamides. It is the only chemotherapeutic drug which has no toxic properties—in the ordinary sense of the word it is almost impossible to give an overdose—so there is no medical reason for underdosage. It is the administration of too small doses which leads to the production of resistant strains of bacteria, so the rule in penicillin treatment should be to give enough. If more than enough is given there is no harm to the patient but merely a little waste—but that is not serious when there is a plentiful supply.

But I am not giving you a discourse on penicillin. Suffice it to say that it has made medicine and surgery easier in many directions, and in the near future its merits will be proved in veterinary medicine and possibly in horticulture.

The spectacular success of penicillin has stimulated the most intensive research into other antibiotics in the hope of finding something as good or even better.

GRAMICIDIN AND TYROTHRICIN

But even before penicillin was publicized another antibiotic had been introduced by Dubos in 1939. This was a substance made by the *Bacillus brevis*, which had a very powerful inhibitory action on the Gram-positive bacteria. This substance was originally named gramicidin, but later the name was changed to tyrothricin, when it was found to be a mixture of two antibiotic substances—true gramicidin and tyrocidine. Gramicidin has proved to be a very useful local application to infected areas. It has an inhibitory power on bacteria far in excess of its anti-leucocytic power, but unfortunately it is toxic when injected, so that it cannot be used for systemic treatment. If penicillin had not appeared it is likely that gramicidin or tyrothricin would have been much more extensively used, but penicillin, which is quite non-toxic, can be used either locally or systemically for almost every condition which would be benefited by gramicidin.

STREPTOMYCIN

Waksman in 1943 described this antibiotic, which is produced by *Streptomyces griseus*. This substance has very little toxicity and has a powerful action on many of the Gram-negative organisms. It has been used in tularaemia, undulant fever, typhoid fever, and *B. coli* infections, but the greatest interest has been in its action on the tubercle bacillus. *In vitro* it has a very powerful inhibitory action on this bacillus, and in guinea-pigs it has been shown to have a definite curative action. In man, however, the clinical results have not been entirely successful, but in streptomycin we have a chemical which does have *in vivo* a definite action on the tubercle bacillus and which is relatively non-toxic. This is a great advance and may lead to startling results. One possible drawback may be that bacilli appear to acquire rapidly a fastness to streptomycin, much more rapidly than they do to penicillin or even the sulphonamides.

Many other antibiotics have been described in the last five

years. Most of them are too toxic for use, but there are some which so far have promise in preliminary experiments. Whether they are going to be valuable chemotherapeutic agents belongs to the future.

TO-MORROW

Let us now consider the future. There are now certain definite lines on which research is proceeding in antibacterial chemotherapy.

Fildes's theory of the action of chemotherapeutic drugs has already led to certain results—not sufficiently powerful to have made wonderful advances in practical therapeutics—but the work goes on, and from it at any time some new antibacterial chemical combination may emerge. All this is dependent on further fundamental research on the essential metabolites necessary for the growth of different bacteria.

Bacteriologists and mycologists are, by more or less established methods, investigating all sorts of moulds and bacteria to see if they produce antibiotic substances. The chemist concentrates or purifies the active substance, and then the experimental pathologist tests the concentrate for activity and toxicity. There are teams of workers who are thus investigating every bacillus and every mould in the collections which exist in various countries. This is useful team work and may lead to something of practical importance, but it is reminiscent of the momentous German researches lacking in inspiration but which by sheer mass of labour bear some fruit. . . .

It seems likely that in the next few years a combination of antibiotics with different antibacterial spectra will furnish a "cribrum therapeuticum" from which fewer and fewer infecting bacteria will escape.

Then the work on antibiotics has led to the discovery of many new chemical combinations possessing antibacterial power. Most of the antibiotics have certain disadvantages—many of them are too toxic—but it may not be beyond the powers of the organic chemists to alter the formula in such a way that the antibiotic power is retained, but the toxic power reduced to such an extent that these substances can be used therapeutically. . . .

As to chemotherapeutic research in general, I would like to conclude with a quotation from Mervyn Gordon: "No research is ever quite complete. It is the glory of a good bit of work

that it opens the way for something still better, and this rapidly
leads to its own eclipse. The object of research is the advancement, not of the investigator, but of knowledge."

1946

Surgery

JOHN THWAITES

SURGEONS tend to attract more of the limelight than their brothers
in medicine. This is not surprising. There is the stuff of drama
in surgery, and what goes on behind the closed doors of operating theaters—where laymen rarely penetrate except as patients—
makes rich material for lively imaginations. Reality is seldom
what the imagination would make of it, but nevertheless the
history of surgery is not lacking in dramatic episodes. And those
who have played its leading rôles have been men, and later
women, of great ability amply endowed with that special brand
of courage which those who accept responsibility for the lives
of others must have. Many renowned figures have adorned the
surgical scene, men who became famous for the dexterity and
speed with which they performed their operations. Their deeds,
and their mannerisms too, are enshrined in hospital legends, and
the names of many of them have come down to the present
day attached either to some surgical technique or operation which
they invented or to an instrument they devised. They were
masters of their art, and many a surgeon of present eminence
owes his position to the fact that he served his apprenticeship
under one of these great craftsmen of the past. Yet, important
though good craftsmanship must always be, surgeons today
would be the first to agree that the fundamental advances in
their specialty have not been due in the main to improvements
in operative techniques but almost entirely to medical discoveries
which have enabled surgery's basic problems to be overcome.
Medical science has made bigger and better operations possible,
while surgical science has produced the men and the tools for
carrying them out. It has been a happy and fruitful partnership.

Surgery's basic problems are pain, sepsis (germ infection),
hemorrhage and shock. In varying degrees some or all of these

may be associated with every operation, and only as means were discovered for overcoming them was any progress made. Pain, at one time the greatest obstruction to surgical advance, was conquered in the first place by Morton's ether and Simpson's chloroform. Thanks to a wide range of efficient and relatively harmless analgesic drugs the problem of post-operative pain is also now a thing of the past, and a patient may now submit to the healing knife, if not with pleasurable anticipation, at least in the knowledge that his passage through the mill will be comparatively comfortable and certainly free from severe pain.

Surgery's other great enemy at the time of the discovery of anesthesia was sepsis. As with anesthesia and pain so, too, scientific discovery came to the aid of surgery in its state of misery and frustration over sepsis. Joseph Lister, a young Glasgow surgeon of promise, lately moved from Edinburgh, where he had been trained, was quick to appreciate the lesson which could be learned from Pasteur's recent discoveries about the nature of micro-organisms. If the germs that caused putrefaction and fermentation could travel through the air and could come to rest on any kind of object, it was pretty certain, Lister thought, that septic infection of wounds was also caused by airborne germs and those that contaminated the hands of surgeons and their assistants. The answer then was clear—kill the germs.

Aseptic surgery, meaning operations conducted in an environment free from living, harmful micro-organisms, followed naturally upon antiseptic surgery. Unlike the latter, whose object was to kill germs, aseptic surgery aimed at preventing germs from coming anywhere near the field of operation.

Provided the modern aseptic technique is religiously adhered to, the risk of wound infection occurring is small. Nevertheless it is real. There are cases in which the slightest infection, while not serious to health, can undo some or all the good of the operation. Skin-grafting is one of them. When infection occurs under a skin graft it will not take root. The graft dies and sloughs off, and the whole procedure has to be gone through again. Infection means inflammation, and when inflammation subsides fibrous tissue invades the recently inflamed part and causes scarring. Scar tissue is hard, inelastic and functionless, and as it ages it tends to contract, distorting the shape of the tissues near it. When visible it is ugly. Any infection in an operation wound on the face or neck therefore must be carefully guarded against lest it results in a disfiguring scar which is highly embarrassing, to say the least, to a sensitive patient. The scar of an uninfected wound, on the other hand, is as a rule a faint thin line often unnoticeable except on the closest inspection. Again, excessive fibrous tissue formation following operations on internal organs may result in a scar which contracts and presses on and obstructs hollow structures. Bowel obstruction may occur in this way, and sometimes the passage of bile through the bile duct leading from the liver to the duodenum may be prevented by pressure from a mass of scar tissue, or adhesion, as it is called, following an operation for removal of the gall bladder. Contamination from an outside source cannot always be blamed for wound infection. Sometimes the surgeon has to operate on a part already infected by the disease he is seeking to relieve. The operation of appendectomy for the removal of an acutely inflamed appendix (the disease known as appendicitis) is an example. Here there are germs aplenty in and around the appendix, and the inflammation may have spread to other parts of the abdominal cavity before a surgeon has a chance to intervene. The story is the same wherever inflammation or abscess formation exists. But whatever its source, infection constitutes a surgical problem, and long after aseptic technique was well established surgeons continued to be apprehensive. For instance, they hesitated to embark on certain operations because the consequences of spreading infection already present would be so grave as to constitute an unjustifiable risk.

Nor was fear of infection the only thing that stayed surgeons' hands. They had no sure means of combating the shock that inevitably accompanied any operations which involved extensive damage, and the certainty of overwhelming hemorrhage effectively prevented them from operating on the heart or great blood vessels. Anesthesia, too, was not sufficiently advanced to allow the chest to be opened. As a result progress was halted— or so we realize now, in the light of modern experience. At the time, however, it appeared as if the operator's skill had reached its zenith. So much had been achieved, and it was generally accepted that those realms of the body which were still unexplored were unexplorable, and would remain so. Lord Moynihan, one of the greatest British surgeons of this century, thought so at least. In 1934 he said: "The craft of surgery has in truth nearly reached its limit in respect both of the range and of safety."

But the surgeons had not reckoned on a further helping hand from medical science. There came the sulfa drugs, Ehrlich's dreamed-of magic bullet against bacteria, and close on their heels penicillin and the other antibiotics. They practically solved the problem of surgical infection—for the time being, at all events. They did not, of course, make aseptic surgery out of date, but they did remove from the surgeon's mind the haunting fear of the consequences should asepsis fail. Now at least he had something up his sleeve for dealing with such an eventuality. He also had something which was effective against any sepsis already present, and which his probings and manipulations might easily flare up into a spreading fire of infection. The confidence that antibiotics gave to surgeons was tremendous. They felt they could advance in safety in many directions where previously they had feared to tread. A notable instance was the progress that became possible in the surgical treatment of tuberculosis of the lung, always before a forbidden field for surgery for fear of spreading the infection.

But it is a common experience that a big step forward sometimes fails to take firm hold and an inch or two of ground must be yielded before stability is secured. This was the case with antibiotics. Strains of bacteria resistant to them developed, and once more the infection bogey reared its head. Resistant strains of staphylococci in particular appeared here and there in hospital wards and caused outbreaks of infection which did not respond to the more readily available antibiotics. This is still the case today, and hence the search for new antibiotics to beat the resistant bacteria continues. The surgeon is on the watch once again, and now he is joined in his vigil by the bacteriologist— an example of the growing co-operation between the medical sciences.

Meanwhile science was aiding surgery in other directions, notably in the way of further discoveries on the nature of blood groups. In the 1920s blood transfusions were exceptional, and when they were given the amount seldom exceeded one pint and at the most two. Little was known about blood groupings beyond the ABO classification which Landsteiner formulated in 1900. Methods of cross-matching for compatibility were somewhat rudimentary and, of course, there were no blood banks to draw from. Donors had to be found in a hurry in emergencies, and unless the patient's need was very urgent surgeons hesitated to transfuse for fear of fatal reactions. They had to rely, therefore, mainly on their operative skill in preventing blood loss, since once lost they could not count on replacing it. Thanks to the work of hematologists, such as Race in this country and Wiener in America, great advances in the knowledge of blood antigens were made and several new groups, including the important RH group, were discovered. These had a direct bearing on transfusion practice, and more accurate methods of cross-matching became possible as a result. Then the discovery that blood remained fresh for a long time when stored in refrigerators at -5 °C. provided the answer to the crying need for ready-made transfusions available immediately on order, and blood banks were gradually established in main centers all over the country. To these were added stocks of dried plasma for use in appropriate cases. Thus the lack of the essential treatment for cases of shock and hemorrhage, which for so long handicapped surgeons in their work, was remedied, and these two problems have now joined their companions, sepsis and pain, in the ranks of those which may be faced with greater confidence.

Antibiotics, advances in anesthesia, and modern methods in blood transfusions were all unforeseen at the time Lord Moynihan was prognosticating that the scope of surgery had almost reached its limits. Nor could he guess to what extent surgery was also to benefit from the researches of physiologists, biochemists, biophysicists, endocrinologists—from, in fact, all branches of medical science. In particular, these contributed toward improvements in that essential preliminary to any operation—diagnosis. From being a man somewhat apart, the surgeon today works closely with his medical colleagues, and he may consult with any number of them on special problems. Any modern operation, a heart operation—say—is planned with all the preliminary staff work of a military campaign. Likely hazards are assessed in advance and plans made for countering them. Advice on the best way of doing this and that is sought from the appropriate expert on the subject. Thus when the moment comes for the surgeon to take over supreme command he does so with all the resources of scientific medicine behind him. It is he who has the patient's life at his finger tips and it is upon his skill that the fortunes of the day rest, but it is to medical science as a whole, in which surgery today is one of the active partners, that the credit for victory must ultimately go, for science makes the operation possible.

Wars have a habit of hastening the pace of medical progress, and in no branch of medicine has this been truer than in surgery. Wars call for courage in fighting men, and they also call for courageous methods in dealing with their wounds. It is surprising how often a surgical boldness which would scarcely be contemplated in less exacting circumstances pays dividends, and many an operation now a standard practice was born out of some desperate emergency in a battle casualty. Wars, too, of grim necessity provide surgeons with a concentration of practical experience which they would have to wait years for in civil life, and many a young surgeon thrown in at the deep end of casualty surgery has emerged in a short time with a mastery of his craft such as he could not have attained under other conditions.

When World War II began surgeons were well prepared with detailed schemes to meet the new conditions associated with mobile warfare. Experience had shown that moving badly wounded men any distance before they received preliminary treatment often tipped the scale against their survival. What was needed was treatment on the spot in the form of first-aid repairs and rest until the initial shock had passed. Therefore arrangements were made whereby mobile operating teams, complete with all equipment, toured the forward areas and set up shop wherever they were needed. Surgeons went to the wounded instead of the wounded being brought to the surgeons, and many a tricky operation was performed while a battle raged all about. But it was particularly about the prevention and treatment of the condition called shock and sepsis—together with hemorrhage the principal and most dangerous complications of wounding—that so much of value was learned in World War II.

The number of lives saved by penicillin can never be calculated. Wounds were so grossly contaminated with earth, bits of clothing, pieces of missile, etc., that asepsis in treating them had little meaning. Surgeons had to return to the principles enunciated by Lister, but instead of carbolic they had its modern and so much more effective successor penicillin as their antiseptic. How well it played its part is one of the most wonderful stories in the records of surgery. Surgeons also learned that, as a preventive against infection, it was essential to cut away wholesale all dead and damaged tissues and blood clot from wounds until healthy tissue was exposed, for dead tissue and blood make excellent culture media for bacteria, particularly the dangerous anaerobic bacilli of gas gangrene. This sometimes drastic but entirely necessary spring-cleaning procedure is know as débridement.

Shock—the surgical variety and not to be confused with a state of emotional upset such as might be engendered by sudden bad news—is a condition which has plagued surgeons as long as surgery has been practised. When severe it is highly dangerous and may be fatal. It results from the body's reaction to severe injury, and its manifestations are due to a failure of the circulation and the deprivation of oxygen from the tissues owing to insufficient blood supply. Unless the condition is quickly reversed the functioning of vital structures is depressed to a degree from which they are unable to recover. In shock the patient is collapsed, although often conscious, ashen grey in colour, icy cold in the extremities, a cold sweat on the brow and a feeble pulse. He lies still and quiet.

Some degree of shock is invariably associated with any injury but, as a rule, the more violent the injury the more severe the shock. It occurs in two stages, primary and secondary. Primary shock is of short duration, and in mild cases of injury recovery ensues within an hour or so and all is well. In more severe cases of injury secondary shock sets in after an interval, while in very severe injuries secondary shock usually follows closely and without interval upon primary shock, one condition merging imperceptibly into the other.

For years there was a great deal of controversy about the nature of the body's reactions which led to the state known as shock, and many theories were advanced. These naturally influenced its treatment. The theory most generally subscribed to in the period between the two wars was, broadly speaking, that the impact of injury on the system had the effect of paralysing the autonomic nervous control over the contractile tone of the walls of the smaller arteries, with the result that these vessels dilated widely. As a consequence the fluid capacity of the vascular system was greatly increased and, instead of being nicely full to the brim, the fluid level in the "tank" fell right down. There was a relative but not an actual reduction in blood volume and the patient was said to have "bled into his own vessels." If hemorrhage happened to complicate the injury, then some actual loss of fluid was added to the relative loss, and the degree of

shock increased accordingly. As an outcome of this fluid loss
the pumping machinery, which is designed for working on a
full tank, failed in efficiency and the circulation was impaired.
The treatment adopted was that of heating up the patient with
hot bottles or a hot-air cradle and plenty of warm covering, and
giving hot, sweet drinks—traditionally tea. Secondary shock,
when it occured, was thought to be but an extension of the
state of affairs existing in primary shock, and it was assumed that
it supervened because the blood vessels failed to recover their
tone—a failure, some believed, owing to the presence of toxins
of an unknown nature. The treatment for secondary shock was
the same as that for the primary condition.

Experience in World War II led to entirely new views on
shock, and their correctness has since been confirmed by observations on civilian casualties. Post-war research, too, has been
aided by the ready availability of all the tools of modern science.
Radioactive isotopes, for instance, to mention one only, have
proved invaluable as a means of accurately calculating blood
volume. Present-day experts do not greatly disagree with the
pre-war theory on primary shock, but they are convinced that
secondary shock is due to a set of circumstances quite different
from those that rule in primary shock. They regard the initial
vasodilatation of primary shock as a passing phenomenon of no
great consequence. Indeed, any of us who has experienced the
feelings of faintness and slight nausea that follow a blow on, say,
the "funny bone" of the elbow knows they are transient, although
possibly severe enough to make us sit or even lie down for a
time. The same syptoms occur, though more markedly, in more
severe injuries such as fractures, but, again, they are not dangerous unless there are complications, and they pass off with treatment. Not so the potentially dangerous failure of circulation in
secondary shock. This has now been shown to be due not to a
relative reduction in blood volume, as was originally thought,
but to an actual reduction of blood volume owing to loss of
fluid, either blood or plasma, from the vascular system. The
severity of the shock depends upon the amount lost or, in other
words, upon the amount by which the volume of circulating
blood is reduced. Thus wounds and operations too, for that
matter, which cause severe hemorrhage, cause far more shock
than those in which there is little bleeding. Extensive burns also
cause profound shock, initially because of the severe pain and

secondarily because of the large leakage of plasma from the areas of raw tissue exposed by the destructive effects of heat. Nor was it realized until recently how much hemorrhage can occur into the tissues in internal injuries, such as fractures, in which there is no external wounding. It is now known, for instance, that it is possible for a man with multiple fractures causing extensive laceration of surrounding structures literally to bleed to death into his own muscles. A method of estimating the amount of internal hemorrhage in fracture cases by measuring the amount of swelling in the injured part has proved most valuable as a guide to treatment. Of course, hemorrhage sufficient to cause severe shock occurs in fractures only when the causative injury is sufficiently violent, as in a car smash for instance, to cause equally violent movements of the ends of the broken bones. These may be of razor sharpness and quite capable of slicing through blood vessels and any other tissues into which they are forced.

The great lesson on secondary shock learned in World War II and after was, that nothing else really mattered in its prevention and treatment than that blood lost must be replaced, and the sooner this was done the better. Once secondary shock is well established, it does not take long before vital structures such as the brain, the liver, the kidneys and the heart itself begin to feel the effects of an impaired circulation and oxygen deprivation, and unless quickly rescued from their plight their function may be so interfered with that it progressively declines to a level from which there is no return. Rescue can come only from a restored circulation, and the circulation can be restored only by restoring the blood volume, and replacing what has been lost. Transfusion, therefore, is the life-saver. Whole-blood transfusions are best, but in war these could not always be available, and transfusions made up from dried plasma were extremely valuable. Transfusions and first-aid repairs, splinting fractures and preventing further hemorrhages were the prime duties of mobile surgical teams, and right well they performed them.

A second important lesson on shock learned during World War II, and also since confirmed, was that heat treatment is positively harmful, and in more ways than one. First, by dilating surface vessels it has the effect of diverting blood into them and away from vital centers where it is urgently needed. Second, as we know from experience in hypothermia, tissues stand up to oxygen deprivation better when their temperature is low than when raised. No attempt is now made, therefore, to warm shocked patients unless they complain of feeling cold, which is a sure indication that recovery is beginning. It is a golden rule, and one which any of us might be called upon to apply in an emergency, that an injured person who is shivering and complains of cold may be warmed, but one who feels icy cold but does not complain should not be warmed. Fortunately, in these cases the customer is always right, if only we will listen to him.

The motto of the Royal College of Surgeons of England calls surgery "an art which is helpful to all men." There might have been some doubt about the strict truth of this statement at the time when the college was granted its royal charter in 1800, but today its Fellows could with justification even go so far as to add to it the words, "and to all parts of men." There are few regions of the body left unexplored, and as each one came within the ambit of the surgeon so each claimed its band of specialists, who gave all their time to this one part. Thus surgery has become a series of specialties within a specialty. It was inevitable that it should, for no man could keep pace with new developments and be equally skilled in everything.

I cannot hope to trace the progress of all surgical specialties. Whole books have been written on the surgery of, for instance, the ear, the throat, the nose and the eye, to mention a few of the small but highly important organs, and there are abdominal surgeons and surgeons who specialize on parts of the abdomen, neurosurgeons who operate on the brain and nervous system, orthopaedic surgeons who deal with the body's framework, and, most recently of all, thoracic surgeons who explore the hitherto unexplored regions inside the chest. Advances have been made in all these specialties, but I can describe here in broad outline only those which have made probably the most outstanding contribution to human welfare. Awarding priority in choice is not easy.

Out of World War I, the first time that the medical profession had ever experienced dealing with injury on a mass scale, was born after an interval an organized fracture service in Britain. It was clear that the best results in these potentially crippling and deforming types of injuries could be obtained only if they were dealt with by surgeons who treated enough of them to become familiar with their particular problems. Largely as a result of the recommendations of a British Medical Association expert committee on fractures in 1935, every main hospital in the country set up a special fracture department with its own surgical staff. The standard of treatment improved greatly, and nowadays it is exceptional for any but perhaps elderly fracture patients not to be able to resume full activities after their discharge from hospital.

As with fractures, so to some extent with other cases of injury. A tendency, of which there was evidence before the war, is growing, though perhaps not as fast as it should, to delegate to specialist surgical teams the treatment of accidents. One and a quarter million accidental injuries needing at least one attendance at hospital occur every year, though many are only trivial in nature. Thirty-five thousand children receive more or less severe burns or scalds each year, and 20,000 people are injured on the roads. The result is a great deal of chronic invalidism and a yearly cost to the community. Accidents, then, are a formidable national problem. They present a medical problem too. In treating them a surgeon willy-nilly has to take things as they are and not as he would like them to be. Unlike elective surgery, he has little time to choose his plan of action, on which a patient's life may barely be waiting, and yet on the soundness of his immediate decisions may hang the patient's future as an able-bodied or at least not-too-maimed person. Experience therefore counts for much.

Large though the number of accidents is, when spread over the whole country it does not amount to a great many in any one locality—certainly not enough for every surgeon to become expert in the special field of traumatic surgery, as the surgery of injuries is called. It was because of this that the Birmingham Accident Hospital and Rehabilitation Centre, to give its full title, was opened in 1941 as a specialist center to which all cases of injury occurring within a reasonable distance in this densely populated area could be taken, and where they could get the treatment they needed from those experienced in the work. It is staffed by surgeons who give all their time to accident surgery, and associated with them are a number of ancillary workers whose job is to help patients towards a return to as useful a life as possible as speedily as possible. This is what is meant by rehabilitation. Thus there are physiotherapists who work on wasted muscles and stiffened joints, re-educating them in their proper functions. Occupational therapists teach new occupations to those who will never be fit to return to their old ones and give temporary occupations to idle hands and minds wearied by weeks of inactivity. Artificial-limb makers fit new limbs and demonstrate how best to use the second best. Social workers help to sort out the pressing present problems and the none-the-less-real but more remote ones of people who have been cut off in midstream from control over their affairs. Watching over all, guiding, directing and operating when necessary, are the surgeons. From the first blood transfusion to the last treatment, teamwork is the watchword, and everything and everybody is co-ordinated for the one purpose of making patients well quickly. The Birmingham experiment, for such it was to begin with, has amply proved itself. Other hospital centers have organized accident departments on similar lines, and the policy is paying dividends. There are many who think it should be extended and that more hospitals entirely for accident cases should be built.

The number of patients with burns, particularly from among the ranks of air crews, mounted tragically in World War II, and as a result of the experience gained the treatment of burns has become a surgical specialty. Blood transfusion and penicillin were the lifesavers in these cases during the war. In fact, penicillin did double service, for it saved patients from the general effects of sepsis and, by quickly cleaning dirty wounds, it enabled the skin grafting which burns so urgently need to be done without too much delay. It is little wonder that this new antibiotic drug was looked upon by hard-pressed surgeons as a heaven-sent ally. Plastic surgery came into its full flowering in treating these cases, but for its beginnings we must turn back to World War I, whose receding tide left high and dry a collection of human wreckage of a kind never seen before in such quantity. Their disfigurements presented doctors with an entirely new problem, and to meet it there came forward a small but gifted band of surgeons. They were pioneers with little previous experience of the work that confronted them and with little to help them beyond their own skill and ingenuity. Bit by bit and with infinite patience they molded, built and fashioned anew, until from the ruins of human frames there gradually emerged new features which, if not exactly as before, were at least clearly recognizable as human. The specialty of plastic surgery was born.

From 1918 to 1939 the number of plastic surgeons steadily increased; there was work for all. Theirs is a job which cannot be hurried. One case may need twenty or more operations spread over three or four years. It was many years, therefore, before the last of the war wounded were dealt with and, as experience was gained, the work was always being improved. Its scope was extended to operations on some of the congenital malformations which result from faults in development in unborn babies. Cleft palates and hare lips clamored for attention and remarkably satisfactory repairs were done on them. Modern results are even better, and for these the credit must again go largely to penicillin for preventing the infection which so often in the old days caused the newly-stitched wounds in the always germ-laden mouth and throat to break down and spoil all that had been so patiently achieved. The increasing toll of injuries levied by mechanization in factories and on the roads also provided work for plastic surgery, and there were always burns, so destructive of large areas of the body surface, needing attention.

Skin grafting is a special province of plastic surgery. Whether a new nose or jaw is being fashioned or a large gap in the flesh has to be filled in, skin is needed as a final covering. Raw surfaces will heal by themselves but only slowly, and in the end the skin is paper thin and fragile and the scar is wrinkled, contracted and ugly. Skin grafting is quick and pain-saving and gives a good-looking result. It is a natural protective dressing for open wounds. One of the difficulties of grafting is that, with one exception which we shall come to later, the body will not allow any implanted tissues to take root whose cell material is genetically different from its own. Unless the chromosome arrangement in the cells of soil and plant is identical, the body develops antibodies which attack and in due course throw out the intruder. This means, if it is to "take," that a graft must be either an autograft—that is, material from another part of the patient's body—or a graft from an identical twin. In practice, therefore, skin for grafting must almost invariably be an autograft. When the amount of skin needed is small there is no great problem, but when the surface to be covered is large it may be necessary to do a bit at a time, for Peter has to be robbed to pay Paul. Care, too, has to be taken that the grafted skin is of the same texture as that which it is being used to replace. For example, it would be disastrous to plant hair-bearing skin on a part normally hairless.

Skin grafts may consist of tissue-paper-thin sheets shaved off the surface with a razor, known as Thiersch grafts after the German surgeon who first used them as long ago as 1874, or sheets which include the whole thickness of the skin. The latter are taken either with a special knife called, after its inventor, a "Humby" knife, or an instrument called a dermatome designed to maintain an even thickness throughout the graft. One of these instruments, the Padgett dermatome, enables a surgeon to cut a sheet of skin of any size up to 4 x 7½ inches. The flesh on which a graft is laid must be raw and fresh so that the new skin may gain nourishment to keep it alive. Raw surfaces of wounds, however, are wet from serum secretion, and therefore grafts are apt to float off unless firmly pressed down with a dressing. Yet firm dressings are not ideal because they prevent the new skin from breathing and they keep it too warm, for grafts do better when exposed to cool air. But how to do this and at the same time keep them firmly in place? This was a problem which vexed plastic surgeons for many years, and it was largely solved by a discovery in 1943 by Dr. Elisabeth Sano, a pathologist in Philadelphia, of a method of making graft and wound firmly adhere. It is known as plasma fixation. A small quantity of blood is withdrawn from one of the patient's veins and separated into plasma and cell extract. The raw surface of the graft is painted with the latter and the wound surface with the former, and when the two are put together they stick. Fixing grafts in this way now enables surgeons to dispense with pressure dressings, and the results are very satisfactory.

When wounds for repair are deep and much tissue is missing, or when a pliable covering is needed for flexible parts such as joint surfaces, grafts must consist of the tissues under the skin as well as the skin itself. But skin flaps, as these thicker grafts are called, cannot be taken from one part and planted in another in one operation, as skin grafts can be. Unlike skin, which is thin and obtains nourishment from wound serum secretions, sub-cutaneous tissues need circulating blood to bring them their food, and new blood vessels do not grow from a wound surface to a grafted skin flap quickly enough to provide it with the circulation it needs. The flap withers and dies like an unwatered plant. In this type of grafting, therefore, a method had to be devised whereby the flap could carry its blood supply with it during transition from source to destination. The procedure is ingenious but simple, and it is as follows.

Let us suppose that a skin flap has to be transported from the abdominal wall to the forehead. First the size of the graft needed —it might be, say, six inches long by three broad and half an inch deep—is mapped on the surface of the abdomen. Incisions are then made along each side of the mapped area and its underneath is freed by undercutting, but the two ends of the skin flap which has now been obtained are left uncut and remain attached to the abdominal wall. It is as if one cut an oblong of turf and freed all but its ends from its surroundings. The gap in the abdominal wall which is left when the flap is undercut is sewn together and allowed to heal for about three weeks. Meanwhile, the flap, now known as a pedicle because of its stalk-like attachments, and resembling the handle of a suitcase, is accustoming itself to living on the blood supply it receives through its two ends. Radioactive isotopes are often used in finding out when and how well this new circulation has established itself. The next step is to cut through one end of the pedicle in preparation for planting elsewhere. One or other forearm is chosen as its new "bed." Since the object of the operation is eventually to transfer the whole pedicle to the forehead, and as a forearm may be placed on the abdomen or the forehead with equal ease, it makes a convenient vehicle for the purpose. An incision is therefore made in one forearm, and it is brought over to meet the free end of the pedicle, which is planted in the bed prepared for it and securely stitched in place. The position now is that forearm and abdomen are joined together by a living bond in the form of the pedicle. This position is maintained for three or four weeks, not without some discomfort to the patient, by which time the forearm end of the pedicle has rooted itself and acquired a nourishing blood supply from the tissues into which it was planted. Provided this blood supply is satisfactory, and here again radioactive isotopes may be used, it is now safe to cut the abdominal end of the pedicle from its attachment. This is done, with the result that the forearm with pedicle attached is freed from its anchorage. The next step is to prepare a bed on the forehead for the free end of the pedicle, and when this has been done the forearm is brought up to the forehead and the pedicle is planted, thus joining forearm to forehead. When in due time the pedicle is well rooted in the forehead its other end is cut away from the forearm and the transportation is finished. The surgeon has a living, healthy skin flap, which has been kept in touch with nourishment at all stages of its journey, firmly attached where he wants it.

Using the pedicle-planting technique, a skin flap can be transported from almost anywhere to almost anywhere. The mechanics of the maneuver (for instance the pedicle may be planted elsewhere than in the forearm) and the number of plants that have to be made vary with the requirements of the situation, and right from the beginning the surgeon must visualize the final result and know exactly how he is going to achieve it. Every step must be planned. Things like eyebrows, for instance, must be thought of, and these are usually borrowed at the appropriate time from the scalp by taking a piece of hair-bearing skin from the side of the head—remembering, of course, that the hair must be aligned in the right direction. Reconstruction must always be natural.

Skin is not everything in plastic surgery. Foundations have to be laid first. Fortunately, bone is good grafting material for this and usually "takes" well. Pieces of bone from the pelvis and ribs, cut to size, are the usual basis of new jaws and noses. Pieces of fat and muscle, borrowed from where they can be spared, are used to fill up hollows and restore rounded surfaces. Artificial materials, like rubber and plastic, have also been used but, on the whole, the body does not take kindly to the intrusion of unnatural substances. Dental surgeons play a big part in reconstructions in and around the mouth by making cunningly designed plates—prostheses they are called—to support new structures, splint fractured bones and fill in gaps. Eye surgeons and ear, nose and throat surgeons also join the plastic surgical team when their special skill is needed.

Plastic repair surgery was bound to be limited by the amount and the nature of building material that could be spared from other parts of the patient's body. But a big step forward was made when it was discovered that there were certain types of tissue which could be taken from one person's body and grafted into that of another without the latter resenting it. This meant that grafts of these tissues need not be autografts and could be homografts—homograft meaning a graft taken from one of the same species. At once exciting possibilities opened up in the field of grafting, including that of "spare part" replacement so often dreamed of by surgeons.

The types of tissue it was found could be homografted were those that are not normally fed from blood vessels but which get their nourishment from the lymph in which they are bathed. They are few in number but, luckily, they are very valuable for building and replacement purposes. The three main ones are cartilage, big arteries and the cornea. The latter is the transparent membrane, or "window," covering the pupil of the eye. All these structures, or parts of them, may be removed from one person and planted in another and they will "take." The host will not attempt to throw them out. The earliest application of this discovery was to a precedure known as corneal grafting. Many cases of blindness are due to opaqueness of the cornea as a result of disease, usually an acute infection, in early life. The visual mechanism of the eye is unaffected, however, and were the window not clouded sight would be normal. In the operation of corneal grafting, the diseased cornea is removed and a healthy one taken from another person's eye is put in its place. It is delicate work. Great care must be used to prevent hemorrhage under the graft, and at all costs infection must be avoided. It needs only a trifling mishap and the new window becomes as dirtied as the old. Penicillin is the great preventer of mishaps of this kind. The crucial moment for knowing whether success has been achieved comes three weeks later when the bandages are removed. Does the new cornea let light through? Can the patient distinguish objects? I am happy to report that in the majority of cases he can. Many people who today can see the world around them quite clearly, some of them for the first time, because of this operation, never expected anything but a life of perpetual darkness.

At first the number of cases of homografting was limited by a difficulty in obtaining grafts. Sections of large arteries cannot be removed from living persons, however willing they may be to donate part of themselves to help a near and dear one because, of course, they could not survive the loss. It would be a case of killing Peter for Paul. Not would surgeons sacrifice an eye of a living person for the sake of a problematical cure of blindness in another. In most cases, therefore, the only source of material for a homograft was the body of one who had recently died. It is now possible to make in advance the necessary arrangements for a speedy collection of the material for grafting. But the great contribution towards homografting, and one which opened the way for tremendous advances, was the discovery a few years ago by Drs. A. S. Parkes and Audrey Smith, of the National Institute for Medical Research, Mill Hill, near London, that adding a small amount of ordinary glycerine to tissue cells and then putting them into a deep freeze (at $-79°C$.) makes it possible to keep them in suspended animation for many months, maybe years. When taken out and thawed they are alive and healthy. Using this technique, a rabbit's heart, for instance, has been made to beat again with full vigor after several weeks of cold storage.

The fillip this scientific discovery gave to the surgery of replacement with homografts was enormous. Storage banks of spare parts, comparable to blood banks, became a possibility, and now a surgeon planning a grafting operation may have a length of aorta or a cornea or a piece of cartilage to order from the store. With grafting material ready to hand more operations could be performed and surgeons had more chance to develop their skill and try new techniques. Vascular surgery—the surgery of blood vessels—advanced rapidly as a result, aided and abetted by hypothermia and controlled respiration anesthesia.

The great arteries of the body are liable to many defects. Some of these are congenital. For instance, we may be born with a segment of our aorta constricted, usually in that part of it where the vessel makes a $180°$ bend just after it leaves the heart. This condition, known as coarctation, impedes the flow of blood as it is pumped out of the heart, and as a consequence the latter has to beat with greater force. Muscle, and heart muscle is no exception, becomes larger with increased use, and in coarctation of the aorta therefore, the heart enlarges. It reaches a stage when it can enlarge no further and it gives up the uneven struggle of trying to force blood through an unyielding bottleneck obstruction. In the past nothing could be done for patients in this state. Now surgeons in some cases are able to cut out the two or three inches of narrowed vessel and replace it with a segment of normal aorta. The obstruction is relieved and a tired heart regains its strength. The operation is quickly done, but even so it involves cutting off the main blood flow for several minutes and hypothermia is necessary to reduce the tissue's oxygen requirements for the time being.

From the wear and tear of years of service weak spots are apt to develop in the walls of main arteries in the elderly. These weak places sometimes give way before the pressure of the blood stream and a bulge like a blister appears. This is called an aneurysm. It gradually increases in size and may burst if nothing is done, causing fatal hemorrhage. This can be prevented nowadays in many cases by cutting out the weakened part of the vessel and replacing it with a healthy homograft. Arteries, too, like other pipes, are apt to get furred up after long use and their lumens narrowed. The blood flow is reduced—to a mere trickle in extreme cases—and the parts supplied by the vessel are deprived of nourishment. When the whole length of an artery is affected little can be done, but when—as is often the case—only a few inches are involved, the diseased part may be cut out and, as in the other conditions, replaced by a homograft. Recently, and with more successful results, an operation has been performed in which the blocked section of artery is by-passed instead of being replaced. A graft is connected up to the artery above the bottleneck and carried down to a point below it, thus diverting the traffic round the block and bringing it back again into the main road where it is clear.

Prostheses—artificial substitutes for parts surgically removed or missing—have their place in vascular surgery despite the availability of deep-freeze stored natural substitutes. Tubes made of nylon and similar synthetic substances have been used to replace arteries, and they have certain advantages over homografts. They are easier to handle, much easier to sterilize, available in quantity and of a guaranteed quality. Whether they or homografts will be the thing of the future remains to be seen. Probably both will continue to be used and the choice will depend partly on the nature of the particular operation and partly on the surgeon's preference.

At the moment no prospect appears of a general solution to the homograft problem, by which grafts of any tissue from any donor could be made to survive permanently in any recipient. A complete spare-part service—new hearts for old, for instance —therefore appears as remote as ever, even supposing the purely technical difficulties of the operations could be overcome, which is problematical in some cases. One line of research, however, is being followed up here and in America which may lead to a little progress, at all events so far as skin homografting is concerned.

It has recently been found possible in animals to induce tolerance to the tissue of a particular donor by injecting the animal at an early stage in its life history with cells from the donor in question. In some species the injection has to be made before the animal is born, but in others injection soon after birth suffices. The theory is that if foreign tissue is introduced into the body before it is capable of antibody formation, further introduction of the same foreign tissue in later years will not stimulate defensive action because, from its early acquaintance with it, the body will regard it as friend, not foe. Whether tolerance to certain tissues can safely be induced in the human infant at birth remains to be discovered. If it does prove possible, then there is a prospect of inducing tolerance in children to the skin of their parents, and if ever a child should suffer a severe burn a homograft of skin from its father or mother could be used for replacement purposes.

Whether this procedure, if it proves feasible, could be extended to other tissues is a matter for speculation. Perhaps it could in the case of kidneys. Already the operative difficulties of transplanting kidneys have been surmounted, and there are a few recorded instances of a kidney having been successfully removed from one identical twin and put in to the other. Similar attempts with homograft kidneys taken from a parent or near relative, however, have all failed. In no case did the donor kidney survive for more than a few months.

The kidneys, together with the lungs, are the body's main agents for maintaining the constancy of the chemical constituents of the blood. By providing two kidneys nature has endowed us with ample reserves against mishap, for we can be perfectly healthy with only one kidney functioning. But under such conditions the margin of safety is reduced by half and there is no reserve. Complete failure of both kidneys lasting more than a few days is fatal, for poisonous waste products accumulate in the blood to a level which is intolerable to living tissues. When both kidneys fail as a result of chronic progressive disease nothing can be done surgically other than grafting a new kidney, and the instances in which this is feasible are rare, as we have seen. There are cases, however, in which the functioning of otherwise normal kidneys is temporarily but completely interfered with by some acute catastrophe, but where recovery is possible if only the patient can be tided over the acute crisis. In these cases a patient's life may be saved if the kidneys' essential work can be done for them until they are able once more to act for themselves. Since new kidneys cannot be fitted, this means in effect that artificial means must be employed.

Dr. W. Kolff was the first man to build an artificial kidney. He did so in Holland during the war under the noses of occupying Nazi forces. He passed blood from an artery in the patient's arm through a tube and into the hollow center of a rotating drum round which was wound a permeable membrane made of sausage skin. The drum revolved in a bath filled with a solution of salts and other substances in water, and by regulating the nature and the concentration of the dissolved substances Kolff was able to control the diffusion of chemicals from the blood to the water in the bath. The sausage skin membrane, in fact, functioned in very much the same manner as do the tissues of the kidney. Valuable substances like glucose, salt and protein were retained in the blood, and waste products were diffused into the bath and removed. After flowing through the drum the blood was returned via a tube to a vein in the elbow. Clotting, which would have brought the operation to an untimely end, was prevented by the use of heparin.

During the last ten years technical improvements have been made in the artificial kidney, but the principle on which the more modern machines work is the same as in Kolff's original apparatus. Cases in which it is needed are uncommon, but in these it is essential. Renal failure in shock from a severe injury is one of them, and during the Korean war a number of badly wounded soldiers' lives were saved because the work of their kidneys was temporarily taken over by the machine. Only a few large hospital centers possess an artificial kidney at present. Because of the limited demand for its services and because only doctors experienced in its use can operate it, that the number will increase very much is unlikely. Occasionally patients urgently needing this treatment have to be brought by air to the nearest center where it can be obtained.

Undoubtedly the most dramatic chapter in the story of medical progress is that of advances made in the surgery of the heart. Most of it has happened since 1945, but the story begins in 1939, when Robert E. Gross, of Boston, Massachusetts, cured a congenital defect in a child's heart. Except for the five years during which surgery went to war, progress has been continuous ever since, and British surgeons have played an outstanding part in it. The principal factors responsible for this rapid advance have been, first, the courage of the surgeons who ventured into what had always been considered a surgically untouchable structure of the body; second, antibiotics; third, controlled respiration anesthesia; fourth, hypothermia; and fifth, a better understanding of the physical forces at work within the heart as it propels the blood ever onward round the body. In a word, success in cardiac surgery must be attributed to the scientific team of which the surgeon is the captain.

The object of heart surgery is to repair mechanical defects in the pump. There is no other curative treatment for them, and until the surgeons took a hand the most that could be done was to give medicines that strengthened the heart beat and restrict the patient's activities within the limits imposed by his incapacity. Some defects in the heart's mechanism are, of course, slight and interfere little if at all with its efficiency, and many a person with a fault of this kind lives to a ripe old age without being aware of anything amiss. Surgeons do not intervene in these cases—there is no need. Severe defects, on the other hand, cause disability and invalidism, and the inability of doctors in the past to do anything effective in these cases made them despondent. Great was their joy therefore when it was found that surgery offered a cure in some and improvement in many others. There is no lack of patients needing treatment. About one in every thousand children is born with a defective heart, and they account for two of every hundred cases of organic heart disease. Far more numerous, however, are those who have acquired defects in their hearts during life as a result, in the main, of an attack of rheumatic fever. Not by any means all of these suffer disability, but sooner or later, as their hearts begin to tire from the continual strain of inefficient pumping, many of them may. Probably four-fifths of them will require treatment at some time and, because of modern medical and surgical discoveries, they may now rest assured that they will get it.

The heart is divided by a septum into a right side and a left side. Each side is subdivided into a smaller chamber, known as the atrium, and into a larger one, known as the ventricle. Blood returning to the heart from its travels round the body enters the right atrium via two big veins, the superior and inferior vena cava. From the right atrium it is pumped into the right ventricle and from thence via the pulmonary artery to the lungs, where it is oxygenated. From the lungs the blood returns to the left atrium via the pulmonary veins, and from the left atrium it passes into the left ventricle. The left ventricle pumps it into the aorta through which and its branches it is distributed throughout the body. Both sides of the heart contract in unison, first the atria and then the ventricles. When the atria contract the ventricles are relaxed and vice versa. This is in accord with the dynamic principles of a pump. Also necessary to any pump are valves to prevent resurgence of fluid against the direction of the flow, and each atrium therefore is separated from its corresponding ventricle by a valve which opens as the atrium contracts and closes as the ventricle contracts. That on the right side is known as the tricuspid valve because it has three cusps, or leaves, which come closely together in the closed position, and that on the left side is known as the mitral valve, and has two cusps, which, when closed, have a resemblance to a bishop's miter—hence the name. At the beginning of the pulmonary artery and the aorta there are also valves, known as the pulmonary and aortic valves respectively, which open when the ventricles contract and close when they relax.

Congenital malformations of the heart are of various kinds. They may occur singly or in combination, and in one of the commonest types of defect, that which causes "blue babies," three may be present. Accurate diagnosis is an essential preliminary to operations for curing them, for time is against the surgeon at the crucial stage of his manipulations, and once inside the heart he must work by feel. Therefore it saves valuable moments which otherwise might have been wasted in fruitless exploration if he knows in advance what he is going to find. Examination of the patient and the history of the case are, of course, helpful in arriving at a diagnosis, but by themselves they do not provide enough information, and until recently imperfect preoperative diagnosis handicapped cardiac surgeons. A great advance was made with the introduction of a procedure known as cardiac catheterization. This consists of inserting a fine, flexible, plastic tube, called a catheter, about twice the thickness of a matchstick, into a vein in the arm and gently pushing it along until its tip enters the heart via the superior vena cava. The catheter is opaque to X rays and its passage along the vein and its position in the heart may be watched on a fluoroscopic screen. The catheter serves at least three useful purposes. First, its behavior inside the heart sometimes shows the surgeon what is wrong. Second, by attaching it to a manometer readings can be taken of the pressures in the different chambers of the heart. Impediments to a flow of fluid cause an increase in pressure on the near side of the obstruction and a drop of pressure on the far side. By watching the position of the tip of the catheter and at the same time noting pressures, the whereabouts of a defect may be diagnosed with accuracy. Third, blood may be drawn off through the catheter and its oxygen content measured. Blood from the left side of the heart should be fully oxygenated while that from the right side, being venous blood, should have a reduced oxygen content. A change from the normal indicates that a defect in the septum dividing the two sides is allowing arterial and venous blood to mix.

Another technique, first used by Sir Russell Brock at Guy's Hospital, London, in 1957, for ascertaining the pressure inside the left ventricle and aorta, consists of plunging a hollow needle through the patient's chest and into the ventricle, A fine plastic catheter is then fed through the bore of the needle until it makes its way into the ventricle and on, when required, into the aorta. Pressure readings from both situations are taken. The patient, of course, is anesthetized. This somewhat alarming-sounding procedure of literally stabbing a person in the heart with a fairly large needle is really quite safe, and it shows what the heart will stand up to. One may add, superfluously perhaps, that the margin of safety is in the skill of the operator and these things are best left to those who know how to do them.

The heart begins to beat before birth and before the lungs are in use. To avoid blood being pumped through the respiratory apparatus before it is functioning, therefore, the flow in the pulmonary artery is diverted along a by-pass tube into the aorta. The by-pass tube is called the ductus arteriosus. It should close soon after birth, but in some cases it fails to do so and blood continues to be diverted along it. In these instances, however, the flow is reversed and passes from the aorta to the pulmonary artery instead of the other way round, with the result that the pulmonary circulation becomes seriously overloaded while the systemic circulation (the circulation in the body apart from the lungs) is denuded. This irregular state of affairs soon leads to trouble in the form of congested lungs, and it was on cases of this kind that Gross first operated in 1939. The plan of his operation was simple even if its performance was not. It consisted in tying a strong ligature of thread round the persistent duct, thus blocking it. The result was completely successful. The circulation soon adjusted itself to its new and normal route and the patients were cured of their trouble. Thousands of these operations have been performed on children in all parts of the world since, and almost invariably with success. What operative risks there are are well worth taking when one considers that the only alternative for the patient is a shortened life, and a severely handicapped one at that. This consideration applies to all heart operations, and knowing that only they can save the patient from the alternative gives courage to surgeons in their venturing.

If one congenital heart defect could be cured surgically, then why not others? After the war, surgeons turned their attention to the "blue babies." In these cases the problems were greater, since there is more than one defect to be overcome. First, the passage from the right ventricle to the pulmonary artery is constricted —"stenosed" is the medical word—thereby impeding the flow of blood to the lungs. Second, there is a hole in the upper part of the septum between the ventricles. Third, the opening into the aorta is out of place and lies between the ventricles instead of fully in the left. As a consequence of the second and third of these defects, the blood which is impeded from entering the pulmonary artery by the constriction in the pulmonary artery —the first defect—is diverted into the left ventricle and aorta, whence it passes into the systemic circulation. As it is venous blood the child's skin and lips are cyanosed, which means blue. Since the flood flow to the lungs is severely diminished its oxygenation is also reduced, and this further increases the cyanosis. Lack of oxygen in the blood causes shortness of breath, and severely affected children can scarcely walk more than a few yards without panting, and running is out of the question.

Hearts malformed to the extent of those of blue babies presented (at one time) too formidable a problem for direct repair, and some other way had to be found for relieving the condition. Dr. Alfred Blalock and his physician colleague, Dr. Helen Taussig, of Johns Hopkins Hospital, Baltimore, found it. They believed that they could get more blood through the lungs if they joined one of the main branches of the aorta—the right subclavian artery —to the right pulmonary artery. The effect of this, they decided, would be to bring some of the blue blood that was being diverted inside the heart into the aorta back into the pulmonary circulation where it properly belonged. For a whole year Blalock, the surgeon of the partnership, practised this operation on dogs to make himself expert and, together with Dr. Taussig, to observe the results. The size and arrangements of a dog's arteries are very similar to a child's and therefore well suited for the purpose. Not for the first time, the dog proved himself a friend of man. Drs. Blalock and Taussig were satisfied with what they learned, and late in the year 1944 Blalock performed for the first time on a child the operation of anastomosing—that is, joining—the sub-clavian artery to the pulmonary artery on the right-hand side. It was successful. Since then thousands of these operations have been done, with a better than 80 per cent record of success, and the lives of those who have had the operation have been trans-formed into one of happy activity.

Despite the remarkable feats of Gross and Blalock, the cure of cardiac defects by operations directly on the heart itself had yet to be accomplished. Surgeons were held back by two diffi-culties which had to be overcome. First, how to operate inside the chambers of the heart without letting so much blood escape as to endanger the patient's life and, second, how to do what was necessary on a moving target and without interrupting the essential beating of the heart. In 1948, Sir Russell Brock (then Mr. Russell C. Brock) of Guy's Hospital devised an alternative to the Blalock-Taussig blue baby operation in which he made a direct approach to the stenosed pulmonary valve through the right ventricle. He did this without too much hemorrhage result-ing and without stopping the heart-beat. He introduced a small spearlike instrument through a small hole cut in the wall of the right ventricle and directed the sharp-edged point of the spear into the orifice of the narrowed valve, which he then enlarged by cutting through the constricting tissues. Alternatively he used a special dilating instrument called a valvulotome. Not only did this maneuver prove successful in relieving the obstruction, but it proved that the heart was a more robust organ than was sup-posed and would stand up to quite a lot of surgical handling. By 1955 Sir Russell Brock had operated on ninety-four cases of pulmonary stenosis by this method, and with very good results considering that he was dealing with patients who were already in poor condition. He had only thirteen failures.

Russell Brock's success with his operation for congenital pulmonary stenosis led naturally to the next step of operating on adults with valvular defects of the heart acquired as a result of rheumatic fever. There was no lack of these cases in need of help. The most common of them, stenosis of the mitral valve, constitutes as much as 25 per cent of cardiac defects compared with the 2 per cent of the congenital variety. In mitral stenosis the two flaps of the valve are stuck together, leaving only a small gap between them. As a result the flow of blood from the left atrium to the left ventricle is severely obstructed, and the back pressure which builds up along the pulmonary veins as a consequence obstructs in its turn the pulmonary circulation, and so throws a strain on the right side of the heart. The longer the obstruction has been present the greater the strain, until eventually the heart tires and can carry on no longer. The only thing that can be done is to relieve the obstruction by separating the stuck-together mitral valves, thus restoring the orifice between the left atrium and left ventricle to its proper size. Brock and other surgeons approach the valve from above through the atrium. At the top of the atrium is a small extra chamber known as the atrial appendage, and a clamp is put on this at its junction with the atrium, shutting it off from the main chamber of the atrium. A suture is then threaded round it, the needle being passed in and out of the heart muscle, in the manner of the string which surrounds the neck of an old-fashioned purse. In fact, this type of suture is known as a purse-string suture. In the next stage of the operation a small cut is made in the wall of the appendage just big enough to take the surgeon's index finger. This is inserted through the hole, and at the same time the clamp is removed to allow the finger to enter the atrium. As the clamp is removed an assistant pulls on the ends of the purse-string suture, thus drawing the edges of the hole closely round the surgeon's finger, which is then literally plugging the hole and preventing an escape of blood. Meanwhile the heart is beating away as usual. The surgeon now presses downwards with the tip of his finger until it enters the orifice of the valve, and very gently he strips the two flaps apart. It may take ten minutes before the gap is widened to his satisfaction, for if he kept his finger at work in the valve all the time the flow of blood through the heart would be stopped. It is a matter of doing a little, desisting for a while, then doing some more, and the greatest gentleness is always needed. Sometimes the flaps of the valves are so firmly stuck together and hardened from deposits of chalk that mere pressure of the finger will not separate them. In this case they are cut apart by means of a tiny but very sharp knife which is mounted on a ring that fits on the surgeon's finger. When the valves have been parted the finger is withdrawn, the clamp is reapplied and the purse-string suture pulled tight. This closes the hole in the appendage and the clamp may then safely be removed. Apart from sewing up the chest wound the operation is complete.

Today, provided the case is a suitable one, most people with mitral stenosis can undergo the operation of valvotomy and be the better for it. Three-quarters of them may hope to return to full productive work.

One other type of valvular defect of the heart remained for the surgeon to operate on—stenosis of the aortic valve. To get at this the aorta has to be opened, and before this can be done the circulation must be stopped, otherwise the loss of blood from the great vessel would be overwhelming. Normally the brain cannot survive having its blood supply cut off for more than three minutes and, quickly though he may work, a surgeon cannot reckon on completing the manipulations within the aorta necessary for valvotomy in so short a time. Therefore in this operation the patient must be cooled. At 29° C. the brain can survive for ten minutes without oxygen, and this is long enough for the surgeon. Since the heart has to be exposed in any case, hypothermia in heart operations is as a rule induced by direct cooling of the blood. A cooling apparatus is used and the method is as I described it elsewhere. Clotting of the blood, always a bugbear to the heart surgeon, is prevented by giving the patient heparin, a routine treatment in all operations on the heart and blood vessels. At the critical moment in the operation for aortic valve stenosis all the great vessels leading to and from the heart are clamped, the aorta being clamped some two inches above its exit from the left ventricle. The circulation is thus cut off; no blood can enter the heart and none can leave it, but it goes on beating. Next the blood is drawn off from the left ventricle by puncturing its wall and inserting a thin catheter. The heart is now "dry," and the surgeon is able to open the wall of the aorta between the clamp and the heart without a flood of blood escaping. Through his incision in the aorta the surgeon passes a cutting or dilating instrument downwards into the stenosed valve opening, and he proceeds to enlarge this until the passage is clear. The instrument is then withdrawn and the hole in the aorta sewn up, as is also the small hole in the ventricle where the catheter was inserted. The clamps are removed from the great vessels, first from the veins, to allow the heart to fill up with blood again, and second from the aorta, and the circulation is restored to normal. Total time for the actual valvotomy procedure—five to seven minutes. The whole operation may take six hours or more from the moment of the first incision into the chest wall to the time of putting in the final stitch, and as much as six pints of blood may be lost. But thanks to modern anesthetic methods and blood transfusion, which goes on continuously throughout the operation, the patient suffers no ill effects.

Hypothermia gives a surgeon enough working time for operations for clearing blocked heart valves but not enough for him to undertake more delicate and precise procedures such as are necessary for repairing holes in the septum between the two sides of the heart. Congenital defects in the septum between the ventricles and the atria are relatively common, and heart surgeons will not rest content until they feel competent to cure them. Most promising beginnings have been made, and there is little doubt that shortly this type of operation will be performed as regularly and with as much confidence as the now well-established valvotomy operations. But a great deal depends on the development of mechanical devices which will take over the duties of the patient's heart and lungs during the time his circulation is stopped and his heart is being repaired.

The idea of an artificial "heart-lung" machine is not new, nor is it in theory at all impossible. The aim is temporarily to disconnect the heart from the circulation, including the pulmonary circulation, by turning off the taps at the main, so to say, by clamping the great vessels near the heart, and to maintain the circulation and oxygenation of the blood by drawing off blood from a main vein, passing it through an electric pump and an oxygenator and returning it to a main artery. The mechanics of the procedure are similar to those of the artificial kidney. But of course so many problems arise when one attempts to hand over a physiological process to the care of a non-living piece of machinery, however cunningly devised, that it is not surprising that several years went by before a heart-lung apparatus was devised which could be used with safety on a human being.

By 1953 successful experiments in substituting a mechanical device for the heart and lungs in animals had been reported from various medical centers throughout the world. Dr. D. G. Melrose and his colleagues at Hammersmith Hospital, London, had perfected a machine which worked well in dogs, and in June, 1954, Professor Ian Aird of the same hospital reported in the *British Medical Journal* that he had used Melrose's pump-oxygenator in a human patient in an operation for aortic stenosis. It was successful. Dr. F. G. Dodrill, of Detroit, reported in the *Journal of the American Medical Association* in the same year four operations in which a mechanical heart was used. Reports were also coming in from other centers. In some cases the whole heart—which means the lungs too—was by-passed, and in others only one side of it. When the pulmonary circulation was not cut off—that is, when only the left side of the heart was by-passed only the pump and not the oxygenator of the machine was used. Whichever way it was used, the machine gave surgeons up to twenty-five minutes' uninterrupted access to the inside of a dry heart during which they could actually see, instead of merely feeling, what they were doing, and they could do their work deliberately and in a comparatively leisurely manner.

It was being able to gain access to the inside of the heart which made it possible, in 1957, for Sir Russell Brock, with the aid of a heart-lung machine imported from the United States, successfully to repair a hole in the septum between the ventricles in a blue-baby patient aged 6. The operation was done at Guy's Hospital. At the same time the septum was repaired the stenosed pulmonary valve was widened (as in Brock's earlier type of blue-baby operation, but in this case it was done under direct vision), and thus the three defects which are responsible for the blue-baby symptoms were cured and, what is more, cured in one operation. Shortly afterwards Sir Russell Brock and his assistant, Mr. D. N. Ross, repeated the operation with equal success in a boy of 12. Brock, however, was not quite the first in the field. The "record holder" for this operation was a little blue-baby boy of 19 months who, shortly before Brock did his first case, was flown from England to the Mayo Clinic in the United States, where the defects in his heart were repaired. But before he had returned Brock's first patient was out of hospital and back in her own home.

The same surgeons who operate on the heart also undertake

operations on the lungs. They are known as thoracic surgeons, because they specialize in the surgery of the thorax, or chest cavity. For a long time major operations on the lungs were prohibited by the danger of lung collapse, which inevitably followed when the air tight seal of the chest wall was opened. The invention of the cuffed endotracheal tube and controlled respiration overcame this difficulty. Now whole lungs or parts of them may safely be removed, and the surgical treatment of pulmonary tuberculosis has gone ahead rapidly as a result. Before pneumonectomy, as removal of a lung is called, was possible little could be done for many cases of chronic tuberculous infection, especially when it had got to the stage of eating out large cavities in the tissues. Pneumonectomy is life-saving, too, in early cases of cancer of the lung and, with the recent rise in the number of those suffering from this disease, surgery is becoming increasingly important here. The invention of the bronchoscope, a tube-like instrument which is introduced into the main bronchial tubes by passing it down the windpipe, and through which the surgeon can get a direct view of the walls of the bronchi, has made early diagnosis of lung disease easier. With its aid also, foreign bodies, which surprisingly often are inhaled into the lungs can be removed. The contrast medium diodone has proved most valuable in X-ray diagnosis of chest disease.

And so the story goes on—or could go on. It would need a whole book and more to cover the recent discoveries in all branches of surgery. I have had space only to indicate some of the advances as they apply to surgery as a whole and to give one or two examples of progress in special fields. Of these, heart surgery is the most spectacular, but we must not forget that surgery is "an art which is helpful to all men," and man is made of many parts. The surgeon deals with them all. Orthopedic surgeons, for instance, do for crippled bodies what heart surgeons do for crippled hearts, and by ingenious operations, in which sound muscles are transplanted to take the place and do the work of paralyzed ones, they bring fresh hope to polio victims and others in similar plight. Brain surgery, too, has made great progress—again thanks to penicillin, anesthesia and hypothermia —and the neurosurgeon is in part an explorer who maps out the areas of the brain as he operates on its living tissues, thus adding to our knowledge of its function. Much more needs to be known about how the brain works, and this is a business on which medical science as a whole is employed, not only the surgeon. In fact, all medical discovery is becoming more and more a matter for scientific teamwork.

1958

The Transplantation
of the Kidney

JOHN P. MERRILL

IF THE human body were a simpler sort of mechanism, it might be possible to save many lives by replacing defective organs and tissues with healthy "spare parts" taken from the bodies of donors, either living or recently dead. The blood bank, of course, already functions as an approximation of this idea. Some hospitals also store corneas and sections of blood vessel, both of which can be transplanted by surgery. It is usually impossible, however, to transplant a whole organ such as a kidney, or even to graft skin successfully from one person to another.

The nature of this impasse is suggested by the familiar fact that blood must be "typed" and matched with care if transfusion is to be helpful and not disastrous. The tissue of each individual has its own chemical identity. Upon exposure to foreign tissue it rallies the most powerful defensive mechanism it possesses, the immune response, to destroy and reject the foreign tissue. The apparent exceptions—blood, cornea and blood vessel—each in its way proves the rule. Properly matched blood does not evoke the response, nor does the biologically rather inert corneal tissue. Transplanted blood vessels serve merely as "bridges" to guide the regeneration of the body's own tissue. The successful achievement of true "homografts" thus remains for the present a frontier of experimental surgery and of research in biochemistry and immunology. At the Peter Bent Brigham Hospital and the Harvard Medical School a group of us has been working at this frontier with results so far that give promise only to the extent that they have added to general understanding of the underlying problems. We work with the kidney, an organ eminently suited for transplantation. Most individuals have two normal kidneys and can live perfectly well with one. The elective surgical removal of one kidney involves little risk, and the surgical connection of the blood vessels of the donated kidney to the vessels of the recipient is generally not prohibitively difficult. Many chronic kidney-diseases are progressive and cannot be arrested by any therapy. Kidney tissue destroyed by disease heals by scarring, and the fibrous scar-tissue in turn tends to destroy more functional units of the organ. Thus the only possible cure often seems to be a new kidney.

E. Ullmann of Vienna made the first attempts to transplant the kidney in experimental animals at the beginning of the century. He was able to remove a kidney from an animal and then restore it to the same animal (an autograft), but could not successfully transplant the organ from one animal to another of the same species (a homograft). In 1908 Alexis Carrel transplanted kidneys in both dogs and cats. He observed that the transplanted kidney was infiltrated with plasma cells, a species of white cell found in the bloodstream. All subsequent observers have noted infiltration by these cells and their next of kin: the lymphocytes. In 1923 C. S. Williamson of the Mayo Clinic attributed the infiltration of the grafted kidney to a "biological incompatibility" between donor and recipient.

In an extensive series of investigations beginning in the 1940's, W. J. Dempster, a British experimental surgeon, gave further substance to this concept of biological incompatibility. He knew that it had been demonstrated that a second transplant of skin from one animal to another of the same species was much more speedily rejected than the first. He extended these observations and found that if the animal had been made "immune" to a donor by a skin graft, it would react in the same way to a kidney transplanted from the same donor. By this time it was believed that an important role in the immune response is also played by the so-called antibodies: molecules that are produced by the blood-forming tissues and perhaps also by the white cells and that react with great specificity to foreign molecules. In his microscope studies Dempster found indications that not only did the host react against the graft; in some cases the kidney graft itself was evincing an immune reaction against the host.

The first attempt to transplant a kidney in man is recorded in Russian medical literature of the 1930's; the effort was not successful. In this country unsuccessful attempts were reported in 1950. In France somewhat later healthy kidneys taken immediately from guillotined criminals failed to survive transplantation into patients chronically ill with uremia.

Our work at Peter Bent Brigham dates from the attempt by Charles A. Hufnagel and Ernest K. Landsteiner to attach a kidney to the arm of patient acutely ill with uremia. The kidney secreted a few drops of urine but never developed measurable function. The patient, however, recovered from her attack of acute kidney failure. In 1955 David M. Hume, Benjamin F. Miller, George W. Thorn and I reported our experience in nine similar procedures. All of the patients were terminally ill and required treatment with artificial kidneys. Indeed, without the artificial kidney we could not have undertaken this procedure in patients as sick as these. The transplanted kidneys came from patients who had died of chronic heart disease. In eight cases we grafted the kidney into a "pocket" fashioned in the skin on the middle of the upper thigh. We connected the blood vessels of the kidney to the vessels of the thigh. The ureter, the tube that drains urine from the kidney into the bladder, was led to an opening in the skin. Three considerations prompted the placing of the kidney in this bizarre position: the surgical procedure was somewhat less extensive than placing it in the abdomen; we could measure urine as it came directly from the kidney, thus avoiding the complicating factor of the output of the two defective kidneys; and we could more easily remove the kidney if the procedure failed or if the kidney became infected, leaving the patient certainly no worse than before. Four of the nine transplanted kidneys functioned; two did so well that the patients had some relief of symptoms. In one of the two patients, a South American physician with severe uremia and high blood-pressure, the kidney functioned for five and a half months before it failed; the patient was even able to leave the hospital for three months.

These results in human patients were far more encouraging than experiments with animals had led us to expect. In dogs grafted kidneys had functioned for only five to 12 days; then blood appeared in the urine and the kidneys suddenly failed. Moreover, microscopic examination revealed that the changes in the transplanted human kidneys were much less drastic than those in the dog. At first we thought that the species difference between dogs and men might account for the difference in behavior of the transplants.

In 1953, however, I was fortunate enough to be in Paris to observe a case in which a kidney had been transplanted. A healthy young man had fallen from a roof and severely injured a kidney, which was then removed by a surgeon in a hospital outside of Paris. Unfortunately the kidney turned out to be the only one the patient possessed. A week later surgeons in Paris transplanted a kidney into the young man from his mother. The immediate results were striking. The kidney began to form urine and functioned well for three weeks, greatly decreasing uremia and improving the patient's condition. But on the 21st day blood appeared in the urine and soon the kidney stopped functioning.

In the post-mortem examination we found that this kidney, transplanted from a healthy donor into a previously healthy recipient, had behaved very much like the grafted dog kidneys. The microscopic picture was almost identical. We now realized that the difference between grafted dog and human kidneys that we had observed had stemmed not from any species difference but from the fact that we had transplanted kidneys from chronically ill individuals into other chronically ill individuals. Our sick subjects apparently did not react as violently against sick kidneys as healthy subjects (or dogs) do against healthy kidneys. Skin grafts to chronically ill uremic patients confirmed this deduction; the grafts survived seven to 10 times as long as those on normal healthy recipients. Apparently the general depression of body function in these patients also depresses the immune response to the homograft.

At this juncture we listed our accomplishments: We had acquired a good deal of technical experience in transplanting kidneys and in the care of critically ill uremia patients, and we had learned that the immune response was not so violent in chronically ill people.

In 1954 we were confronted with a unique opportunity to apply this experience. David Miller, an alert physician in a nearby U. S. Public Health Service hospital, was caring for a young veteran who was dying of severe kidney failure and high blood-pressure. A daily visitor to his bedside was his apparently identical twin. Miller knew of our work on kidney transplantation. He also knew that biological incompatibility was the reason transplantation of tissues generally failed. He reasoned that if the two young men were identical twins, their tissues might not be biologically incompatible. As is well known, identical twins develop from a single fertilized egg; they not only resemble each other in appearance but also have a high degree of biological identity. What is more, skin transplants between identical twins have succeeded. With these considerations in mind Miller referred the patient and his brother to the Peter Bent Brigham Hospital.

To be sure that these twins were identical we transplanted skin from each to the other. Knowing that such a transplant might "take" for a prolonged period (though not permanently) in the sick twin, we were especially concerned to observe the result in the healthy twin. Both grafts took normally. Although this was the critical test, we thoroughly investigated other significant similarities that might confirm identical inheritance. A geneticist carefully compared the boys' facial features, iris color and pattern, hair color and form, shape of the ears and even taste similarities. A hematologist found their blood groups identical in all the major categories and in 20 separate subcategories. Extensive examinations convinced us that the healthy twin was free from all kidney and other diseases. Thus we had adequate medical and genetic bases for proceeding with the transplantation.

On the other hand, we had no precedent for the removal of a perfectly normal kidney from a healthy individual, and this consideration weighed heavily in our deliberations. Meanwhile the sick twin grew sicker. His uremia became so bad that it required treatment with an artificial kidney; his blood pressure continued to rise, with dangerous effects upon his heart and blood vessels. Finally, two days before Christmas, 1954, a normal kidney was removed from the donor twin by J. Hartwell Harrison and transplanted by Joseph E. Murray into the sick recipient.

Murray placed this kidney not in the thigh but in the hollow of the pelvis, inside the abdominal cavity, where its surroundings resembled its normal habitat. He connected the kidney's artery to a branch of the large iliac artery and its vein to a vein in the pelvic cavity through which blood flows from one leg. The operation cut off the blood supply of the healthy kidney for almost an hour. In spite of this delay, when the clamp was released from the artery to which the grafted kidney was attached the kidney became a healthy pink, and within minutes urine began to drip slowly from the end of the ureter. Murray thereupon implanted the ureter directly into the bladder so that the urine would drain normally. In this case we wanted no possibility of technical failure to compromise our very real chance to avoid the immunologic barrier.

By the time the patient had left the operating room, urine was definitely flowing, and over the succeeding days and weeks the kidney gradually improved its function. The patient's uremia cleared up; his appetite and mental processes improved. Then— and this was beyond our expectation—we observed a drop in blood pressure. Six weeks after the transplantation we performed two operations, the first to remove one of the patient's diseased kidneys and the second to remove the other kidney. Following the second operation the blood pressure at last fell to normal, where it has remained ever since. All signs of heart strain and hemorrhage from smaller blood vessels soon disappeared.

This was a dividend we had not fully anticipated. The role of the damaged kidney in causing high blood-pressure had been investigated in experimental animals for many years. This case provided the first opportunity to study in a human subject the kidney's role in high blood-pressure by first adding a normal kidney in the presence of two diseased ones and then removing the diseased kidneys in separate operations. We have now been able to make the same observations in six successful kidney transplants between identical twins; in each case the sick twin was a victim of severe hypertension.

Since 1954 we have transplanted a total of 13 kidneys between identical twins. Each of the 13 recipients had been terminally ill with uremia; 10 are alive and healthy today.

The kidney is of course one of the most complex organs in the body. It not only disposes of wastes but also delicately regulates the content and balance in the blood of salts and other substances. Our 10 successful transplants show that it can continue to do so in a totally different location in a different individual. Furthermore, the kidney functions even though its nerve connections are severed. This was indicated some time ago in animal-kidney autografts, and has been proved by our successful human transplants.

The moral problem of taking a healthy kidney from a healthy donor is acute, we feel, when the twins are minors. In such cases we have asked court permission to perform the graft. Permission has been granted on the ground that the healthy child would suffer more from the psychical loss of his twin than from the physiological loss of a kidney that can be spared.

The graft failed in one of our 13 cases because a congenital abnormality of the blood vessels in the donated kidney prevented them from fitting the vessels of the recipient. The other two deaths, following initially successful transplantation, gave us a critically important insight into the working of the immune response.

We found that these two patients had died because their transplanted kidney developed the nephritis (Bright's disease) from which they had suffered before the operation. Why was this finding important? For many years workers have been able to produce in animals a disease that appears to be the equivalent of human nephritis. To do this they make a serum from ground-up rat kidney and inject it into a rabbit. The immune response in the rabbit produces antibodies against this foreign material. When serum from the rabbit's blood is injected into the rat, the antibodies attack the rat's kidneys, causing the disorder that so resembles nephritis. A condition even closer to human nephritis is produced by injecting the ground-up rat kidney into a duck. When the duck serum is injected into the rat, the duck antibodies somehow mask the rat's kidneys so that the rat's tissues no longer "recognize" them. The rat then produces antibodies that act against its own kidneys.

Such investigations had strongly suggested that in human nephritis the body has formed antibodies against the kidneys. Proof of this hypothesis, however, had been lacking. Now we had transplanted normal kidneys into patients with nephritis, and had seen these kidneys contract the disease. Apparently in man, as well as in the rat, either antibodies circulating in the blood plasma or sensitized lymphocyte white cells had attacked the grafted kidney. Since skin grafts had taken in both of our cases, we knew that the attack upon the transplanted kidneys was no ordinary immune reaction to a graft.

The identical-twin grafts have demonstrated that where an immunological barrier does not exist kidneys can be successfully transplanted to cure otherwise incurable kidney and vascular disease. This limited success in surgery furnishes an additional motive for investigation of the immunological barrier, which is a problem of great fascination in itself. From long experience with skin grafts, investigators have a clear picture of the normal course of the immune response. A piece of skin from one person transplanted to the forearm of another will assume a firm, healthy appearance for several days as blood vessels grow into it. Four to five days after transplantation, however, the small vessels begin to be plugged, the skin becomes discolored in a patchy fashion and the skin cells become necrotic and die, to be overgrown by the epithelial cells of the host's skin. After this the host will react much faster in rejecting a new skin transplant from the same donor. This acceleration in the reaction suggests that the recipient's tissues have in some way learned to "recognize" as foreign the tissue from the donor.

The recognition system involves the reticuloendothelial tissues of the body, which are found in the bone marrow, in the lymphatic system and spleen and in the liver. These are the blood-forming tissues and also the generators of the immune response, as the source both of white cells and of antibodies. In some way contact with antigens produced by a graft of foreign tissue "teaches" the reticuloendothelial system to recognize the foreign material. After the "lesson" by a first graft from a particular individual, the system is sensitized and the rejection of any subsequent graft of any kind of tissue from that individual is speeded up.

One tortuous detour around the immune response is suggested by the fact that the response is not fully developed in many animals until after birth. Thus day-old chicks may tolerate skin grafts from other chicks. In rats this neutral period when skin grafts may be accepted can extend to as late as 10 days after birth. The maturing reticuloendothelial system of the young animal is still learning to recognize the tissues of the animal; a hypothetical "self-marker" in these tissues presumably tells the reticuloendothelial system not to develop antibodies to them. R. E. Billingham and P. B. Medawar of University College London have injected the spleen cells of brown mice into embryonic white mice and found that as adults these white mice tolerated skin grafts from brown mice [see "Skin Transplants," by P. B. Medawar; SCIENTIFIC AMERICAN, April, 1957]. The immature recognition system of the embryonic mice apparently accepted the foreign cells as having the "self-marker."

In solving the problem of tissue transplantation in man, however, we do not expect to make popular the injection of cells from a prospective donor into the human fetus. There is another approach that is receiving consideration. This is the destruction or incapacitation of the crucial centers of the reticuloendothelial system by means of total body irradiation, followed by the transplantation of bone marrow. The idea is to obliterate the patient's own recognition system and replace it with one compatible with the tissue to be grafted. The feasibility of this admittedly heroic procedure has been supported by limited success in terminal cases of leukemia, in which the massive irradiation is, of course, directed to the destruction of malignant cells. In experimental animals destruction of the bone marrow by radiation has made it possible to graft marrow and other tissues not only from other animals but from animals of a different species!

We have attempted to use this procedure in two terminal cases of kidney disease to condition the patient for transplantation of a kidney. In both cases the bone-marrow transplant eventually failed. Indeed, there is no evidence from the world's medical literature that transplanted bone marrow has ever functioned in man for more than a few weeks.

Recently we have attempted another experiment that combines experience both with irradiation and with the reduced intensity of the immune response in cronically ill patients that we have noted in our first series of kidney grafts. This experiment also applies the knowledge, gained from more recent work with experimental animals, that a large dose of antigen introduced into the bloodstream may produce tolerance to foreign tissue where a small dose excites the immune response. We transplanted a kidney from a healthy man to his critically uremic brother. Though the men were probably not identical twins, we hoped that their relationship might make for some immunologic compatibility. The recipient was chronically and dangerously ill, and he was given a total dose of X-rays large enough to depress his reticuloendothelial tissues severely. Immediately after the last irradiation, the kidney was transplanted. A transplanted kidney of course introduces a large dose of antigen directly into the bloodstream. As the patient's reticuloendothelial system recovers from the radiation, it may be forced to become familiarized with the antigens of the transplanted kidney and accept them as carrying a "self-marker," after the precedents in research with animals. It is as yet too early to evaluate the results of this transplant, but initially it appears to be successful. Obviously the combination of circumstances favoring its success is unusual. The general principles, however, are universal, and give us some idea of the way in which not only kidneys but other living tissues may eventually be routinely transplanted.

1959

Hope for Victims of Stroke

ROBERT A. KUHN

IN THE foyer, the librarian bends busily over her glass-topped desk. She is humming softly, an almost inaudible sign of contentment, and occasionally she lifts her head to look affectionately at the scattered groups of peaceful, semisomnolent readers. Then, satisfied that her domain is functioning well, she returns to sorting check-out cards.

This plain, kindly soul is about to experience a terrifying ordeal. Sudden disruption of her brain function is several hundred seconds away. What could an expert medical detective offer on shrewd appraisal now, before this catastrophe? Surely there must be telltale signs of impending disaster, perhaps even some method of prevention?

Physically, the librarian gives the impression of exceptional good health. Fiftyish, spare and neat, she wears her smooth gray hair in an efficient knot. Her movements are quick and sure. Only in recent years has she needed her rimless glasses. One would suspect, and rightly, that here is a woman who seldom wastes a jot of patience on those who pamper colds and coughs by staying home when they could just as well be working. We decide with reasonable certainty that Miss Helen is medically well-nigh indestructible. But this brief survey has already eaten up all but a few precious remaining moments, and still we have found no helpful clues—no way to guess what is about to happen.

But wait: perhaps there is some hidden flaw of constitution? Some illness passed on from forebears, a silent diabetes or unsuspected essential hypertension? Later, we shall find out that, to the contrary, the librarian comes of long-lived, sturdy stock, untroubled by chronic disease. Now the seconds move inexorably by. Miss Helen flips another card, her face serene. One must watch closely now, for there will be little warning.

We are six seconds removed from terror. She swivels her chair to the typewriter, turns a card in with a practiced twist, and begins to type. Some vague premonition of disaster wrinkles her brow slightly; the rapid chatter of the machine slows, stops. One hand comes up tentatively to touch the scalp. She seems to be sensing an indefinable inner discomfort at the back part of her head. One second now. A sudden savage pain tears at the nape of her neck, totally unlike anything this mild lady has ever experienced. Defenseless, she stiffens in rigid surprise before her typewriter. In the next few interminable seconds bursting agony floods to a peak. The hushed quiet of the library is profaned by her scream. Her vision blurs and fades into the nothingness of merciful oblivion. The slight figure pitches forward on the desk.

For an instant there is frozen silence. Then pandemonium swirls about her. No one knows what has happened. She is gently lifted and laid carefully on a couch by a fat man, terrified and now perspiring freely, who had only just been about to take out a book. It is apparent that though Miss Helen is deeply unconscious, she is still alive. The words "heart attack" and "stroke" ricochet through the little knot of bystanders. Someone thinks finally to call an ambulance. By the time the white-garbed crew arrive, the patient is partly awake. She is very nauseated and begins to vomit repeatedly. She mumbles over and over of her bursting, unremitting headache—the while holding her temples desperately with both hands. Although half conscious, she seems to be using all four limbs with normal strength and co-ordination. She even helps to move herself to the stretcher as she is being lifted.

Those who were very close beside her, and were especially observant, might have been struck by the fact that her eyes no longer seemed exactly parallel, and one pupil was much larger than the other. But most would remember for a long while just a wretchedly sick little lady who had had some kind of terrible and painful seizure. One hour after arrival at the hospital, examination of her spinal fluid showed the presence of fresh blood. Our indestructible librarian has been the victim of a hemorrhagic stroke.

In a moment we shall follow our patient to the hospital and trace the steps which will be taken to investigate and treat her illness. Let us digress for a moment to consider the crippled ranks this woman has joined.

It is estimated that 500,000 Americans yearly are felled by some sort of stroke. Moreover, the huge number of victims seems to be steadily growing a little larger. The increase is probably a normal accompaniment of the rising average age of the population—strokes are more frequent in the elderly. And there is every indication that incidence of strokes will continue to mount, unless we find some way to reverse the trend.

What are the social implications of this problem? We can gain an idea from the fact that 1,250,000 individuals who have had one or more strokes live on in hospitals, nursing homes and other institutions. This figure represents about one in every 150 persons—of all ages—in our populace. Typically, these unfortunates are at least partially paralyzed, many without speech or power to recognize those about them, living out their years in hopeless invalidism. A few lucky persons recover "spontaneously" from stroke. Many have long since ceased to live in any real sense. Those permanently crippled constitute an incalculable drain on the mental and financial resources of their families. Sadly, many of the victims are experienced, highly trained men and women at the height of their productive powers, stricken at the moment when their contributions to society are at a maximum. We can ill afford to squander such talent. Happily, we are now in a position to help many of these victims.

It is not generally realized that today, for the first time, we have the means to deal effectively with strokes. Depending very much on the type of stroke, appropriate measures can cure or greatly help many of the victims. It remains now to begin to apply these methods with concerted skill and diligence.

First of all, there must be some common understanding in regard to usage of the word "stroke." It is true that certain easily observed features of a stroke—such as paralysis—are generally recognized by everyone as characteristic or typical. But what, precisely, does the term mean?

"Stroke" has no precise meaning. It represents a medical way of saying paralysis, or coma, or loss of consciousness or any other of a series of symptoms which have usually been found in the past to accompany this condition. It does not really matter which of the synonyms is used, for they can be—and are—interchanged freely and still connote a stroke. But all these words suffer from the serious flaw of being purely descriptive. None of them gives us any information about the possible cause of the catastrophe.

There have been unfortunate consequences in the past of using this word as a diagnosis: in other words, of using the designation "stroke" as a label applied to all who develop paralysis. Not long ago, comparable terms such as "rheumatism" and "growing pains" were respected medical diagnosis. With the advent of modern investigative techniques, these vague terms have all but vanished, to be replaced by exact designations of the illness of which they are the symptoms. In modern medical parlance, blanket terms such as arthritis, rheumatism and heart disease are frequently called "wastebasket diagnoses." They do actual damage by strongly implying the same causal agent, same clinical course, same treatment for all the patients lumped under each general heading.

Such a word is "stroke."

A medically accurate description of a stroke is a disruption of brain function due to some cause—we know not precisely what. The all-important answer as to where, and what, and how will come only after the systematic and patient application of special tests. Treatment must rest upon the solid bedrock of precise diagnosis.

For many years, once it had been established that a stroke had indeed occurred, little attempt was made to pursue the matter. The damage was done, the outlook was grave, and main efforts were directed toward making the patient as comfortable as possible. But during the past several years we have witnessed the development of a new and startling change in attitude toward the medical tragedy of the stroke victim. Universal hopelessness has been replaced by cautious optimism. What has happened to produce this revolutionary change in a period of only a few years?

It is not surprising that the brain—the monarch of all organs—has been more reluctant than the heart, the stomach, the lungs to yield its secrets to the scientific probe. The unusual sensitivity of even a normal brain to slight disturbances of its stable state has confronted investigators with hazards not lightly dismissed nor easily surmounted. A sick brain is even more susceptible. Yet as research advanced, technical difficulties crumbled with dramatic suddenness.

Today we have three effective methods of studying brain

structure, and through it the why and wherefore of strokes: cerebral angiography, pneumoencephalography and electro-encephalography—words more difficult to pronounce than to understand, as you will soon see. But before describing these tests, it might be pertinent to consider the external appearances of a stroke. What exactly do we mean by "disruption of the brain function," what actually happens to the patient?

There are many different causes of strokes, and one patient who has the same kind of paralysis as another might well have developed his stroke for an entirely different reason.

Most frequently, during the course of a stroke, paralysis of part of the body occurs. The most usual combination of paralysis involves the upper and lower limb and lower one-half of the face, all on one side. Though paralysis is present in all three sites, the degree of paralysis may be greater in the arm or the leg, depending on the exact spot in the brain of the damage. If paralysis is total in both limbs it is termed hemiplegia; if partial (meaning that some movement in the affected limbs is still possible), it is called hemiparesis. Variations in the severity of paralysis and in the limb hit hardest are due to slight differences in location and varying severity of brain damage.

Hemiplegia and hemiparesis are the usual kinds of paralysis shown by those labeled as having had a "stroke." (Note, though, that our librarian had no limb paralysis at all, yet would have been ordinarily considered a stroke victim by the layman.) Since paralysis of half the body is the most familiar mark of a stroke, it has been assumed to be an invariable sign of such an attack, yet this easily detected symptom of stroke may often be absent.

Onset of a stroke may be abrupt and violent—the "vascular accident" of the brain. Even small hemorrhage into brain substance usually causes symptoms within seconds; if the patient is deeply unconscious within a minute or so, we may be fairly certain some kind of bleeding has occurred. Sudden block of a large brain artery by a clot propelled by the heart may be almost as dramatic in onset, but coma is usually absent. At the other end of the scale are "little strokes," brief periods of paralysis or numbness in the same limb pattern as seen in severe strokes, but which clear up spontaneously after each episode. Such attacks may be repeated many times before the first "real stroke" happens, and are invaluable warning signs that serious trouble is brewing and that investigation is sorely needed.

Symptoms as innocent as dizziness or vertigo continued over a period of many days may be the initial manifestation of a stroke. The very first sign of some strokes is an epileptic attack, and in other strokes such seizures never occur. Sometimes insidious mental changes diagnosed as early senility are the first indications—in fact, personality changes constitute a most important clue in development of some types of strokes. Despite popular belief, a stroke is no respecter of youth: certain kinds of strokes are found to occur typically in adolescents. There are no age restrictions in those affected by this illness.

A hodgepodge of signs and symptoms might indicate warning of a stroke. Such an attack could be manifested in a number of ways. A greatly simplified analogy will point up the difficulties in study of such an illness: if a sudden cutoff of electric power plunges half of our home into darkness, hurried inspection will disclose only uniform absence of light in the blackened rooms—the dark rooms representing the external evidence of electric-power failure. Within itself, the darkness carries no distinguishing features indicating its cause. We must search for the cause, excluding one by one a spate of possibilities, from a shorted circuit to a prank-playing youngster.

So, also, with the outward manifestations of a stroke. Cursory external examination of a patient paralyzed in an arm or leg, or both, may be totally unrevealing as to whether that paralysis was caused by bleeding from an artery deep in the brain substance, or by any of the different kinds of brain tumor, or by a closed-off artery in the brain, or one in the neck, or by infection. It is the rule, rather than the exception, that strokes produced by these widely different causes are externally the same. No singular marks of identification—no magic clues—set apart paralysis due to one cause from that due to another.

It is not possible, therefore, for even a highly trained specialist to determine, by clinical or neurological examination, the precise reason for any stroke. His years of experience may enable him to narrow the field down to a remarkably small area of the brain. He may occasionally be able to pinpoint, within a fraction of an inch, the exact pathways that have been injured in the brain. Yet, even then, the all-important cause of the damage remains incompletely known. It might be a total block of the tiny brain artery irrigating that site. The site might just as easily have been "starved" by impaired blood flow through the parent vessel which is its main source of supply and is located in the neck. Precise knowledge of why that particular area is affected might mean life or death to the patient.

Today the "why" of a stroke can be discovered with precision and accuracy by systematic application of special tests.

Until recently, one of the important tests for those with suspected brain disease involved taking X rays of the head. X-ray pictures are contrast photographs, depending entirely on the different densities (or compactness) of body tissue. X rays penetrate dense tissues poorly and porous tissue strongly—hence the contrast on the resulting picture. Skull bone, being very dense, shows clearly. The brain and its coverings and fluid jacket, however, are much the same density; therefore, in X rays taken of the head there is no contrast—only bony structures show.

Because of this limitation of X rays, investigative techniques have been developed which rely on "contrast substances" to outline structures within the head. Gas and dye are two such substances.

For many years, medical investigators searched for a contrast liquid which, when injected into an artery headed for the brain, would outline the blood-vessel "tree" clearly on an X ray simultaneously taken. The technique finally developed, called cerebral angiography, has truly revolutionized medical approach to vascular diseases of the brain.

Using special X-ray equipment, it is possible to follow the column of dye as it surges up the large arteries at the base of the neck, up through the neck itself, and finally into the brain. If we scrutinize these films with knowledge of what the normal blood-vessel pattern should be, any deviations from normal become apparent. For example, if a stroke is due to a slowly enlarging tumor, that tumor will produce a characteristic distortion of the blood-vessel pattern. If, on the contrary, the paralysis has resulted from chronic obstruction of a large artery in the neck, quite another pattern will show on the X ray. A third possibility is bleeding into the brain, which frequently results from rupture of a "ballooning" or weak spot in an artery wall. In such an instance, dye studies are the only method of making an accurate diagnosis.

During the early days of cerebral angiography, as is often the case with a new procedure, it had a somewhat dubious reputation. Dye injection was accompanied by an appreciable number of complications and an occasional death. Two factors were mainly responsible: first, the adverse response of the brain to the dye then used; second, the frequently desperate condition of the patient, which made the attempt to help a necessity, but which also increased the risk. This second factor has not changed, but the manufacture of new contrast liquids has, for all practical purposes, eliminated risks previously due to the dye itself.

The pneumoencephalogram, though originated many years ago, continues to be one of the most useful tools for the investigation of brain disease. In this test, gas is injected into the spinal canal and, as it rises into the brain, is seen in X-ray pictures as a delicate tracery of shadows within the skull. These pictures, taken at various angles, show the internal and external surface of the brain in silhouette, and yield extremely valuable information. Pneumoencephalography has certain drawbacks—none of the blood vessels or finer details of brain anatomy can be visualized using this method. However, combined with cerebral angiography, it is of enormous value, and is one of the principal techniques used for the investigation of suspected brain tumors. When used with certain normal precautions, this method cannot be matched in terms of information gained and safety to the patient.

A third testing procedure of major importance in evaluating brain function, particularly in locating an accumulation of blood within the brain, is the "brain-wave recording" or electroencephalogram. Electrodes pick up incredibly small currents in the brain, and an amplifying apparatus converts this electrical energy into movements of a pen which "writes" on a moving sheet of paper. Each wavering line represents moment-to-moment changes in electrical potential between two electrodes.

What, exactly, has happened to our stricken librarian? Is it possible that she can be helped—perhaps completely cured? By using one or more of the tests described above, can we determine precisely what felled her in such a brutal fashion? It will be recalled that the onset of her stroke was explosive, with terrific head pain and almost immediate loss of consciousness. In addition—and in this she is not typical of others with stroke—she does not seem to be paralyzed. The reason for this becomes apparent only after we have conducted an examination in the emergency room at the hospital. Violent onset, unbearable headache, boardlike neck and incessant vomiting—all are explained by the bloody fluid found when her spinal column is tapped.

The patient has experienced a classic sequence of events for brain bleeding. She has had a hemorrhage somewhere within her head—we can even make an educated guess as to the location. We know, for example, that a massive hemorrhage within the substance of the brain itself almost always causes paralysis of one or more limbs. She has had no such paralysis, so we speculate that this hemorrhage has occurred from an artery within the skull, but before it enters the substance of the brain.

It is now vital to determine the exact point of artery leakage. For this we schedule the patient for arteriography.

In the X-ray special-study room, dye-injection studies of the librarian are performed. On the film series there can be seen quite clearly a small weak spot, or blister, like the bulge of a weak spot in an automobile inner tube, located at the junction of two medium-sized arteries beneath the brain. This blister, undoubtedly present since a very early age, has for some unknown reason chosen this particular moment to rupture. It let loose a raging arterial stream into the skull and then subsided momentarily for reasons as obscure as those surrounding the rupture. Sealing of the hole took place—or she certainly would have expired within a minute or two.

It is well known that after one such bleeding, future rupture at the same weak point is very likely to recur, and that chances of surviving subsequent attacks are exceedingly slim. So now Miss Helen faces brain surgery to clip off the malformed blood vessel. Though there is considerable risk, her outlook for survival and cure is far better than it would have been ten years ago—when she might well have been released from the hospital only to suffer a second and fatal hemorrhage.

It is probably that about one third of all strokes are due to hemorrhage within the head. A large number of those affected, particularly those in the older age groups, have in the past been said to have "spontaneous" bleeding, in that the exact reason for hemorrhage was at the moment not completely clear. There are fairly accurate data concerning those who die as a result of intracranial bleeding, for in many of these instances autopsy is requested and performed. But if our only information about brain hemorrhage is derived from examining those who have died from it, our attitude toward brain bleeding will surely be pessimistic.

This pessimism is unwarranted. After all, one does not make generalizations about an extremely poor outlook for all patients with peptic ulcer by considering only those dying in the throes of an acute hemorrhage! It is possible to offer real help to some brain-hemorrhage victims through surgical removal of the clot if it is done shortly after the initial bleeding. There seems little doubt that many people have brain hemorrhages which go undetected and from which they recover. Many of these could be protected against further bleedings by alert and vigorous surgical management. These surgical triumphs occur more and more often with early accurate diagnosis, for which cerebral angiography is indispensable.

It was assumed in the past that strokes are due to three main causes: cerebral thrombosis (thickening and closing off of a blood vessel in the brain), cerebral embolism (block of a brain artery by a particle being carried by the blood stream), and cerebral hemorrhage (rupture of a vessel in the brain). Hemorrhage is indeed responsible for about 30 per cent of strokes, embolism for about 10 per cent. But the remaining 60 per cent of strokes have been erroneously lumped together as due to cerebral thrombosis.

Recently there have been a number of thorough studies of several groups of patients with hemiplegia or hemiparesis due to initially unknown causes. The strokes, which were alike in that each patient showed partial or complete paralysis of one side of the body, were fully investigated, using modern methods. Causes of these apparently similar strokes were discovered to be as follows:

One-third of the patients had complete or partial occlusion in the neck of one or both of the main (carotid) arteries carrying blood for the brain.

The importance of this unexpected finding can hardly be overestimated. In the past, disease of the main artery to the brain had been considered so rare as to be a medical oddity. The extraordinary frequency of carotid blockage is only now becoming apparent—more and more of such cases are turning up each day. Yet stroke due to this cause cannot be differentiated from stroke due to another cause unless special studies are made. Symptoms as innocent as vertigo, dizziness and brief periods of numbness of an arm or leg are warning signs of such trouble. These warnings are usually ignored—with development of a real stroke within weeks or months. Most of these cases slip by unrecognized even today, at least until severe paralysis has occurred.

Victims of carotid occlusion are, in one way, extremely fortunate. The artery is readily accessible to direct operative exposure and to remedial surgery—much more so than if the clogged vessel were within the brain. Certain patients with stroke due to carotid occlusion in the neck can therefore be cured or vastly improved by prompt surgery to remove or bypass the obstruction. Naturally the sooner warning signals bring the patient to the doctor, the better his chances are.

One-third of the patients had developed blocked arteries within the brain itself. These are the individuals who have stroke due to what was once considered the most typical happening—closing off of a major artery in the brain, or of one of the important branches.

There is mounting evidence that patients with diseased arteries in the brain can be helped by special anticoagulant drugs. There is even some indication that if the patient can be carried over the critical period of the acute attack, a certain amount of reconstruction of the canal in the narrowed vessel may be achieved through intensive treatment. So diagnosis of cerebral-vessel disease scarcely warrants despair—vigorous early treatment may still restore much function.

One-quarter of the patients had tumors or enlarging accumulations of blood within the head. Excluding certain types of malignant brain growths, these conditions represented a most hopeful aspect. Such patients are primarily neurosurgical problems. Early diagnosis is particularly important to effect a cure, since under ideal circumstances and with early operation some of the happiest results occur with these cases. If the mass of blood or tumor tissue is sharply circumscribed, and has not irreparably damaged adjacent brain substance by pressure or by squeezing off its blood supply, brain operation can often convert the desperately ill patient to complete normality.

The remaining small percentage of strokes were found to be due to relatively rare causes, such as infection of the brain, injury to it from a blow, or involvement by disease spread elsewhere in the body. The correct diagnosis is established by exclusion. After the usual tests have failed to uncover the commoner diseases, there are only a few known possibilities to be considered. Some small hint eventually shifts medical attention from the external appearance of the "stroke" to focus on the true disease culprit.

Looking over the groups of stroke victims described above, we see that most of them needed specific treatment of one type or another. The application of a battery of investigative techniques was the only possible way to sort them into groups according to cause. Appropriate and specific therapy was the next step. The number of individuals in these groups who might "get well by themselves" is microscopically small or nonexistent.

Due to the relative newness of these concepts, it is not surprising that testing procedures are not yet routine. As with any other scientific advance, there is some lag between development of a new method and its mass application. There are factors which hinder present-day routine use of such tests, especially in smaller hospitals. Radiographic equipment is bulky, elaborate and expensive. A special room for the techniques must usually be set aside. Each of the tests is time-consuming, and requires collaboration of a number of specialists in allied medical fields. But these are relatively minor difficulties, and there is no doubt that they will soon be overcome.

Several years from now it may be that routine cerebral angiography will form an integral part of annual medical examinations for all those reaching fifty. Today, utilizing certain warning signals of impending stroke, medical or surgical treatment can effectively prevent a stroke from developing. Modern medical techniques have established a major breach in the wall surrounding vascular diseases of the brain. The next decade should witness consolidation of the ground we have gained, and a steadily brightening future for victims of stroke.

1960

Sick Minds, New Medicines

ROBERT S. DE ROPP

MENTAL illness takes many forms. A psychosis draws a veil between its victim and the outer world, clouds the mind with hallucinations which make purposive action difficult or impossible. The psychotic individual can play no active part in life. He must, for his own good and that of others, be separated from his normal surroundings and cared for in a special hospital until he re-establishes contact with reality.

A neurotic, on the other hand, does not lose contact with

reality. He can continue his work and deal with most of the situations that confront him. Nonetheless he is sick emotionally and mentally and his sickness colors his waking and possibly also his sleeping hours. Because of it he can never really enjoy his existence. His neurosis hovers over him like the mythological Harpy, and whatever choice morsel life offers him in the way of pleasure it swoops upon and carries off. It distorts his every feeling and colors his every impression, poisoning with suspicion, fear, guilt, apprehension, envy, or malice the very fountainhead of his existence. The psychiatrists spend much time delving into the subconscious of such a one to discover the old griefs, traumas, repressions, complexes which set this poison flowing. The chemist prefers to leave the complexes alone and to pin his faith on the dictum, "All is chemical." He believes that the sufferings of these hapless neurotics have a chemical basis, that there can be neither guilt, anxiety, depression, nor agitation without some sort of chemical imbalance within the body.

Where should we seek the basis for such imbalance? If we consider the mental and emotional life of man we see that it changes its tone from day to day and from hour to hour. Today he is elated, tomorrow depressed; in the morning an optimist, in the afternoon a pessimist; a lover after lunch, a misanthrope before it. And on what do these ceaseless variations of mood depend? They depend on an endless sequence of minor changes in the outpourings of those glands whose blended secretions make up the chords of man's inner symphony. From pituitary and adrenals, from thyroids and gonads flows the stuff of which man's feelings are created, partially regulated by processes in the brain which, like a conductor struggling through a difficult symphony, does not always produce a very distinguished performance. Neurosis and psychosis alike must be the result of a breakdown in glandular harmony: too much adrenalin here, too little thyroxine there, a shade too much testosterone or too little progesterone, a shortage of ACTH, an insufficiency of cortisone, too little serotonin or perhaps too much. Why should we enmesh ourselves in a tangle of complexes when the root of all evil lies in chemical disharmony? Let us take as our motto the dictum of R. W. Gerard: "There can be no twisted thought without a twisted molecule."

So, from this standpoint, to use a slightly different analogy, we can depict the ever-changing moods of man as a more or less continuous spectrum composed of many colors. From hour to hour man's ego, that which he feels to be himself, moves to and fro across this spectrum under the influence of inward and outward events. At one end of the spectrum lies the infrared of melancholia or depression. At the opposite end lies the ultraviolet of mania or extreme agitation. A normal, balanced man remains for the most part in the middle region of the spectrum and strays into the extreme regions only rarely. If he does enter those regions he can, without too much difficulty, remove himself from them. The dark or the frenzied mood passes. The needed chemical adjustments are carried out. Harmony is restored, the inward symphony trips along smoothly again, *allegro ma non troppo*.

In the mentally sick individual, however, this healthy chemical adjustment does not take place. Such a one may become permanently stuck at one end or the other of the psychological spectrum. If stuck at one end he is said to be suffering from depression or melancholia; if stuck at the other he is said to be suffering from agitation or mania. Quite commonly such a sick individual fluctuates between the two extremes in a condition known as a manic-depressive psychosis. Now like a god he strides on the clouds above Olympus, feeling himself to be capable of anything and everything; a few hours later, falling with a crash from the heights, he creeps through the glooms of the infernal regions, feeling lower than a worm. There is, in this case, an obvious effort on the part of the ruling chemical mechanism to correct the imbalance which has arisen among the lesser hormones. The correction, however, is always overdone, so that the mood of such an unfortunate swings from one extreme to the other and his personal symphony fluctuates between a frenzied *presto agitato* and an almost unendurably dreary *largo*.

To treat conditions such as these the physician will seek a remedy among two very different classes of drugs. The patient at one end of the spectrum, overactive, agitated, tense, nerves "frayed" with anxiety, requires a medicament that will soothe and tranquilize. But the patient at the opposite end of the spectrum, whose load of depression is so heavy that he can scarcely raise his head, whose life is an empty, meaningless, valueless void, and whose pale apathetic face gazes indifferently alike at the prizes and penalties offered by this life, obviously needs a very different sort of drug, one which, by opening the dampers that regulate our inner fires, will restore that healthy glow now almost stifled in a cloud of poisonous smoke.

We will consider first the tranquilizing agents, the ataraxics. What are these drugs whose action is so special that we have to borrow a new Greek word to describe it? The first of the ataraxics is not new at all. It is an extremely ancient remedy and has been used for at least 2,500 years in India by practitioners of a system of medicine known as the Ayur-Veda. This drug, known in India by the name *sarpaganda*, is the powered root of a small bush belonging to the family *Apocynaceae*, the Latin name of which is *Rauwolfia serpentina*, a name bestowed upon it by Plumier in honor of Dr. Leonhard Rauwolf, a sixteenth-century German physician who had traveled widely in India collecting medicinal plants.

It is curious indeed that a remedy so ancient and one on which so much excellent research had been carried out by several Indian scientists should have been ignored by Western researchers until the year 1947. This situation resulted, in part at least, from the rather contemptuous attitude which certain chemists and pharmacologists in the West have developed toward both folk remedies and drugs of plant origin, regarding native medicines as the by-products of various old wives' tales and forgetting that we owe some of our most valued drugs (digitalis, ephedrine and quinine, to name only a few) to just such "old wives' tales."

That the secret of Rauwolfia's potent action was finally brought to light was due to the curiosity of an eminent biochemist, Sir Robert Robinson, and the enterprise of Dr. Emil Schlittler of the Swiss pharmaceutical firm of Ciba, at Basle. Sir Robert was interested in an alkaloid of Rauwolfia called adjmaline and persuaded Dr. Schlittler to prepare this substance from the ground roots of *Rauwolfia serpentina*. After the adjmaline had been crystallized there remained large amounts of muddy, unattractive residue which Schlittler, with that thrift which is the hallmark of every good chemist, refused to discard until he had further explored its make-up. His exploration of this muddy resinous residue proved profitable beyond his wildest dreams, for the pharmacologists to whom he sent this material discovered, on testing it in animals, indications of that curious tranquilizing effect for which the drug has now become justly famous. Spurred on by this report, Dr. Schlittler set out to isolate the chemical substance responsible for this activity.

In September of 1952, just five years after Sir Robert Robinson had presented his request for some adjmaline, the three Ciba scientists, Schlittler, Muller, and Bein, finally published an account of their labors. The few grams of shining white crystals they had obtained from the muddy resinous extract of Rauwolfia represented the fruit of a prodigious amount of work. Every crystal was equivalent in activity to more than 10,000 times its weight in the crude drug. "We have long intended," wrote Schlittler and his colleagues, "to isolate the sedative substance of crude Rauwolfia extracts. This hypnotic principle had been examined earlier by Indian authors, but they did not get any further than the crude 'oleoresin fractions.' Starting from these fractions, we have now been able to isolate the carrier of the sedative effect in pure crystalline form." To this crystalline substance they gave the name reserpine.

A few months later Dr. Bein published a second report which revealed that reserpine, besides producing sedation, also lowered the blood pressure of the experimental animals. The drug reduced blood pressure slowly and safely, taking a fairly long period to attain its maximum effect. As high blood pressure is a particularly common ailment in America it is not surprising to find that one enterprising American physician, Dr. Robert W. Wilkins of Boston University, had already given the crude Indian drug a trial. Pure reserpine was not available to him. It had not at that time been isolated. Instead he used tablets of the crude drug imported from India with which he treated more than fifty patients suffering from high blood pressure.

By 1952, Wilkins and his colleagues were able to report progress:

> We have confirmed the clinical reports from India on the mildly hypotensive (blood-pressure lowering) effect of this drug. It has a type of sedative action that we have not observed before. Unlike barbiturates or other standard sedatives, it does not produce grogginess, stupor or lack of co-ordination. The patients appear to be relaxed, quiet, and tranquil.

One of the doctors at a later scientific meeting supplied this statement: "It makes them feel as if they simply don't have a worry in the world."

It was this observation, that the drug not only lowered blood pressure but also relaxed the tensions and anxieties by which high blood pressure is often accompanied, that aroused the interest of psychiatrists. Here, they reflected, might be the drug for which they had so long been seeking. Until the discovery of Rauwolfia no drug available to psychiatrists would really tranquilize the agitated, anxious, restless patients who so often came to them seeking help. The bromides were short-acting and apt to be toxic. The barbiturates made the patients too sleepy to carry on with their work; chloral and paraldehyde suffered from the same drawbacks.

As soon as the drug did become available a flood of scientific publications poured from the presses; indeed so great was the interest that for a time one rarely opened a medical journal without finding within it at least one article on Rauwolfia.

Reserpine is an extraordinary drug in more ways than one, and its mode of action is hard to understand. It acts slowly and takes several weeks to exert its full effects, and these effects when they come follow a definite pattern. Dr. Nathan S. Kline, who has used reserpine extensively on mental patients in Rockland State Hospital, Orangeburg, New York, summarizes his findings as follows: When reserpine is given by mouth, very little response is noted for several days. This suggests that the drug is transformed in some way in the body and that the substance which really produces the effect may not be reserpine itself but some product of reserpine. When the effects do begin to be seen they follow a very definite sequence. First comes the sedative phase. Patients behave more normally. They become less excited, assaultive, and agitated, appetite improves, and they begin to gain weight. Then, at the end of the first week, the patient enters the turbulent phase. During this phase the mental state seems suddenly to worsen. Delusions and hallucinations increase. Patients complain of a sense of strangeness; they do not feel like themselves, do not know what they are going to do next, have no control over their impulses. A physician who does not expect such manifestations may be alarmed at these symptoms and discontinue the use of the drug. Medication, however, should not be reduced until the patient has been able to get "over the hump." The turbulent phase may last for two or three weeks or may pass in a few hours. In some patients it was not observed at all. Finally, if all goes well, the patient enters the integrative phase, becomes quieter, more co-operative, friendly, and more interested in his environment. Delusions and hallucinations become less marked. This is followed by recognition on the patient's part that he has actually been ill.

The statistics offered by Dr. Kline are impressive. In a series of 150 chronically disturbed psychotics who had failed to improve when treated with electroshock or insulin, 84 per cent showed improvement with reserpine, and 21 per cent of these patients maintained their improvement after medication had been discontinued. Electroconvulsion treatment was largely abandoned. Dr. L. E. Hollister and his colleagues report from California that reserpine produced significant improvement in 98 out of 127 chronic schizophrenics. Drs. Tasher and Chermak (Illinois) report excellent results in 221 chronically ill schizophrenics.

Needless to say, this chorus of praise contains a few discordant notes. Dr. J. C. Muller and his co-workers, in an article in the *American Journal of Medicine*, declare that the tranquilizing action of reserpine may on occasion go too far and lead to a depression. High doses of the drug produce definite side effects which may be troublesome. It is definitely not a medicament to be taken without medical supervision, but the side effects it produces are of minor importance compared with the tremendous benefits it can confer.

The second of the new ataraxics has a history entirely different from that of reserpine. Here there was no romantic background of ancient folk medicine. The remedy originated in the chemical laboratory and its full title, 3-di-methyl-amino-propyl-2-chlor-phenothiazine hydrochloride, is awe-inspiring to anyone but a chemist. The Rhone-Poulenc Specia Laboratories in France, which developed this valuable drug, gave it the name chlorpromazine, by which it is now generally described. To ensure the greatest possible confusion, however, various trade names were also given to this substance. In the United States it is met with as Thorazine, in Great Britain and Canada it goes under the name of Largactil. It has also been called R.P. 4560 and Megaphen.[1]

Chlorpromazine, like reserpine, rose to fame with rocket-like velocity. In 1953 it was almost unheard of; in 1955 it was known to every physician in the country and reports on its use were

---

[1] Reserpine may also be met with under various trade names, such as Serpasil (Ciba). Raunormine (Penick) is not reserpine but a closely related alkaloid from Rauwolfia canescens.

eagerly studied, especially by those responsible for the care of the mentally sick. Dr. Douglas Goldman of Cincinnati published one of the first reports on large-scale use of this medicament in a mental hospital. So encouraging were the effects that, in the words of his colleague, Dr. Fabing, he took a new lease on life.

The reduction in assaults, the lessened use of restraint, the increased granting of privileges to locked-ward patients, the lessened need for repeated electroshock treatment to control explosive behavior, and the beginnings of an improved discharge rate of patients from the hospital all stem from the use of this drug in his hands and parallel the kind of improved state of affairs which Kline reports with reserpine at Rockland.

Goldman likes to tell the story about Willie. Willie was a disheveled, mute, untidy schizophrenic who had to be spoon fed and who managed to tear off just about all the clothes anyone tried to put on him. Willie received an eight-week trial with chlorpromazine, but at the end of that time Goldman was not greatly impressed with his improvement. He announced that he was going to withdraw Willie's drug, whereupon an orderly raised a clamor, pleading for its continuance, insisting that Willie was much better. He said, "Wait a minute. I'll prove it to you. I'll get Johnny." In a moment he returned with Willie's identical twin. "See, they were both alike two months ago," he said. They stood side by side. Johnny's hair fell in his face, he was soiled, his pants were torn, and he was barefoot. Willie was fully clothed, barbered, shaved, clean and wore shoes. The difference was obvious. Instead of taking a patient off chlorpromazine he put another one on.

Goldman also pointed out that chlorpromazine, when used with barbiturates, so greatly enhanced the effectiveness of these drugs that excited patients could be sedated with doses of a barbiturate which would barely have produced somnolence if given by itself.

In the same issue of the *Journal* Dr. Robert Gatskie reported enthusiastically on the value of chlorpromazine in the treatment of emotionally maladjusted children. Such children, rejected by their parents on account of their aggressive, violent, and destructive behavior, were housed in a cottage-type treatment center, 150 of all ages ranging from four to sixteen years. Nine of these children were treated with chlorpromazine and within a week all showed improved behavior. They became calm, co-operative, and more communicative. Their social behavior improved and they became more amenable to cottage supervision. Last but not least, they established rapport with the therapist.

On occasion chlorpromazine exerts an influence that may quite justifiably be called miraculous. An example is given by Dr. L. H. Margolis and coworkers in their paper, "Psychopharmacology." The patient on whom the drug was tried was the despair of psychologists, a thirty-four-year-old paranoid schizophrenic who had been treated with insulin coma and electroconvulsions, despite which his condition had remained unchanged. His brain was filled with delusions of grandeur and of persecution and his whole life was spent amid a collection of systematized delusions. As neither insulin nor electroconvulsion had helped him lobotomy was recommended, but his wife refused to consent to the operation. Finally in August 1954 chlorpromazine was recommended "as a desperation measure in a hopeless case." If it failed, lobotomy and/or return to the state hospital were planned.

Soon after treatment with chlorpromazine was started the night staff began to report a subtle change in the patient's attitude. On the fiftieth day of treatment he began to emerge from his world of delusions. By the fifty-seventh day he ceased to show any evidence of mental derangement. He developed an interest in the world of reality, broadened his interests and soon began to lay plans for his future. For the first time since he had been committed to the state hospital he was allowed to go home, where his wife was so impressed by his improvement that she began at once to make plans for his discharge and return to normal life. This patient was fortunate indeed. Only by his wife's refusal of her consent was he saved from a mutilating operation which, while it might have freed him from some of his delusions, would have left him with an irreparably injured brain. Chlorpromazine accomplished all that might have been done by the surgeon's knife without doing any damage to those precious lobes on the integrity of which the highest aspects of the personality depend. Some workers have referred to the action of chlorpromazine as "chemical lobotomy." It produces some of the good effects of the operation without the mutilation.

Another new member of the ataraxic group is azacyclonal, a synthetic substance manufactured by the William S. Merrell Co.

of Cincinnati under the name of Frenquel. It seems valuable in those cases where confusion or hallucination is the result of the action of some poison, and is useful for the treatment of senile patients who often go through troublesome confusional states. For the treatment of schizophrenics, however, it seems not to be in the same class with the great ataraxics, chlorpromazine and reserpine.

The other new ataraxic, meprobamate (trade names Miltown or Equanil), is a member of a group of chemicals classed as muscle relaxants, some of which also have sedative effects. In "Miltown" the tranquilizing action seems to predominate over the muscle-relaxing effect, though it is very probable that the two go hand in hand. It has been shown by several psychological studies that the condition we call "anxiety" is accompanied always by certain muscular tensions, indeed it is questionable whether anxiety could be experienced by any individual whose muscles were perfectly relaxed. It is exactly in this connection that Miltown is so effective. It promotes general muscle relaxation, which results in a reduction of tension, irritability, and restlessness. Tension headache, discomfort due to abdominal cramp, conversion hysteria, and the tremors of paralysis agitans may all be greatly relieved by this drug. Clinical tests by Drs. Selling and Borrus show that Miltown is remarkably non-toxic, for despite its muscle-relaxing qualities it does not seem to affect the heart or respiration. In short this is a valuable remedy for those lesser ailments of the spirit whose chief manifestations are anxious fear and inward tension. For the more major ailments, the hallucinations and delusions of schizophrenia for example, Miltown appears to be not so promising.

Passing to the opposite end of the psychological spectrum, the gloomy infrared of depression and melancholia, we must now consider remedies for these conditions. Melancholia, to use the time-honored name whose origin goes back to the days of Hippocrates, when the condition was thought to be due to an overproduction of black bile, is a much commoner condition than is generally realized.

"What potions have I drunk of Siren tears/Distilled from limbecs foul as hell within," writes Shakespeare who, to judge by certain passages in *Hamlet*, was personally familiar with every aspect of melancholia. The chemist must now try to reach that "foul alembic" and analyze its products, a task which is likely to tax his skill to the utmost. What shall he seek, where shall he seek it? Is melancholia also the result of an error in metabolism which leads to the production of a poison similar to the hypothetical "M" substance in schizophrenia? If so where shall we look for the poison? In blood, in urine, in lymph, in spinal fluid? But perhaps no poison is involved. Perhaps melancholia results simply from an imbalance of those potent hormones on whose quantitative relationships depend the inner harmonies of man's emotional life.

Since we cannot uncover the causes of melancholia, our quest for agents that will cure this condition has to be on a strictly trial-and-error basis. In the old days a good deal of reliance was placed on various weird concoctions known collectively as "nerve tonics."

Far more specific in their action on the melancholy humor are various drugs belonging to the amphetamine group, whose best-known member is amphetamine itself, more familiar to the public under its trade name of Benzedrine. Benzedrine acts directly on the central nervous system. It stimulates, cheers, elevates, and enlivens. Its relative, Dexedrine is even more active in this respect. Considerable studies have been carried out on this drug, especially on its use under war conditions to combat the fatigue that results from prolonged strain or effort. Reifenstein and his co-workers reported progress of a depressed individual under the influence of this drug. He was, at the outset, "hopeless in his outlook and lacking ambition." An hour after taking the drug he became talkative and three hours later was feeling much better. On the fourth day he remarked that he was very happy, cheerful and alert. On the sixth he was jovial, by the tenth he was singing and appeared to have reached approximately his normal state. The improvement, however, was not maintained and by the fourteenth day the depression began to return.

The same authors obtained favorable results in a case of catatonic schizophrenia in which the prevailing symptoms were dullness, listlessness, inactivity, and passivity.

It appears from this that these analeptic drugs, as they are called, do have some value in the treatment of depressed states, especially the condition called narcolepsy, in which the patient keeps falling asleep at inappropriate moments. But both Benzedrine and its close relative Dexedrine are apt to produce annoying side effects. For one thing they reduce appetite, so much so that Dexedrine is incorporated into several varieties of reducing pills.

For another they tend to overstimulate the nervous system in such a way that sleep becomes difficult or impossible. On this account their use in the treatment of depression has been limited.

More recently pipradrol, a close relative of Frenquel, produced by its makers (William S. Merrell Co.) under the name of Meratran, has gained some fame as an antimelancholic. Dr. Howard Fabing found it a valuable drug, for it does not, as do the amphetamines, seriously reduce appetite or interfere with natural sleep. "On occasion the response of patients with reactive depression is sudden and dramatic, in that they note an elevation of mood and a quickening of their retarded psychomotor state within two hours after ingesting the first tablet."

That curious nervous disorder narcolepsy, which may in some ways be allied to melancholia, also responds to medication with Meratran. The disorder can be well illustrated by one of Dr. Fabing's cases. A housewife began at the age of twenty to have attacks of narcoleptic sleep. Regular doses of Meratran relieved her of these symptoms, but if she stopped taking the drug the symptoms recurred within forty-eight hours.

Meratran appears to be useful only in states of pure depression. Where depression is mixed with anxiety it tends to make the anxiety more severe. As Fabing puts it, "The manic patient becomes more excited, the deluded patient becomes more actively paranoid, an obsessive patient becomes more obsessive, an anxious patient becomes more anxious, and an agitated patient becomes more agitated." In short, to quote from Dr. W. Begg's article in the *British Medical Journal*, "The chief drawback to this drug's therapeutic usefulness is its tendency to exacerbate pre-existing anxiety."

On the whole it must be admitted that the ideal drug for the treatment of melancholia seems not yet to have been discovered. It is a hard problem for the pharmacologist, for one cannot produce melancholia in experimental animals. What we really need is a naturally melancholic guinea pig, the depth of whose gloom can be measured by some means or other. We could then try, by chemical agents, to restore its *joie de vivre*. But until someone devises such a beast the quest for the perfect antimelancholic will be almost as problematical as was the hunting of the Snark.

We can now consider the impact which some of these newly discovered drugs have made on that complex, costly, and prolonged procedure loosely referred to as psychoanalysis. Behind the analyst, says Freud, stands the man with a syringe. Shall we now put all our faith in the syringe and forget about the analyst?

It is still far too early to answer this question. We can say, however, that the task of the therapist may be eased if he makes intelligent use of some of the chemical agents now available. Psychoanalysis is a procedure frequently rendered impossible by the inner fears of the patients which persistently block those very memories and damaging experiences from rising to the surface from the depths of the subconscious. In this way the health-giving cleansing or catharsis is prevented. It is this blocking which can to some extent be overcome by the judicious use of drugs, particularly such barbiturates as thiopental (Pentothal), which, for reasons known only to journalists, has been frequently referred to in the press as "truth serum." The drug is injected intravenously and, as it begins to take its effect, the tense, anxious, uncommunicative patient becomes more or less unguarded, receptive, friendly, and expansive. Unfortunately, this communicative stage lasts for a rather short time. As the action of the barbiturate continues the patient becomes increasingly drowsy and is apt to fall asleep on the analyst's couch, which makes the procedure highly unprofitable for the patient.

Attempting to overcome this difficulty, Drs. Rothman and Seward combined the soporific Pentothal with a stimulant of the Benzedrine type called methamphetamine, administering both drugs intravenously. This procedure decreased the excessive tension of the patient and at the same time promoted a state of alertness, spontaneity, and well-being. The isolation of the patient was broken down, a gate opened in the wall of fear and tension with which he had formerly been surrounded, wide enough for the analyst to squeeze through and establish contact.

Another chemical key that has been used to unlock the closed rooms of the mind is LSD. It seems strange that this potent drug, whose effect so closely resembles the symptoms of schizophrenia, should prove of value in the psychotherapy of neuroses. Dr. R. A. Sandison and his colleagues have tried it, however, and report favorably on its effect when used under proper conditions:

> Our clinical impressions have convinced us that LSD, when used as an adjunct to skilled psychotherapy, is of the greatest value in the obsessional and anxiety groups accom-

panied by mental tension. We cannot emphasize too strongly, however, that the drug does not fall into the group of "physical" treatments and that it should be used only by experienced psychotherapists and their assistants.

Before we leave the subject of the sick minds, mention should be made of that much-misunderstood ailment, epilepsy. This illness, so dramatic in its manifestations, has occupied the attention of physicians from the earliest times. In the days of Hippocrates it was known as the "Sacred Disease," a concept which aroused the scorn of the Father of Medicine who, with his usual common sense, rejected the idea "that the body of man can be polluted by a god." He wrote a treatise on epilepsy and announced, with an insight surprising for the times, that "its origin, like that of other diseases, lies in heredity." By the Jews, however, it was regarded as a form of demonic possession, as may be seen from the well-known passage of the Gospels: "And lo, a spirit taketh him, and he suddenly crieth out, and it teareth him that he foameth again, and bruising him hardly departeth from him."

It is in connection with epilepsy that that wonderful instrument, the electroencephalograph, has given us so much information. All the outward symptoms of epilepsy are the direct results of an electrical storm in the brain. The storm begins with violent electrical discharges from a small group of neurones. This violence, like panic in a densely packed crowd, spreads to the other neurones until in a few seconds the whole great mass of the cortex is discharging in unison. These massive discharges, registered by the pen of the electroencephalograph, are so distinctive that the veriest amateur can spot them. Each kind of epilepsy shows its own kind of disturbed brain wave. The three-per-second "dome and spike" of "petit mal" are entirely different from the eight-per-second spikes of "grand mal" which, in turn, differ from the slow waves of the psychomotor seizure. Oddly enough, these abnormal brain waves may occur in people who have never had an epileptic fit. They have, however, a tendency to the disease and, if exposed to certain stimuli, such as a flickering light flashing at a critical rate per second, may develop the outward symptoms of epilepsy.

Few ailments have yielded more dramatically to the combined attack of the modern chemist and pharmacologist than has epilepsy. Research on the disease was made possible by the discovery that convulsions typical of epilepsy could be induced in cats by passing an electric current through their heads. Here was a tool which could be used for the mass screening of chemical substances for anticonvulsive activity. It was seized upon by Merritt and Putnam of Parke, Davis, who tested 700 chemicals for their ability to prevent such artificially induced fits, and emerged triumphantly with diphenylhydantoin (Dilantin). Dilantin differs from the bromides and such barbiturates as phenobarbital, both of which have been used in the treatment of epilepsy, in not rendering the patient drowsy. It appears to act by preventing the spread through the brain of that electrical storm of which the convulsions and unconsciousness are the outward and visible signs. Dilantin is effective against "grand mal" and psychomotor epilepsy. Complete relief from seizures is generally experienced by 60 to 65 per cent of patients suffering from grand mal, and in 20 per cent the number and severity of convulsions are reduced. For those afflicted with petit mal another drug, trimethadoine (Tridione), is available. It will generally keep the patient completely free from seizures. In addition to these two agents several other anticonvulsants are on the market. Their names are legion: Mesantoin, Mysolin, Miltonin, Hibicon, Diamox, Paradione, Phenurone, Gemonil, Peganone. If one proves ineffectual the physician can always try another. In this particular disease he has a remarkably wide choice of remedies.

Unfortunately for the epileptic, public education has not kept pace with these triumphs of the pharmacologist. The old horror which, in the past, was associated with epilepsy is still far too prevalent today, and the epileptic suffers more from public ostracism than he does from his illness. In actual fact even grand mal epilepsy need not interefer too seriously with the life of the individual who suffers from it. Epileptics are frequently perfectly normal intellectually. They may be outstanding. Dostoevsky and Julius Caesar both suffered from the disease. With modern medication it is generally possible to prevent the development of convulsions. Even when they cannot be prevented there is no reason why one who suffers them should be treated as a leper. His ailment actually, except in extreme cases, is no more serious than migraine or dysmenorrhea. Obviously one prone to epileptic seizures should not work with dangerous machinery or drive a car, but otherwise there is no reason why he should not perform a useful function in society. If he happens to develop a fit it is merely necessary to loosen his clothing, prevent him from hurting himself, and put a gag in his mouth to stop him from biting his tongue. Horror and disgust will not help him and are not called for. There are about 1,000,000 epileptics in the United States, the majority of whom can perform a useful function if society will let them and abandon its rather medieval attitude toward this disease.

NOTE: Recently an immense amount of research has been devoted to discovering other substances like iproniazid (Marsilid), which Dr. Nathan Kline defined as a psychic energizer. Substances in this group have one thing in common. They inhibit the action of an enzyme called monoamide oxidase which plays a role in the inactivation of adrenalin. Substances having this action are often quite active antidepressants and a number of new ones have now appeared on the market under such trade names as Catron, Nardil, and Niamid. Deaner, another new antidepressant, belongs in a somewhat different chemical category. At this time (October 1959) it is too early to say just how valuable these new drugs are going to prove.

1959

The Therapeutical Use
of Radioactive Isotopes

FERNAND LOT

CLINICAL EXPLORATION

WHETHER as tracers for special examinations or as sources of radiation in the treatment of disease, the use of radioactive isotopes has undergone considerable expansion in the field of therapy. Used as tracers, they enable all sorts of clinical exploration to be conducted which enlarge our knowledge of the pathogenesis and etiology of diseases, bringing material of the greatest value in diagnosis.

Thus the functional state of the thyroid gland can be determined by administering a few microcuries of radioactive iodine. The subsequent determination of the radioactivity of the gland gives information on its ability to fix mineral iodine. It is also possible to determine the rate of utilization of iodine in the production of the thyroid hormone by assessing the radioactive iodine content of the iodized proteins of the plasma. Pierre Sue and Maurice Tubiana have developed an apparatus which enables a whole map of the thyroid's endocrine activity to be prepared, by means of curves showing regions of the hyper- or hypo-functioning of the gland.

With radioactive iodine it is also possible to detect cancerous growths originating from the thyroid which develop in the lungs, the liver or any other part of the body.

Similar investigations are current practice today in hospitals, and for some years past thousands of cases of diseased thyroids have thus been examined.

THE LOCATION OF CEREBRAL TUMORS

The normal techniques (radiology, ventriculography) often fail when the doctor is endeavoring to determine the exact location of a brain tumor. New tissues that are growing rapidly, as is the case with cancers, contain appreciably more phosphorus than do normal adult tissues. When radiophosphorus is introduced into the body, it is selectively accumulated in the diseased tissues, which can therefore be located accurately through the beta radiation of the phosphorus.

On the day before the operation, the patient is injected with radiophosphorus in the form of a solution of sodium phosphate. Fortunately, the substance of the brain can be pierced without damage and, after trepanning, the surgeon searches in the exposed brain with a needle, not exceeding 2.5 millimeters in diameter, which contains a tiny counter. When the needle is introduced into the tumor, the counting rate suddenly increases. Each determination only takes a few seconds. It is therefore possible to carry out, in a short time, a number of explorations sufficient to determine the general shape and the position of the tissues which are to be removed. Note that in this case diagnostic research has to be conducted on the exposed brain, since radiophosphorus only emits beta radiation, which would be stopped by the skull and would thus not be detectable from the outside.

RADIOGALLIUM AS A DIAGNOSTIC AGENT

Since it is selectively fixed by bone tissues, particularly those which are in process of proliferation, radiogallium (gallium is a metal closely related to aluminum) can also be used diagnostically for certain malignant tumors. For example, cancer of the breast often gives rise to metastases and to extensions in bone tissue; and it is extremely important to detect these multiplication from malignant cells as soon as possible, so that they can be destroyed. If a weak dose of radiogallium is digested (it is too poisonous to be used for curative purposes), part of it is immediately eliminated, while part is fixed by the bony tissue being attacked; in this way it is possible to photograph the lesions before they give rise to any clinical signs. Radiotherapy can then be applied, and it is possible to continue to follow the evolution of the lesions. In successful cases, the fixations of gallium in the bones resolve and disappear, which is an indication of the regression of the tumors. The curve of activity determined is a faithful reflection of the progress of the disease and enables treatment to be accurately controlled. If there are no malignant localizations, the pattern of gallium fixation enables the diagnosis to be corrected.

THE STUDY OF THE BLOOD

The study of blood circulation by means of radioactive elements (radiophosphorus, radiosodium, radiocobalt, radio-iron, radiochromium) has also been extremely fruitful. By injecting marked red corpuscles into a surface vein, it is possible to measure the speed of circulation in different parts of the body and to discover, for example, the position of vascular occlusions. It is also possible to follow a complete circulatory cycle, to measure the time of pulmonary circulation, or to measure the cardiac output. The technique of transfusion has greatly benefited from these methods. By following the radioactivity of the blood, it is possible to determine the proportion of transfused red corpuscles which disappears and the proportion which remains in circulation. If the quantity of radioactivity injected is known, together with the total blood content of the patient, it is possible to calculate the quantities of red corpuscles destroyed and the quantities utilized. By varying the conditions of storage of the blood (e.g., the temperature, anticoagulant, etc.) so as to obtain the largest possible number of viable corpuscles, considerable improvements have been made.

WHEN FRACTURES ARE HEALING

In Germany, specialists have used radioactive elements to observe the progress of healing of a fracture. They have been able to show that considerable quantities of phosphorus are rapidly directed to the fractured bone during the first days of healing, calcium being mobilized only much later. Calcium injections are, therefore, now only given two weeks after the fracture, because if administered too soon they are quite useless. Further, since considerable quantities of proteins are needed during the healing process, and their synthesis calls for much energy, proteins are broken down in other parts of the body to obtain the energy required; this explains the apparently paradoxical phenomenon that the total quantity of proteins in the human body diminishes after a fracture, although the body produces more during the healing process.

"TRACEABLE" MEDICINES

Penicillin, by means of the atom of sulphur contained in its molecule, can be marked by radiosulphur. By cultivating penicillium stocks in environments containing radioactive sulphur, it is possible to obtain penicillin which can be followed in the body. In this way, the usefulness of various means of administration has been examined: the ultimate fate of the penicillin is the same, whether given by the mouth or injected.

The speed of absorption of different insulins has been measured by radioactive iodine. By means of radioactive sodium it has been possible to examine the passage into the blood, and the amounts fixed by the lungs, of substances administered in the form of aerosols.

It has been possible to prepare radioactive cortisone by incorporating an atom of tritium in the molecule, which enables us to extend considerably our knowledge of the remarkable results obtained by cortisone in the treatment of certain cases of rheumatism.

Radioactive chlorides of sodium and potassium have been used to show the resistance of the protective covering of medical capsules to the action of the digestive juices. As soon as the capsules have been penetrated, the radioactive element spreads into the blood stream and is detected by a counter placed at the level of the hand; another counter enables the radiation to be followed along the alimentary canal. In this way; it is possible to determine the position in the stomach or intestine, where the capsule opens. By means of radioactive elements, it is also possible to measure the speed with which the skin absorbs any particular medicament. It is only necessary to spread a radioactive ointment on the skin and to observe the rate at which the radioactivity of the ointment decreases.

CURATIVE RADIOACTIVE ELEMENTS

Radioactive iodine offers other possibilities, apart from its infinitely valuable function as a radioactive trace. It is, in fact, capable of reducing the activity of cells affected by its radiation, and even to destroy them, in the same way as X rays. It can thus be used for combating cancers localized in the thyroid or dispersed in distant metastases.

In diseases of the thyroid, radioactive iodine represents the best of these agents. It was already known that goiter was sensitive to the action of radiation, and radiotherapy, that is, irradiation of the gland externally, had for some time been considered a conventional method.

Iodine-131 has a half life of eight days, long enough therefore for the radiation to persist for a certain time and yet short enough for the secondary risks inherent in any too prolonged irradiation to be reduced to a minimum. Furthermore, it emits beta radiation of medium energy, i.e. radiation sufficiently "hard" to produce effective irradiation; the gamma rays which it also emits form only a tiny proportion of the total irradiation from the iodine but enable it to be followed from the outside by means of a counter. Finally, the conditions are also very favorable from the physiological point of view, the concentration of the iodine in the thyroid being 10,000 times greater than in the blood. This selective fixation is very rapid. Six minutes after ingestion of the solution of radioactive iodine radioactivity can be detected at the level of the neck. In one hour, 75 per cent of the dose has been absorbed, and in less than six hours the concentration has reached its maximum. Once fixed, the iodine remains in the thyroid a long time, and the physiologically most active areas of the gland fix most iodine and therefore receive most radiation.

In the treatment of hyperthyroid conditions and in the struggle against cancer of the thyroid, the results have been such that there are now hundreds of treatment centers in the world using radioactive iodine.

RADIOPHOSPHORUS OVERCOMES POLYCYTHAEMIA

Radiophosphorus has proved effective in the treatment of certain diseases of the blood, especially polycythaemia (Vaquez's disease or erythraemia), characterized by an excessive number of red corpuscles in the blood, which can cause serious accidents (sometimes fatal) and which hitherto has been treated by tele-radiotherapy, by medicines or by the old-fashioned method of bleeding, in no way affecting the process of the actual formation of red corpuscles in too great number. By employing radio-phosphorus it is possible to act directly on the erythropoiesis (formation of the red corpuscles) itself, which can be slowed down.

REMOTE COBALT THERAPY

Radiocobalt (cobalt-60) emits gamma radiation comparable to that of radium. But whereas radium is extremely rare and consequently very expensive, radiocobalt is one of the isotopes which today are obtained readily in atomic piles by subjecting the stable isotope, cobalt-59, to neutron bombardment. It can thus be acquired cheaply in as great a quantity as is required. By means of this element, radiotherapy has ceased to be a luxury treatment. Apart from its ready availability and low cost price, radiocobalt has therapeutic advantages. Whereas radium contained in a needle may, in the event of a fracture, pass into the blood stream and be deposited in the bones (which is dangerous for the patient), radiocobalt, being in solid form, is not likely to break up. Even were it to pass into the blood, it would not be fixed in any particular place in the body, and would be quickly eliminated by the kidneys. Since, unlike radium, it has no break-down products which are dangerously radioactive, it can be introduced without danger into the deepest parts of the body.

Finally, radiocobalt can be used for radiation at a distance— cobalt teletherapy. The radioactive source is placed in the center of a spherical protecting mass, a "bomb" of lead and steel. The thickness of the wall is sufficient to absorb the radiation emitted in all directions other than the radiation channel, which directs a beam through an opening that can be adjusted or closed by

GREAT ADVENTURES IN MEDICINE

means of a series of diaphragms and a shutter. The bomb is supported on a movable arm attached to a fixed column, and can be moved by an electrical mechanism. The whole is installed in an insulated, air-conditioned room, access to which can only be obtained through a concrete wall provided with a baffle opening. In the wall there is a window of lead glass, partially opaque to gamma radiation; this allows the operator to supervise the patient, with whom he remains in oral communication by means of a telephone. Why have so many precautions to be taken? Because the cobalt source enclosed in the metal sphere, although it weighs only a few grams, is equivalent to two kilograms of radium (at the present time, in the whole world there only exists about a kilogram and a half of isolated radium). The flux of radiation is therefore very intense, and advantage is taken of this to reach lesions situated very deep below the skin with doses of radiation considerably greater than those which could be supplied to these regions by the X ray apparatus at present in use. The radiation produced by the cobalt corresponds to the energy of a beam of X rays that would be produced by electrical apparatus operating at the enormous voltage of 3.5 million volts (instead of the 200,000 volts customarily employed). With the new radiation, it is possible to send 57 per cent of the energy to a depth of 10 centimeters below the skin, instead of 30 per cent as hitherto. Furthermore, the resulting skin reactions are appreciably less intense than with X rays; the general reaction of the body is also less acute. This represents great technical progress. Of course, the dose of radiation to be given in each case is calculated extremely accurately, and curves of equal doses are rigorously prepared. Particularly suited to treatment by cobalt teletherapy are tumors of the lungs, esophagus, brain and uterus, as well as the more superficial lesions such as those of the breast and larynx.

The first cobalt teletherapy apparatus was made in Canada. Since its appearance, apparatuses of this type have multiplied in many countries. There are more than two hundred in the U.S.S.R. In France, several anti-cancer clinics, as well as private clinics, are equipped with them. Numerous improvements are constantly being made, and among those proposed is a multifocal installation, whereby four or six patients could be treated at once.

RADIOACTIVE CAESIUM AGAINST CANCER

Radiocaesium also provides a powerful source of radiation and can be used in treating cancer. Numerous British hospitals have recently requested radioactive capsules for this purpose, the first of which has been installed in the Royal Marsden Hospital. This caesium is obtained as a fission by-product in the Windscale piles in Cumberland. The caesium salt is contained in a platinum capsule 7 centimeters long by 3 centimeters in diameter. The capsule is placed in a block of lead and uranium weighing about a ton.

USE OF GOLD

Important experiments with radioactive gold have been conducted in the U.S.A. for the treatment of inoperable tumors of the chest. This radioactive gold, obtained from Oak Ridge, has to be used extremely quickly because its half-life is very short.

Radioactive gold 'seeds' are frequently used in the United Kingdom as implants round tumors in the same way as radium needles. Owing to the short half-life of gold, 28 days, removal after treatment is unnecessary. Colloidal gold, pumped into a bladder or sac, is often used in the treatment of tumors in cavities such as the bladder and the intestines.

1958

Radiations and the Genetic Threat

WARREN WEAVER

THE PLOT

WE ALL remember that Dickens used to start some of his novels with two or three chapters which appeared to be wholly unconnected. Then the relationship would gradually and dramatically come to light. Since our common purpose here is clarity rather than suspense, I will tell you at the outset that our plot will, in a way, be similar. Chapter I will be devoted to the villain of the piece—radiations. Chapter II will deal with the innocent victim—the genes. Chapter III will describe the crime—mutations. And Chapter IV will then give the verdict of society, will indicate, at least in modest part, what we ought to do about this.

THE VILLAIN—RADIATIONS

What is radiation? It is energy on the move, energy being transmitted from one location in space to another. But this remark requires an immediate modification. For not all energy on the move is radiation. A thrown baseball or the moving stream of water from a hose—these involve moving energy, but these are purely mechanical effects, rather than radiation. So we must be more accurate and say that radiation is electromagnetic energy being transmitted. I am not speaking here of electricity in wires, but rather of electromagnetic waves—radio or television waves— moving freely through space, or as we very inaccurately some- times say, "through the air." (This is really a bad phrase, for insofar as the air plays any role at all, it tends to stop such waves rather than transmit them. A century ago scientists used to say that these waves moved through the "aether," but they just invented this word to diminish their worry over the fact that they didn't understand what was happening. We don't either, but we have abandoned the verbal tranquilizer.)

The most familiar instance of an electromagnetic wave is light, the visible light which affects our eyes. And fortunately this familiar instance is a completely typical instance, as we will see in just a moment.

Any wave disturbance can be partly characterized by its wave length. In the case of a water wave, this wave length is simply the distance from one crest to the next adjacent crest. One can also speak of the frequency of a wave motion, this being simply the number of waves which in each second pass a fixed point. Granting a fixed speed for the waves (and this is the case with electromagnetic waves), the longer the wave length, the fewer of them pass a given point. Quantitatively, if you double the wave length, you halve the frequency. It is often useful to speak both of wave length, which is familiar to us from the water-wave case, and of frequency, which is familiar from the case of sound waves. When one speaks of an "octave" on the piano, the fre- quency of the upper "do" is just twice the frequency of the lower "do"; so using the sound analogy one can speak of two electromagnetic radiations being an "octave" apart, one of them having a frequency twice that of the other.

In these terms (mixing the sound and light cases) we can think of a great "light-piano." Suppose its keyboard covers about seventy octaves. In the center of it, rather less than one octave wide, is the visible light that affects our eyes. To the right stretch out octave after octave of progressively higher frequencies (smaller and smaller wave lengths). First come about eleven octaves of so-called ultraviolet, the light that is bluer than blue. Then come four octaves of the still shorter wave length X rays, six octaves of so-called gamma rays, and finally, shortest of all in wave length and highest of all in frequency, some sixteeen octaves of very high energy gamma rays derived from cosmic rays.

To the left of the central octave of visible light we find about fifteen octaves of infrared light, then about six octaves of radar waves[1], and finally some twelve octaves of ordinary radio waves.

That is to say, these physical entities with differing names— radio waves, infrared, visible light, ultraviolet light, X rays, gamma rays, and cosmic rays—are now all known to be electro-magnetic radiations which are alike except that they differ in wave length and hence in frequency. They range from the deep base of the radio waves at the left end of our radiation piano, up to the ultra-high tenor of the cosmic rays at the right end. The only part of this whole spectrum of which we are immediately conscious is the less than one octave of visible light in the middle.

Speaking broadly, the very long wave length radiations tend to flow around any obstacle they meet, while the very short wave lengths tend to penetrate right into an obstacle. Since we are concerned here with radiations which are able to penetrate into our bodies, we see that we are dealing with the tenor half of the radiation piano, namely, with X rays, the still more pene-trating gamma rays and the most of all penetrating cosmic rays.

At this point it will be useful to take note of the most common source of radiations. Most ordinary atoms are stable—their insides stay put. But some atoms are inherently unstable. Their insides have a tendency to readjust into a new pattern of arrange-ment. It is not possible to predict, for one particular atom, when this readjustment will occur. These unstable atoms—they are often called radioactive—are like alarm clocks wound up and set for unknown times. Eventually the alarm goes off, and the

[1] That is to say, waves of wave lengths which are very short when con-sidered as radio waves, although not in the least short from the point of view of the entire electromagnetic spectrum.

inside of that atom readjusts into a more stable arrangement. When that readjustment occurs, the atom sends out a burst of radiant energy, and this process is in fact the commonest origin of radiations.

Although one cannot at all say when one given radioactive atom will pop off, one can give a useful description of the time behavior of a lot of similar radioactive atoms. One does this by specifying the interval of time within which half of the atoms will pop off. This interval is called the half-life. Starting out with a large number of unpopped atoms of half-life equal to, just as an example, one day, half would be popped by the end of the first day, half of the remaining half of unpopped atoms would then pop in the second day (or a total of three fourths of the original number), again half of the remaining quarter of unpopped atoms in the third day (or a total of seven eighths of the original number), and so on. Some radioactive atoms have half-lives of minutes, hours or days. There are some so transient that they have half-lives as short as a millionth of a second, and others so nearly stable that they have half-lives of thousands or even millions of years.

To return now to the general subject of this chapter, namely the radiations which are capable of penetrating our bodies, part are furnished by nature, and part are caused by man. The part furnished by nature is often referred to as the background radiation, this implying an inevitable and omnipresent base to which is added whatever man causes. Of this background radiation a certain amount comes up from the radioactive material in the rocks and soil. In the top layer of depth one foot there exists on the average, per square mile of earth surface, two grams of radium, eight tons of uranium, and twelve tons of thorium; so clearly the earth under our feet is an important and inescapable source of radiation. On the other hand, part of the background radiation comes down from the sky. This part is due to cosmic rays, so very penetrating that they can pass through ten centimeters of lead, and so universally present that as you read these lines some two to three hundred bursts are passing through your body each second. These two contributions, up from the soil and down from the sky, add together to form the background radiation.

In addition to this background that has been flooding man throughout the centuries are the radiations which man has recently learned how to produce. In this latter category there are two main kinds. First, there are the X rays so widely used in medicine for both diagnostic and therapeutic purposes. Second, there are the rays (from our point of view the gamma rays are the important ones) produced in nuclear experiments, in atomic weapons testing and in nuclear power plants. In addition to these two main kinds there are various other radiations, usually of minor importance or affecting fewer persons, such as are produced by luminous dials, encountered in certain industries, experienced by certain miners, etc.

The advent of atomic weapons has drawn attention to the possible dangers to man from all sorts of radiations. In the explosion of an atom bomb, in fact, there are produced about 175 kinds of what the physicist calls isotopes—abnormal variants of the ordinary elements. Some of these isotopes from an atom bomb are stable, and the unstable radioactive ones have half-lives which vary from a few seconds to 1,000,000,000 years. About 1,000 pounds of radioactive material are produced per ten-megaton shot.

In the explosion of an atom bomb there are three discernible stages. The first, involving truly awful destruction from immediate radiation, heat, and blast, lasts for the order of one second and extends out, one supposes, to a ten-to twenty-five-mile radius. The second stage involves a radiation dose due to immediate fallout, which is directly dangerous or even lethal to those receiving it. This lasts for a few days, and extends over an area which presumably may be 10,000 or perhaps in special circumstances even 100,000 square miles. The third stage is that of the eventual "fallout." The finely dispersed radioactive material is carried high into the atmosphere, drifts with the winds, settles down at various rates, or is brought down with rain. This stage lasts over months or years, and extends over the entire planet. This third stage is what is usually meant by "fallout," and the word will be used here in this sense.

So now we have met the villain. It consists of blobs of penetrating energy produced by the popping off of wound-up atoms. Some of these atoms nature herself winds up, but many of these the modern physicist has learned how to wind.

THE INNOCENT VICTIM—THE GENES

Every cell of a person's body contains a great collection, passed down from the parents, the parents' parents, and so on back, of diverse hereditary units called genes. These genes singly and in combination control our inherited characteristics.

These genes exist in every cell of the body. But from the point of view of heredity the ordinary "body cells," which make up the body as a whole, are not comparably as important as the "germ cells" which exist in the reproductive organs, and which play the essential roles in the production of children.

Ordinarily genes are passed on unchanged to children, grand-children and more remote descendants, but occasionally they do change. They are changed by certain agents, notably by heat, by some chemicals and by radiation. It is at this point that we begin to see the villain plotting against the innocent victim.

THE CRIME—MUTATIONS

When a gene becomes thus permanently altered we say it mutates. The gene is then duplicated in its altered form in each subsequent cell division. If the mutant gene is in an ordinary body cell, it is merely passed along to other body cells. The mutant gene, under these circumstances, is not passed on to progeny, and the effect of the mutant gene is limited to the person in whom the mutation occurred.

However, it cannot safely be assumed that this body-cell effect is a negligible one on the person in whom the mutation occurred. For various kinds of cellular abnormalities are known to be perpetuated within an individual through body-cell divisions; so these effects are genetic in the broad sense. In fact, although the quantitative relations are not yet clear, it is nevertheless clear that certain malignancies such as leukemia, and certain other cellular abnormalities, can be induced by ionizing radiations. There is also some evidence that effects of this sort measurably reduce the life expectancy of the individual receiving the radia-tion.

But to return to a consideration of the risks which are passed on to progeny: the mutant gene may exist in a sperm or an egg cell as a result of a mutation having occurred either in that cell or at some earlier cell stage. In this case, a child resulting from this sperm or egg will inherit the mutant gene.

We are now in a position to indicate why it is that radiations, such as X rays or gamma rays, can be so serious from the genetic point of view. For although the genes, as described above, normally remain unchanged as they multiply and are passed on from generation to generation, they do very rarely change, or mutate; and radiation, as we have already mentioned, can give rise to such changes or mutations in the genes. Mutation ordinarily affects each gene independently; and once changed, an altered gene then persists from generation to generation in its new or mutant form.

Moreover, the mutant genes, in the vast majority of cases, and in all the species so far studied, lead to some kind of harmful effect. In extreme cases the harmful effect is death itself, or loss of the ability to produce offspring, or some other serious abnormality. What in a way is of even greater ultimate importance, since they affect so many more persons, are those cases that involve much smaller handicaps, which might tend to shorten life, increase disease, reduce fertility, or to be otherwise detrimental.

In assessing the harm done to a population by deleterious genes, it is clear that society would ordinarily consider the death of an early embryo to be of much less consequence than that of a child or young adult. Similarly a mutation that decreases the life expectancy by a few months is clearly less to be feared than one that in addition causes its bearer severe pain, unhappiness, or illness throughout his life. Perhaps most obviously tangible are the instances, even though they be relatively uncommon, in which a child is born with some tragic handicap of genetic origin.

A discussion of genetic damage necessarily involves, on the one hand, certain tangible and imminent dangers, certain tragedies which might occur to our own children or grandchildren; and on the other hand certain more remote trouble that may be experienced by very large numbers of persons in the far distant future.

This is not a suitable occasion on which to go into details. But due to well understood genetic principles it is possible to state some important conclusions concerning the danger which is inherent in a radiation-mutated gene. First of all, the change produced by mutation is practically always a change for the worse. Second, the amount of mutation varies directly with the amount of radiation. Third, there is no minimum amount of radiation which is genetically safe—all radiation is genetically bad. A little radiation is a little bad, and a lot is a lot bad. Fourth, once exposed to some radiation, this never "wears off": that is to say, the genetically important number of mutations depends on the total dose that one accumulates from his own conception up to the time of conception of his last child. Fifth, the radiation that is important genetically is only that which reaches the gonads —that is to say, the male testicles and the female ovaries. Sixth, what counts from the point of view of society as a whole is the total number of mutated genes. Thus a small radiation dose to a large number of persons is, socio-genetically speaking, equivalent to a large dose to a few.

The resulting damage may, in a small proportion of cases, appear promptly in one's children or grandchildren, or it may be hidden for many generations; but it is usually not completely hidden and almost always imposes some small handicap on all generations. Moreover these small handicaps accumulate, and the mutated gene eventually eliminates itself through disaster— the disaster of a person whose life span is so shortened or whose fertility is so impaired that no progeny is possible, and this particular genetic line dies out.

THE VERDICT OF SOCIETY

Crime, we ordinarily say, does not pay. One's natural inclination, knowing that any and all radiation is genetically bad, is to say, "Let's just eliminate radiation." But we couldn't do that if we really wanted to, and we wouldn't dare if we could.

We couldn't if we wanted to because of the background radiation which comes up from the soil and rocks, and down from the sky. This background is such as to give each person, on the average in the United States, a reproductive lifetime dose (say, over thirty years, from conception to the birth of the "average" child) of about 3 roentgens.[2]

As a practical matter, moreover, it would be virtually impossible to eliminate man-made radiation also; but this is the part that we wouldn't really dare eliminate even if we could. To

___

[2] A roentgen is the common unit in which radiation dose is measured. You get a gonad dose of about 0.005 roentgen from a dental X ray, from 0.1 to 1.0 roentgen from a pelvic X ray, and up to 2 roentgens in a fluoroscopic examination of the pelvis. In the original report of the Genetics Committee of the National Academy of Sciences the background dose was estimated at 4.3 roentgens and the average dose from diagnostic and therapeutic medical X rays was estimated at about 3 roentgens. A large amount of additional data has now been analyzed, and the result has been to decrease the estimate of the background dose to 3 roentgens, and to increase the estimate of the medical X-ray dose to about 4.5 roentgens. The estimate for the sum of the two thus remains nearly unchanged.

consider one type of man-made radiation: at the present time a person in the United States receives a reproductive lifetime dose of about 4.5 roentgens from diagnostic and therapeutic medical X rays. Any of this that could be avoided without interfering with really necessary medical procedures should, of course, be eliminated. But obviously this involves careful and technical judgments in deciding, in each instance, which is the more acceptable risk—the genetic risk or the medical risk which would result in not using the X rays.

In addition to the substantial doses from background and from medical X rays, there is the dose—up to the present time small—due to the radioactive fallout from atomic tests. And in the future we certainly face the possibility of significant doses from nuclear power installations.

The reproductive lifetime fallout dose has recently been estimated (assuming no increase in number or size of weapons tested) to be about 0.1 roentgen. There is a considerable uncertainty, and fluctuation from place to place, in this figure; and it may be a fifth as large as stated or, on the other hand, may perhaps be five times as large.

When we think of the genetic risk from any of these sources of radiation we should always, of course, think in terms of comparing two risks—the risk from the radiation, and the risk we would incur if we eliminated the radiation. We all have to compare risks every day, even though we usually do not do so explicitly, but rather in a vague and unformulated way which invokes experience.

If a person must go from New York to San Francisco, he could look up the traffic statistics, and could thus compare two actual numbers representing the traffic deaths per mile of automobile or of air travel. But in the case before us there are reasons which make any attempted comparison of risk very difficult indeed.

We wish to compare Risk A, the genetic risk from radiation, with Risk B, the medical, economic, political and military risk which might result from decreasing X rays, from handicapping the development of nuclear power, and from weakening our position of world leadership and our capacity to defend ourselves. Our difficulties result from the very basic facts that we do not as yet know enough about human radiation genetics to give precise and quantitative estimates of the radiation Risk A; that we certainly cannot give any accurate estimates of the medical, economic, political or military Risk B; and that even if we could describe both Risk A and Risk B, there would be the final and baffling difficulty that these two risks are inherently unlike and hence essentially incomparable.

To speak only of Risk A, we must remember that our knowledge of genetics is very largely derived from experiments with lower forms of life—fruit flies, corn, mice. Large-scale and controlled genetic experiments with human beings are obviously out of the question. Genetics, moreover, is an inherently complicated and subtle subject, almost no quantitative facts concerning radiation harm are known with high precision, and the great but necessary leap from mice to men is one which unavoidably introduces uncertainties. But do not make the mistake of concluding, from these discouraging comments, that the geneticists have little to offer in the way of knowledge and advice. On the contrary, and despite uncertainties about details and exact values, geneticists are in firm agreement on practically all of the really basic points.

Many of you will, at this point, want to make a protest, or will at least want to voice your confusion. If the basic genetic facts are indeed firm and agreed, how can different informed persons, all of whom are clearly intelligent and socially sensitive, appear to hold such diverse views? Take the much publicized case of fallout. How can some be worried about this as a serious menace, while others even refer to it as "harmless" or "negligible"?

The recent report of the National Academy of Sciences suggested that we ought to plan our medical and nuclear affairs so that an average U. S. citizen would receive a reproductive lifetime dose, from man-made radiation, of not more than 10 roentgens. Such an amount would probably not double our present genetic load, in the sense of doubling the long-established and long-tolerated rate of natural mutations from background radiation and from other agents (heat and chemicals) which cause radiations. Thus, the report concluded, perhaps 10 roentgens of man-made radiation will not result in an unreasonable burden to society. Well, if 10 roentgens thus gets enthroned as reasonable,[3] isn't the 0.1 roentgen from fallout negligible?

It is certainly not surprising that some persons, deeply and

[3] Reasonable, mind you; not harmless.

properly concerned over the military and political importance
of nuclear weapons, answer that question in the affirmative.
But the geneticists, if I interpret them correctly, answer in the
negative. How can this be?

I think that this is to be explained, and that some of the
differences in emphasis among the geneticists are also to be
explained, in terms of two paradoxes, one numerical, the other
temporal.

The numerical paradox is the one which applies most directly
to the fallout problem. The paradox arises by virtue of the fact
that some persons are impressed by relative figures, some by
absolute amounts.

A fallout dose of 0.1 roentgens is, for example, only 1/100 of
the 10 roentgens set as "reasonable" by the NAS report. It is
only about 1/500 of the dose that would presumably be required
to double the natural rate of mutation. If I am already running a
certain risk (and after all surviving in spite of it) then ultimately
to add to this risk by only one part in 500 doses, when put in
this relative way, seems pretty negligible.

But look at the question in other terms. At the present time,
roughly 4.5 per cent of the babies born in the United States have
serious defects (congenital malformation, mental defects, epilepsy,
cutaneous and skeletal defects, visual and aural defects, etc.). Of
these, it seems likely that about half are genetic in origin. Let us
roughly assume that 2 per cent of the babies born have defects
of mutational origin.

Now all the persons now alive in the world—all the persons
who at this moment face this problem—will have, before they are
all dead, something of the order of 15,000,000,000 babies
(1.5×10^9). The immediate genetic risk to this vast set of babies
—the world's next set of persons—may well be increased, due to
fallout, only by one part in 5,000 (2×10^{-4}).[4] The increase in risk
is very small, but the increase applies to a vast number of persons.
The estimated result, in fact, is 6,000 additional handicapped babies.
Now what impresses you as more significant: that 6,000 is a good
many babies to subject to serious handicap, or that 1/5000 is a very
small fraction and correspondingly is very small relative addition

[4] This factor is the product of 1/500 (a reasonable ratio of fallout to
the doubling dose) by 1/10 (a reasonable estimate of the fraction of total
damage which would be expressed in the first generation).

to the 30,000,000 babies that, without fallout, will have serious genetic handicaps? And remember that this calculation underestimates the total radiation effect in two ways: it speaks of first-generation damage (whereas there will be increasing amounts of damage in later generations), and it speaks only of gross abnormalities (which, if we accept the evidence from lower forms of life, constitute only a small part of the total genetic damage).

In connection with these remarks about the numerical paradox there is one aspect of the problem of genetic risk which probably deserves some explanation. Increasing some types of risk to individuals by one part in 5,000 might just result in each individual person experiencing a small amount of additional harm —each one might, in an average year, say, have a certain type of physical distress for a total of 5,001 minutes rather than for 5,000 minutes, as previously. But genetic harm does not work that way. Mutations differ a great deal in their seriousness, of course. But for a given mutation, it either occurs or it does not occur. Thus when a lot of persons are subjected to a low radiation dose, almost all of them experience no harm whatsoever, but in the case of a few persons mutation will occur. When a mutation occurs it occurs, so to speak, completely. The result for the person in whom it occurs is just the same as though the mutation had been caused by a larger dose of radiation. In other words, a small dose actually affects a small proportion of the exposed population, and a larger dose affects a larger proportion; but those individuals who are affected experience the same result in the two cases.

The temporal paradox is also a difficult one. What impresses you as more important—a relatively little tangible and tragic suffering encountered promptly, by your own children and grandchildren, say—or a great deal more of rather vague and remote suffering to be encountered by the next fifty or one hundred generations?

Some sincere and intelligent persons, including some geneticists, think it is difficult enough to try to play short-range God, without attempting, or worrying about, the problems of a long-range God. These persons, moreover, have a substantial comfort in their confidence that man's intellect will succeed in finding ways out of the long-range difficulties, so that we are justified in trying to deal only with the next few generations.

On the other hand, there are equally sincere and intelligent persons, again including some geneticists, who think that we may well have no greater responsibility than that of protecting the genetic heritage of the future; and that that responsibility does not in the least excuse our committing genetic crimes simply on the grounds that they will not be found out for a long time.

I hope that the statement of these two paradoxes may help you interpret certain statements which might otherwise confuse you and—worst of all—might lead you to think that this situation is so mixed up that the best thing to do is disregard it. Whatever we do, we must not disregard this problem. A massive discontinuity was introduced into life by the discovery of nuclear fission. We have to learn to live with it, for the alternative is that we do not live.

1957

INDEX

Aaron, 46, 47
Abel, Prof. John Jacob, 619, 620
Abernathy, John, 157, 199
Abrams, Albert, 13, 14
Académie Française, 262, 276
Achot, 37
ACTH, 496
Adams, Charles Francis, 471
Addison's Disease, 620
Adrenal Cortex, 619-621
Adrenal Gland, 615, 619, 620
Adrenalin, 524, 620
Aesculapius. *See* Asclepius
Agramonte, Aristides, 562-586
Ague, cures for, 147
Aird, Professor Ian, 805
Alcithous, 88, 89
Alcoholism, 148, 159, 745
Alexander and Leidy, 713
Alexander, Dr., 305
Allan, 622
Alloway, 713
Alvarez, Walter C., 4, 5, 9-27, 31
Amenorrhoea, 610
Ameresis, 90, 91
American Association for Cancer Research, 762
American Cancer Society, 751, 753, 760
American Journal of Medicine, 833, 834
American Public Health Association, 577
Amulets, 20, 32, 41, 44, 45, 132
Anatomical Tables, 112
Anatomy, 26, 33, 54, 76, 97, 107-113, 115-118, 120, 161, 178-180, 182, 186, 189, 193, 198-200, 222, 225, 232, 237, 330, 374

Anatomy Act, 199, 200
Andrewes, 722
Androgens. *See* Hormones
Anemia, 605, 606, 607, 608, 609
Anemia, pernicious, 496, 606-608
Anesthesia, 26, 27, 204, 265, 278, 306, 340, 401-426, 667, 668, 777, 797, 806
Angioneurotic edema, 745
Ansfield, Dr. Fred J., 755, 756
Anthrax, 61, 65, 206, 207, 292, 519
Antibiotics, 767-776
Antisepsis, 204, 206, 235, 256-262, 279, 357
Aortitis, 741-742
Apoplexy, 104
Appendicitis, 4, 26, 440, 482, 688, 745, 778
Archigetes, 51
Aretaeus, 667
Aristotle, 25, 33, 75, 118
Arteries, 18, 32, 97, 98, 121-124, 360, 624, 627, *See also* Blood Circulation
Arthritis, 15, 25, 285, 745
Artificial kidney, 796, 804
Ascania, 104
Aschheim-Zondek Test, 623
Asclepius, 6, 75
Aspenwall, Dr. Wm., 174
Asthma, 150, 745
Asuero, 13
Athenian Plague, 63, 64
Atlee, Dr. Washington, 378
Atoxyl, 694, 695
Atterbury, 149
Aubrey, John, 120, 125
Auenbrugger, Leopold, 101
Autopsies, 20, 25, 162, 289, 571, 614. *See also* Dissections